AMPHIBIANS AND REPTILES OF TRINIDAD AND TOBAGO

AMPHIBIANS AND REPTILES OF TRINIDAD AND TOBAGO

John C. Murphy

KRIEGER PUBLISHING COMPANY
MALABAR, FLORIDA
1997

Original Edition 1997

Printed and Published by
KRIEGER PUBLISHING COMPANY
KRIEGER DRIVE
MALABAR, FLORIDA 32950

Library of Congress Cataloging-In-Publication Data

Murphy, John C., 1947–
    Amphibians and reptiles of Trinidad and Tobago / John C. Murphy.
        p.   cm.
    Includes bibliographical references.
    ISBN 0–89464–971–X (hc : alk. paper)
    1. Amphibians—Trinidad and Tobago.   2. Reptiles—Trinidad and Tobago.   I. Title.
    QL656.5.T7M87   1997
    597.6'0972983—dc20   95–36455
                                                                           CIP

10   9   8   7   6   5   4   3   2

For Kathie, Sara, and Mary Margaret
with love

Contents

COLOR PLATES FOLLOW PAGE 98

PART 4   REPTILIA SPECIES ACCOUNTS

Introduction

Trinidad and Tobago are lush, tropical, continental islands with a herpetofauna of extremes in size. Included in the 130 taxa recognized here are the world's largest snake and turtle, two of the largest lizards in the Western Hemisphere, and one of the largest, if not the largest, anuran in the hemisphere. Also within the fauna are some of the smallest snakes, lizards, and anurans found in the hemisphere. More spectacular is the diversity of adaptations present in this fauna. Trinidad and Tobago frogs use at least nine different reproductive modes. There are several endemic and near endemic lizards, at least one parthenogenetic lizard, amphisbaenids with symbiotic relationships with leaf-cutting ants, and snakes with highly specialized habitats and diets. Alien species, species introduced by man, can also be found in these islands, as can species with economic and cultural importance. What makes this fauna remarkable is the high diversity of form and function within the relatively small area of these two islands.

Trinidad Indian middens dated 500–2100 years before present (BP) contained the remains of one amphibian and seven reptile species (Wing and Reitz, 1982), which suggests tribal people exploited the herpetofauna for food. Extensive hunting in the last century most likely contributed to the decline of sea turtles and tortoises, DeVerteuil (1858) commented.

The supply of food derived from the great class of reptiles is much greater than is, perhaps first thought. From the Spanish Main alone, the town of Port of Spain receives, on average, 4000 pounds of turtle per annum, to which we may safely add 4000 pounds more, as representing the quantity supplied to all other parts, including, however, a quota from the island itself; thus the whole quantity of turtle consumed in the island would amount to 8000 pounds; if to this we add 1000 pounds more for morocoys [=*Geochelone denticulata*], lizards, matos [=*Tumpinambis teguixin*], we shall then have a grand total of from 9000 to 10000 pounds of flesh supplied from the grand class of reptiles.

Relatively recent deforestation and other environmental degradations are reducing amphibian and reptile habitats. However, the resilient nature of amphibian and reptile populations is not to be underestimated. During this investigation amphibians and reptiles were surprisingly easy to find and some species, particularly those adapted to life in the savanna, have flourished with human changes. This raises the question of how many forest species may have disappeared from the islands in the last 150 years as well as what other species were not able to adapt to the environmental change wrought by humans. There are a number of species known from single, or relatively few, specimens collected in the last 150 years (*Leptodactylus knudensi, Lithodytes lineatus, Typhlonectes* sp., *Gonatodes albogularis, Bachia flavescens, Gymnodactylus geckoides, Anolis* cf. *lemurinus, Kentropyx striatus* (on Tobago), *Drymarchon corias corias, Erythrolamprus aesculapii aesculapii, Erythrolamprus bizona, Leptophis riveti, Liophis reginae* ssp., *Typhlops brongersmianus, Typhlops trinitatus, Crocodylus acutus*). These species may be secretive or present at low population densities; some may be species that failed colonization attempts due to competition, lack of habitat, or bad luck; some may be remnants that hang on in small populations until their habitat disappears due to human intervention; and a very few may be the result of errors in locality data. Accurately sorting taxa into these various categories is not possible. Recent additions have been made to the fauna of both islands suggesting older collections are incomplete, and I have every reason to believe that there are still new additions to the herpetofauna of these islands forthcoming. Species represented by specimens from the islands that have been declared locality errors by some authors (Oliver, 1948; Emsley, 1963) have subsequently been shown to be present; *Leptophis riveti* is an excellent example. This snake, first collected on Trinidad in 1937, was not collected again until 1987. It is for this reason species of questionable occurrence are included in the species accounts.

Amphibians and reptiles play a colorful role in the folktales of the islands. Ashtine (1966) recounts nine folktales commonly told to the children of Trinidad and Tobago. Two of these (Young and Old Nelson; Why The Tortoise's Back Is Cracked) contain three reptile characters: a *Boa constrictor;* a yellow-footed tortoise, *Geochelone denticulata;* and a horsewhip snake, *Oxybelis aeneus.* To provide the reader with a sense of the rich history and folklore associated with these animals, quotes from earlier publications are used here. Some are excellent observations of a species biology, others represent pure folklore, and many are a mixture of fact and folklore. All are of interest and illustrate the role these vertebrates play in the islands' cultures.

The purpose of this book is to allow naturalists to identify the amphibians and reptiles of Trinidad and Tobago and to provide them with some information on the animals' distribution and natural history. It is not intended to be a comprehensive taxonomic revision of the fauna, a guide to museum specimens from the area, a detailed zoogeographical work, or a source of extensive ecological, and behavioral information on any single taxon. The book has numerous gaps that should serve to generate future study, and the herpetofauna has enough interesting problems to keep generations of students busy with systematic, ecological, and behavioral studies. Trinidad and Tobago provide an easily accessible continental South American fauna for the scientist, amateur herpetologist, and ecotourist. I ask these people, and the people of Trinidad and Tobago, to treat the fauna with respect. Noncommercial collecting will do little to damage populations, but commercial collecting and market hunting can decimate populations. Unfortunately, rampant habitat destruction and pollution are a much greater and more immediate threat to the herpetofauna of these islands; and the only way to combat these problems is through education and environmental activism.

This project has provided the author with endless hours of enjoyment, adventure, and intellectual stimulation. It is hoped that the reader will also be entranced with the island's herpetofauna and that this work will lead to a better understanding of the herpetofauna and stimulate further investigations.

Acknowledgments

Numerous individuals and organizations have provided the author with assistance in the production of this book. Some of their names may be lost in my memory, but to all go my sincerest thanks. The following people have contributed to the project in innumerable ways and without them it would not have been completed. Kathie and Sara Murphy have supported the project from the start, providing excellent logistical support in the field, museum, and home. Field work was accomplished with the aid of Chicago Herpetological Society members Ron and Dottie Humbert, Mike Dloogatch, Mel Bruns, Mike Miller, Steve Barten, Gerry Hermann, and Ralph Shepstone; John Seyjagat of the Emperor Valley Zoo; and students Kris Krammer, David Alderson, and Chad Spangler. Jack and Carol Price, Edward and Janice Rooks, Ronnie Hernandez, and Richard Quiaman made our visits to Simla and the Asa Wright Nature Centre enjoyable and provided an enormous amount of useful information. Simla visitors often provided information, specimens, and friendship including: April Allgaier, Jenny Boughman, Jack Bradbury, Hugh Brittin, John and Roger Downie, J. Dave Hardy, J. Ellen Marsden, Bill Montgomery, Morley Read, John Reed, David Reznick; the crew collecting insects from the Cincinnati Zoo, and particularly John Bindernagle (UN-FAO) and family. Charles and Pat Turpin at Man-O-War Bay Cottages and the staff of the Blue Waters Inn made our visits to Tobago comfortable. Hans E. A. Boos (Emperor Valley Zoo) provided a variety of help, including the loan of John Seyjagat. Julius Boos, Julian Kenny, Keith Harding, William Lamar, Allan Markezich, and Van Wallach participated in discussions that helped clarify the nature of the islands' fauna. The Trinidad and Tobago Forestry Department has been helpful with issuing permits, information, and assistance; thanks go to: Carol James, Dennis Garcia, Howard Nelson, and Bheesham Ramdial. Special thanks go to Julie Niznik-Perisco for the original art work and redrawings of others. Also contributing to the illustrations were Missy Bowker, Maria Bucio, Ramiro Nava, Shelley Calabrese and Sara Murphy, Nick Alberini, and John Polykandriotis. Ashley Mills translated literature and Ria Tsaliagos compiled tables. The Division of Amphibians and Reptiles of the Field Museum of Natural History provided laboratory space and endless help in obtaining specimens on loan and finding references; special thanks go to Alan Resatar, Hymen Marx, Harold K. Voris, Molly Ozaki, Janet Uvarji, and Cassie Redhead. Other people and their institutions that have been particularly helpful: Ronald I. Crombie, W. Ronald Heyer, Roy McDiarmid, Robert P. Reynolds, and Addison Wynn (USNM); Jose P. Rosado (MCZ); Charles J. Cole and Charles W. Myers (AMNH); James R. Dixon (Texas A&M University); C. J. McCoy (CMNH); Joseph R. Bailey, (Duke University); Elizabeth S. Wing and David L. Auth (Florida State Museum); William E. Duellman and David Cannatella (KU); Juan Rivero (University of Puerto Rico); Jon Mendelson and Edward Miller (Governors State University); and Ray Pawley (Chicago Zoological Society). Seven people have done extensive reading of the manuscript and have been extremely helpful in making it as error-free as possible: Robert W. Henderson, William W. Lamar, James D. Lazell, David L. Auth, Greg Cleven, Mike Dloogatch, and Tom Anton. Any remaining errors are mine alone. The staffs of the Field Musuem of Natural History library and the Plainfield Illinois Public Library did an outstanding job in tracking down hard-to-find books and journals. Jim Harding, Phil Drajeske, and Paul Gritis also acted as sources of hard-to-obtain articles. Peter J. Murphy is to be commended for his efforts in the computer layout of the figures and maps.

PART 1

General Information

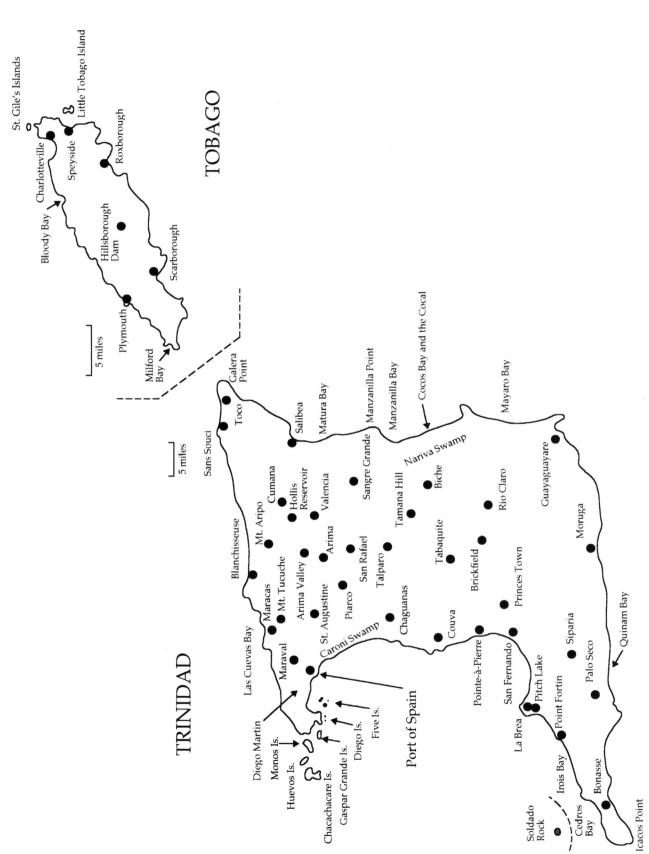

Locations of frequently collected areas of Trinidad and Tobego

TOBAGO

St. Gile's Islands

Little Tobago Island

Roxborough

Speyside

Charlotteville

Bloody Bay

Hillsborough Dam

Scarborough

Plymouth

Milford Bay

5 miles

TRINIDAD

Galera Point

Toco

Sans Souci

Salibea

Matura Bay

Manzanilla Point

Manzanilla Bay

Cocos Bay and the Cocal

Mayaro Bay

Nariva Swamp

5 miles

Cumana

Mt. Aripo

Hollis Reservoir

Valencia

Sangre Grande

Tamana Hill

Biche

Rio Claro

Guayaguayare

Blanchisseuse

Maracas

Mt. Tucuche

Arima Valley

Arima

San Rafael

Talparo

Tabaquite

Brickfield

Princes Town

Moruga

Las Cuevas Bay

Maraval

St. Augustine

Piarco

Chaguanas

Couva

Caroni Swamp

Diego Martin

Monos Is.

Huevos Is.

Chachacare Is.

Gaspar Grande Is.

Diego Is.

Five Is.

Port of Spain

Pointe-à-Pierre

San Fernando

Pitch Lake

Siparia

Palo Seco

Quinam Bay

La Brea

Point Fortin

Bonasse

Irois Bay

Soldado Rock

Cedros Bay

Icacos Point

Physiographic Features and Geology

Beard (1944) wrote, " . . . The mountains of Tobago constitute the last and most easterly link in the great coastal cordillera of Venezuela. Tobago, the Northern Range of Trinidad and the Paria Peninsula of Venezuela are the three ridges of related structure arranged parallel and *en echelon.*" I fully support this assertion and treat these islands as extensions of mainland South America throughout the text. It is only in this context that the herpetofauna's zoogeography can be fully understood.

Trinidad lies between 10°3′ and 10°51′ north latitudes and between 61°55′ and 60°55′ west longitudes. Tobago lies between 11°8′ and 11°30′ north latitudes and 61°5′ and 60°28′ west longitudes. Figure 1 shows the position of both islands. Politically both islands are considered to be the southernmost islands of the West Indies (Lesser Antilles), but the geological structure, flora, and fauna indicate that these islands are better regarded as outliers of the South American continent.

Trinidad

Trinidad is separated from Venezuela by a strait 11 km wide, and is located just north of the Orinoco Delta. At its greatest north-south axis Trinidad is 105 km long, and it averages 77 km in width; in total area it is 4769 km^2. The island has been divided into five physiographic regions (Figure 2) by Liddle (1946); a short description of each follows.

1. The Northern Range is a low series of parallel ridges that is an extension of the Coastal Cordillera of Venezuela. The highest peaks are Aripo (940 m) and Tucuche (936 m). The Range is cut by a suite of northwest-southeast striking faults which abut the El Pilar Fault System. The Northern Range is 11–16 km wide and about 88 km long. In profile it is shorter and steeper on the north side, and has extensive foothills on the southern edge. Most of the region lies between 150–456 m in elevation, but the majority of peaks and ridge tops are between 456 and 760 m in elevation. Fifteen valleys dissect the Northern Range; three more to the west are now drowned and represent open waterways. Most of the streams are transverse and the largest drain to the south. These south draining streams have cut deep valleys; the exceptions are the alluviated Tucker and Diego Martin valleys west of Port of Spain. Metamorphic rocks, phyllites, quartzites, and recrystallized limestones of Jurassic-Cretaceous age compose the Northern Range. Figure 3 shows a profile of the Northern Range in an east-west section.

2. The Northern Basin (includes the Caroni Syncline of Farfan, 1985) is composed of a dissected alluvial terrace and a peneplain, most of which is at elevations between 15–60 m above sea level. During the Miocene and Pliocene much of this appears to have been covered by shallow seas that were filled by clastics and limestone. The average width of the basin is about 16 km, but on the western side of the island it widens to about 25 km and contains the Caroni Swamp. Caroni Swamp is about 103 square kilometers of mangroves supplied with freshwater from the Northern and Central Ranges as well as saltwater from the inundating tide; salinity approaches 25 ppt during the dry season. The higher central portion of rolling terrain divides the drainage systems. The upland runoff is carried to the west by the Caroni drainage system; and the runoff to the east is carried by the Oropuche River.

3. The Central Range is a belt of low hills dividing the island into northern and southern halves. The average width of the range is 5–8 km and the elevation varies between 60–300 m. These hills run diagonally across Trinidad from Manzanilla to Pointe-à-Pierre, a distance of about 60 km. Tamana Hill is the highest point, reaching 307 m in elevation. The uplifted Brasso and Tamana Formations form the backbone of the Central Range. On the southern edge are the poorly defined

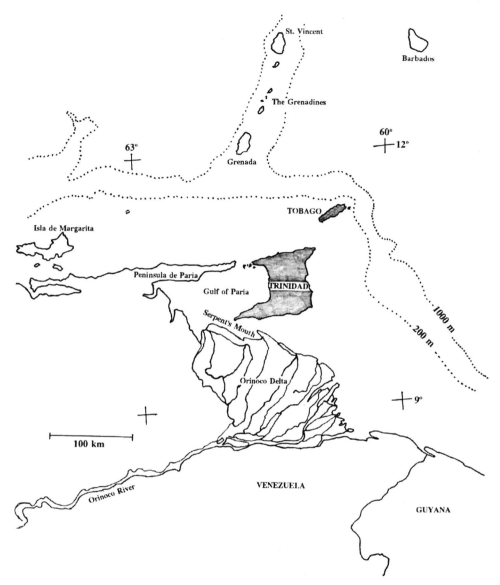

Figure 1. The position of Trinidad and Tobago.

Naparima Hill and Central Range Fault Systems. Drainage is mostly to the northwest into Caroni Swamp, and to the southeast into Nariva Swamp and the tributaries of the Ortorie River. Shales, quartzites, and limestones compose this range.

4. The Southern Basin (includes the Naparima Fold Belt of Farfan, 1985) is a gently rolling area south of the Central Range with elevations below 60 m. The Naparima Fold Belt is bound to the north and west by the Central Range and the Naparima Hill Faults, and to the south by an irregular, east-to-west line extending from approximately Mosquito Creek to just north of Radix Point. The higher, central portion divides the drainage into eastern and western systems. To the east the waters of Nariva and the Ortorie reach the Atlantic, and

to the west the Oropuche River and lagoon empty into the Gulf of Paria. The area has a northeast-southwest orientation from which the Nariva Formation outcrops. Nariva Swamp is a 258 square kilometer complex of palm marsh, mangroves, and herbaceous swamp. Farfan (1985) defined the Southern Basin as the area south of the Naparima Lowlands where a thick Upper Miocene to Pleistocene group of distinctive sediments are preserved. The Basin is a broad, intensely folded, and faulted syncline with an axis that strikes east-west, and has trapped oil, which is being exploited.

5. The Southern Range is a series of discontinuous low hills forming a barrier to the Atlantic on the southern edge of the island. Elevations are generally lower than

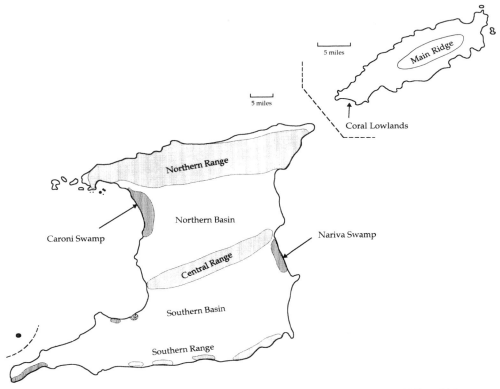

Figure 2. The physiographic regions of Trinidad and Tobago. Modified from Liddle (1946).

150 m, but the Trinity Hills in the southeast reach 303 m. These low hills represent tectonic uplift of Southern Basin Sediments. The major drainage systems all discharge to the south, into the Serpents Mouth. In the west is the Erin River, the central system is the Moruga River and in the east is the Piolte River.

Trinidad is separated from Venezuela by the Gulf of Paria which reaches depths of 27–38 m. To the south is the Serpent's Mouth, a strait 11 km wide, with a minimal depth of 13.7 m and a maximum depth of 38 m, which separates Trinidad from the Orinoco's delta. To the northwest is the Boca Grande, a strait 6–10 km wide separating Trinidad's Chacachacare Island from Venezuela's Península de Paria. To the southeast of the Península de Paria is Patos Island, now considered part of Venezuela. The Boca Grande channel is relatively deep and may represent one or more drowned valleys recently scoured out by currents. To the east are the Dragons' Mouths, a series of three channels (40–246 m deep) separating islands which are peaks and ridges of drowned valleys that were at one time much higher, and connected Trinidad's Northern Range to the Península de Paria of Venezuela. Chacachacare Island is about 7 km² and reaches 239 m in elevation; Huevos Island is about 1 km² and reaches 198 m in elevation; and Monos Island is about 9 km² and reaches 280 m in elevation. All of these islands have a herpetofauna. In the shelter of the Gulf of Paria, on the south side of Trinidad's northwest peninsula

are the islands of Gasparillo (0.3 km long); Gaspar Grande or Gasparee (2.5 km long); the Diego Islands: Cronstadt and Carrera (both about 0.3 km long); and the Five Islands: Little Centipede, Carrera, Caledonia, Lenagan and Nelson (all are very small). All of these have a herpetofuana. On the north side of the northwest peninsula is Saut d' Eau, a small island with at least one reptile species. Soldado Rock reaches about 42 m in elevation and is located in the Gulf of Paria about 9 km WNW from the tip of the Trinidad's southwest peninsula. It has a herpetofuana of at least two species of lizards.

Tobago

Tobago is about 36 km northeast of Trinidad, with an interisland channel that reaches a depth in excess of 91 m. Much of the channel is less than 72 m. Tobago is 51 km long and 18 km at its widest point, with an area of approximately 300 km²; and its most prominent physiographic feature is the Main Ridge which runs in an east-west direction for about 24 km. The highest point on the ridge is an ill-defined peak that reaches 549 m. The surrounding landscape is steep, broken terrain, with ridges, and deep gullies cut by numerous fast-moving streams. The only coastal plain is at the extreme southwest end of the island which is formed from coral reefs. In this area are two marshes, Kilgwyn Swamp and Bon Ac-

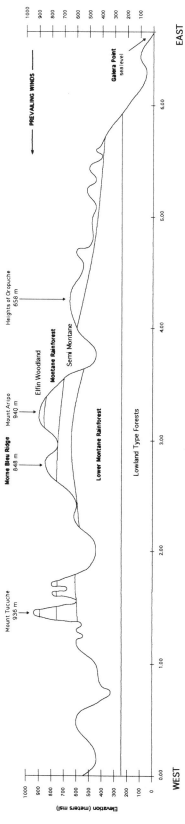

Figure 3. A profile of Trinidad's Northern Range, showing major peaks and their altitudes, vegetation types, and the direction of the prevailing wind. Redrawn from Beard (1946).

cord Lagoon, which have extensive development in and around them.

The following description is based upon Rowley (1979). The northern third of Tobago is composed of the North Coast Metamorphic Group which is a broad anticlinorium dipping gently to the northeast. Overturned isoclinal folds and small-scale faulting with maximum displacements of a few meters are general features. The metamorphics are subdivided into three formations: the Main Ridge, the Parlatuvier, and Mt. Dillon. These are composed of greenschists, quartzites, mica-schists, and greenstones.

The Main Ridge rocks are the oldest on the island, with the possible exception of the fault-emplaced slivers of ultra-mafics found within these rocks. The Main Ridge is mostly platy, hematite-stained, sericitie-schists, and phyllites interbedded with significant amounts of grey-brown quartzites, greenstones, and smaller quantities of schistose metavolcanics. The oldest metamorphics form the core of the anticlinal structure and grade upward into the Main Ridge Formation. The boundary between the Parlatuvier and the Main Ridge Formation is where the metavolcanics become the dominant rocks. The Parlatuvier Formation overlies the Main Ridge schists and phyllites. It is dominated by massive greenstones and greenschists. Rocks of this formation are almost continuous around the coastline in the metamorphic belt. The Mt. Dillon Formation is characterized by rust-colored quartzites that are thinly bedded and folded.

A belt of igneous rocks covers a little more that one-half of the island, between the Northern Coast Schist Group and the Tertiary-Quaternary sediments of the southwest. The northern portion of the igneous belt is a complex, Lower Cretaceous, dioritic plutonic body that intrudes into the metamorphic belt on the north and a volcanic belt on the south side of the pluton. Maxwell (1948) divided the volcanics that intrude into the pluton into the Goldsborough Formation, the Bacolet Formation, the Merchiston Formation, and the Hawk's Bill Formation. Two ultramafics occur throughout the pluton, as do a number of dike systems.

The southwestern tip of Tobago was inundated in the Pliocene and resulted in the sedimentation of drowned river valleys in the southwestern lowlands. Outcrops of these deposits occur at localities between the Bacolet River and Canoe Bay to the west, and form the Rockly Bay Formation. Quaternary reef facies cover the southwestern end of the island from sea level to elevations of 30 m. These are composed of massive coral heads and mollusc remains, in other areas calcareous sands represent the limestone formations. The variable topography has contributed to the diversity of the islands' flora and fauna by presenting a structurally complex environment containing many microhabitats.

Islands and rocks around Tobago that may, or do, harbor a herpetofauna include the following: Sister Rocks off the north coast; St. Gile's Islands, Goat Island, and Little Tobago Island off the northeast coast; and Queen Island, Richmond Island, and Smith Island off the south coast. The latter three are all very small, less than 150 m in length.

Tectonics of Trinidad And Tobago

Both islands have a complex and controversial tectonic history. Maze (1984) presented a map (his Figure 5) showing northern Venezuela including the Península de Paria as being allochthonous and stated the materials in this area have been accreted or obducted since the end of Jurassic time. It is unclear if Trinidad and Tobago are included in this accreted mass. Case et al. (1984) considered Trinidad's Northern Range and Tobago as part of the Cordillera De La Costa geological province, while the southern portion of Trinidad is in a separate Trinidad Province. Mattson (1984) argued that the southern margin of the Caribbean Plate adjoins the mostly continental South American Plate. In the eastern part of the margin, in the Caribbean Mountains of Venezuela and the offshore islands, a complicated history of subduction, uplift, and nappe formation extended from the Jurassic through the Eocene. Vierbuchen (1984) stated that north of the El Pilar fault [at the southern edge of the Northern Range] is an east-west trending mountain range called the eastern Cordillera de la Costa in Venezuela and the Northern Range in Trinidad; and that these mountains are underlain by a deformed, low-to-medium-grade metamorphic terrane of Mesozoic age. Metamorphic rocks also crop out offshore on Isla Margarita and on smaller islands to the east and west. The most easterly exposures of metamorphic rocks are on Tobago. Duncan and Hargraves (1984) presented a model showing the Villa de Cura complex being torn off the Pacific coast of Colombia about 100 million years BP and pushed northeastward and accreted to its present position in northern Venezuela about 38 million years BP. This model is in direct opposition to Speed (1985) who explained the tectonics of the Trinidad area by an ongoing right-oblique collision between the Lesser Antilles arc and northeastern continental South America, noting the major tectonic elements engaged in, or created by, the collision are the southern Lesser Antilles magmatic arc, forearc basin, the Araya-Tobago terrane, a South American foreland thrust and fold belt, and a foreland basin. He suggested the southern boundary of the Caribbean plate is a non-rigid, discontinuous assembly of microplates. The Araya-Tobago terrane includes Trinidad's Northern Range and Tobago, prompting Speed to propose a proximal, rather than exotic origin for this material, which was accreted to the Lesser Antilles forearc during its transit of the ocean basin, continental slope, and outer shelf.

Robertson and Burke (1989) argued the Mesozoic metamorphic rocks of Trinidad's Northern Range were formed during a Late Cretaceous–Early Paleocene arc-continent collision and since their formation they have rafted eastward at least 1000 km in the northern wall of the El Pilar fault. Speed et al. (1991) took exception to this, stating the maximum age of metamorphism and first ductile deformation in Northern Range schists is 20–30 million years old based upon argon dating and structural studies, and the range was about 500 km from present position based upon plate velocities at the

Cayman Trough. Russo and Speed (1992) proposed a model of the transition zone between the Lesser Antilles arc and continental South America emphasizing the steepening, detachment, and then sinking of the Atlantic lithosphere that is attached to northern continental South America. The continental wedge overrides the slab and is overridden by terranes attached to the Caribbean plate, and the structural and kinematic transitions are the consequence of the continuing collision between South America and the overriding Caribbean terranes.

Sea Level Changes in the Quaternary

The degree to which tectonic events have influenced the current herpetofauna is uncertain. It seems likely that more recent fluctuations in sea level during the Quaternary which connected and isolated the two islands and the mainland have had a greater influence in determining the composition of the extant herpetofauna.

Dawson (1992) reviewed the evidence for Late Quaternary sea level changes, noting that it is astonishingly difficult to reconstruct the pattern of sea level changes. He summarized the problems as follows: (1) determining sea level in formerly glaciated environments is complicated by geoidal attraction of ocean water to ice sheets; (2) the pattern of geoidal sea surface change is unknown for the Late Quaternary; (3) disaggregation of Late Quaternary hydro-isostatic and tectono-eustatic changes from glacio-eustatic and glacio-isostatic is very difficult; and (4) there is no such thing as a global eustatic sea level curve, the curves have only regional significance. Despite the aforementioned problems, Dawson noted the close correlation of sea level fluctuations estimated by Shackleton (1987) from studying emerged New Guinea coral reef terraces, to the independently collected plankton and benthic ^{18}O isotope data. Dawson also cited studies in Barbados, Haiti, Japan, and Alaska which have produced similar curves for Late Quaternary sea level fluctuations.

Using Shackleton's curves, and assuming they are applicable to the Caribbean, as data presented by Dodge et al. (1983) and Fairbanks (1989) imply, it appears sea level exceeded current levels and would have flooded most of the Northern and Southern Basins of Trinidad lying below 10–25 m above current sea level, reducing the land area to the foothills, peaks, and ridges of the Northern Range, the Central Range, and the Southern Range between 115,000–125,000 years BP, and again between 2,000–6,000 years BP. Superflooding thus turned the three ranges into island refugia for terrestrial flora and fauna during these time periods.

However, between 25,000–115,000 years BP sea level flucutated 10–50 m below current levels. And, at two points in time, about 135,000 years BP, and again about 20,000 years BP, sea level plunged to 130 m lower than current levels. Gascoyne et al. (1979) reported evidence that sea level was reduced even more, to 160 m, during the Mid-Quaternary.

Considering that the maximum current depth of the channel between Trinidad's south coast and Venezuela is 38 m, Trinidad and the mainland have been connected a minimum of five times and possibly as many as seven times in the past 140,000 years, but more revealing is the fact that for about 65% of the last 140,000 years (a total of 91,000 years), Trinidad was connected to the mainland. Assuming that 91 m is, and has been, the maximum depth between Trinidad and Tobago, these two islands were connected by dry land at least twice, possibly three times in the past 140,000 years. The total time involved in the connections appears to be 18,900 years, or 13.5%, of the past 140,000 years. Land bridge connections in the past 140,000 years between the two islands and the mainland were not just brief, ephemeral episodes, but extended periods of time; nine times longer than the history of civilization for the connection of Trinidad to the mainland. A history long enough to provide considerable time for faunal exchange and gene flow. Thus, connection, isolation, reconnection, followed by more isolation, etc. help account for the diversity and the similarities in the populations seen between the two islands and the mainland.

Climate

Trinidad

Despite Trinidad's relatively small size, it has a high degree of variability in local climates. Undoubtedly, this has influenced the number of species of amphibians and reptiles that the island can support by creating numerous microhabitats.

Trinidad's temperature and precipitation regimes are described by Beard (1946) for the years 1935–1940 and by Granger (1982) for the years 1921–1966. Temperature data collected between 1921–1966 show that the monthly mean temperature of Trinidad has a relatively consistent distribution. The annual range of temperature is about 1.9°C. The mean diurnal range during this time period was 10.4°C. The mean daily maximum temperature was 32°C, while the mean daily minimum was 21.6°C. There were two temperature maxima, one in May (27.6°C) and the other in October (27.2°C). The wet season (June-December) was the warmest period, presumably from increased solar radiation due to longer days combined with maximum cloud cover that decreases heat loss. The annual mean temperature for Granger's 46-year period was 26.7°C, with an annual range of 2.9°C. Beard (1946) reported similar temperatures, and noted the average monthly maximum temperature varies between 30.2°C in January and 32.1°C in May; and that the average monthly minimum temperature ranged from 19.7°C to 22.1°C in February. Beard (1946) provided some anecdotal data on the temperatures at the higher elevations in the Northern Range. On 10 March at 288 m on Mt. Aripo the temperature was 28°C. When entering the forest at 486 m at noon the temperature was 23°C, and at 1600 h in camp at 700 m the temperature was 19°C. During the night the thermometer fell to 16°C. On a subsequent trip to Aripo, Beard (1946) found the nighttime temperature in February to be 14.4°C.

The humidity approached 100% at night and fell to 60% in afternoons during the dry season and 75% in the afternoons of the wet season. Sunshine averaged 6–7 hours per day. Wind speed in Port of Spain, at sea level, averaged 6 kph, with the maximum recorded (except during hurricanes) at 40 kph. Hurricanes are uncommon in Trinidad because it lies at the southern edge of the hurricane belt. The hurricane of 1810 may have done some damage to the forests in the Northern Range, but the severe gales of 1884, 1891, and 1892 probably did little damage to the forests. In 1933 a hurricane struck the south coast of the island and severely damaged the forests (Beard, 1946). Hurricanes have occurred since, the most recent in 1993, but have done only minimal damage. Granger (1982) found no relationship between their occurrence and rainfall deviation from the monthly mean.

Precipitation varies widely on the island. Figure 4 summarizes mean monthly rainfall at 11 stations on Trinidad (based on data from Beard, 1946 and Granger, 1982). February is usually the driest month, but March and April are also relatively dry. June, July, and August are the wettest months. None of these stations represents conditions at the higher elevations in the Northern Range, and Beard (1946) suggested that humidity must be very high, sunshine very low, and rainfall of at least 5080 mm must occur at the high elevations. Even during the dry season the ground at higher elevations is soggy, and in the wet season rain may be almost continuous. The peaks of Aripo and Tucuche are shrouded nightly with mist and clouds during the dry season, and during much of the day and night during the wet season.

The Northern Range probably has localities receiving in excess of 5000 mm of rain per year, while there are localities in the southwest peninsula and offshore islands near the northwest peninsula that receive less than 1140 mm of rain per annum (see Figure 5). Droughts occur, and in dry years the rainforest catches fire. The dry season occurs from January to early May, and the wet season from late May to December. A break in the rains in September or October is locally referred to as the *petit careme*.

The climatic regions of Trinidad (Figure 6) follow Beard (1946). Most of the island falls into a "wet seasonal" climate region where there are wet and dry seasons. The Northern Range is in a "lower montane" climatic region, where rainfall is supplemented by condensing water on the vegetation. And, there is a narrow strip along the eastern coast receiving about 1651 mm of rain per annum, and it is continually subjected to prevailing winds off the ocean that carry salt spray. Beard terms this a "coastal" climate.

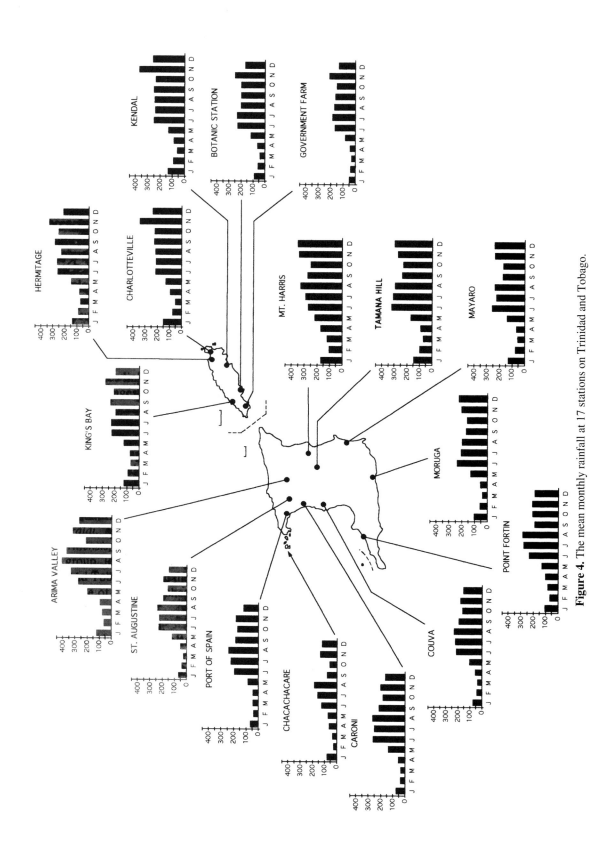

Figure 4. The mean monthly rainfall at 17 stations on Trinidad and Tobago.

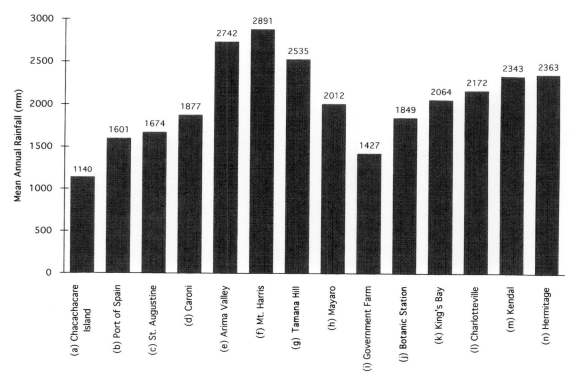

Figure 5. The mean annual rainfall at 14 stations on Trinidad (a-h) and Tobago (i-n).

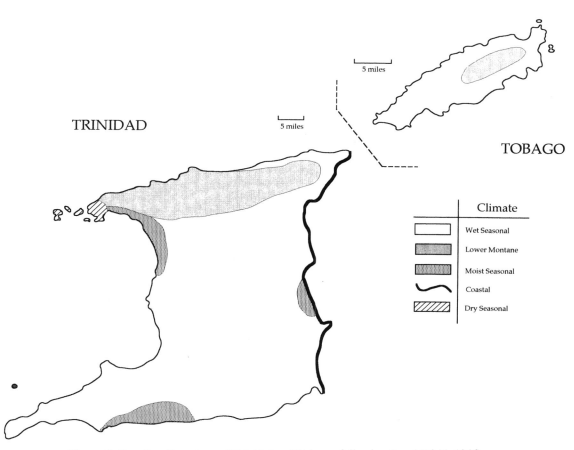

Figure 6. The climatic regions of Trinidad and Tobago, following Beard (1944; 1946).

Tobago

Tobago's climate is similar to that of Trinidad, and Beard (1944) compared the climate on Tobago to that of the Toco District of northeastern Trinidad. The year is divided into wet and dry seasons with the dry season lasting from January to May and the wet season extending from June to December. Rainfall decreases slightly in October, but not to the degree seen in Trinidad. Rainfall varies from one locality to another; the Government Farm in the southwest receives an average of 1427 mm per annum and Hermitage in the northeast receives about 2363 mm per annum. The southwest station's rainfall varies from 798–3470 mm and the northeast station's rainfall varies from 1742–3367 mm per annum; the Main Ridge receives an average of 3810 mm per annum. The graphs in Figure 4 illustrate mean monthly rainfall at six stations in Tobago. Figure 5 summarizes the mean annual rainfall at the six Tobago stations (i-n) and is based on data from Beard (1944).

Little information is available on Tobago temperatures. Beard (1944) suggested that they are similar to temperatures on Trinidad, but that the humidity is lower. The prevailing wind is the northeast trade which blows with some regularity, but no data are available. Figure 6 summarizes the climatic regions of Tobago, based upon Beard (1944).

Vegetation

Vegetation of Trinidad

Trinidad's vegetation is complex due to the variation in rainfall and the variety of soils occurring on the island, and is described by Williams et al. (1928), Marshall (1934), Beard (1946), and others. Beard's (1946) monograph is most useful for descriptions of plant communities and an analytical key to plant formations. Since the heterogeneous nature of the vegetation contributes support to the large herpetofauna, the natural vegetation is summarized here.

When Columbus discovered Trinidad in 1498, during his third voyage, the island was covered with forest and inhabited by Arawak Indians living along the coast; savanna environments were restricted to small areas of poorly drained soils. Figure 7 is an attempt to reconstruct the pre-Columbian vegetation. At glacial maxima, lower sea levels and more xeric conditions resulted in the reduction of forests and the expansion of savanna habitats. During interglacial periods, forest expanded and savanna was reduced. Beard (1946) presented a model of Late Pleistocene vegetation at glacial maxima on Trinidad, and it has been modified in Figure 8 to include Tobago. It should be noted that much of the natural vegetation that existed during Beard's study has been changed by human activities. What remains are small islands of natural vegetation, often connected with secondary growth and agricultural areas. The following summary of the major plant formations is based on Beard (1946).

Evergreen seasonal forest is the most widespread naturally occurring forest in Trinidad, covering the lowlands, the Central Range, as well as the foothills and lower slopes of the Northern Range; and it receives rainfall that is less than 2000 mm (Bacon, 1978) per annum. The upper canopy is discontinuous, with some trees emerging to 30–46 m, while the middle canopy is continuous between 12–27 m, and contains an understory subcanopy between 3–9 m. Lianas and epiphytes are well developed, and the latter include bromeliads, aroids, ferns, and orchids. This formation includes the extensive Mora forests where *Mora excelsa* makes up 85–95% of the canopy. Enormous buttress roots support these trees and collect leaf litter, making an attractive microhabitat for some of the herpetofauna.

Semi-evergreen seasonal forest occurs in areas subject to seasonal drought. But, the lack of water is not necessarily due to lack of rain; steep topography, exposure to wind, and free draining soils contribute to the lack of available moisture. The forest is open and supports a well-developed shrub layer; the canopy occurs between 6–12 m with trees emerging from the canopy that may reach 25 m. Lianas and epiphytes are few and most epiphytes present are bromeliads. Although sunlight penetrates to the forest floor, there is little ground cover.

Beard (1946) could not find any undisturbed examples of deciduous seasonal forest in Trinidad. The canopy is low, 3–9 m, and lianas and epiphytes are almost absent; some emergent trees may reach 18 m. This formation did occur on islands off the northwest peninsula, on the peninsula, and in the vicinity of Port of Spain; but housing developments have replaced much of this forest.

Trinidad's littoral woodland may be a windswept thicket a few feet high, or a loose stand of trees 12 m tall, with some palms reaching 30 m. All trees are evergreen and have leathery, cutinized leaves; lianas are numerous and bromeliads are on large trees and on the ground. Salt spray and wind are dominant factors in this formation, and it occurs along the eastern coast where coconut palms have not taken over.

In Trinidad, lower montane rainforest is confined to the Northern Range between 243–760 m. There is no seasonal drought, and the forest receives 1778–3810 mm of rain per annum. There is a closed canopy between 21–30 m, with an average tree height of 27 m. Emergent trees are absent, lianas are poorly represented, and epiphytes are restricted to the crowns of trees. A discontinuous understory occurs at 6–12 m, and ground vegetation is very sparse.

The largest area of montane rainforest occurs on the Aripo massif, in the Northern Range, above 760 m, and at a few other locations in the Northern Range (Figure 3). There is a closed canopy between 15–18 m and no trees over 22 m. An understory is present between 6–12 m. Lianas and

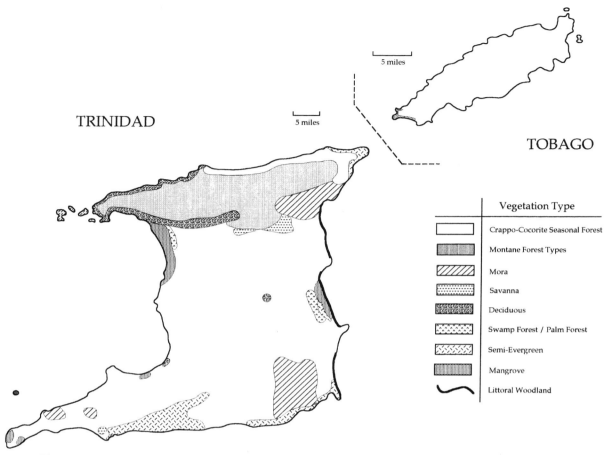

Figure 7. A modified version of Beard's (1946) model of Pre-Colombian vegetation on Trinidad and Tobago.

epiphytes are luxuriant from the canopy to ground level. Ground plants are few, with the exception of prominent terrestrial bromeliads.

Elfin woodland is restricted to the summit of Aripo (above 851 m), and the summit of Tucuche shows elements of this formation, as does a small area on Morne Bleu Ridge (Figure 3). The canopy is formed by a dense layer of tree ferns and small palms at about 3 m, and some trees emerge from the canopy attaining 6–7 m. There is a constant supply of moisture, from rain and condensation on vegetation; and all of the woody vegetation is enveloped with mosses and lichens.

Swamp forest occupies the landward edge of Nariva Swamp, and the mouth of the Oropuche River in areas that are continually inundated with freshwater. Swamp bloodwood, *Pterocarpus officinalis,* dominates the habitat, and larger trees have enormous plank buttresses, and form a canopy at about 20 m.

Palm swamp is composed of *Roystonea* or *Mauritia* palms that are scattered and do not form a canopy. The palmiste palm, *Roystonea oleracea,* occurs on the seaward margins of Nariva Swamp and Los Blanquizales Lagoon, while the moriche palm, *Mauritia setigera,* occurs on the landward margins of these freshwater swamps. An under-

story of scrub or forest may be found between 3–18 m, but the palms do not form an enclosed canopy and the forest is patchy. *Roystonea* reach more than 30 m, while *Mauritia* attain 25 m.

Herbaceous swamp occurs in areas continually inundated with water that may be 1–1.5 m deep. Clumps of the giant flat sedge, *Cyperus giganteus,* along with aroids and grasses compose this formation. Deeper parts of swamps and lagoons support growths that reach 3 m high. Caroni, Nariva, and Roussillac swamps, and Los Blanquizales and Icacos lagoons support this formation. At some locations this is a fire-maintained habitat.

Mangrove woodland occurs in all coastal areas where the land is tidally inundated with brackish water. Caroni Swamp is dominated by three red mangrove species, but black, white, and button mangroves are also present. The canopy may reach 24 m, is somewhat open, and has no understory except for young mangroves. The best growths occur in areas where the surf is broken by offshore sandbars, and the salinity is close to 36 ppt.

Marsh forest is confined to a few square kilometers near Long Stretch at Valencia. A canopy formed by palms between 3–9 m has emergent trees that may reach 24 m, but do

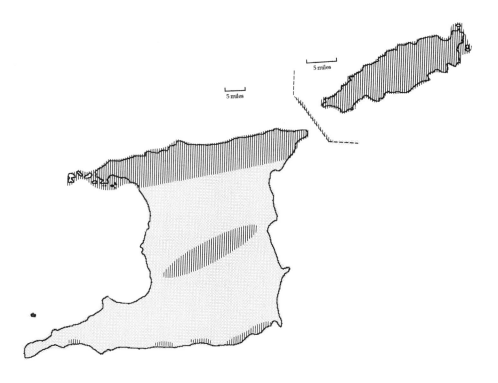

Figure 8. A model of late Pleistocene vegetation at glacial maxima. Based upon Beard (1944) for Tobago; and Beard (1946) for Trindad. Crosshatching represents areas of forest, vertical marks represent savanna.

not form a canopy. Beard suggests that this is a specialized community adapted to the leached, clay-pan soil.

In the palm marsh, as well as in the savannas, there are waterlogged habitats that support *Mauritia-Chrysobalanus* associations. This community is found in the Erin savanna, where *Mauritia* palms emerge to 20 m from a low, thicket-like growth that is 3–9 m high; and the ground vegetation is composed of ferns and sedges.

Savannas are short grass-sedge formations with scattered shrubs attaining 4 m; they occur in small, localized areas of the Northern and Southern Basins as well as in some hill-mountain areas. Beard (1952) noted the Erin and St. John savannas are small patches growing on the remnants of a recently uplifted ancient peneplain, and the savanna exists because the soil is waterlogged during the wet season and desiccated during the dry season. The small Piarco, Mausica, and O'Meara savannas occur on terraced-plateaus with poor drainage; while the large Aripo savanna complex occurs in an area of high rainfall (about 2600 mm per annum) with poor drainage and an ironpan subsoil. In the Aripo savannas the dominant vegetation is sedge, and the area contains a large number of endemic plants. The St. Joseph savanna occurs on a steep southerly slope with the quartzite bedrock close to the surface. This savanna is also the result of soil factors rather than lack of precipitation. Other savannas are derived from human alterations of the forest environment.

Arima Valley Ecology

The Arima Valley is situated in the center of Trinidad's Northern Range and because it has been and continues to be the site of numerous biological studies, its environment is relatively well known and worthy of discussion. The valley floor is cut by the Arima River draining to the south. The southern end of the valley is near sea level and it rises to just over 730 meters at Morne Bleu Ridge. The climate is wet and warm and Beebe (1952) reported the mean rainfall from three stations as ranging from 2591 to 3073 mm (for 3 to 5 years). Mean relative humidity ranged from 77–89%. The low point is normally about 50% which is reached about noon; the dew point is reached almost every night. Mean monthly temperatures ranged from 23.3°C in February to 25.8°C in May. The maximum recorded temperature is 32.8°C, while the minimum recorded temperature is 17.8°C. No wind records are available, but the valley is well sheltered from the prevailing northeast trade winds. The southern end of the valley is savanna with poorly drained soil. Much of this is now developed for housing, agriculture, and industry. Proceeding northward there is derived savanna from cut forest, much of which is developed. Patches of deciduous seasonal forest, transitional forest between deciduous seasonal forest, and lower montane rainforest exist in the area. A relatively undisturbed section of transitional forest can be found on the ridges above St. Patrick's Estate. From this area northward the valley's natural vegetation is lower montane rainforest, but some of this has been cut and planted with cocoa, citrus, bananas, and more recently christophine (*Sechium edule*). The Asa Wright Nature Centre and the government of Trinidad and Tobago protect much of the higher areas of the valley.

Herpetologically, the Arima Valley is of interest because it contains 75 species of amphibians and reptiles, 64% of the herpetofauna known from the island. The high diversity is due to the complex series of successional stages that generate numerous microhabits for wildlife due to agriculture in the lower valley grading into the relatively well-protected forest in the upper valley. Additionally the number of biologists that visit the area have also made the fauna of this area very well known (Plates 1, 2).

Vegetation of Tobago

Discussing the origin of Tobago's vegetation Beard (1944) wrote, "The flora of Tobago is entirely continental in its affinities. Belonging structurally to the South American mainland and not to the Lesser Antilles, Tobago is no oceanic island, . . . the flora corresponds in a close degree with that of Trinidad. It is by no means as rich, due to the disparity in size of the two islands. Trinidad, twelve times as large, contains many plants of swamps, savannas, and high mountain woodlands . . . assemblages which are not found in Tobago." Beard also noted plant communities have a curiously Antillean stamp, attributing the similarity to the Antillean-like climate of Tobago. The following description of Tobago vegetation is based upon Beard (1944).

Most of the coastal swamps in Tobago have been drained and reclaimed for cultivation, and now exist only in relatively small areas where the combination of tidal mudflats and brackish water permit the establishment of mangrove forests. Tobago's mangrove woodland was similar to other mangrove habitats in the Caribbean.

Littoral woodland is a stunted, windswept community similar to that described for Trinidad. It occurs on shoreline cliffs, rocks, sandbanks, and on small islets off the coast in areas where rainfall is high enough to promote growth, but the plants are structurally dwarfed by the wind and salt spray.

Before humans disturbed Tobago's vegetation most of the lower slopes of the island were covered with seasonal forests. These forests were cleared for agriculture and are no longer present; however, the island of Little Tobago still retains its seasonal deciduous forests. Beard suggested that because Tobago's lowlands are very dry and the Main Ridge is so wet that at one time the island had a series of transitional communities ranging from seasonal deciduous forest to evergreen-seasonal forest and rainforest.

Lowland rainforest occurs at altitudes between 243–364 m, and has a closed canopy at about 36 m, with a lower mid-dle story between 12–24 m, a lower story between 3 and 12 m, and a shrub and ground layer below that. The understories are poorly defined. Beard considered this forest to be the optimal habitat for plants on Tobago because it contains enough moisture during the dry season to support growth.

Lower montane rainforests occur from 243 m to the top of the Main Ridge, but only on schist soils. The canopy is closed at about 30 m, buttressing is absent, and most of the trees have simple leaves. At the summits of the Main Ridge the canopy may be reduced to 18 m. Bromeliads and terrestrial vegetation are lush; this community is more exposed to wind, cooler temperatures, and a greater, more constant rainfall. The schist soil is several feet deep and has more water-holding ability than igneous soils.

Xerophytic rainforest occurs at elevations above 243 m on igneous soils. It has a continuous canopy between 12–18 m, with emergent trees attaining 27 m. Epiphytes and lianas are scarce, a shrub layer is absent, and ground vegetation is sparse. Beard attributes this forest to the shallow igneous soil and notes that roots rarely extend much below 450 mm. Thus, this community is the result of soil factors, not a lack of rainfall; this may account for the oxymoronic name of this forest.

Historical Changes in the Tobago Vegetation

The sugarcane industry made Tobago a valuable piece of real estate. Before 1814, sugarcane was virtually the only crop cultivated on the island and most of Tobago's landscape was converted to its culture. Beard (1944) wrote, "Old maps exist showing the boundaries of the sugar estates. . . . From these maps it appears that the areas which are now the Crown Lands and Forest Reserves were never cultivated, being too inaccessible." Since that time a variety of tree crops and other agricultural activities have prevented the landscape from returning to its climax.

Vegetation of Little Tobago

The vegetation on the 97 hectare island lying off the northeast coast of Tobago is described by Beard (1944), " . . . while it is well known that parts of the island were formerly cultivated it is entirely covered today with a vegetation which has all the appearance of being a climax. . . . The vegetation corresponds fairly closely in physiognomy with that of the island of Chacachacare, off Trinidad. . . . The vegetation of Little Tobago is a deciduous seasonal forest . . . expressing a marked deciduous period coincidental with the dry season . . . " Littoral woodland and transitional littoral woodland–deciduous forest are also present on Little Tobago. Today this island is a nature preserve, uninhabited, but frequently visited; and it contains a small herpetofauna.

Previous Herpetological Investigations

The earliest notes regarding the Trinidad and Tobago herpetofauna are scattered in the literature of early explorers. One of the earliest is in the writings of the Carmelite friar Antonio Vásquez de Espinoza (1628); his manuscript was discovered and translated by C. U. Clark. It is unclear whether Vásquez de Espinoza actually visited Trinidad or related descriptions from other travelers. He wrote,

> On the island of Trinidad and in the other tropical forest regions there are certain birds which the Indians call conotos, of the size of doves, very handsome, with black and yellow plumage, a long yellow bill, and an agreeable song. Heaven provided them with a natural instinct such that, to keep monkeys and snakes from eating their eggs and young, they pick out the tallest and most isolated trees, and build their communities of nests in large numbers on the branches so that the monkeys and snakes cannot reach them without slipping off and getting killed.

This is a very accurate description of the yellowtail or crested oropendola, *Psarocolius decumanus*. In another place he discussed an island between Guiana and Trinidad that was used to obtain iguanas for food. From the description it seems likely that this island is part of the Orinoco Delta. He states that it is made of sand and the iguanas hide in burrows.

The herpetofauna of Trinidad and Tobago is taxonomically relatively well known compared to areas in mainland South America. Of the possible 130 taxa of amphibians and reptiles on these two islands, about 23% were described in the 18th century by Linnaeus, 10% were described in the 18th century by workers other than Linnaeus, 40% were described in the 19th century, and 23% were described in the 20th century. Additionally, another 3 taxa (2.3%) are currently undescribed, but under review by herpetologists. The majority of Trinidad and Tobago taxa were described from specimens collected elsewhere in their range, usually mainland South or Central America.

The earliest attempt at summarizing the Trinidad herpetofauna is a list compiled by Court, and published in De Verteuil's (1858) volume on the island's resources. A second early list was published by Danish zoologists Reinhardt and Lutken (1863). They demonstrated that the Trinidad herpetofauna is more similar to that of South America than to other Caribbean islands. Cope (1879) listed four reptiles and one anuran from Tobago based on a collection made by Frederic Ober; however, Tuck and Hardy (1973) found that none of the Ober specimens Cope listed actually came from Tobago. R. R. Mole, a Trinidad newspaper editor, and F. W. Urich, a government entomologist, published a preliminary list of the island's herpetofauna in the *Journal of the Trinidad Field Naturalist's Club,* in 1894. In 1914 Mole published a paper on Trinidad snakes with the aid of Boettger's identifications, Boulenger's *Catalogue of Snakes in the British Museum* (1893), and private correspondence with Boulenger. Mole also included anecdotal information from Urich and A. B. Carr of Caparo, Trinidad. Mole's paper appeared in two publications in 1914: in the *Proceedings of the Agricultural Society of Trinidad and Tobago;* and in the *Fauna of Trinidad,* edited by Guppy and Tripp. Boettger (1896) listed four snakes and one anuran from Tobago, and Ober (1898) published a book on his experiences in Tobago which contains some minor comments on the island's herpetofauna. In 1910 Mole suggested Tobago has only six or seven species of snakes. However, Barbour (1916b) published a list of three amphibians and 19 reptiles from Tobago based upon collections made by H. L. Clark of the MCZ and supplemented with material collected by W. E. Broadway at the Scarborough Botanical Gardens. In 1924 Mole published yet another paper on Trinidad snakes containing short species accounts with ecological information; it lacks keys and references, but contains photographs useful for identification. The 1924 paper is famous for its natural history information, including the first report of the egg-laying habits of the bushmaster, *Lachesis muta.* It also seems likely that Mole wrote the anonymous article on harmless and useful snakes that appeared in the 1926 *Zoological Society Bulletin.* This may be an extraction from the *Trinidad Guardian* newspaper series on Trinidad snakes. In 1926 J. Roux reported on a small collection of amphibians and reptiles from Trinidad made by H. G. Kugler and E. Lehner. Adolopho Lutz visited Trinidad for 6 days in 1925 and published an annotated list of the anurans he found, as well as ones that had been previously known to occur on the island (Lutz, 1927). Also, in the mid-1920's G. Netting visited Trinidad and made observations on the breeding habits of the frog *Eupemphix trinitatus* (= *Physalaemus pustulosus*) and commented on its systematic status.

The New York Zoological Society sent a scouting expedition to Trinidad in the summer of 1934 to collect animals, primarily reptiles. The field work was done by A. Greenhall and chronicled by *New York Sun* reporter, W. Bridges. The field trip is recounted in *Snake-Hunter's Holiday* (Ditmars and Bridges, 1935), and while this is not a major contribution to science, it did serve to popularize and heighten interest in the island's fauna and herpetology.

H. W. Parker of the British Museum contributed significantly to the knowledge of Trinidad's herpetofauna with annotated lists of Trinidad's frogs and lizards (1933, 1934a, 1935b, 1936) as well as descriptions of several new taxa (1926, 1934, 1935c). Most noteworthy of the forms Parker described is the lizard *Proctoporus shrevei,* a microteiid endemic to the Northern Range. In 1939 Parker wrote a paper describing luminous organs in the males of this species, probably based upon information obtained from Ivan Sanderson (see Sanderson's 1939 account). This paper is controversial, but Parker was cautious and suggested the so-called luminous organs may actually be simple reflectors. The bioluminescent capabilities in this lizard are highly improbable; see Roth and Gans (1960).

Relatively few papers on Trinidad and Tobago's herpetofauna appear in the 1940's and 1950's. Johnson (1946) collected in the vicinity of Tucker Valley in the spring of 1944 and published some miscellaneous notes. F. Wonder, a collector for the Chicago Natural History Museum (now the Field Museum of Natural History), visited Trinidad in 1947 to collect vertebrates for the museum. His collection has not been described, but his specimens are included in this work. Lynn (1957) visited Trinidad for 6 days in 1952 and reported on the species observed. W. Beebe contributed indirectly to a knowledge of Trinidad reptiles with his work at Caripito, Venezuela, and Kartabo, British Guiana; both of these localities have many of the same species found in Trinidad (Beebe, 1944a,b, 1945, 1946). In 1952 Beebe described the ecology of the Arima Valley in Trinidad's Northern Range and listed the amphibians and reptiles found in the valley. J. P. L. Wehekind, former field assistant to F.W. Urich, commented on Trinidad snakes in the mid- and late 1950's (1955, 1960). Brongersma (1956a,b) reported on a collection of amphibians and reptiles made in 1929 by D. C. Geijskes and in 1953–54 by G. F. Mees.

Kenny, V.C. Quesnel, and G. Underwood commented on Trinidadian anoles (1959); and G. C. Gorman and colleagues also worked with anoles in the late 1960's and early 1970's. Gorman's work described the interaction between *Anolis trinitatis* and *Anolis aeneus* and the hybrids they produced. In 1962, Underwood published a survey of the herpetofauna of the eastern Caribbean, and included notes, keys, and lists of the Trinidad and Tobago herpetofauna, minus the snakes. A popular booklet on the reptiles of Trinidad by H. Boos and Quesnel was published by the Trinidad and Tobago Ministry of Education and Culture in 1968. J. P. DeVerteuil (1968) compiled a list of Tobago reptiles including 10 lizards and 16 snakes. R. Mertens collected on Tobago in the late 1960's and produced a series of papers on the island's herpetofauna (Mertens, 1969, 1970, 1972, 1973, 1974). Kenny (1969) worked on Trinidad amphibians from 1955 to 1961 and from 1963 to 1965. This is the most thorough treatment any aspect of the Trinidad herpetofauna has received to date. In the early 1960's M. Emsley contributed to the literature on Trinidad snakes, discussing species reported in error and describing the status of Tobago's *Erythrolamprus* population; and, in 1977 he published an article on Trinidad snakes that included species accounts, keys, and common names.

Freshwater chelonians are strikingly absent from most of the literature on Trinidad's herpetofauna. Underwood (1962) had some comments, but only one article dealt with nonmarine turtles (Kearney, 1972) and it was an anecdotal account of one week of turtle collecting in Trinidad. However, some Trinidad and Tobago turtle data are included in Pritchard and Trebbau's (1984) book on Venezuelan chelonians.

Medem's (1983) second volume on the crocodilians of South America includes a chapter on Trinidad and Tobago, and this is the most extensive treatment these animals received in the literature to date.

Trinidad and Tobago marine turtles are discussed in a number of reports from the late 1960's to the early 1980's authored by P. R. Bacon and colleagues.

J. D. Hardy produced a series of works on Tobago in the early and mid-1980's, reporting new species records from the island and commenting on the faunistic composition of the island. Boos continues to publish papers on the Trinidad herpetofauna. Winstel also published a short series of nontechnical papers on collecting Trinidad amphibians and reptiles. Without the foundation of these earlier works, this text would not exist.

Species Erroneously Reported or of Questionable Occurrence

Questionable records of species reported from Trinidad, Tobago, and surrounding islets are discussed here. Species that are represented by museum material or reliable eyewitnesses are noted here and included in the species accounts because the possibility exists that they may be eventually encountered; these are included in the lists, keys, and species accounts. Parker (1935b) pointed out collections made by Plée and l'Herminier were apparently made elsewhere (probably Hispaniola) but have been somehow mislabeled as being from Trinidad. Tuck et al. (1973) noted the collection of amphibians and reptiles made by Ober and reported on by Cope (1879) are probably from one of the following locations: Martinique, Grenada, St. Vincent, or the Grenadines. These errors have been transported deep into the literature of the last 100 years. The following is a summary of some major problems. Smaller issues are noted in various species accounts.

Anura

Leptodactylus pentadactylus: Mole and Urich (1894a) listed this species from the island. Kenny (1969) also reported it from the island, but his photograph clearly shows his listing to be based upon *Leptodactylus bolivianus* (Kenny, 1971). There is a single specimen of *Leptodactylus knudseni* (see that account) from Trinidad, a species that was long confused with *L. pentadactylus.* Hardy (1982) discussed *Leptodactylus* cf. *pentadactylus* on Tobago suggesting its presence or former presence on the comments made by Ober (1898) and a large, subfossil frog femur from a cave. It seems probable that references to *L. pentadactylus* on either island are more likely based upon *L. bolivianus* or *L. knudseni* considering the complete lack of *L. pentadactylus* specimens from Trinidad and Tobago.

Lithodytes lineatus: There is a single specimen of this frog from Trinidad. The locality data may be in error, but it is included in the species accounts.

Gymnophiona

Typhlonectes sp.: The presence of a caecilian on Trinidad is based upon a single, now lost specimen. A species account for *Typhlonectes* is included.

Chelonia

Claudius angustatus: Wing and Reitz (1982) reported remains of the narrow-bridged musk turtle, *Claudius angustatus* (Kinosternidae), from an Indian midden at St. John's on the northern shore of the southwest peninsula of Trinidad. The middens are in a protohistoric level dated at 1000–1500 BP. There is no evidence that this turtle is extant on Trinidad. However the remains suggest two hypotheses to explain the species presence on Trinidad. First, *Claudius* once had a greater distribution than it currently does. This may have occurred at glacial maxima, or it may be much older. Secondly, the aboriginal people of Trinidad may have done extensive traveling or trading with other Mesoamerican cultures in the Caribbean.

Geochelone carbonaria: Its presence in the area is based upon literature references, zoo specimens, and specimens that may represent feral animals. See this account.

Podocnemis expansa and *P. unifilis:* These species probably do not occur on Trinidad. The species accounts presented here are based upon literature records of waifs. See accounts.

Crocodylia

Crocodylus acutus and *Crocodylus intermedius:* These are discussed in species accounts based upon literature records and subfossil material from Indian middens. See accounts.

Sauria

Ameiva major: Dumeril and Bibron (1839) reported it from Cayenne and Trinidad. This same name is used by Court (1858). Boulenger (1885) considered *A. major* to be a synonym of *A. punctata* and listed the species as being on Trinidad. The species is then reported as present on Trinidad by Mole and Urich (1894a). Boulenger (1887) placed *A. major* and *A. punctata* in the synonymy of *A. erythrocephala.* Parker (1935b) examined the specimens and concluded the "Trinidad" specimen is most similar to *Amevia cineracea* from Guadeloupe. There is no evidence that this lizard occurs on Trinidad or Tobago.

Anolis cf. *lemurinus:* Its presence is based upon a single specimen; the locality data may be in error. See account.

Cnemidophorus murinus: Boulenger (1885) stated it inhabits the Guianas and Trinidad, but mentions no Trinidad specimens. Parker (1935b) noted the inclusion of Trinidad is apparently based upon a manuscript entry in the British Museum catalog of the receipt of two specimens from a Mr. Cooper between the years 1845 and 1856. The specimens were apparently lost before Boulenger's 1885 catalog was compiled. Thus, there is no evidence that this Curaçao and Bonaire lizard occurs on Trinidad, Tobago, or mainland South America.

Gonatodes albogularis: Its presence in the area is based upon one Tobago specimen, now lost, and one Trinidad specimen (a poorly preserved hatchling and an egg shell, making identification uncertain). See account.

Gymnodactylus geckoides: The first report of this lizard on Trinidad is in this work. It is based upon a single specimen; the locality data may be in error. See account.

Kentropyx intermedius: This lizard is not present on Trinidad, although it was reported from Trinidad by Barbour (1930b) and Underwood (1962). Hoogmoed (1979) listed Trinidad in the range of this species in his Suriname account. See the comment in the *Kentropyx striatus* account.

Leiocephalus herminieri: This was described by Duméril and Bibron (1837) from material collected by Plée and l'Herminier undoubtedly on Martinique, where it is an extinct endemic. Duméril and Bibron list Trinidad as the type locality, apparently confusing it with Trinite, a town on the northeast coast of Martinique. See comments by Parker (1935b) and Schwartz and Henderson (1988).

Serpentes

Anilius scytale: Emsley (1977) found the "Trinidad" specimen to be from Trinidad, Bolivia.

Bothrops asper: Emsley (1977) noted two AMNH specimens of *B. atrox* [recognized as *B. asper* here] reputed to be from Tobago are undoubtedly errors in labeling.

Bothrops lanceolatus: Tuck et al. (1973) found that two USNM specimens labeled as being from Tobago are from the Ober collection. There is no evidence this snake occurs on Trinidad or Tobago.

Leptotyphlops goudotii: Emsley (1977) noted that it is known from Patos Island, which was politically part of Trinidad until 1942. There is no evidence this snake occurs on Trinidad or Tobago.

Mastigodryas amarali: Stuart (1941) reported this species as being present on Tobago based upon the Ober collection. See the comment in the *Mastigodryas boddaerti dunni* account.

Oxybelis fulgidus: Underwood (1962) listed this snake from Tobago; Emsley (1977) noted that it is known from Patos Island that was politically part of Trinidad until 1942. There is no evidence this large, distinctive snake occurs on Trinidad or Tobago.

Pseudoboa coronata: Emsley (1977) suggested reports of this species from Trinidad are based upon misidentifications of *Pseudoboa neuweidii.* This species does not occur on Trinidad or Tobago.

Typhlophis squamosus: Peters and Orejas-Miranda (1970) stated this snake occurs on Trinidad. Boos (1975c) questioned the validity of the report, and I have been unable to locate any literature references or specimens from Trinidad or Tobago.

Zoogeography

The Origins of the Trinidad and Tobago Herpetofauna

DeVerteuil (1858) observed, "The four grand divisions of reptiles have their representatives in the islands, viz., the chelonia, the sauria, the ophidia and the batrachians. Of these a few are to be met with in the other West India islands, whilst many are common to Trinidad and the neighboring continent, but none seem to be peculiar to this island alone."

Boettger (1895) wrote that Tobago and Trinidad were connected and that Tobago "obtained its Reptiles and Batrachians by active or passive migration from this island [Trinidad]."

Darlington (1957) stated, "The amphibians and reptiles of Trinidad are more numerous and generically more diverse than those of the West Indies proper, and include relatively more snakes and few lizards, as the continental fauna does."

Lescure (1980) observed that there is a break in the number of species between Tobago and Grenada, and that the greater the distance between an island in the Lesser Antilles and mainland South America, the fewer elements of the South American herpetofauna are present. He considered the Lesser Antilles (excluding Trinidad and Tobago) to be a distinct biogeographical unit from the Greater Antilles. Prior to this, West Indian ornithologist James Bond had noted the dramatic change in bird species between Grenada and Tobago. Lack (1976) named this 140 km saltwater gap "Bond's Line."

Hardy (1982) stated, "The herpetofauna of Tobago is clearly of South American origin."

Williams (1989) wrote, "Periodically interrupted land bridges are like stable land bridges except (1) that access in both directions is periodically interrupted by water gaps, and (2) faunas on one or both sides may be reduced by the extinction caused by the restriction of area during these periods of separation. Examples are such 'continental islands' as Trinidad and Tobago, which are on the South American continental shelf."

Clearly, a diverse group of authors over the past 130 years are in agreement that the Trinidad and Tobago herpetofauna is South American. This conclusion from the past is again supported here. However, what has been missing in previous examinations is an analysis of the species distributions of these two islands, and which macrohabits are used by these species. Populations have expanded, contracted, become extinct, and evolved during the islands' histories extending backward into deep time. Today's herpetofauna is the product of the species that have survived complex changes in the environment wrought by time and most recently, by human activity. The macrohabitats may provide some clues as to why some species are absent from one island or present on another. The macrohabitat(s) that a species uses will determine if a population survives a cool, dry period, or a warm, wet period; and determine whether or not a population expands or contracts its distribution during changing climatic regimes.

Distributional Categories

In this investigation, the distribution of each taxon on Trinidad and Tobago is examined and placed in one of eight broad distributional categories. The classification system is based on the one used by Hoogmoed (1979b; 1983), with some modifications. Table 1 lists each taxon, its presence or absence on Trinidad and Tobago, its distributional classification, and its macrohabitat(s). Included in the list are all of the taxa discussed in the species accounts, including those considered to be of questionable occurrence, or waifs. By comparing the macrohabitat used by taxa in the distributional categories, patterns in the fauna may be detected that will support or refute vegetational models that have been proposed for the islands, such as Beard's (1946) model (Figure 8) for Late Pleistocene vegetation.

1. Widespread (W) Taxa

Widespread (W) taxa have distributions that extend into Middle or North America, or occur on both sides of the Andes Mountains. Most of these originated in Amazonia and dispersed northward after the closure of the Panamanian portal. Thirty-five taxa (27% of 130) fall into this category: 10 (28% of 35) frogs; a questionable record of 1 (2.7% of 35)

Table 1. The distribution, origin, and macrohabitat use of the Trinidad and Tobago herpetofauna

Family	Species	Trinidad	Tobago	Distribution	Habitat
	CLASS AMPHIBIA				
	Frogs and Toads (Order Anura)				
Bufonidae	*Bufo beebei*	x		OB	S
	Bufo marinus	x	x	W	RES
Centrolenidae	*Hyalinobatrachium orientale tobagoensis*		x	CCR	RE
Dendrobatidae	*Mannophryne olmonae*		x	CCR	RE
	Mannophryne trinitatis	x		CCR/TTE	RE
Hylidae	*Flectonotus fitzgeraldi*	x	x	CCR	RE
	Hyla boans	x		W	R
	Hyla crepitans	x	x	W	ES
	Hyla geographica	x		A	RE
	Hyla microcephala misera	x		OB	S
	Hyla minuscula	x		OB	S
	Hyla minuta	x	x	A	RES
	Hyla punctata	x		A	RES
	Phrynohyas venulosa	x	x	W	ES
	Phyllodytes auratus	x		CCR/TE	R
	Phyllomedusa trinitatis	x		CCR	RES
	Scinax rubra	x	x	W	S
	Sphaenorhynchus lacteus	x		A	ES
Leptodactylidae	*Adenomera hylaedactyla*	x		A	RE
	Eleutherodactylus charlottevillensis		x	CCR/TOE	R
	Eleutherodactylus johnstonei	x		LA	U
	Eleutherodactylus cf. *rozei*		x	CCR/ToE	RE
	Eleutherodactylus urichi	x	x	CCR	RE
	Leptodactylus bolivianus	x	?	W	S
	Leptodactylus fuscus	x	x	W	S
	Leptodactylus knudseni	x	?	A	RE
	Leptodactylus macrosternum	x		A	S
	Leptodactylus nesiotus	x		OB	?
	Leptodactylus validus	x	x	CCR	RES
	Lithodytes lineatus	x		A	R
	Physalaemus pustulosus	x	x	W	S
Microhylidae	*Elachistocleis ovalis*	x		A	S
	Elachistocleis surinamensis	x		W	R
Pipidae	*Pipa pipa*	x		A	RES-Aq
Pseudidae	*Pseudis paradoxa caribensis*	x		OB	S-Aq
Ranidae	*Rana palmipes*	x	?	A	R
	Caecilians (Order Gymnophiona)				
Typhlonectidae	*Typhlonectes sp.*	?		OB	Aq
	CLASS REPTILIA				
	Turtles and Tortoises (Order Chelonia)				
Chelidae	*Chelus fimbriatus*	x		A	RES-Aq
	Phrynops gibbus	x		A	RES-Aq
Cheloniidae	*Caretta caretta*	x	x	Cos	M
	Chelonia mydas	x	x	Cos	M
	Eretmochelys imbricata imbricata	x	x	Cos	M
	Lepidochelys olivacea	x		Cos	M
Dermochelyidae	*Dermochelys coriacea*	x	x	Cos	M
Emydidae	*Rhinoclemmys punctularia punctularia*	x	?	A	RES-Aq
Kinosternidae	*Kinosternon scorpioides scorpioides*	x		A	RES-Aq
Pelomedusidae	*Podocnemis expansa*	?	?	A	RES-Aq
	Podocnemis unifilis	?	?	A	RES-Aq
Testudinidae	*Geochelone carbonaria*	?	?	A	RE
	Geochelone denticulata	x	?	A	RE

Key: The presence of a taxon on an island is denoted by an "x." [1. *Gymnopthlamus specious* occurs only on Chacachacare Island in the area under study.] Distribution codes: W = Widespread; A = Amazonian; CCR = Caribbean Coastal Range; LGE = Lowland Guiana Endemic; OB = Orinoco Basin; LA = Lesser Antilles; Cos = Cosmopolitan; TTE = Trinidad and Tobago Endemic; TE = Trinidad Endemic; ToE = Tobago Endemic; UK = Unknown. Habitat codes: R = Rainforest; E = Forest-edge; S = Savanna; Aq = Aquatic; M = Marine; U = Urban; I = Introduced; "?" denotes questionable status.

Table 1. The distribution, origin, and macrohabitat use of the Trinidad and Tobago herpetofauna (*continued*)

Family	Species	Trinidad	Tobago	Distribution	Habitat
Crocodilians (Order Crocodylia)					
Alligatoridae	*Caiman crocodilus crocodilus*	x	x	A	RES-Aq
Crocodylidae	*Crocodylus acutus*	?	?	W	RES-Aq
	Crocodylus intermedius	?	?	OB	RES-Aq
Amphisbaenids (Order Squamata: Suborder Amphisbaenia)					
Amphisbaenidae	*Amphisbaena alba*	x		A	RE
	Amphisbaena fuliginosa fuliginosa	x		LGE	RES
Lizards (Order Squamata: Suborder Sauria)					
Gekkonidae	*Gonatodes albogularis*	?	?	W	ES-U
	Gonatodes ceciliae	x		CCR	R
	Gonatodes humeralis	x	x	A	RE
	Gonatodes ocellatus		x	ToE/CCR	RE
	Gonatodes vittatus vittatus	x	x	CCR	ES
	Gymnodactylus geckoides	?		UK	ES
	Hemidactylus mabouia	x	x	Cos	U
	Hemidactylus palaichthus	x	x	OB	ES
	Sphaerodactylus molei	x	x	CCR	E
	Thecadactylus rapicauda	x	x	W	RES
Gymnophthalmidae	*Bachia flavescens*		x	LGE	R
	Bachia heteropa alleni		x	ToE/CCR	RE
	Bachia heteropa trinitatis	x		CCR	RE
	Gymnophthalmus speciosus	1		W	ES
	Gymnophthalmus underwoodi	x		OB	ES
	Proctoporus shrevei	x		TE/CCR	R
Iguanidae	*Anolis aeneus*	x		LA	U,I
	Anolis chrysolepis planiceps	x		LGE	RE
	Anolis extremus	x		LA	U,I
	Anolis cf. *lemurinus*	?		W	R
	Anolis richardii		x	LA	E,I
	Anolis trinitatis	?+		LA	I,U
	Iguana iguana	x	x	W	RES
	Polychrus marmoratus	x	x	A	E
	Tropidurus plica	x		A	RE
Scincidae	*Mabuya bistriata*	x	x	W	RE
Teiidae	*Ameiva ameiva*	x	x	W	RES
	Cnemidophorus lemniscatus	x	x	W	ES
	Kentropyx striatus	x	?	OB	ES
	Tupinambis teguixin	x	x	A	RES
Snakes (Order Squamata: Suborder Serpentes)					
Anomalepididae	*Helminthophis* sp.	x		TE/CCR	R
Boidae	*Boa constrictor constrictor*	x	x	W	RES
	Corallus hortulanus cookii	x	x	W	ES
	Epicrates cenchria maurus	x	x	W	ES
	Eunectes murinus	x		A	RES-Aq
Colubridae	*Atractus trilineatus*	x	x	LGE	RES
	Atractus univittatus		x	CCR	R
	Chironius carinatus	x		W	RE
	Clelia clelia clelia	x		W	RES
	Dipsas variegata trinitatis	x		CCR	RE
	Drymarchon corais corais	x	x	A	RE
	Erythrolamprus aesculapii aesculapii	x		W	R
	Erythrolamprus bizona	?		CCR	R
	Erythrolamprus ocellatus		x	ToE/CCR	RE
	Helicops angulatus	x		A	RES-Aq
	Hydrops triangularis neglectus	x		LGE	RES-Aq
	Imantodes cenchoa cenchoa	x	x	W	RES
	Leptodeira annulata ashmeadi	x	x	OB	RES
	Leptophis ahaetulla coeruleodorsus	x	x	OB	RE
	Leptophis riveti	x		CCR	R

Table 1. The distribution, origin, and macrohabitat use of the Trinidad and Tobago herpetofauna (*continued*)

Family		Species	Trinidad	Tobago	Distribution	Habitat
		Snakes (Order Squamata: Suborder Serpentes) (*continued*)				
		Liophis cobella cobella	x		LGE	RES-Aq
		Liophis melanotus nesos	x	x	CCR	ES
		Liophis reginae ssp.		x	ToE/CCR	R
		Liophis reginae zweifeli	x		CCR	RE
		Mastigodryas boddaerti boddaerti	x		A	RES
		Mastigodryas boddaerti dunni		x	ToE/CCR	ES
		Ninia atrata	x	x	W	RES
		Oxybelis aeneus	x	x	W	RES
		Oxyrhopus petola petola	x	x	CCR	RES
		Pseudoboa neuwiedii	x	x	W	RES
		Pseustes poecilonotus polylepis	x		W	RE
		Pseustes sulphureus sulphureus	x		A	R
		Sibon nebulata nebulata	x	x	W	RES
		Siphlophis cervinus	x		W	R
		Spilotes pullatus pullatus	x	x	W	RE
		Tantilla melanocephala	x	x	W	RE
		Thamnodynastes sp.	x		LGE	ES
		Tripanurgos compressus	x		W	RE
Elapidae		*Micrurus circinalis*	x		CCR	RES
		Micrurus lemniscatus diutius	x		LGE	RES
Leptotyphlopidae		*Leptotyphlops albifrons*	x	?	A	RE
Typhlopidae		*Typhlops brongersmianus*	x		A	R
		Typhlops trinitatus	x	x	CCR	RE
Viperidae		*Bothrops asper*	x		W	RES
		Lachesis muta muta	x		A	R

crocodilian; 8 (22.2% of 35) lizards; and 17 (49% of 35) snakes. Twenty-four (69% of 35) of these taxa are trans-Andean, extending their distributions to the Pacific side of the Andes. Twenty-five (71% of 35) occur on both Trinidad and Tobago; 10 (29% of 35) occur on Trinidad but not on Tobago; and 1 (2.8% of 35) occurs on neither Trinidad or Tobago, but is restricted to Chacachacare Island, off Trinidad's northwestern peninsula. All of the taxa that occur in this category on Tobago also occur on Trinidad.

Table 2 presents an analysis of these taxa by habitat. Because many of these species use more than one habitat, the percentages will greatly overlap and will equal more than 100%; they reflect the percentage of taxa in this category that use a specific habitat. Note that 36% are habitat generalists, and are present in all three habitat categories (taxa using rainforest, forest edge, and savanna—RES), but if RE (taxa using rainforest and forest edge) and ES (taxa using forest edge and savanna) species are also generalists, the percentage of generalists in widespread taxa increases to 72.2%. Therefore, 24 (69% of 35) of these taxa use rainforests; 24 (69% of 35) use savanna; and 26 (74% of 35) use forest edge situations. Thus, due to the plasticity of their habitat preferences, a large percentage of the taxa in this group can be expected to survive changes in vegetation that occur during the expansions and contractions of rainforest and savanna habitats. These taxa often frequent human modified habitats such as the cocal (Plate 3). Note that only one aquatic species occurs in this category, and no chelonians are in this category. A few of these species may eventually be shown to be composite species and further restricted in range, *Hyla crepitans*, *Elachistocleis surinamensis*, and *Gymnophthalmus speciosus* are likely candidates for change.

Widespread taxa ([TA] denotes trans-Andean taxa): *Bufo marinus*[TA], *Hyla boans*, *Hyla crepitans*, *Phrynohyas venulosa*[TA], *Scinax rubra*[TA], *Leptodactylus bolivianus*[TA], *Leptodactylus fuscus*, *Physalaemus pustulosus*[TA], *Elachistocleis surinamensis*[TA], ?*Crocodylus acutus*, ?*Gonatodes albogularis*, *Thecadactylus rapicauda*[TA], *Anolis* cf. *lemurinus*[TA],

Table 2. Analysis of Widespread taxa by habitat.

Habitat	Amphibians	Reptiles	Total Taxa
RES	1	12	13 (37%)
RE	0	6	6 (17%)
ES	2	5	7 (20%)
S	4	0	4 (11%)
E	0	0	0
R	2	3	5 (14%)

The numbers are the number of species of amphibians and reptiles that exhibit a widespread geographic distribution and use the macrohabitats listed in the left-hand column. Habitat codes are R = rainforest, E = forest edge, S = savanna; RES species use all three macrohabitats, RE species use rainforest and forest edge; ES species use forest-edge and savanna macrcohabits.

Iguana iguana[TA], *Gymnophthalmus speciosus*[TA], *Ameiva ameiva*, *Cnemidophorus lemniscatus*, *Mabuya bistriata*[TA], *Boa c. constrictor*, *Corallus hortulanus cookii*, *Epicrates cenchria maurus*, *Chironius carinatus*[TA], *Clelia c. clelia*[TA], *Erythrolamprus a. aesculapii*[TA], *Imantodes c. cenchoa*[TA], *Ninia atrata*[TA], *Oxybelis aeneus*[TA], *Pseudoboa neuweidii*[TA], *Pseustes poecilonotus polylepis*[TA], *Sibon nebulata nebulata*[TA], *Siphlophis cervinus*[TA], *Spilotes pullatus pullatus*[TA], *Tantilla melanocephala*[TA], *Tripanurgos compressus*[TA], and *Bothrops asper*[TA].

2. Amazonian (A) Taxa

Amazonian (A) taxa have their distribution centered in the greater Amazon Basin and have extended into Trinidad and Tobago and surrounding areas during periods of favorable habitat expansion. This includes two species (*Lithodytes lineatus* and *Phrynops gibbus*) Hoogmoed (1979b) considered peripheral to the Amazon Basin, which are distributed along the western and northern edges of the Basin. None of the taxa in this category are known to occur west of the Andes. This category contains 33 (25% of 130) taxa known to occur or suspected to occur in Trinidad and Tobago: 11 (33.3% of 33) frogs; 8 (24% of 33) chelonians; 1 (3% of 32) crocodilian; 1 (3% of 33) amphisbaenid; 4 (12% of 33) lizards; and 8 (24% of 33) snakes. Twelve (36.4% of 33) of these taxa occur on both islands (note that six of these are of questionable occurrence on Tobago); 21 (65.6% of 33) occur on Trinidad and the mainland.

Table 3 contains an analysis of these taxa by habitat. Note some of these species use more than one habitat, thus the percentages will add up to more than 100%. Habitat generalists (RES) make up 40%, but if RE and ES taxa are added, the number increases to 25, (76% of 33). Of these taxa, 28 (85% of 33) use rainforest, while only 17 (52% of 33) use savanna. Taxa using forest edge situations number 26 (79% of 33) in this category. Ten (66.6% of 15) aquatic species found on the islands occur in this category. Aquatic taxa are also included in the habitat generalist (RES) category because they occur in aquatic habitats contained within all of these terrestrial macrohabitats. Again, many species within this category have the plasticity to survive vegetational shifts between rainforest and savanna.

Amazonian taxa: *Hyla geographica, Hyla minuta, Hyla punctata, Sphaenorhynchus lacteus, Adenomera hylaedactylus, Leptodactylus knudseni, Leptodactylus macrosternum, Lithodytes lineatus, Elachistocleis ovalis, Pipa pipa, Rana palmipes, Chelus fimbriatus, Kinosternon s. scorpioides, Rhinoclemmys p. punctularia, Phrynops gibbus, ?Podocnemis expansa, ?Podocnemis unifilis, Geochelone carbonaria, Geochelone denticulata, Caiman c. crocodilus, Ampisbaena alba, Gonatodes humeralis, Tropidurus plica, Polychrus marmoratus, Tupinambis teguixin, Eunectes murinus, Drymarchon c. corais, Helicops angulatus, Mastigodryas b. boddaerti, Pseustes sulphureus sulphureus, Leptotyphlops albifrons, Typhlops brongersmianus,* and *Lachesis muta muta.*

3. Carribean Coastal Range (CCR) Taxa

Caribbean Coastal Range (CCR) taxa are associated with a montane complex that extends from the Santa Marta region of Colombia, across northern Venezuela and Trinidad to Tobago. Most, but not all, of the taxa in this category reach the eastern limit of their distribution in Trinidad and Tobago. The CCR is an expansion of Lynch's (1979) Northern Forest and includes Santa Marta, Villavicencio at the base of the Cordillera Oriental (the Merida Andes) of Colombia and the Maracaibo Basin, the Falcon District, the coastal range of Venezuela, the Península de Paria, and Trinidad-Tobago. Lynch considered the Northern Forest a transition between the well-differentiated Trans-Andean and Central Cis-Andean Forests; and found the area to have low endemism, suggesting that the endemics that do occur here are due to montane slope species invading the lowland forest. Haffer (1979) supported this argument by considering the Península de Paria and the mountains of Trinidad and Tobago a Quaternary forest peri-Andean refuge, along with the other areas of Colombia and Venezuela considered part of the CCR complex defined here. Trinidad and Tobago endemics are included in this category because historically both islands have been connected to the mainland and the mountain range complex. Thus, Lynch's proposal for the Northern Forest category being transitional is strongly supported by this study. There are 30 (23% of the 130 taxa in this category; 10 (33% of 30) frogs; 7 (23% of 30) lizards; 13 (43% of 30) snakes. Eight of these taxa are shared by Trinidad and Tobago, 11 occur on Trinidad, and 10 occur on Tobago. Twenty-seven (90% of 30) of these taxa use rainforest while only 7 (23% of 30) enter savanna environments, and 18 (60% of 30) use forest edge habitats. On Trinidad, taxa in this category tend to be restricted to the Northern, Central and Southern Ranges; on Tobago they tend to be found on the Main Ridge.

Table 3. Analysis of Amazonian taxa by habitat.

Habitat	Amphibians	Reptiles	Total Taxa
RES	2	11	13 (40%)
RE	3	7	10 (30%)
ES	2	0	2 (6%)
S	2	0	2 (6%)
E	0	1	1 (3%)
R	2	3	5 (15%)

The numbers are the numbers of species of amphibians and reptiles that exhibit an Amazonian distribution and use the macrohabitats listed in the left-hand column. Habitat codes are R = rainforest, E = forest edge, S = savanna; RES species use all three macrohabitats, RE species use rainforest and forest edge; ES species use forest-edge and savanna macrohabits.

Table 4 presents an analysis of the habitat of these taxa. Of 11 rainforest specialists, 8 are Tobago endemics, and 3 probably occur on Tobago and mainland South America, but not on Trinidad. The latter taxa may be considered landbridge relicts, and represent populations that were once more widespread along the Caribbean Coastal Range. The discontinuous distributions are exactly what would be expected from differential extinction during times of dramatic habitat changes. A relatively small percentage (24%) of these forms are capable of surviving the xeric and thermal conditions of a savanna environment, whereas 90% of these taxa are capable of inhabiting rainforest; and there are more rainforest specialists in this category than any other (12 of 30, or 40%). If Beard's model (see Figure 8) is correct, vegetational shifts in Late Pleistocene may have had a dramatic impact on the taxa in this category. The three Trinidad ranges and the Main Ridge of Tobago may have acted as refugia for the rainforest specialist species in this category (and others). Extinctions occur in one place, while populations of the same taxon survive on the mainland or other island. Note that 18 species in this category occur on Tobago (26% of 69 taxa known from the island) when questionable records for that island are included. There is a marked absence of taxa highly adapted for aquatic life styles in this category.

The herpetofaunal clues linking Trinidad and Tobago to the Caribbean Coastal Ranges are those species in the CCR group that have a low dispersal ability. The small burrowing snakes in the family Anomalepididae known from Costa Rica, inter-Andean Colombia and Venezuela typify a group with low dispersal capabilities. The recent discovery of a new species on Trinidad supports this island's connection to the coastal continetal ranges. The presence of the snakes *Erythrolamprus bizona* and *Leptophis riveti* (the only trans-Andean taxa in this category), and the frogs *Flectonotus fitzgeraldi, Mannophryne trinitatis, Eleutherodactylus charlottevillensis, E.* cf. *rozei,* as well as other species within the CCR group, lend support to a vicariance model placing Trinidad and Tobago within the Caribbean Coastal Range complex. Nine of these are shared by Trinidad and Tobago, and another four have closely related species or subspecies on both islands — ([TA] are trans-Andean taxa) evidence that Trinidad and Tobago were connected to each other.

Caribbean Coastal Range taxa: *Hyalinobatrachium orientale tobagoensis, Mannophryne olmonae, Mannophryne trinitatis, Flectonotus fitzgeraldi, Phyllodytes auratus, Phyllomedusa trinitatis, Eleutherodactylus charlottevillensis, Eleutherodactylus* cf. *rozei, Eleutherodactylus urichi, Leptodactylus validus, Gonatodes ceciliae, Gonatodes ocellatus, Gonatodes vittatus, Sphaerodactylus molei, Bachia heteropa alleni, Bachia heteropa trinitatis, Proctoporus shrevei, Helminthophis* sp., *Atractus univittatus, Dipsas variegata trinitatis, Erythrolamprus bizona*[TA]*, Erythrolamprus ocellatus, Leptophis riveti*[TA]*, Liophis melanotus nesos, Liophis reginae zweifeli, Liophis reginae* ssp., *Mastigodryas boddaerti dunni, Oxyrhopus petola petola, Micrurus circinalis,* and *Typhlops trinitatus.*

4. Lowland Guiana Endemic (LGE) Taxa

Lowland Guiana Endemics (LGE) are taxa that are found at elevations below 1000 m on the Guiana Shield and have extended their distribution to Trinidad and Tobago at one time or another. Eight (6.2% of 130) taxa are in this category. One (12.5% of 8) amphisbaenid, two (25% of 8) lizards, and five (62.5% of 8) snakes compose this category. Table 5 provides an analysis of these taxa by habitat. Only two (25% of 8) of these of these taxa occur on Tobago; and only one of these, *Bachia flavescens,* is known to occur on Tobago, but not on Trinidad; it is, however, found on the mainland. Table 5 summarizes the habitats used by the taxa in this category. Seven (87.5% of 8) of these animals use rainforests, while six (75% of 8) are plastic enough in their requirements to use savanna and forest-edge habitats; and two (25% of 8) of these taxa are aquatic.

Lowland Guiana Endemic taxa: *Amphisbaena fuliginosa*

Table 4. Analysis of habitats of the Caribbean Coastal Range taxa.

Habitat	Amphibians	Reptiles	Total Taxai
RES	2	3	5 (16.6%)
RE	5	5	10 (33%)
ES	0	2	2 (6.6%)
S	0	0	0
E	0	1	1 (3.3%)
R	3	9	12 (40%)

The numbers are the number of species of amphibians and reptiles exhibiting a Caribbean Coastal Range distribution and using the macrohabitats listed in the left-hand column. Habitat codes are R = rainforest, E = forest edge, S = savanna; RES species use all three macrohabitats, RE species use rainforest and forest edge; ES species use forest-edge and savanna macrcohabits.

Table 5. Analysis of habitats of the Lowland Guiana Endemic taxa.

Habitat	Amphibians	Reptiles	Total Taxa
RES	0	5	5 (62.5%)
RE	0	1	1 (12.5%)
ES	0	1	1 (12.5%)
E	0	1	1 (12.5%)
S	0	0	0
R	0	1	2 (25%)

The numbers are the number of species of amphibians and reptiles exhibiting a Lowland Guiana Endemic distribution pattern and using the macrohabitats listed in the left-hand column. Habitat codes are R = rainforest, E = forest edge, S = savanna; RES species use all three macrohabitats, RE species use rainforest and forest edge; ES species use forest-edge and savanna macrcohabits.

fuliginosa, Anolis chrysolepis planiceps, Bachia flavescens, Atractus trilineatus, Hydrops triangularis neglectus, Liophis cobella cobella, Thamnodynastes sp., and *Micrurus lemniscatus diutius.*

5. Orinoco Basin (OB) Taxa

Orinoco Basin (OB) taxa are lowland species that have originated in the Orinoco Basin. Twelve (9.2% of 130) taxa are in this category. Five (42% of 12) frogs, three (25% of 12) lizards, two (16.6% of 12) snakes; and two (16.6% of 12) questionable records, one caecilian and one crocodilian, compose this category. The frog *Leptodactylus nesiotus* is known only from the southwestern coast of Trinidad; while the frogs *Bufo beebei, Hyla microcephala misera,* and *Pseudis paradoxa caribensis* occur only in Trinidad's Northern and Southern Basins as well as the Orinoco drainage. The frog *Hyla minuscula* has a slightly larger distribution extending into the Guianas and Brazil paralleling the distributions of the lizards *Hemidactylus palaichthus* and *Kentropyx striatus.* Table 6 summarizes the habitats used by taxa in this category. Only two members of this category use rainforests, the snakes *Leptodeiva annulata ashmeadi* and *Leptophis a. coeruleodorsus.* Nine (75% of 12) however, use savanna, and four (33% of 12) use forest edge environments.

Orinoco Basin taxa: *Bufo beebei, Hyla microcephala misera, Hyla minuscula, Leptodactylus nesiotus, Pseudis paradoxa caribensis, ?Typhlonectes* sp., *?Crocodylus intermedius, Hemidactylus palaichthus, Gymnophthalmus underwoodi, Kentropyx striatus, Leptodiera annulata ashmeadi, Leptophis a. coeruleodorsus.*

6. Lesser Antillean (LA) Taxa

Lesser Antillean (LA) taxa have been introduced to Trinidad and Tobago from islands in the Lesser Antilles. Most (if not all) of these introductions are the result of human activity. Five (3.8% of 130) taxa are included in this category: one (20% of 6) frog and four (80% of 6) lizards. Except for *Anolis richardii* all of these species are very recent arrivals with human help, and *A. richardii* may have arrived the same way. These species tend to use urban habitats in Trinidad and Tobago, or other human altered environments. What is surprising about this category is the low percentage of species from the Lesser Antilles that have influenced the make-up of the Trinidad and Tobago herpetofauna, particularly Tobago. Only one (1.4% of 69) member of the Tobago herpetofauna is from the Lesser Antilles, further emphasizing the continental composition of the fauna.

Lesser Antillean taxa: *Eleutherodactylus johnstonei, Anolis aeneus, Anolis extremus, Anolis richardii,* and *Anolis trinitatis.*

Table 6. Analysis of habitats of the Orinoco Basin taxa.

Habitat	Amphibians	Reptiles	Total Taxa
RES	1	2	3 (25%)
RE	0	1	1 (8.3%)
ES	0	2	2 (16.6%)
S	5	1	6 (50%)
E	0	0	0
R	0	0	0

The numbers are the number of species of amphibians and reptiles exhibiting an Orinoco Basin distribution pattern and using the macrohabitats listed in the left-hand column. Habitat codes are R = rainforest, E = forest edge, S = savanna; RES species use all three macrohabitats, RE species use rainforest and forest edge; ES species use forest-edge and savanna macrcohabits.

7. Cosmopolitan (Cos) Taxa

Cosmopolitan (Cos) taxa have distributions extending to other hemispheres. Sea turtles and the gecko *Hemidactylus mabouia,* with populations in Africa, are in this category. Six (4.6% of 130) of the taxa listed in Table 1 are in this category.

Cosmopolitan taxa: *Caretta caretta, Chelonia mydas, Eretomochelys i. imbricata, Lepidochelys olivacea, Dermochelys coriacea,* and *Hemidactylus mabouia.*

8. Unknown (UK)

Unknown (UK) is a category containing a single species of gecho *Gymnodactylus geckoides.* Its presence on Trinidad is questionable, and it does not fit well into any of the above categories, being known only from Brazil.

Distributional Patterns

Table 7 summarizes the distributional patterns exhibited in the Trinidad and Tobago herpetofauna. The Lesser Antillean fauna has played a minor role in the development of the Trinidad and Tobago herpetofauna, and those Lesser Antillean species present are the result of human-mediated transport. The origin of this fauna is overwhelmingly from South America. Twenty-six taxa (20% of the 130) are trans-Andean, occuring on both sides of the Andes. Eighty-two taxa (63% of 130) are habitat generalists (RES, ES, RE), capable of surviving in two or more macrohabits. This suggests that vegetational shifts between forest and savanna during the Pleistocene-Quaternary on the islands of Trinidad and Tobago would not threaten this large portion of the herpetofauna with extinction. It is also probable that the Northern Range (and possibly the Central and Southern Ranges) of Trinidad, and the Main Ridge of Tobago, served as forest refugia for species during the cool, dry periods of the Pleis-tocene-Quaternary, when savanna expanded, and during times of sea level rise, when the lower elevations of these islands were flooded. Many of the species showing a Caribbean Coastal Range distribution are restricted to these areas, and this category has more rainforest specialists than any other. Table 8 summarizes habitat use by the Trinidad and Tobago herpetofauna for anurans, saurians, and serpents.

The Similarity of the Trinidad and Tobago Faunas

Including questionable records, Trinidad has 118 taxa, Tobago has 69 taxa, and they share 57 taxa. Duellman's (1965) formula is used to calculate the faunal resemblance factor (FRF):

$$\frac{2C}{N_1 + N_2} = FRF$$

where

C = number of shared taxa
N_1 = the number of taxa present in area 1
N_2 = the number of taxa present in area 2

Trinidad and Tobago have an FRF of 0.61. The closer this number is to 1.0, the more alike are the faunas being com-pared. Again, this supports the idea that changes in sea level have alternately connected and isolated the islands histori-cally and that differential extinction has produced the current fauna of these continental islands.

Distributional Patterns within the Islands

There are six species, which tend to be restricted to the Northern and Southern Basins of Trinidad (*Bufo beebei, Elachistocleis ovalis, E. surinamensis, Kentropyx striatus, Helicops angulatus, Liophis c. cobella*). Three (50% of 6) of these species, two frogs and a lizard, are savanna species (*B. beebei, E. ovalis* and *K. striatus*); the two (33% of 6) snakes (*Helicops angulatus* and *Liophis cobella*) are aquatic; and the frog *E. surinamensis* (17% of 6) is forest dwelling and is now restricted to patches of forest. The reasons for the lack of endemism may be the radical habitat changes that have occurred over the past two or three hundred years or it may be the flooding sea invading Trinidad's basin areas 2000–6000 years ago. In any case, the once forest shrouded low-lands contain only remnant patches today, and the fauna pre-sent over most of the basins is decidedly savanna in origin.

Trinidad's Northern Range holds three Trinidad en-demics: the hylid frog *Phyllodytes auratus,* the luminous

Table 7. A summary of the distributional patterns exhibited by the Trinidad and Tobago herpetofauna.

Distribution	Trinidad	Tobago	Total Taxa
Widespread	35 (30%)	25 (36%)	35 (27%)
Amazonian	33 (25%)	14 (20%)	33 (25%)
Caribbean Coastal Range	20 (17%)	18 (26%)	30 (23%)
Orinoco Basin	12 (10%)	4 (5.7%)	12 (9.2%)
Lowland Guiana Endemics	7 (5%)	2 (3%)	8 (6.2%)
Lesser Antilles	4 (3.4%)	1 (1.5%)	5 (3.8%)
Cosmopolitan	6 (5.1%)	5 (7.2%)	6 (4.6%)
Unknown	1 (0.8%)	0	1 (0.8%)
Totals (100%)	118 (100%)	69 (100%)	130

Table 8. Summary of macrohabitats used by the major taxa of Trinidad and Tobago amphibians and reptiles.

Habitat	Anurans	Saurians	Serpents
RES	6 (16.6%)	4 (13.3%)	18 (40%)
RE	9 (25.0%)	7 (23.3%)	12 (27%)
ES	2 (5.5%)	8 (26.6%)	5 (11%)
S	11 (30.5%)	0	0
E	0	3 (10%)	0
R	6 (16.6%)	4 (13.3%)	10 (22%)
U	1 (2.7%)	4 (13.3%)	0
?	1 (2.7%)	0	0

Numbers are the number of species/subspecies using a given macrohab-itat or set of macrohabitats. Habitat codes are R = rainforest, E = forest edge, S = savanna; RES species use all three macrohabitats, RE species use rainforest and forest edge; ES species use forest-edge and savanna macrcohabits.

lizard *Proctoporus shrevei,* and the undescribed snake *Hel-minthophis* sp. The Amazonian forest snake *Erythrolamprus a. aesculapii* and the Caribbean Coastal Range taxa *Lep-tophis riveti* and *Erythrolamprus bizona* also appear re-stricted to the Northern Range, but are known from only one, three, and one specimen respectively. If the distribution is expanded to include the Central Range, the frog *Manno-phryne trinitatis* and the gecko *Gonatodes ceciliae* can be added. All of these species are rainforest dwellers, and five of them are endemics or near endemics. The southwest peninsula of Trinidad shelters a suite of species not known from elsewhere on the island (*Hyla minuscula, Adenomera hylaedactyla, Leptodactylus macrosternum, Leptodactylus nesiotus,* and the undescribed snake *Thamnodynastes* sp.) All of these taxa have populations on the mainland, except for *L. nesiotus* which is known only from Trinidad's south-west coast. Also, none of these are rainforest specialists. They are savanna species, or habitat generalists, and have similar requirements to the taxa described from the Northern and Southern Basins.

Tobago appears to have been disconnected from the mainland for more time than Trinidad, thus a greater number of autochonotus taxa may be expected. *Mannophryne olmonae, Eleutherodactylus* cf. *rozei Gonatodes ocellatus, Bachia heteropa alleni, Erythrolamprus ocellatus, Liophis reginae* ssp., and *Mastigodryas boddaerti dunni* are all Tobago endemics. Undoubtedly much remains to be discovered about Trinidad and Tobago zoogeography, the islands contain elements of both trans-Andean and cis-Andean fauna resulting from its transitional nature between the trans-Andean and central cis-Andean forests as suggested by Lynch (1979).

When Trinidad and Tobago are considered together, *Eleutherodactylus urichi, Leptodactylus validus, Liophis melanotus nesos,* and *Typhlops trinitatus* are endemics common to both islands, and support the idea that both islands share at least a partial common biological history. The timing of the faunal exchange between the two islands and the mainland has yet to be determined, but the data presented by Shackelton (1987) and the discussion in Dawson (1992) suggested that during the past 140,000 years there was ample opportunity for faunal exchange (see discussion in "Sea Level Changes in the Quaternary" in the section on "Physiographic Features and Geology").

A Word about Venomous Snake Bite

Four species of venomous snakes occur on Trinidad; none are known from Tobago. Envenomation from poisonous snakes on Trinidad undoubtedly occurs but the summary of deaths and death rates given in the *1991 Annual Statistic Digest of Trinidad and Tobago* does not separate venomous reptile bites from other forms of injury and poisoning and toxic effects which are listed. Four species of venomous snakes occur on Trinidad that are potentially lethal to human beings. *Micrurus circinalis* poses the least threat due to its small size. During this investigation local people were often seen walking barefoot along the roadside at night, the same roads where we collected *Micrurus circinalis, Micrurus lemniscatus diutius, Bothrops asper,* and *Lachesis muta muta.*

The best way to avoid a bite from a venomous snake is to stay away from it and not to attempt to pick it up, catch it, or kill it! As a rule venomous snakes are fearful of humans since humans are major predators on snakes and much too large to be used as food by venomous species. Attempting to kill a snake often places a person within striking distance, and death from the envenomation of a decapitated head has been documented.

The probability of a bite from an unseen snake can be greatly reduced with proper clothing. Long pants and boots—even thin rubber boots—give a great measure of protection because they keep the snake's head and fangs away from the skin. Placing hands and feet only where they are visible also helps avoid bites. Hiking at night (the time of day when all four species of venomous Trinidad serpents are active) should always be done with adequate light, the brighter the better.

There is serious doubt that popular first aid measures are effective, and should someone be bitten by a venomous snake, the best first aid is a car ride to the nearest hospital or doctor's office. It is important to stay calm. A comforting fact is that many venomous snakes meter their venom; that is the snakes control the amount of venom injected during a bite. Thus, in a defensive bite the snake may not want to waste its venom on a human it cannot eat; venom is rich in protein and protein is expensive to make. Nonetheless, if bitten by a snake believed to be venomous, the patient should go to a hospital immediately because there is no way to determine how much, if any, venom was injected during the bite.

The following first aid suggestions are taken from Campbell and Lamar (1989) and Conant and Collins (1991).

1. Immobilize the bitten limb. If the bite is on the head or torso, keep the patient still.
2. If cardiac (heart) or pulmonary (breathing) arrest occurs, administer cardiopulmonary resuscitation (CPR).
3. Establish an intravenous line with an isotonic fluid such as D_5W, normal saline, or Ringer's lactate.
4. If vomiting occurs, have the patient lie on one side so that the fluid does not block the breathing passages.
5. Avoid harmful medicines and treatments:

- **Do not** administer alcohol or aspirin (oral acetaminophen or codeine phosphate is appropriate).
- **Do not** use "cut and suck" techniques.
- **Do not** apply ice to the bite.
- **Do not** apply tight (arterial) tourniquets to the area above the bite.
- **Do not** apply electric voltage to the bite site.

6. A suction device that can be used safely is the Sawyer Extractor™ (Sawyer Products, Long Beach, California). This device may be of some benefit in removing venom from the bite site through the fang puncture.
7. An elastic bandage may be appropriate for coral snake bites. The bandage should allow circulation and **should not** be used for pit viper bites.
8. Use antivenom injections in the field only if experienced personnel are available.

If the snake responsible for a bite can be safely captured or killed, it should be brought to the hospital for positive identification.

Some harmless snakes in the family Colubridae have oral secretions that contain venom. Thus, these species are capable of causing mild envenomation. In the course of a normal defensive bite, they may not inject any venom, but if they bite a human and chew during the bite, venom may be delivered into the wound. The chewing action may be stimulated by the odor of prey on a human hand. Thus, the odor left on hands by frogs, lizards, other snakes, or rodents may stimulate these snakes to bite and inject venom. Trinidad and Tobago species that fall into this category include: *Clelia clelia clelia, Erythrolamprus* sp., *Helicops angulatus, Leptodeira annulata ashmedi, Leptophis ahaetulla coeruleodorsus, Liophis* sp., *Oxybelis aeneus, Oxyrhopus petola petola,* *Pseudoboa neuwiedii, Siphlophis cervinus, Thamnodynastes* sp., and *Tripanurgos compressus.* Note that these snakes are not a major threat to human health, but bites from them may result in mild envenomation. Avoiding bites should be the first rule when handling these animals.

Methods

The islands were visited between 14 June–12 July 1982; 1–21 July 1983; 20–29 April 1984; 25 June–16 July 1984; 14 June–9 July 1993; 9–16 June 1994. On each of these trips, Simla Research Station in the Arima Valley of the Northern Range of Trinidad served as base camp. The visits to Tobago were short and collecting efforts were focused on the northeastern end of the island (Plate 4). A total of 114 field days were accumulated for this study. Much of the time was spent in Arima Valley area because of convenience and the the excellent and varied habitats present in this area, but trips to other parts of the islands were frequent. Field collecting was done by hiking through an area and turning cover, looking in vegetation and in leaf litter. Streams and ponds were seined and examined with dip nets; roads were driven day and night for amphibians and reptiles; and frog choruses were examined. Road killed specimens were collected and retained. Live specimens were collected, photographed, and frequently released if they were already well represented in collections.

Museum collections examined were the Field Museum of Natural History (FMNH) (Chicago); the National Museum of Natural History (USNM) (Washington, DC); the American Museum of Natural History (AMNH) (New York); the Museum of Comparative Zoology (MCZ) (Harvard University, Cambridge, MA); the Carnegie Museum (CM) (Pittsburgh, PA). Additional material was borrowed from the British Museum of Natural History (BM) and the Florida State Museum of Natural History (FSMNH). Material collected by the author is housed in the Field Museum of Natural History; with some material in the Museum of Natural History, the University of Kansas (KU); and the Natural History Museum at the University of Illinois (UIMNH).

Accounts for species and subspecies are presented for all taxa known to occur within the geographic area, and include species of questionable occurrence which have been documented in the literature or with specimens accompanied by questionable data. Recognition of subspecies is often controversial, particularly in the neotropics where the fauna is not well known. Subspecies are recognized here, and I have attempted to follow the most recent revision of the group, making no taxonomic judgment unless it is discussed in the comment section. In cases where researchers have noted that subspecies are not valid I have either commented or not used the trinomial; *Ameiva ameiva* is an excellent example. Scientific names are used throughout to encourage the user to learn and use them.

Within orders and suborders, the families, genera, species, and subspecies are arranged in alphabetical order. In writing the introductory information for higher categories I have relied on three sources and have not referenced them each time a bit of information was taken from them. They are Duellman and Trueb (1986), Halliday and Adler (1986), and Zug (1993). If other references were used, they are noted. Names are in chronological order by date of publication, thus the description of the recognized species or subspecies may not be the first entry. Only the earliest use of a name applied to Trinidad and Tobago populations is listed. The names appear as they do in the original citation, including typing errors. The type localities are listed for each taxon, and if they have been revised, it is noted. The common names given are the ones that occur in the literature for the islands and the citations listed for each are the earliest use applied to Trinidad and Tobago populations. New combinations of names are avoided, despite the fact that some are warranted.

The comment sections in the accounts alert the reader to taxonomic controversy, express published opinions that the author may or may not agree with, or express the author's opinion regarding status of a taxon, or some problem with determining the presence or absence of the taxon on Trinidad or Tobago.

The distributions include an overview of the species range, usually based upon a recent reference; a list of Trinidad and Tobago locations based upon the literature; locations reported in field notes; and a list of locations based upon verified museum material. Spellings of place names follow: Ottley (1969); Map of Trinidad (ed. 5), Lands and Surveys Division, Ministry of Planning and Development 1990; and Map of Tobago (ed. 3), Lands and Surveys Division, Ministry of Planning and Development 1992. Some museum specimen locality data are difficult if not impossible to determine because of spelling or name changes. Many Trinidad and Tobago specimens are accompanied by no specific data other than the name of the island; if these specimens are included in the materials list, they are simply listed as "no data." Also, included in the distributions are locations based upon field notes when they are not supported by museum material.

Open circles on range maps represent localities reported in the literature, field notes, and museum specimens not verified by the author. Solid circles represent localities with museum specimens verified by the author. Question marks denote locations the author has reason to doubt, and arrows are used to mark coastal localities, small islands, and offshore rocks. A map is provided with some of the most commonly collected locations cited in the text. The user may refer to this map when attempting to locate a specific locality. Note that the maps lack the county and parish boundaries. While some museum data contain references to these much of it does not, and it is often difficult if not impossible to resolve which county or parish a specimen came from. Thus I have avoided trying to decipher on which side of a boundary line to place a dot and have attempted a best guess. Some parts of the islands have been collected many times by many people (i.e., the Arima Valley, Trinidad, and Charlotteville, Tobago), while other areas of the islands are poorly collected. The range maps reflect these biases. The Trinidad and Tobago range maps are drawn to different scales. For each map the bar under the map represents 5 miles. Data for specimens are more often given in miles than kilometers from a particular reference point and the island roads have milepost markers, which makes locating a specific place relatively easy.

Descriptions were usually written while looking at preserved material and photographs, but some descriptions are based on live specimens. In some cases it was not possible to use specimens from Trinidad and Tobago populations, i.e., sea turtles and crocodilians. Measurements are given in millimeters, and in many cases the data collected here fall within a larger published range. In those instances the larger range was adopted. If a larger maximum size was found, the range is revised upward. If a published record for maximum size for the species is found to be considerably larger, a statement noting maximum expected length is given. These numbers often represent individuals from elsewhere in their range. Scale counts are from Trinidad and Tobago material and may overlap or fall within counts given by others. If only a small sample size was available, counts presented by others are used. Descriptions emphasize characteristics that will separate taxa from others found on the islands or nearby areas; and taxa restricted to Trinidad and Tobago tend to have more extensive descriptions.

Natural history notes include information from observations made on Trinidad and Tobago by the author and field associates. Information collected during this study is designated by "field notes" followed by the person or persons' initials making the observations (JCM = John C. Murphy; MD = Michael Dloogatch; RH = Ron Humbert; MB = Mel Bruns; MM = Michael Miller; SB = Steve Barten; GH = Gerry Hermann; RS = Ralph Shepstone; RIC = Ron I. Crombie; RWH = Robert W. Henderson). Information gathered from the literature at locations other than Trinidad and Tobago are noted as such and are added to provide comparative information. Information within the natural history section includes habitat, food, reproduction, abundance, predators, defense behavior, folklore, and human uses.

Material listed is material examined and material upon which specimen descriptions are based, and is not all inclusive. Keys were constructed using Trinidad and Tobago specimens, and the illustrations used include original material, as well as redrawn and modified drawings from a variety of sources.

PART 2

Keys

Keys to the Amphibians and Reptiles of Trinidad and Tobago

A. Key to the Higher Taxa of the Trinidad and Tobago Herpetofauna

1a. A body covered with smooth skin, may have tubercles; usually moist or slimy to touch; no scales or plates ....Amphibia (go to 2)

1b. Body covered with plates or scales; skin dry to touch ....
....Reptilia (go to 3)

2a. Frog or toad: Adults with four limbs; moveable eyelids; no tail ....
....Anura (go to B)

2b. Adults worm-like, smooth skin, no limbs; eyes covered by skin ....Gymnophiona (*Typhlonectes* sp.)

3a. Turtle: a bony shell, or leather-like shell; no teeth on jaws ....
....Chelonia (go to J)

3b. Not a turtle: no bony or leather-like shell; teeth present 4

4a. Crocodilian: longitudinal cloacal opening; toes webbed ....
....Crocodylia (go to O)

4b. Not a crocodilian: a transverse cloacal opening; if limbs present, toes rarely webbed 5

5a. Lizard: both forelimbs and hindlimbs present; ear opening and moveable eyelids present ....Sauria (go to Q)

5b. Not a lizard: Legs not present 6

6a. Body covered with rectangular scales that are arranged in rings or annuli; eyes poorly developed, covered with opaque scales; scales between orbits paired ....Amphisbaenia (go to P)

6b. Snake: body scales not rectangular; scales not arranged in rings, eyes usually covered with transparent scale; three or more median scales between orbits; no ear openings; no limbs ....Serpentes (go to GG)

B. Key to the Adult Frogs and Toads of Trinidad and Tobago

1a. Fingers not webbed, end in star-shaped disks (Figure B-1); toes fully webbed; body extremely depressed; tongue and eyelids absent; an aquatic frog ....Pipidae (*Pipa pipa*)

1b. Not as above 2

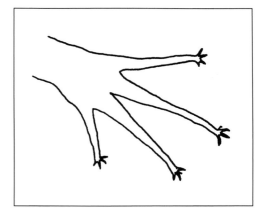

Figure B-1

37

2a.   Upper surfaces of finger and toe disks have a pair of dermal scutes (Figure B-2); only a trace of webbing on inner three toes; a small (<30 mm) brown frog, females and juveniles have a bright yellow throat ....Dendrobatidae (*Mannophryne olmonae* on Tobago, *M. trinitatis* on Trinidad, see comment in account.)

2b.   Not as above 3

3a.   Toads: thick glandular skin; paratoid glands present; cranial crest and ridges present (Figure B-3); no teeth in upper jaw ....Bufonidae (go to C)

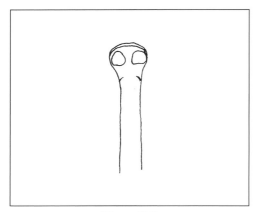

Figure B-2

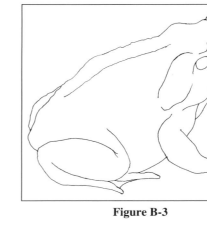

Figure B-3

3b.   Not as above 4

4a.   Snout pointed, short legs, transverse fold of skin across back of head (Figure B-4) ....Microhylidae (go to D)

4b.   Not as above 5

5a.   Toe disks T-shaped (Figure B-5); toes slightly webbed; ventral skin translucent green, internal organs visible; dorsum lime green with dark green and white flecks... ....Centrolenidae (*Hyalinobatrachium orientale tobagoensis*)

5b.   Not as above 6

6a.   Tree frog: almost all of these have granular skin on the belly and/or thighs; most have toes that end in expanded circular disks (Figure B-6a); and the terminal phalanges (ends of finger and toe) are claw-shaped (Figure B-6b); an intercalary cartilage is present in all of these species ....Hylidae (go to E)

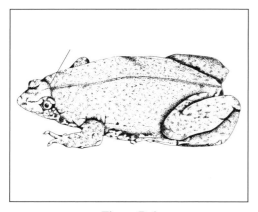

Figure B-4

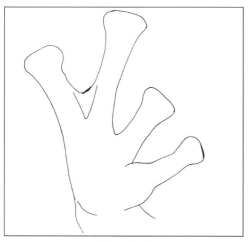

Figure B-5

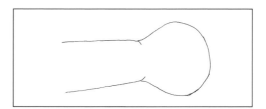

Figure B-6a

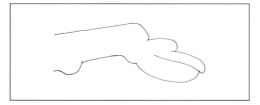

Figure B-6b

6b.   Not as above 7

7a.   Skin mostly smooth, may have rows of glands; if somewhat warty with small parotoid glands; cranial crests and ridges absent; upper jaw with teeth; the proximally concealed surfaces of the thighs, below the cloaca, do not have eyespots; most of these frogs have greatly reduced (or no) webbing between digits; some have granular skin on belly, and/or a ventral discodial disk (Figure B-7); none of the larger (50–70 mm) Trinidad and Tobago species are green ....Leptodactylidae (go to G)

7b.   Not as above 8

8a.   Toes fully webbed, fingers with no webbing; smooth skin with a dorso-lateral fold that starts over the tympanum (Figure B-8); tympanum almost as large as eye; pair of glands anterior to the front legs; green-brown dorsum ....Ranidae (*Rana palmipes*)

8b.   Smooth skin except for a few glands on flanks; a green-brown dorsum; long muscular legs, feet fully webbed, end of each digit swollen into small bulb; upper jaw with teeth; eye-spots present on concealed surface of proximal thigh; dorsolateral fold absent (Figure B-9) ....
....Pseudidae (*Pseudis paradoxa caribensis*)

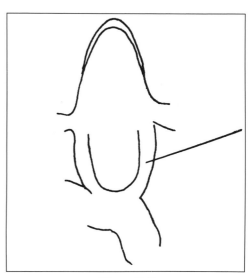

Figure B-7

Figure B-8

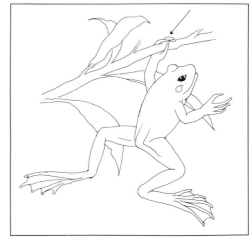

Figure B-9

C. Key to the Trinidad and Tobago *Bufo* (Bufonidae)

1a.   Crainal crests, ridges, and parotids glands present 2

1b.   Skin warty, parotid glands present, but no crainal crests or ridges ....(Go to Key G, Number 2a)

2a.   Nostrils situated on shelf and directed upward (Figure C-1) ....
....*Bufo beebei*

2b.   Nostrils directed anterior and lateral, subnasal shelf lacking ....
....*Bufo marinus*

D. Key to the Trinidad and Tobago *Elachistocleis* (Microhylidae)

1a.   White vertebral line (see Figure B-4); venter uniform in color ....
....*Elachistocleis ovalis*

1b.   Vertebral line absent; venter mottled ....*Elachistocleis surinamensis*

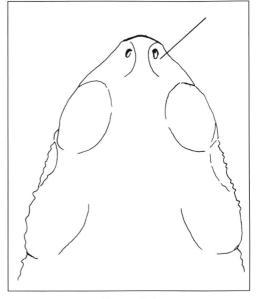

Figure C-1

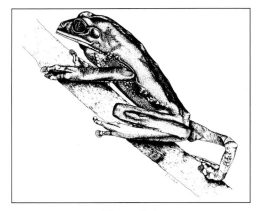

Figure E-1

E. Key to the Genera of Trinidad and Tobago Hylidae

1a. Pupil vertical; no webbing on hands or feet; thumb and first toe opposable; slow moving; adults are large and green (Figure E-1) ....*Phyllomedusa trinitatis*

1b. Pupil horizonal; webbing on hands and/or feet; thumb not opposable..2

2a. First finger longer than second (Figure E-2); very small (25 mm or less); dorsal pouch in females for brooding eggs ....*Flectonotus fitzgeraldi*

2b. First finger shorter than second; no dorsal pouch in female 3

3a. Tooth-like projections on lower jaw (Figure E-3); body very depressed; striped pattern ....*Phyllodytes auratus*

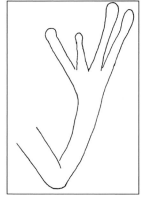

Figure E-2

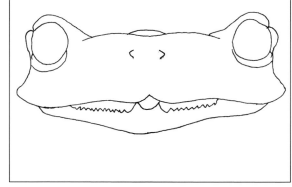

Figure E-3

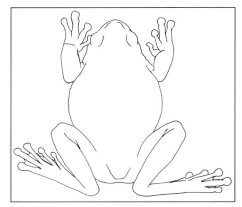

Figure E-4

3b. No tooth-like structures on lower jaw 4

4a. Males have double vocal sacs; both sexes have brown, very glandular skin and large toe disks (Figure E-4) ....*Phrynohyas venulosa*

4b. Males with a single median vocal sac; skin not exceptionally granular; toe disks moderate in size 5

5a. Fingers without webbing or only a trace of webbing, pattern of green and brown stripes ....*Scinax rubra*

5b. Fingers with webbing 6

6a. Snout pointed and projecting over mouth (Figure E-5); skin green; anal region and hind legs trimmed with a thin flap of skin; translucent green in life (yellow to white in preservative) ....*Sphaenorhynchus lacteus*

6b. Snout not pointed or projecting much beyond mouth (Figure E-6); fingers and toes webbed to varying degrees ....*Hyla* (go to F)

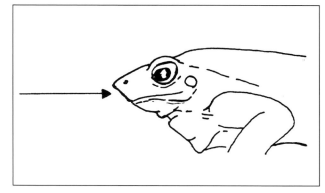

Figure E-5

Figure E-6

F. Key to the Trinidad and Tobago *Hyla* (Hylidae)

1a.   Adults small, 25–26 mm SVL, or less; yellow or yellow-brown in color with dorsum flecked, blotched or with hourglass mark; fingers with at least some webbing; no triangular skin flap on heel 2

1b.   Adults larger than 26 mm, brown or yellow dorsum 4

1c.   Adults larger than 26 mm, green or red dorsum. Webbing between fingers 2–3 and 3–4 reduced (Figure F-1), does not extend more than half way to disk of toe; third toe disk less than the size of tympanum; green or red with light dorsolateral line ....*Hyla punctata*

2a.   Area between eye and nostril (canthus) rounded ....*Hyla minuta*

2b.   Area between eye and nostril (canthus) distinct, forming a raised ridge...3

3a.   Snout flattened from above (Figure F-2); it does not protrude over mouth, 20–25 mm snout-vent length ....*Hyla microcephala misera*

3b.   Snout more triangular (Figure F-3); it slightly protrudes over mouth ....*Hyla minuscula*

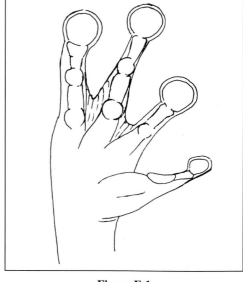

Figure F-1

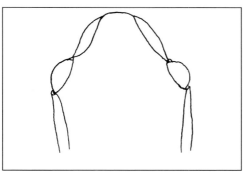

Figure F-2

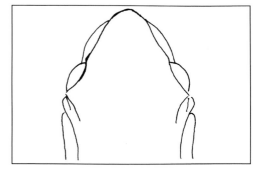

Figure F-3

4a.   All fingers and toes webbed (Figure F-4) ....*Hyla boans*

4b.   Webbing absent from between first two fingers 5

5a.   Webbing between fingers 2–3 and 3–4 present but reduced; webbing does not extend to base of disk (Figure F-5) ....*Hyla crepitans*

5b.   Webbing between fingers 2–3 and 3–4 extends to, or almost to, base of disk (Figure F-6); a large frog, may reach 115 mm SVL ....
....*Hyla geographica*

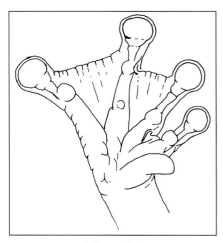

Figure F-4

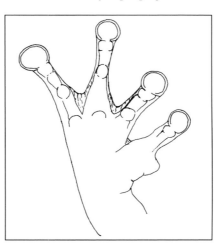

Figure F-5

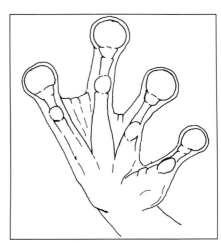

Figure F-6

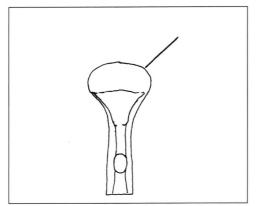

Figure G-1

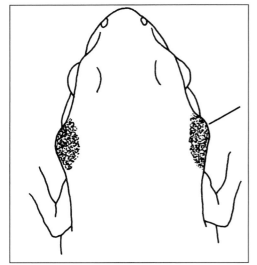

Figure G-2

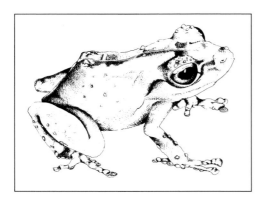

Figure H-1

G. Key to the Genera of Trinidad and Tobago Leptodactylidae

1a.   Fingers and toes with distinctly expanded disks (Figure G-1), each disk has a groove along the edge; skin with small tubercles ....
....*Eleutherodactylus* (go to H)1

1b.   Fingers and toes lack expanded disks; skin warty or with some glands 2

2a.   Small parotid gland (Figure G-2) with warty skin, but crainal crests absent ; males have prominent vocal sac ....*Physalaemus pustulosus*

2b.   Skin with glands, frequently in rows, but parotids absent 3

3a.   Dorsum is brown-gray, no large red inguinal blotch; toe tips form small blunt ends slightly expanded; first finger shorter than second; no obvious vocal sac; small, less than 31 mm SVL ....*Adenomera hylaedactyla*

3b.   Not as above 4

4a.   Dorsum is black with a large red blotch; tips of digits slightly T-shaped; skin has regularly distributed tubercles.....................*Lithodytes lineatus*

4b.   Finger and toe tips knobbed (Figure G-3); first finger longer than second; inguinal (groin) glands absent; brown-grey frogs, most have dorsal dermal folds or small tubercles forming short lateral ridges; and white lip spots..*Leptodactylus* (go to I)

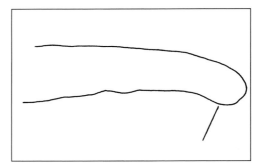

Figure G-3

H. Key to the Trinidad and Tobago *Eleutherodactylus* (Leptodactylidae)

1a.   Skin on belly smooth, wide head....*Eleutherodactylus charlottevillensis*

1b.   Skin on belly granular 2

2a.   More than four or five tubercules on upper eyelid ....
....*Eletherodactylus johnstonei*

2b.   Few or no tubercules on upper eyelid 3

3a.   Eye diameter greater than distance between eye and nostril, gold iris ....
....*Eleutherodactylus* cf. *rozei*

3b.   Eye diameter not greater than the distance between eye and nostril, blue iris (Figure H-1)...*Eleutherodactylus urichi*

I. Key to the Trinidad and Tobago *Leptodactylus* and *Adenomera* (Leptodactylidae)

1a.   First finger shorter than second........................*Adenomera hylaedactyla*

1b.   First finger longer than second 2

2a.   No longitudinal folds (ridges) of dorsal skin, but lateral rows of glands may be present...3
2b.   Dorsal folds or ridges present 4
3a.   A light side stripe present, supratympanic fold does not extend to shoulder ....*Leptodactylus nesiotus*
3b.   Light side stripe not present, supratympanic fold extends to shoulder (Figure I-1) ....*Leptodactylus validus*
4a.   Two longitudinal dorsal folds present, one on each side of body 5
4b.   More than two longitudinal dorsal folds of skin 6
5a.   Posterior surface of thighs uniformly black; head very broad ....
....*Leptodactylus knudseni*
5b.   Posterior surface of thighs mottled, head not very broad ....
....*Leptodactylus bolivianus*
6a.   Snout pointed and extending well beyond mouth (Figure I-2); males have black, external vocal sacs and no thumb spines ....
....*Leptodactylus fuscus*
6b.   Snout rounded, does not extend much beyond mouth (Figure I-3); males have no external vocal sacs, two thumb spines present ....
....*Leptodactylus macrosternum*

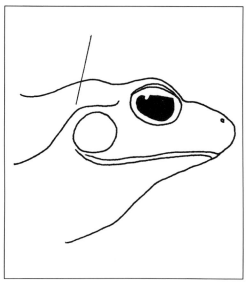

Figure I-1

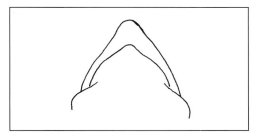

Figure I-2

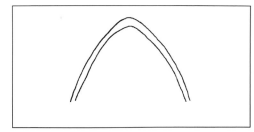

Figure I-3

J. Key to the Families of Trinidad and Tobago Turtles

1a.   Carapace (upper shell) lacks horny plates (leather-like); limbs are paddle-like and without claws; barrel-shaped body (Figure J-1), marine ....Dermochelyidae (*Dermochelys coriacea*)
1b.   Carapace with horny plates (not leather-like) 2
2a.   Limbs paddle-like with zero to three claws; marine (Figure J-2) ....Cheloniidae (go to K)
2b.   Limbs not paddle-like; four or five digits with claws 3
3a.   Neck withdraws into shell in a horizontal plane, side-neck (Figure J-3) ....go to 4

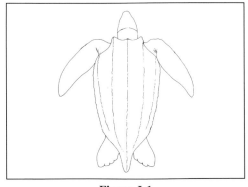

Figure J-1

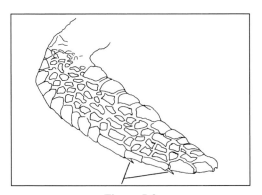

Figure J-2

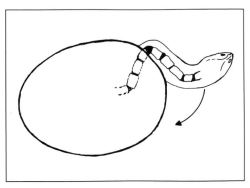

Figure J-3

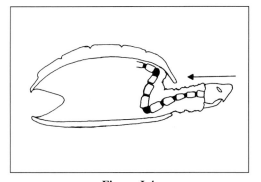

Figure J-4

3b.   Neck withdraws into shell in a vertical plane (Figure J-4) 5
4a.   Nuchal scale present (Figure J-5) ....Chelidae (go to L)
4b.   No nuchal scale..Pelomedusidae (go to M)
5a.   Hind legs columnar (elephant-like) (Figure J-6)....................................
        ....Testudinidae (go to N)
5b.   Hind legs not columnar 6
6a.   Plastron (lower shell) composed of 12 scutes; pectoral scutes form part of bridge with carapace (Figure J-7) ....
        ....Emydidae (*Rhinoclemmys punctularia punctularia*)
6b.   Plastron composed of 11 scutes; pectoral scutes do not form part of bridge with carapace (Figure J-8) ....
        ....Kinosternidae (*Kinosternon scorpioides scorpioides*)

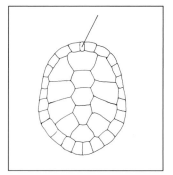

Figure J-5

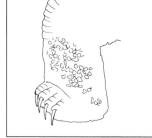

Figure J-6

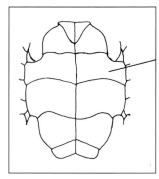

Figure J-7

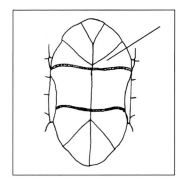

Figure J-8

K. Key to the Trinidad and Tobago Genera of Cheloniidae

1a.   Five or more pairs of costal scales (Figure K-1)....................................2
1b.   Four pairs of costal scales (Figure K-2) 3
2a.   Five pairs of costal scutes, shell narrow, brown or red ....
        ....*Caretta caretta*
2b.   Six or more pairs of costal scutes, shell wide, olive green ....
        ....*Lepidochelys olivacea*
3a.   Scutes on shell overlap; four prefrontals (Figure K-3); posterior margin of carapace serrated. ....*Eretomochelys i. imbricata*
3b.   Scutes on shell do not overlap; two prefrontals (Figure K-4); posterior margin of carapace rounded ....*Chelonia mydas*

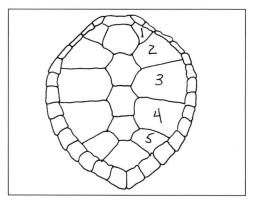

Figure K-1

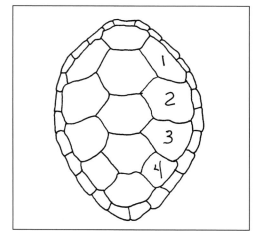

Figure K-2

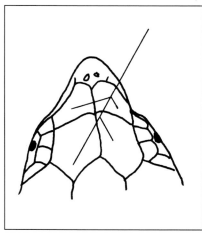

Figure K-3

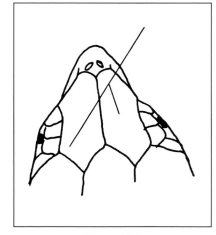

Figure K-4

L. Key to the Trinidad and Tobago Chelidae

1a. Carapace with three rows of keels; neck longer than shell; fleshy appendanges on throat and neck (see Figure L-1) ....*Chelus fimbriatus*
1b. Carapace smooth; neck shorter than shell; no fleshy appendages on throat and neck ....*Phrynops gibbus*

M. Key to the Possible Trinidad and Tobago Pelomedusidae

1a. Carapace flattened and widens posteriorly; a pair of chin barbels present; juveniles have yellow spots on the head ....*Podocnemis expansa*
1b. Carapace slightly keeled on third vertebral scute; only one chin barbel present; juveniles have yellow-orange spots on the top of the head ....*Podocnemis unifilis*

N. Key to the Trinidad and Tobago Testudinidae

1a. Carapace black; shell usually has strong constriction in middle (Figure N-1); scales on front limbs usually tipped with red ....
....*Geochelone carbonaria*
1b. Carapace brown; shell lacks medial constriction (Figure N-2); scales on front limbs orange or yellow ....*Geochelone denticulata*

O. Key to the Trinidad and Tobago Crocodylia

1a. No lower teeth visible when mouth is closed (Figure O-1) ....
....*Caiman crocodilus crocodilus*
1b. Fourth tooth in lower jaw visible when mouth closed 2
2a. Preocular area raised (Figure O-2); snout relatively short; symphysis of lower jaw extends to fourth or fifth tooth ....*Crocodylus acutus*
2b. Preocular area not raised (Figure O-3); snout elongated; symphysis of lower jaw extends to the sixth tooth or beyond..
....*Crocodylus intermedius*

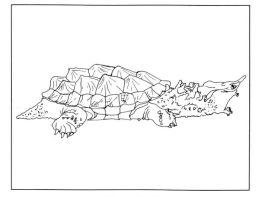

Figure L-1

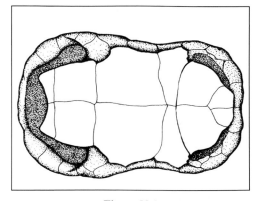

Figure N-1

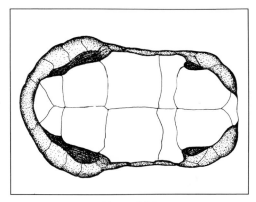

Figure N-2

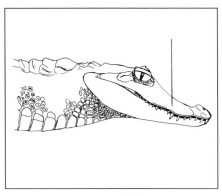

Figure O-1

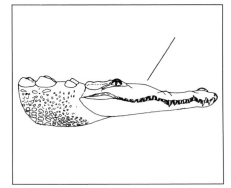

Figure O-2

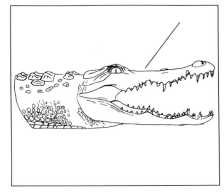

Figure O-3

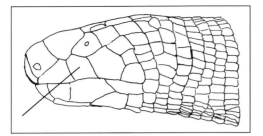

Figure P-1

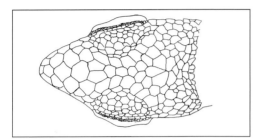

Figure Q-1

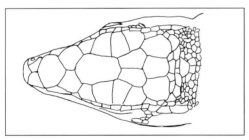

Figure Q-2

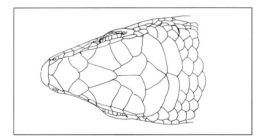

Figure Q-3a

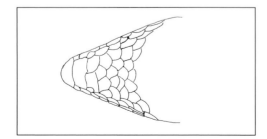

Figure Q-3b

P. Key to the Trinidad and Tobago Amphisbaenidae

1a.   Prefrontals and oculars contact supralabials (Figure P-1); no constricted ring on tail; no black mottling in pattern ....*Amphisbaena alba*

1b.   Supralabials usually not in contact with prefrontals and oculars (only the anterior edge of the ocular touches the second supralabial); constricted ring on tail; dorsal pattern with black mottling ....*Amphisbaena fuliginosa fuliginosa*

Q. Key to the Higher Categories of Trinidad and Tobago Lizards

1a.   Eyelids absent; upper head scales granular; well-developed limbs, with five digits on each...Gekkonidae (go to R)

1b.   Eyelids present; upper head scales not granular 2

2a.   Top of head with irregular scales (Figure Q-1); tongue fleshy and not extensible..Iguania (go to U)

2b.   Top of head with plate-like scales (Figure Q-2); tongue not fleshy and is extensible and bifurcate (two tips) 3

3a.   Head scales overlap (Figure Q-3a); scales on chin small and uniform in size (Figure Q-3b); scales have underlying osteoderms ....Scincidae (*Mabuya bistriata*)

3b.   Head scales juxtaposed; scales on chin both large and small; no osteoderms under skin 4

4a.   Anterior nasal scales not separated by frontal (Figure Q-4), nasals are in contact with each other ....Teiidae (go to W)

4b.   Anterior nasal scales separated by frontal, nasals are not in contact with each other (Figure Q-5) ....Gymnophthalmidae (go to X)

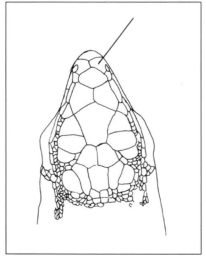

Figure Q-4

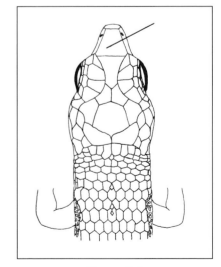

Figure Q-5

R. Key to the Trinidad and Tobago Gekkonidae

1a.   Pupil vertical; digits dialated over entire base 2

1b.   Pupil round; digits only slightly dialated at base 3

2a.   Digits dilated only at base (Figure R-1); digits not connected by web; scales on back unequal in size ....*Hemidactylus* (go to S)

2b.   Digits entirely dilated (Figure R-2); digits connected by web; scales on back equal in size ....*Thecadactylus rapicauda*

3a.   Scales on the dorsum heterogeneous (some larger than others) ....*Gymnodactylus geckoides*

3b.   Scales on the dorsum homogeneous (all about the same size) 4

4a.   Superciliary spine present (Figure R-3); a tiny lizard with toes dilated at tip only ....*Sphaerodactylus molei*

4b.   Toes not dilated at tip ....*Gonatodes* (go to T)

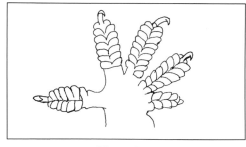

Figure R-1

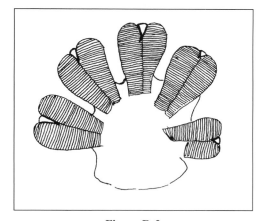

Figure R-2

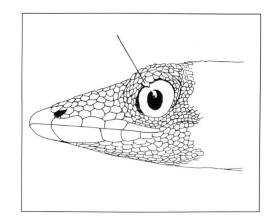

Figure R-3

S. Key to the Trinidad and Tobago *Hemidactylus* (Gekkonidae)

1a.   Tubercles reduced and widely separated by smaller granular scales; lamellae on the fourth and fifth toes do not extend to base of digit (Figure S-1) ....*Hemidactylus mabouia*

1b.   Tubercles large and raised giving the skin a spiny appearance; lamellae on fourth and fifth toes extend to base of digit (Figure S-2)................... ....*Hemidactylus palaichthus*

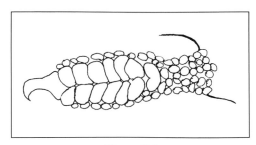

Figure S-1

T. Key to the Trinidad and Tobago *Gonatodes* (Gekkonidae)

1a.   Vertebral stripe bordered with black stripes in males, bordered with spots in female ....*Gonatodes vittatus vittatus*

1b.   No vertebral stripe..2

2a.   At least one pair of dorsolateral ocelli (Figure T-1)*Gonatodes ocellatus*

2b.   No dosolateral ocelli; elongated streaks may be present.......................3

3a.   Head mottled; light pre-axillary stripe with brown border; light dorso-lateral streaks bordered with brown may be present ....*Gonatodes ceciliae*

3b.   Head not mottled 4

4a.   Infradigital lamellae at base of digit not flattened, and not wider than rest of digit; males with bright yellow head ....*Gonatodes albogularis*

4b.   Infradigital lamellae at base of digit flattened and distinctly wider than the rest of the digit; collar-like bar present anterior to front legs ....*Gonatodes humeralis*

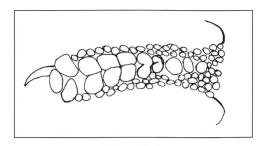

Figure S-2

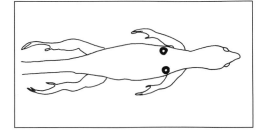

Figure T-1

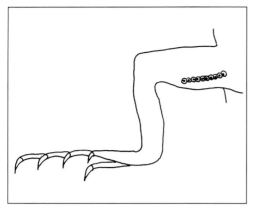

Figure U-1

U. Key to the Trinidad and Tobago Iguanidae

1a. Femoral pores present (Figure U-1) 2
1b. No femoral pores 3
2a. Body laterally compressed; no dorsal crest or spines; third and fourth toes of equal length..*Polychrus marmoratus*
2b. Body cylindrical; dorsal crest or spines present; third toe shorter than fourth ....*Iguana iguana*
3a. Body cylindrical or compressed; digits dialated to some degree; no spiny knobs on head or neck ....*Anolis* (go to V)
3b. Body slightly depressed; digits not dialated; spiny knobs on head and neck ....*Tropidurus plica*

V. Key to the Trinidad and Tobago Anolis (Iguanidae)

1a. Ventral scales keeled..2
1b. Ventral scales not keeled..3
2a. Tibia (lower leg) length greater than head length; paired dorsal blotches on both sides of the middorsal line at the hip; long hind legs..*Anolis chrysolepis planiceps*
2b. Tibia length equal to or less than head length..........*Anolis* cf. *lemurinus*
3a. Hind limb length/SVL ratio about 0.88; a large anole (to 140 mm SVL); males have sculptured head ....*Anolis richardii*
3b. Hind limb length/SVL ratio about 0.70..4
4a. Axillary pigmentation dark, particularly on humerus; in life lizard mossy green with blue-grey on head; dewlap orange with yellow to green scales; keeled dorsal scales ....*Anolis extremus*
4b. Axillary pigment light, particularly on humerus...................................5
5a. Coloration in life green and brown; females are 51–60 mm SVL ....*Anolis aeneus* × *trinitatis*
5b. Coloration in life green or grey-brown 6
6a. Green dorsum; male dewlap yellow with blue scales; 115–132 scales rows halfway around midbody......................................*Anolis trinitatis*
6b. Brown-grey dorsum; dewlap grey-green to yellow with yellow to blue scales; 81–94 scales rows halfway around midbody; smooth dorsal scales ....*Anolis aeneus*

W. Key to the Trinidad and Tobago Teiidae

1a. Ventral scales keeled ....*Kentropyx striatus*
1b. Ventral scales smooth 2
2a. Ventral scales small, forming more than 20 longitudinal rows ....*Tupinambis teguixin*
2b. Ventral scales large, forming 8–10 longitudinal rows 3
3a. Ventrals in 10 longitudinal rows....................................*Ameiva ameiva*
3b. Ventrals in 8 longitudinal rows ....*Cnemidophorus lemniscatus*

X. Key to the Trinidad and Tobago Gymnophthalmidae

1a. Limbs rudimentary, digits clawless; no ear opening.............................
....*Bachia* (go to Y)
1b. Limbs relatively well developed; ear opening present (Figure X-1) 2
2a. Scales on dorsum in three rows, smooth, rounded and overlapping ....
....*Gymnophthalmus* (go to AA)
2b. Scales on dorsum keeled, hexagonal and quadrangular (see Figure Q-5)..*Proctoporus shrevei*

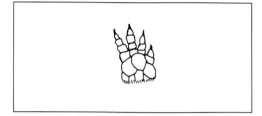

Figure X-1

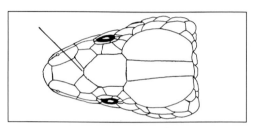

Figure Y-1

Y. Key to the Trinidad and Tobago Bachia

1a. Hindfeet have four distinct digits (Figure Y-1); prefrontals present ....*Bachia heteropa* (go to Z)
1b. Hindfeet have two digits; prefrontals absent. ....*Bachia flavescens*

Z. Key to the Trinidad and Tobago Subspecies of *Bachia heteropa*

1a. Prefrontals not in medial contact (Figure Z-1) ....
....*Bachia heteropa trinitatis*
1b. Prefrontals in medial contact (Figure Z-2) ....*Bachia heteropa alleni*

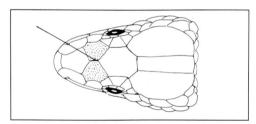

Figure Z-1

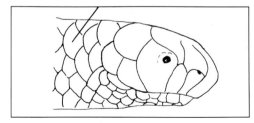

Figure Z-2

AA. Key to the Trinidad and Tobago *Gymnophthalmus*

1a. Dorsolateral stripe extends to tail, may be broken into spots posteriorly; ventrals between pectoral and anal plates, number 23–27; population contains males and females ....*Gymnophthalmus speciosus*
1b. Dorsolateral stripe fades at midbody; ventrals between pectoral and anal plates number 21–24; population contains only females ....
....*Gymnophthalmus underwoodi*

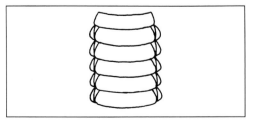

Figure BB-1

BB. Key to the Families of Trinidad and Tobago Snakes

1a. Scales around body uniform in size, or the vertebral row slightly enlarged and cycloid (Figure BB-1) 2
1b. Ventral scales distinctly larger than dorsals (Figure BB-2) 4
2a. 14 scale rows on body ....Leptotyphlopidae (*Leptotyphlops albifrons*)
2b. More than 14 scale rows on body 3
3a. 18 scale rows on body ....Anomalepididae (*Helminthophis* sp.)
3b. 19–20 scale rows on body ....Typhlopidae (go to DD)

Figure BB-2

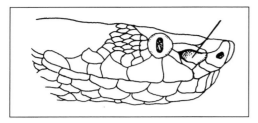

Figure BB-3

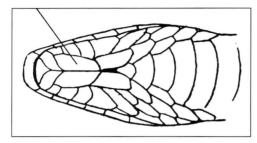

Figure BB-4

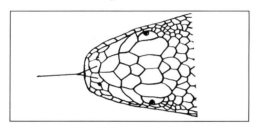

Figure CC-1

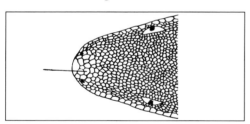

Figure CC-2

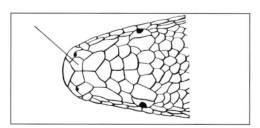

Figure CC-3

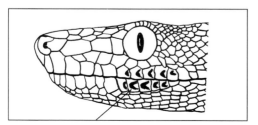

Figure CC-4

4a.   A single pit between the eye and nostril (Figure BB-3) ....
....Viperidae (Go to FF)

4b.   Pits may or may not be present; if present, they are on labial scales (scales bordering mouth)...5

5a.   15 dorsal scale rows; loreal scale absent; very short tail; fixed fangs in upper jaw; body ringed with red, black, and yellow or white.................
....Elapidae (Go to EE)

5b   Not as above 6

6a.   One or more pairs of enlarged chinshields between infralabials (Figure BB-4) ....Colubridae (Go to GG)

6b.   Scales between infralabials (scales on chin) small ....
....Boidae (Go to CC)

CC. Key to the Trinidad and Tobago Boidae

1a.   No pits in labials; anterior teeth no larger than others 2

1b.   Pits in labials; anterior teeth distinctly larger than others 3

2a.   Divided nasal scales in contact; nostrils dorsal (Figure CC-1); ventrals very small ....*Eunectes murinus*

2b.   Nasal scales separated by four or more tiny internasals Figure CC-2); nostrils more lateral, large ventrals ....*Boa c. constrictor*

3a.   Pits in labial scales shallow; internasal scales present (Figure CC-3) ....*Epicrates cenchria maurus*

3b.   Pits in labial scales deep (Figure CC-4); nasals in broad contact ....*Corallus hortulanus cooki*

DD. Key to the Trinidad and Tobago *Typhlops*

1a.   Small, less than 250 mm; 11 rows of dark brown stripes; tail yellow; dorsals 388–389 ....*Typhlops trinitatus*

1b.   Large, to 325 mm; dorsum yellow-brown; dorsals 195–287 ....
....*Typhlops brongersmianus*

EE. Key to the Trinidad and Tobago *Micrurus*

1a.   Black rings on body form triads, with two white rings separating the black rings; a red ring separates each triad ....
....*Micrurus lemniscatus diutius*

1b.   No triads of black; each black ring bordered with a narrow white ring; each red scale has a black spot ....*Micrurus circinalis*

FF. Key to the Trinidad and Tobago Viperidae

1a.   Posterior subcaudals finely divided; keels on middorsal scales conical; supralabials number 9–10 ....*Lachesis muta muta*

1b.   Posterior subcaudals all or most paired; keels on middorsal scales normal; supralabials number 7–8 ....*Bothrops asper*

GG. Key to the Trinidad and Tobago Colubridae

1a.   Dorsal scales smooth (Figure GG-1)...2
1b.   Some or all dorsal scales keeled (Figure GG-2) 21
2a.   Dorsal scale rows number 12 ....*Chironius carinatus*
2b.   Dorsal scale rows more than 12 (Figure GG-3) 3
3a.   Subcaudal scales single (Figure GG-4)..................*Pseudoboa neuwiedii*
3b.   Subcaudal scales paired (Figure GG-5) 4
4a.   Scales at midbody 19 (*Leptodeira* may have 21) 5
4b.   Scales at midbody 15 or 17 10
5a.   Vertebral scale row enlarged; transverse blotches or bands ....
      ....*Tripanurgos compressus*
5b.   Vertebral scale row not enlarged...6
6a.   Preocular scale forming suture with frontal scale; eye in contact with
      fourth and fifth supralabials (Figure GG-6) 7
6b.   Preocular scale not forming suture with frontal scale...........................8
7a.   Pattern of black and red, or solid black, belly uniform...........................
      ....*Oxyrhopus petola petola*
7b.   Dorsum brown, belly flecked with pigment ....*Thamnodynastes* sp.
7c.   Preocular scale not forming suture with frontal scale...........................8
8a.   Dorsal surface uniform in color (except for collar in very young speci-
      mens); eye in contact with third and fourth supralabial; subcaudals in
      64–93 pairs...*Clelia clelia clelia*
8b.   Not as as above 9

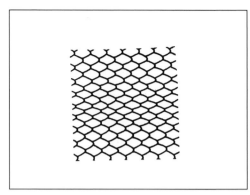

Figure GG-1

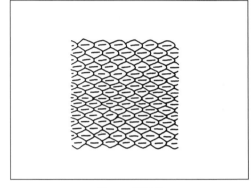

Figure GG-2

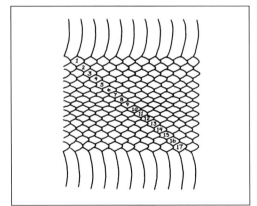

Figure GG-3

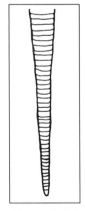

Figure GG-4

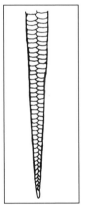

Figure GG-5

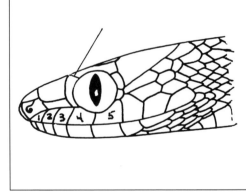

Figure GG-6

9a.   Anal plate single (Figure GG-7); subcaudal scales in 98–118 pairs; eye
      in contact with fifth and sixth supralabial; dorsum variegated with black,
      pink, and yellow..*Siphlophis cervinus*
9b.   Anal plate divided (Figure GG-8); subcaudal scales in 81–89 pairs; ven-
      ter uniform white or cream; scale rows at midbody may be 21 ....
      ....*Leptodeira annulata ashmeadi*
10a. 17 scale rows at midbody 11
10b. 15 scale rows at midbody 16
11a. Anal plate single 12
11b. Anal plate divided 13
12a. A large, diurnal, terrestrial-arboreal snake; head distinct from neck;
      nasal single ....*Drymarchon corais corais*
12b. A small, fossorial snake; head barely distinct from neck ....
      ....*Atractus univittatus*

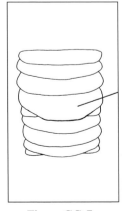

Figure GG-7

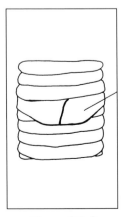

Figure GG-8

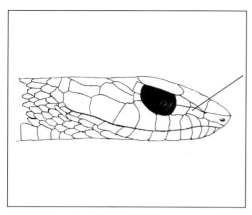

Figure GG-9

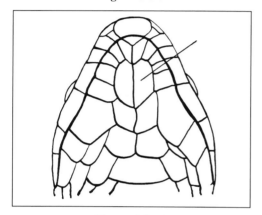

Figure GG-10

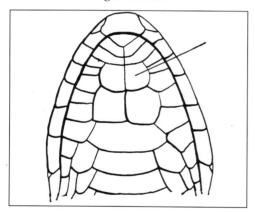

Figure GG-11

12c.   Divided nasal scale, transverse crossbars or uniform pattern ....
....*Oxyrhopus petola petola*

13a.   Subcaudals less than 82 ....*Liophis* (go to HH)

13b.   Subcaudals more than 82...14

14a.   Loreal usually absent; a very thin snake that resembles a twig; head elongate ....*Oxybelis aeneus*

14b.   Loreal present (Figure GG-9) 15

15a.   Vertebral scale row not enlarged; ventral scales number 163–204; racer-
like snake...*Mastigodryas* (go to JJ)

15b.   Vertebral scale row enlarged; ventrals number 220–267; a thin-bodied,
blotched snake with a large head ....*Imantodes c. cenchoa*

16a.   Anal plate single 17

16b.   Anal plate divided 19

17a.   Head indistinct from neck; dorsum brown with three or four dark
stripes; a very short tail, subcaudal scales number 11–19; a fossorial
snake...*Atractus trilineatus*

17b.   Head distinct from neck 18

18a.   Anterior chin shields larger than posterior (Figure GG-10); sixth supralabial largest; the fourth and fifth supralabials contact eye ....
....*Sibon nebulata nebulata*

18b.   Anterior chin shields shorter than posterior (Fig. GG-11); two pairs of
lower labials touch mental groove; third and fourth supralabials in contact with eye ....*Dipsas variegata trinitatis*

19a.   Pattern uniform or with three to five longitudinal stripes; head and nape
with dark blotch forming a hood........................*Tantilla melanocephala*

19b.   Pattern with crossbands..20

20a.   Nostrils and eyes directed dorsally; nasal plates in contact behind rostral;
one internasal shield; pattern of 54–74 black annuli...............................
....*Hydrops triangularis neglectus*

20b.   Nostrils and eyes directed laterally; nasals separated by two internasals;
pattern of black bands in triads on Trinidad; on Tobago a pattern of black
ocelli ....*Erythrolamprus* (go to KK)

21a.   Scale rows number 21,23 or 25 ....*Pseustes* (go to II)

21b.   Not as above 22

22a.   Number of scale rows even, 16 or 18 ....*Spilotes pullatus*

22b.   Scale rows odd, 15, 17, or 19 23

23a.   Scale rows 15; a green vertebral stripe present ......*Leptophis* (go to LL)

23b.   Scales in 19 rows..24

24a.   Eyes lateral; a small, blue-black snake; frequently with a white or orange
occipital blotch; venter uniform, except for black bordered scales on the
subcaudals ....*Ninia atrata*

24b.   Eyes dorsal; one internasal; an aquatic snake with black-edged crossbands; venter with dark olive or black spots or crossbands ....
....*Helicops angulatus*

HH. Key to the Trinidad and Tobago *Liophis*

1a.   Pattern does not include longitudinal stripes ......*Liophis cobella cobella*

1b.   Longitudinal stripes in pattern...2

2a.   Black vertebral stripe on the middle five scale rows, and a second black
stripe involving scale rows four and five ....*Liophis melanotus neosus*

2b.   No vertebral stripe, black stripe on each side of tail ....
....*Liophis reginae zweifeli*

2c.   No vertebral stripe, but a stripe of cream or tan present on scale row
four ....*Liophis reginae* ssp. (Tobago)

II. Key to the Trinidad and Tobago *Pseustes*

1a.   All rows of scales keeled, except outermost rows (Figure II-1); three postocular scales ....*Pseustes sulphureus sulphureus*
1b.   Only middorsal scale rows strongly keeled; two postocular scales; 23 scale rows at midbody ....*Pseustes poecilonotus polylepis*

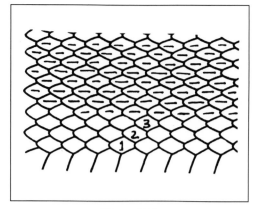

Figure II-1

JJ. Key to the Trinidad and Tobago Subspecies of *Mastigodryas boddaerti*

1a.   Two lateral stripes ....*Mastigodryas boddaerti dunni*
1b.   One lateral stripe ....*Mastigodryas boddaerti boddaerti*

KK. Key to the Trinidad and Tobago *Erythrolamprus*

1a.   Body pattern composed of rings of red, black, yellow; a coral snake mimic...2
1b.   Body pattern composed of 22–29 black ocelli, most with a white center, red ground color ....*Erythrolamprus ocellatus*
2a.   No nuchal collar, subcaudals probably fewer than 49 ....
      ....*Erythrolamprus aesculapii aesculapii*
2b.   Nuchal collar present, subcaudals probably number more than 51 ....*Erythrolamprus bizona*

LL. A Key to the Trinidad and Tobago *Leptophis*

1a.   Scales on rows one and two not keeled..
      ....*Leptophis ahaetulla coeruleodorsus*
1b.   All scale rows keeled, oblique bands on body ....*Leptophis riveti*

PART 3

Amphibia Species Accounts

Class Amphibia

Amphibians differ from most vertebrates in having glandular skin which lacks epidermal scales, feathers, or hair. During their 380 million year history amphibians have generated numerous adaptations which have allowed them to successfully colonize the land. Today three living orders—Anura (frogs and toads), Caudata (salamanders and newts), and Gymnophiona (caecilians)—comprise 34 families and about 4000 species, with new species being described annually. Modern amphibians tend to be small. The large salamanders and caecilians reach 1.5 m, and the largest frog attains 300 mm, but most amphibians are much smaller and rarely exceed 50 mm. Most live in the tropics, and most are greatly dependent upon water for reproduction. Amphibians produce shell-less eggs which usually hatch into swimming, fish-like larvae. The larvae or tadpoles then feed, grow, and metamorphose into an adult stage which may live on land or stay in the water. One order of Amphibia occurs on Trinidad and Tobago, Anura; but the Gymnophiona have been reported from Trinidad on the basis of a single specimen, which is now lost. Thus, 10 amphibian families with 19 genera, and 37 species are suspected to inhabit Trinidad and Tobago. Trinidad and Tobago frogs show a remarkable diversity of life history adaptations, including nine different modes of reproduction. Amphibians are important in nature's economy, controlling insects, taking part in the recycling of matter in the ecosystem, and serving as indicators of environmental quality.

Order Anura

The tailless amphibians, commonly called frogs and toads, are the most successful group of modern amphibians in terms of the number of species contained within the order. Worldwide more than 3500 species are known, and while most occur in the tropics, many have invaded temperate latitudes, and a few enter the Arctic Circle. Nine families with 18 genera and 36 species inhabit Trinidad and Tobago, including one of the smallest New World frogs, *Hyla minuscula,* and one of the largest, *Bufo marinus.* Adults feed mostly on insects or other animals, while the larvae may be herbivores, grazing or filtering bacteria and algae from the water, or they may be carnivorous, feeding on small animals, even their siblings. Vocalizations are usually used by males to attract females and advertise their presence to other males; but the calls will also attract the attentions of humans and sound-activated predators. DeVerteuil (1884) commented on the anuran voices of Trinidad.

During the whole rainy season, and also after heavy showers, toads of all kinds and sizes unite their varied croakings in discordant concerts—from the most acute falsetto to the gravest bass, occasionally drowned by the accompaniment of a chorus from our larger species; they are generally assisted, in the minor notes by frogs. Hearken! the loud croak from this cluster of bamboos by the bank of the river, and in the still of the night, is the harsh and solemn "FROG-FROG-FROG" of one of our hylas; another species is often met with in some obscure corner of a house, where its croaking is a sure announcement of coming rain. If placed in a bottle with water, it generally keeps motionless at the bottom during dry weather, but rises to the surface and commences its croak on the slightest indication of a shower.

Order Anura
Family Bufonidae: True Toads

The bufonids are almost cosmopolitan, inhabiting every major land mass except Australia–New Guinea (but they have now been introduced there by man), Antarctica, Greenland, and Madagascar. Most adult toads are terrestrial and have thick, glandular skin, with or without warts; large, alkaloid-producing parotid glands are usually present. Eggs are laid in water, and the tadpoles are free-swimming. There are about 25 genera with approximately 335 species; two species of the genus *Bufo* occur on Trinidad and one of these species occurs on Tobago. They can be distinguished from all other frogs by their cranial crests and large parotid glands. Locally toads are called crapauds. Niddrie (1980) wrote,

Litigating Tobagonians, wishing to silence a hostile witness, frequently sew up the mouth of a crapaud with cotton thread and toss it into the house the night before the court case, as a grim reminder of his vulnerability should his evidence go against the plaintiff! Others wishing to indicate impending misfortune for an individual will comment "Crapaud smoke your pipe!"

Bufo beebei Gallardo

Map 1. Plate 5.

Bufo granulosus: Parker, 1933:4. *Bufo granulosus beebei* Gallardo, 1965:114. Type locality: "Churchill-Roosevelt Highway, Trinidad, B.W.I." *Bufo beebei*—Rivero et al. 1986:2.

Comment: Crombie (in Frost, 1985) suggested the *Bufo granulosus* group was in need of revision, and noted that a number of races had been raised to specific status and that more should be expected to follow, considering range overlap in *B. g. beebei* and *B. g. humbolti* and some races approach each other without evidence of intergradation. Rivero et al. (1986) raised this subspecies to specific status without comment, and that arrangement is followed here. However, further justification is needed to support this position.

Distribution: *Bufo beebei* is endemic to the Orinoco Basin and Trinidad; and it occurs throughout most of the lower elevations of Trinidad. Published Trinidad localities include: Quarakoon River, sw peninsula (Alkins-Koo,

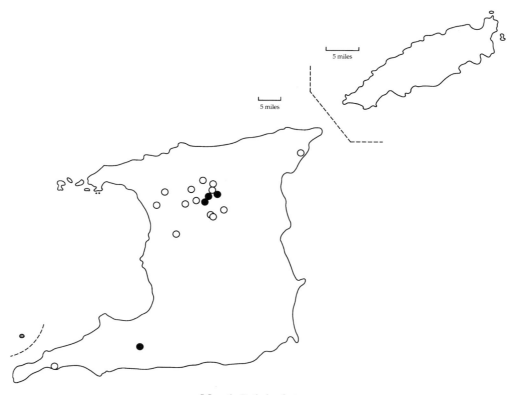

Map 1. *Bufo beebei*

1990); Arima Valley (Beebe, 1952); Bamboo Grove in the Northern Basin (Kenny, 1969); Tacarigua (Brongersma, 1956b); St. Augustine (Lynn, 1959); Aripo Savanna (Schwab, 1988). Field notes (JCM) list it from the lower Arima Valley, the road to Arena Dam, just west of Cumuto; Cumuto Rd.; Guanapo Valley; Mexico Road; Waller Field. Museum material documents the following Trinidad localities: Arima; Aripo Savanna; St. Augustine; San Rafael; Chaguanas; Laurie Pond, Siparia; Balandra, Ne coast; Mausica Rd. east, St. George Co.; and Piarco Airport. Parker's (1933) record of this toad from the summit of Mt. Tucuche is most likely in error; Tucuche's highland is densely forested and this is a savanna species.

Description: Males 51 mm, females 61 mm SVL. Head elongate, snout protruding due to subnasal ridges; eyes about twice the diameter of tympanum; orbit outlined by well developed crest extending posteriorly over tympanum; parotids large, extending to axillary region; top of head with orbital crests extending posteriorly toward a light vertebral line. Dorsum with small granular warts that become smaller laterally and ventrally; first finger about equal to the second in length, or slightly longer than second; two subarticular tubercles (enlarged pads on wrists); hind limbs short; heel reaching tympanum; feet with very little webbing; tarsal fold may or may not be present. Coloration light to dark brown, with some mottling on dorsum; venter light with some spots or mottling; males with darkly pigmented, medial vocal sac; females with pointed gular and pectoral granules. This toad

can be confused with *Bufo marinus,* but the nostrils of *B. beebei* are directed dorsally from a subnasal shelf, while the nostrils of *Bufo marinus* open laterally. It could also be confused with *Physalaemus pustulosus;* however, *P. pustulosus* lacks cranial crests.

Voice: Kenny (1969) described the voice as "A sustained tremulous low pitched whistle."

Natural History: A lowland, savanna-dwelling toad. On Trinidad, *B. beebei* inhabits canefields, rice fields, and other open agricultural areas; it will penetrate forests by following roads and lumber tracts (Rivero, 1961; Kenny, 1969; Hoogmoed and Gorzula, 1979). Field notes (JCM) report it in disturbed, open habitats such as roadside ditches, construction sites devoid of all vegetation, and grassy areas adjacent to man-made ponds. Males call from the edges of shallow puddles in June and July with *Physalaemus pustulosus* and *Leptodactylus fuscus.* Massive spawning in June, August, and September; the eggs have a wrinkled appearance, and hatched within 24 hours; metamorphosis occurs at about 4 weeks (Kenny, 1969). Prey reported includes ants, snails, and hemipterans (Lynn, 1959; Rivero, 1961). A population density of one individual per 3.8 square meters was estimated for this species at San Fernando de Apure, Venezuela (Dixon and Staton, 1976) .

Material: Trinidad—FMNH 43667 Aripo Savanna; 218784 Laurier Pond, Siparia; 219617 between the Eastern Main Road and Churchill-Roosevelt Highway east of Arima; 49603–4 San Rafael.

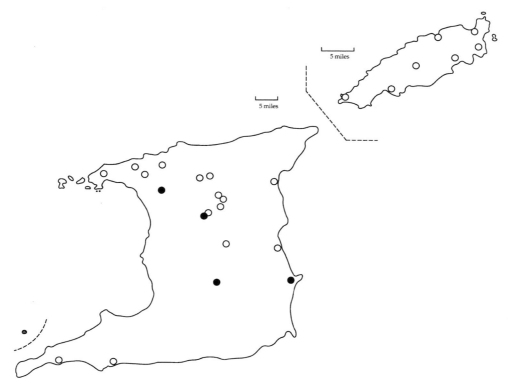

Map 2. *Bufo marinus*

Bufo marinus Linnaeus

Map 2. Plates 6, 7.

Rana marina Linnaeus, 1758:211. Type locality:"Americas", restricted to Suriname by Muller and Hellmich (1936). *Bufo marinus:* Schneider, 1799:219. *Bufo strumosus:* Court, 1858:441. *Bufo agua:* Clark, 1916:13. *Bufo marinis* [*sic*]: Barbour, 1916b:222 (Tobago). *Bufo m. marinus:* Mertens, 1969:64. *Bufo marinus marinus:* Mertens, 1972:9.

Common Name: "Crapaud" (DeVerteuil, 1858:441).

Distribution: *B. marinus* is a widespread species, occurring from extreme southern Texas to northern Brazil, and its distribution is increasing throughout the world's tropics with the help of humans. On Trinidad and Tobago it occurs from sea level to the highest peaks. Zug and Zug (1979) considered the Trinidad and Tobago populations to be natural (not introduced by man). Published Trinidad localities include Quarakoon River, sw peninsula (Alkins-Koo, 1990); Arima Valley (Beebe, 1952); throughout Trinidad at low elevations (Kenny, 1969); Tamana Caves (Kenny, 1979a); Aripo Savanna (Schwab, 1988). Field notes (JCM): road to Arena Dam, just west of Cumuto; the Cocal area of Manzanilla-Cocos Bay Beach; the summit of Mt. Tucuche; the Guanapo Valley; Matura Beach; Quinam Beach; 5 km SSW of Valencia on Nicaragua Rd.; Waller Field. Trinidad museum material documents the following localities: Brickfield; San Rafael; St. Joseph; St. Augustine; Marval Valley; Mt. St. Benedict; Tucker Valley. Published Tobago localities include Scarborough (Mertens,

1970). Tobago localities based on museum material include Milford Bay; Bloody Bay; Roxborough-Bloody Bay Rd., 1.7 km W of junction of Windward Rd. in Roxborough; Hillsborough Dam; Charlotteville; and SW of Speyside 1.45 km W of junction with Windward Rd. It also occurs on Little Tobago Island.

Description: Maximum size about 238 mm SVL, females larger than males. Head wide, rounded snout; tympanum one-half to two-thirds the eye diameter; anterior and supraorbital crests well developed; posterior and subocular crests incomplete or missing; nostrils directed laterally; parotid glands large, pitted, extending past axillary region; upper eyelids and area in front of the tympanum tuberculate. Dorsum with irregular, tubercles (red in males), often each with a spine outlined in dark pigment; venter mottled; tubercles become very small ventrally. First finger slightly longer than second; hind feet heavily webbed compared to *Bufo beebei*. Juveniles and adult females mottled with brown, often have a middorsal stripe and dark scapular blotches; juveniles with dark interorbital blotch; adult males unicolored red-brown, with rugosities on inner side of first digit. Small individuals difficult to distinguish from juvenile *Bufo beebei* without checking the position of the nostrils. Small specimens readily distinguished from *Physalaemus pustulosus* by the presence of cranial crests in *Bufo marinus*.

Voice: "A low pitched staccato drumming sustained up to 30 sec." (Kenny, 1969).

Natural History: A ubiquitous toad, occurring through-

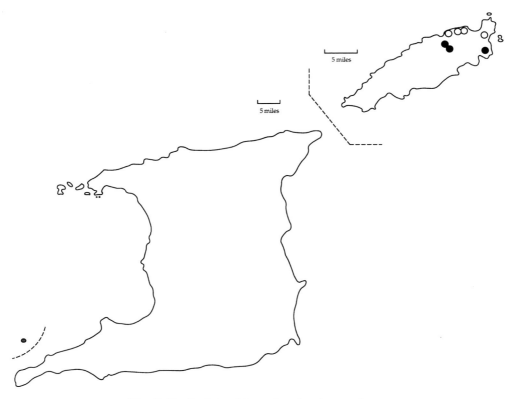

Map 3. *Hyalinobatrachium orientale tobagoensis*

out the two islands in most terrestrial habitats. Drainage ditches, open areas, agricultural areas, gardens, caves, and forests (Johnson, 1946; Kenny, 1969). Field notes (JCM) report it abundant in secondary forests and in open areas around buildings that are occupied; lights on buildings and in yards attract nocturnal insects upon which the toads feed. Adults and juveniles present on summit of Tucuche where there is little or no standing water; oviposition may take place in cavities created by fallen trees that fill with water. Observed within 2 meters of ocean at Quinam Beach and at Man-O-War Bay, Tobago; and on Matura Beach eight individuals with SVLs of approximately 10 cm emerged from the surf shortly after dark. Food includes anything that can be swallowed; Alexander (1964) reports Florida animals eating nonliving food such as pet foods, meat, and vegetables; Quesnel (1986) reported this toad feeding on a fledgling cowbird; and ffrench (in Quesnel, 1986) described one feeding on the coral snake *Micrurus circinalis*. Reproduction year round with peaks at the height of the dry season and early in the wet season; wet season reproduction occurring in temporary bodies of water, while dry season spawning occurs in rivers. Males vocalized in late April (the end of the dry season) and throughout June and July (the height of the wet season); in April males called from artificial ponds; during the wet season males called from stations both in and out of the water, and amplexing pairs were occasionally seen on land (Kenny, 1969; field notes, JCM). Eggs hatched within 36 hours and metamorphosis occurred at 6 weeks (Kenny, 1969). Ditmars and Bridges (1935) de-

scribed a site near St. Joseph as " . . . infested with them and there must have been thousands in five or six acres of grassy land around the house." Field notes (JCM) report them abundant at Laurie Pond near Siparia, estimated density exceeds one animal per square meter. The toxic nature of its skin has been known for some time (Abel and Macht, 1911), and dogs quickly learn to avoid the species because of its noxious skin secretions (Krakauer, 1968). Cooper and Bacon (1981) note that this species may be used for dissection in secondary school biology classes. Aitkens et al. (1968) reported the tick *Amblyomma dissimile* from Trinidad *Bufo marinus*.

Material: Trinidad—FMNH 49605 Brickfield; 49606–7 San Rafael; USNM 102401 St Joseph, Mayaro Co.; 103348–69 St. Augustine, St. George Co.

Order Anura
Family Centrolenidae: Glass Frogs

Glass frogs range from southern Mexico to Argentina, Boliva, and southeastern Brazil. They are small, usually less than 30 mm, distinctive green frogs with transparent skin. The tips of the toes are T-shaped. Most species lay small clutches eggs on leaves above streams; males of some species guard one or more clutches during their development; upon hatching the elongated tadpoles drop into the water below, where they develop in the stream's substrate. Four genera with 65 species, one species occurs on Tobago; the family is unknown from Trinidad. Hardy (1983b) commented on the Tobago centrolenlid,

The *Centrolenella* of Tobago is, indeed, a remarkable tree frog. I call it the instant anatomy frog. The dorsal surfaces are magnificent pale green, sometimes flecked with pure ebony, but the belly is as transpaprent as air so that the inner organs — heart, intestines, gall bladder, liver, and all — are constantly displaying in living, moving colour.

Hyalinobatrachium orientale tobagoensis (Hardy)

Map 3. Plates 8, 9.

> *Centrolenella orientalis* Rivero, 1968:308. Type locality: Cerro Turumiquire, 1200 m, Estados Sucre-Monagas, Venezuela. *Centrolenella* cf. *orientalis:* Hardy, 1982:71. *Centrolenella orientalis tobagoensis* Hardy, 1984d:165. Type locality: Roxborough-Partatuvier Road in the vicinity of Bloody Bay, St. John Parish, Tobago. *Centrolenella orientalis:* La Marca, 1992:21. *Hyalinobatrachium orientale:* Ruiz-Carranza and Lynch, 1991:24.

Comment: Hardy (1984d) described a centrolenid from Tobago, naming it *Centrolenella orientalis tobagoensis.* Cannatella and Lamar (1986) made a strong case for placing *Centrolenella orocostalis* Rivero in the synonymy of *Centrolenella orientalis;* using the principle of first reviser they selected the name *C. orientalis* over *C. orocostalis,* which is described three pages earlier in Rivero (1968). They argued that *C. o. tobagoensis* is invalid and *C. orientalis* is a widespread species made up of disjunct populations ranging from Colombia to Guyana. Ruiz-Carrera and Lynch (1991) split the genus *Centrolenella* into several genera, and placed the animals under discussion in the genus *Hyalinobatrachium.* Preliminary observations of the type material of *Centrolenella orientale* and *Centrolenella orocostalis* and Tobago material suggest the three populations may be distinct at the species level and that further investigation into their relationships is warranted. Thus, I am recognizing the race described by Hardy pending further investigation.

Distribution: *H. orientale* ranges from Cordillera Oriental above Villavicencio, Meta, Colombia, mountains of northern Venezuela, and the Sierra de Lema in the Venezuelan Guyana, and northeastern Tobago. *H. o. tobagoensis* is known only from northeastern Tobago. It occurs along streams that transect the road leading to Bloody Bay from Roxborough, approximately 3–5 km south of Bloody Bay. Museum material supports the following Tobago localities: Windward Rd near Lambeau Crown Trace at milepost 22.5; vic. Bloody Bay; Northside Road at mileposts: 27.5, 29.5, near milepost 30; on Northside road 3.75 mi WSW of milestone 27.5; vicinity of Bloody Bay on Roxborough-Parlatuvier Road; Windward Road near milepost 22.5; at intersection of Windward Road and Merchiston Road.

Description: Males 18–21 mm SVL, females 20–22 mm SVL. Head round in dorsal view and truncated in lateral view; canthus very rounded and indistinct; nostrils not protuberant; eyes large with a gold iris; eye-nostril distance is about 51% of the eye diameter; tympanum not visible. Dorsum smooth, usually with many melanophores; ventral skin is granular. Fingers have reduced webbing; toes are moderately webbed; finger disks T-shaped with angular edges; tubercle on the palm is not obvious. Ground color lime green with scattered dark green flecks and white to yellow spots on the dorsum; venter transparent to translucent green, heart visible; visceral peritoneum white. Of the frogs known from Tobago this species cannot be confused with any other because of its color and unique translucent/transparent skin. However, should it eventually be found on Trinidad it could be confused with *Hyla punctata* and *Sphaenorhynchus lacteus.* It can be distinguished from both of these species by the lack of an intercalary cartilage, claw-like terminal phalanges, and its T-shaped finger and toe disks. *Hyla punctata* has a dorsolateral cream stripe which this species lacks, and *Sphaenorhynchus lacteus* has a uniquely shaped sloping snout and horizontal pupil not present in this species.

Voice: a low, single, high pitched "peep."

Natural History: A frog of small, fast-moving forest streams, often near waterfalls. Calling males in July near Cambelton, outside Charlotteville, and south of Bloody Bay sit on the upper or lower surface of a leaf over a stream. The frogs sit 5–50 cm above a small, fast-moving stream, the usual oviposition site for members of this family. Tadpoles drop into streams upon hatching. Myers and Daly (in Cannatella and Lamar, 1986) and Cannatella and Lamar (1986) report it mostly near waterfalls in forested streams, from a few feet to about 8 feet above the water, and describe two clutches of eggs arranged in monolayers on the underside of leaves; the eggs contained pale green larvae.

Material: Tobago—FMNH 251215–7; USNM 195031–34.

Order Anura
Family Dendrobatidae: Arrow Poison Frogs

Dendrobatid frogs range from Nicaragua to Bolivia and southeastern Brazil. Many of them are small, less than 50 mm, and brightly colored. Species that are brightly colored tend to have toxic skin secretions, while those that are drab in color tend to lack them. The eggs are usually few in number with large yolks and are laid on land, tadpoles are transported to water on the back of an adult, and some species feed their tadpoles unfertilized eggs. At least six genera hold about 125 species. In Trinidad and Tobago *Mannophyrne* is common along streams in the Northern and Central Ranges of Trinidad and in the northeastern portion of Tobago. Wells (1980) described male combat in *M. trinitatis.*

> Two males approaching one another for wrestling would assume elevated postures, with the forelegs held in stiff upright positions and heads tilted up . . . Two opponents often charged one another head on, standing erect on their hind legs and grappling with their forelegs. Sometimes one male would clasp the other around the head or body. The bottom male would move rapidly in a circle, attempting to shake off his opponent. Most of these encounters lasted less than 1 min but one lasted 11 min.

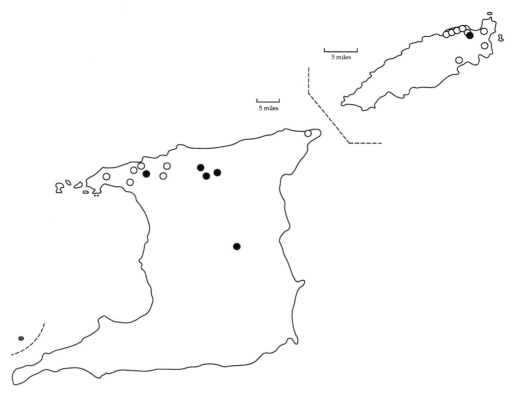

Map 4. *Mannophryne olmonae* (Tobago)
Mannophryne trinitatis (Trinidad)

Mannophryne olmonae (Hardy)

Map 4. Plate 10.

> *Phyllobates trinitatis:* Mertens, 1970:4. *Phyllobates trinitatis trinitatis:* Mertens, 1972:8. *Colostethus* [sp.]: Hardy, 1977:1. *Colostethus* cf. *dunni:* Hardy, 1982:73. *Colostethus olmonae* Hardy 1983a:47. Type locality: " . . . Bloody Bay, St. John Parrish, Tobago, West Indies." *Mannophryne* [*olmonae*]: La Marca, 1992:32.

Comment: Hardy (1983a) named the Tobago population *Colostethus olmonae* distinguishing it from *trinitatis* on the basis of the facial mask pattern, webbing between the toes, the call, and the number of tadpoles riding on the backs of males. Due to its isolation, the Tobago population may have evolved enough differences to be reproductively isolated from *trinitatis*. However, examination of external morphology of Trinidad and Tobago material by this author suggests these populations are conspecific. The face masks are variable in both populations. Webbing between the toes is variable and those in Hardy's drawings show variation that is contained within the Trinidad population alone. Hardy stated *trinitatis* males carry 7–12 tadpoles, while *olmonae* males carry 11–19. Pradeiro and Robinson (1990) reported males in a Venezuelan population of *trinitatis* carry 6–18 tadpoles, and found clutch size is seasonal and is influenced by permanent versus temporary water. The call differences reported by Hardy may represent calls from different social situations; Wells (1980) illustrated an advertisement call and a courtship call from male *trinitatis* on Trinidad which are at about 4 kHz as are

Hardy's, but at different timings. The possible call differences are the only characteristic that suggest these two populations should be recognized as different species; however, Hardy's harsh call described for *olmonae* may be a warning or an alarm call. In the absence of additional call data and hard evidence that *olmonae* and *trinitatis* are conspecific, this species is retained to avoid prematurely resynonymizing this species.

Distribution: Northeastern Tobago. Literature records from Tobago include Moriah (Mertens, 1970). Tobago localities based upon museum specimens: Northside Road: vicinity of milepost 27.5, 28.75, 29.75, between mileposts 31.3 and 31.4; Windward Road between mileposts 22.5–23; 2.2 m N and 2.0 miles W of Roxborough; on Lambeau Hill Crown Trace, 1.1 km W of turn to King's Bay Water Treatment Plant; Pigeon Peak Trail, 2 km south of Charlotteville. It also occurs on Little Tobago Island.

Description: See that for *Mannophryne trinitatis*.

Natural History: Probably very similar to that of *M. trinitatis*.

Material: Tobago—FMNH 217252–5 Cambleton.

Mannophryne trinitatis (Garman)

Map 4. Plates 11, 12.

> *Phyllobates trinitatis* Garman, 1887b:13. Type locality: "Trinidad". *Prostherapis herminae:* Boettger, 1892:37. *Prostherapis trinitatis:* Mole and Urich, 1894a:87. *Prostherapis trinitatis trinitatis:* Rivero, 1961:159. *Colostethus trinitatus:* Edwards, 1971:148. *Mannophryne* [*trinitatis*]: La Marca, 1992:32.

Common Name: "Yellow-throated frog" (Mole and Urich, 1894b).

Distribution: *M. trinitatis* occurs in Venezuela's Carribean Coastal Range, and the Northern and Central Ranges of Trinidad. Published Trinidad localities: Arima Valley (Beebe, 1952); Tacarigua (Brongersma, 1956a); Northern Range and Mt. Tamana (Kenny, 1969). Museum material supports the following localities: Trinidad—Aripo Valley; Arima Valley; Mt. St. Benedict; Blue Basin; Caure Valley; Marval Valley; Morne Bleu Ridge; Toco; St. Ann's Valley; on trail to Maracas Valley; and ca. 13 km NNE of Port of Spain. Mt. Tamana; Mt. Tucuche.

Description: Males 25 mm, females 28 mm SVL; recently metamorphosed individuals 9–11 mm. Snout truncated in lateral view, blunted in dorsal view; tympanum about one-half eye diameter; nostrils located three-fifths distance between the anterior edge of the eye and the center of the snout. First two fingers about equal length, or the first slightly shorter; fingers free; inner three toes with reduced webbing; small, distil, tarsal fold. Dorsum is smooth with some tubercles in the posterior region. Dorsal color usually dark brown with varied blotches and mottling; venter usually white; females have bright yellow chin, and very distinctive collar; males have grey or black chin. Calling males jet black; when vocalization is completed, or they are disturbed, they quickly return to the normal brown color. This species can be distinguished from all other small, brown frogs by the pair of dermal scutes on the dorsal surface of each digit.

Voice: A sustained "peep, peep, peep" followed by short chirps.

Natural History: A terrestrial, diurnal, forest, and forest-edge frog that uses streams and stream-side habitats. Abundant in damp forests along rocky edges of streams that are densely shaded; a large population of these frogs occurs in Tamana caves, and depends upon the bat guano and the insects that feed on the bat waste (Kenny, 1969; 1979a). Field notes (JCM) report this frog in the leaf litter, near and away from streams; density estimated to be 4–5 per square meter along the trails of the Asa Wright Nature Centre. Males vocalize during the day from prominences in or near moving water; during the display the male is black. Wells (1980) reported at least three different calls for this species. Calling stations are in or near a female's territory. When a female approaches, the male's behavioral display leads her to a terrestrial oviposition site under leaves or in a crevice where up to 12 eggs may be laid. Kenny (1969) and Van Meeuwen (1977) reported males attending eggs, but Wells (1980) found two nests unattended. About 3 weeks after oviposition the tadpoles are transported to a nearby stream on the male's dorsum. Males are more mobile than females and apparently move among female territories. In Venezuela, Praderio and Robinson (1990) reported the smallest gravid female as 19 mm SVL and the largest as 25 mm; the number of yolked ovarian follicles ranged from 6–19 and average 11.4 in the dry (March-May) season and 13.1 in the wet season; mean

number of larvae carried by males is 11.6; and egg developmental time at terrestrial sites is not certain, but is a minimum of 11 days. Kenny (1969) found tadpoles at Tamana caves reach densities of several thousand per square meter, and suggested they feed on bacteria and organic debris washed from bat guano in the cave; metamorphosis occurred at about 8 weeks. Mole and Urich (1894b) described predation by the snake *Liophis cobella*. Test et al. (1966) reported predation by the snakes *Oxyrhopus petola petola*, *Liophis reginae zweifeli*, and *Imantodes cenchoa cenchoa* in Venezuela; these same snakes occur in Trinidad and Tobago. This is the only record of *O. p. petola* feeding on a frog, and it is doubtful that this diurnal frog would be eaten by a nocturnal snake; thus this record may be in error. Kenny (1979a) also considered *L. r. zweifel* an important predator upon this frog. Field notes (JCM) describe this snake foraging along a small stream where this species is abundant.

Material: Trinidad—FMNH 22513, Mt. St. Benedict; 49707–49765 Morne Bleu; 49766–68, 49769–772, 172547–561 Arima Valley. AMNH 87382–91 Mt. Tamana.

Order Anura
Family Hylidae: True Tree Frogs

Tree frogs occur in both the Western and Eastern Hemispheres, but most of the 38 genera and 650 species inhabit the Neotropics. They have flattened, slender bodies, large eyes, long legs, and frequently webbed toes and fingers; each digit ends in a circular disk; all have an intercalary cartilage and claw-like digits. Hylids are diverse in structure and habits; many of the 38 genera are arboreal, but a few are aquatic or fossorial. Most of them lay large numbers of eggs in open water that hatch into free-swimming tadpoles; however, some lay few eggs and have parental care. Seven genera represented by 13 species occur on Trinidad, four of these genera are represented by five species on Tobago. DeVerteuil (1858) wrote about Trinidad treefrogs.

There exists in the colony many tree-frogs, or hyliforms; besides the ones already mentioned, I know a very small one of a brown colour above, and gray beneath; another, of nearly the same colors, but much larger, and found in cacao plantations, generally sticking on the inferior surface of some leaf (*Hyla Xerophylla*?); a third of a milky colour (*Hyla Lactea*?).

Flectonotus fitzgeraldi (Parker)

Map 5. Plate 13.

Gastrotheca fitzgeraldi Parker, 1934:123. Type locality: ". . . 3000 ft on Mt. Tucuche . . . , Trinidad." *Nototheca fitzgeraldi*: Bokermann, 1950:218. *Nototheca spec. inc.*: Mertens, 1972:8 (Tobago). *Flectonotus fitzgeraldi*: Duellman, 1977:11. *Flectonotus* cf. *pygmaeus*: Hardy, 1982:70 (Tobago).

Distribution: *F. fitzgeraldi* occurs on the Península de Paria, Venezuela; Trinidad and Tobago. It is a species of the

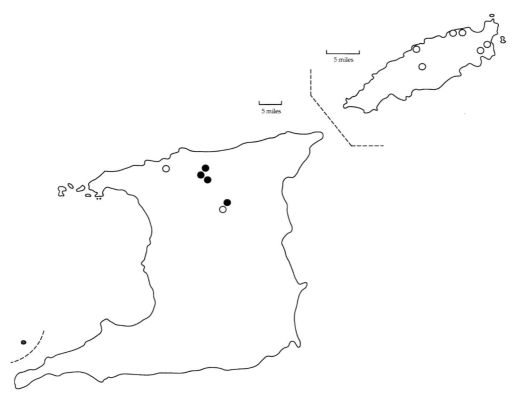

Map 5. *Flectonotus fitzgeraldi*

Caribbean Coastal Range and Northern Forests. Literature records for Trinidad localities: Arima Valley (Beebe, 1952); Aripo Savanna (Schwab, 1988). Kenny (1969) stated it is found throughout Trinidad; however he has seven major study sites and reports the species from only one, Mt. Tucuche. Trinidad localities based on museum material: Arima Valley; road to Arena Dam, just west of Cumuto; Morne Bleu Ridge; and Mt. Tucuche. Tobago museum material includes: Northside Rd. at the 22.5, 27.5 mileposts and between mileposts 31.3 and 31.4; Hillsborough Dam; Speyside; and Windward Road near Lambeau Crown Trace.

Description: Males 21 mm, females 25 mm SVL. Snout rounded from above, blunted in profile; canthus rostralis has a slight ridge. Eyes large, about one and one-half times the eye-nostril distance; tympanum about one-third the eye diameter. Dorsal skin smooth; ventral skin granular. First finger longer than the second, a characteristic readily distinguishing it from all other Trinidad and Tobago hylids; fingers free; toes slightly webbed. Dorsum brown, venter translucent white; a dark canthal streak continues over the tympanum toward the groin, but breaks up before reaching the groin. Males with a subgular vocal sac; females with dorsal longitudinal folds of skin forming a brood pouch, the only Trinidad and Tobago species to have one.

Voice: "A soft click or chirp repeated at frequent intervals and usually only within the first hour after sunset" (Kenny, 1969). These frogs sound very much like crickets.

Natural History: An arboreal, crepuscular, forest frog

that uses leaf axials of epiphytes and rolled leaves of terrestrial plants. Duellman and Gray (1983) considered *F. fitzgeraldi* to be terrestrial by day and arboreal at night. Field notes (JCM) describe the following habitats and activities: in rolled-up *Heliconia* leaves during the day; at dusk, leaping from branch to branch in a bromeliad festooned tree and entering bromeliads; the long leaps are extremely fast, making capture difficult; on rainy nights crossing forest roads. Kenny (1969) stated calling usually occurs within the first hour after sunset; and we have heard these frogs calling just before and just after sunset, the lowering light intensity may stimulate vocalization. Clutch size in this species is the smallest in the species group, 2–6 (n = 6, x̄ = 3.5) (Parker, 1934; Kenny, 1969; Duellman and Gray, 1983; field notes, JCM). Amplexus and oviposition behaviors are unknown for this species, but Duellman and Maness (1980) described these behaviors for *F. pygmaeus*. During axillary amplexus the male opened the female's dorsal brood pouch with his feet, caught the eggs between his heels, moved each egg past his cloaca, and placed each egg into the female's pouch with a pelvic thrust; the female carried the eggs, until they hatch and then deposited the tadpoles in a leaf axial pond. *F. fitzgeraldi* most likely has similar reproductive behavior. Possible multiple broods per season in *F. fitzgeraldi* has been suggested but further observations are needed (Duellman and Gray, 1983). Tadpoles hatched in advanced stages (39–41 of Gosner, 1960), and are well supplied with yolk; Kenny (1969) found 26 tadpoles in the base of the giant

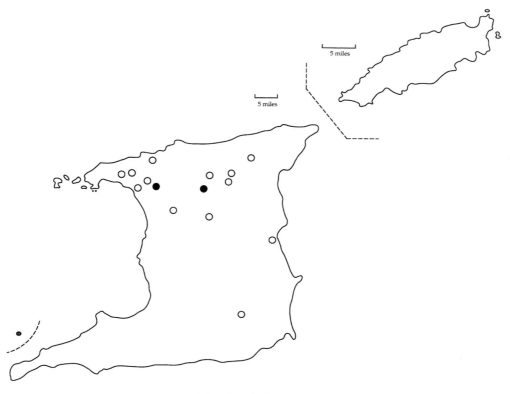

Map 6. *Hyla boans*

aroid *Xanthospora,* containing about 200 ml of water; metamorphosis occurred after 5 days of leaving the parent. Field notes (JCM) report recently transformed individuals, SVL about 2–3 mm, sitting on leaves 1–1.5 m above the ground at 2300 h.

Material: Trinidad—FMNH 218790–1 Morne Bleu Ridge. KU 192399–400 Simla, Arima Valley. USNM 166625–6 Spring Hill Estate, Arima Valley.

Hyla boans (Linnaeus)

Map 6. Plates 14, 15.

Rana boans Linnaeus, 1758:213. Type locality: "Americas." *Hyla boans:* Daudin, 1803:64. *Hyla maxima:* Werner, 1899:482.

Distribution: *H. boans* is a widespread species, ranging from eastern Panama and the Atrato Valley of northwest Colombia southward to Bolivia and northern Brazil. On Trinidad it is widespread, but may avoid the higher elevations. Trinidad localities in the literature include: Arima (Werner, 1899); Arima Valley (Beebe, 1952); Maraval (Brongersma, 1956b); Kenny (1969) notes its presence in the Northern and Central Ranges and at Maracas, Bamboo Grove, Valencia, and Nariva. Field notes (JCM) report it in the Guanapo Valley; and south of Rio Claro in the southeastern portion of the island. Additional localities based upon museum material are: St. Augustine; Arima Valley; the Caroni River; the Hollis Reservoir; near San Rafael; San Antonio Estate, Guanapo Valley; Diego Martin; and Oropuche Cave.

Description: Maximum SVL for Trinidad males 100 mm; 115 mm for females (in Central American populations males attain 132 mm, and females 117.5 mm); this is the largest tree frog on Trinidad. Snout is rounded from above, blunted in profile; eye diameter about two-thirds the eye-nostril distance; tympanum about two-thirds the eye's diameter; canthus distinct and raised. Dorsal skin smooth; ventral skin granular. Fingers and toes heavily webbed to base of disk; rudimentary thumb (pollex) present; a small triangular flap (calcar) present on the heel; and the lower eyelid has a reticulated pattern. *H. crepitans* is similar but lacks the reticulated lower eyelid; and *H. geographica* is similar but has webbing absent or greatly reduced between fingers 1 and 2, and it has distinct vertical bars on the flanks and thighs. Dorsal coloration a tan-grey to dark chocolate brown; it may or may not have a middorsal stripe from snout to vent; the ability of these animals to change color is considerable. Some evidence of crossbars usually present on the limbs. Ventral skin white or yellow; iris orange; lower eyelid (palpebral membrane) with gold reticulations.

Voice: "A raucous 'wark-wark' repeated at intervals of a few seconds, sustained over periods of an hour" (Kenny, 1969).

Natural History: *H. boans* inhabits stream-side vegetation in humid forests; and it may be heard in tall trees or bamboo (Kenny, 1969; Lutz, 1973; Toft and Duellman, 1979). Field notes (JCM) describe individuals within a few meters of moving water; males calling next to moving water, in shallow moving water, and on roads with water moving across them; small

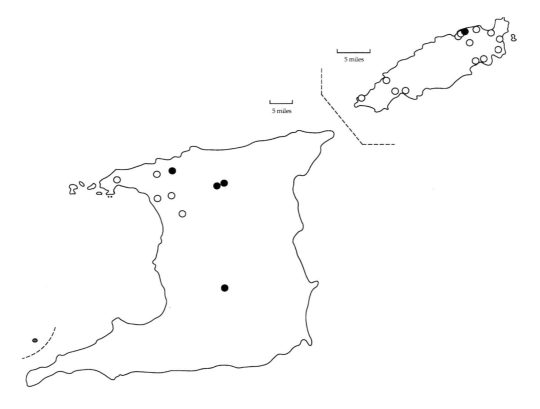

Map 7. *Hyla crepitans*

choruses of 5–8 males along streams in the Arima and Gua-napo Valleys after rains. Reports of food from mainland pop-ulations include crabs, orthopterans, beetles, lepidopteran lar-vae and adults (Beebe, 1925; Rivero, 1961; Duellman, 1978). Reproduction occurs during the dry season (December-April) on Trinidad (Kenny, 1969); males construct shallow basins up to 40 cm in diameter in mud, sand, or gravel floodplains; wa-ter fills the cavity and the males call from the nest (Kenny, 1969; Duellman, 1978). Eggs hatched within 72 hours and metamorphosis occurred at 8 weeks; tadpoles selected stream edge situations to feed on algae; and larvae tolerated low salin-ities at river mouths (Kenny, 1969). Dowling (1960) reported observations on what she believed to be tadpoles of this species in the Arima River, describing large schools of black tadpoles, numbering up to 177 individuals; upon metamor-phosis she states they are "*Hyla maxima.*" Clearly, she de-scribed *Hyla geographica* tadpoles, not *Hyla boans* tadpoles. In Brazil, Caldwell (1989) found the cryptically colored tad-poles of this species are readily eaten by fishes.

Material: Trinidad—FMNH 69776, 22523 St. Augustine; 216454–5 Arima Valley. USNM 17771 no data; 146353–4, 166530–1 Arima Valley.

Hyla crepitans Wied-Neuwied

Map 7. Plates 16, 17, 18.

Hyla crepitans Wied-Neuwied, 1824, pl 47, fig. 1. Type locality: Tamboril, Jiboya and Areal da Conquista, Bahia, Brazil. *?Hyla xero-phyla:* DeVerteuil, 1858:446. *?Hyla Lactea:* DeVerteuil, 1858:446.

Common Name: "Flying frog" (Boos and Quesnel, 1968).

Comment: Kluge (1979) suggested that several species are masquerading under the name *H. crepitans*.

Distribution: *H. crepitans* is a widespread species rang-ing from the central Pacific lowlands of Panama southward through Colombia, Venezuela, and the Guianas to Brazil. Published Trinidad locations include: Maracas and Bamboo Grove, and the southern foothills of the Northern Range from Diego Martin to Arima (Kenny, 1969); and the Caroni Plain (Kenny, 1977); field notes (JCM) add the Guanapo Valley. Museum specimens from Trinidad document: Brick-field; Mt. St. Benedict, Santa Cruz, St. Augustine, and Tucker Valley in the Northern Range. Tobago localities in the literature include: Louis d'Or Settlement (Mertens, 1972). Museum material from Tobago documents: near Anse Fourmi on Northside Rd. at 26 milepost; Arnos Valle; vicinity of Bloody Bay at Bloody Bay River and Roxbor-ough-Parlatuvier Rd.; Buccoo Bay; near Hermitage; 1.45 km W of Windward Road on Lambeau Crown Trace; Man of War Bay; Milford Bay; Northside Rd. vic. of 27.75 milepost; near Roxborough; Scarborough Botanical Gardens; Bird of Paradise Inn at Speyside; the Windward Rd. at the 9.75, 18.25, 22.5 mileposts.

Description: Males 61 mm, females 73 mm SVL. Snout rounded viewed from above; snout blunt in profile; eye di-ameter equal to, or shorter than, the eye-nostril distance; tympanum about equal to the eye diameter; canthus rounded

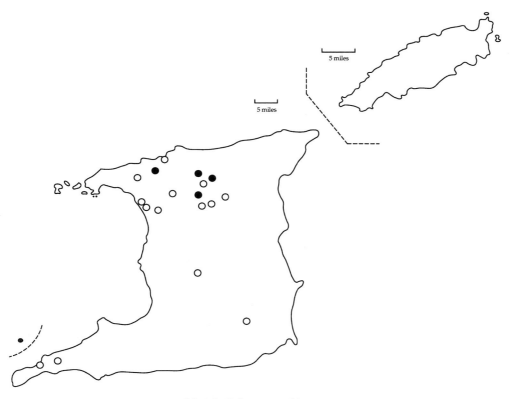

Map 8. *Hyla geographica*

and raised. Dorsal skin smooth, the ventral skin granular. No webbing between the first two fingers, but reduced webbing occurs between the other fingers, toes heavily webbed. This species lacks the reticulations on the lower eyelid that occur in *H. boans* and *H. geographica*. Dorsal skin has a remarkable ability for color change; usually tan or red-brown, once captured it may turn milk white, grey-brown, or a light metallic green. Dorsum usually with large, central, dark blotch, often x-shaped; limbs with crossbars; diffuse spots between the eyes. Flanks and sides with a series of about seven crossbars with areas of yellow-orange between them; chin white; in life the ventral side of the limbs and belly orange; iris metallic green. Newly metamorphosed individuals green.

Voice: "A loud low-pitched croaking rattle" (Kenny, 1969).

Natural History: A savanna and forest-edge frog. Kenny (1969) described it from open country; Hoogmoed and Gorzula (1979) found it in savannas and gallery forests in southern Venezuela. Field notes (JCM) describe males calling on floating vegetation in man-made ponds and from shallow water of roadside ditches; calling males were spaced 1.2–1.8 m apart on a road embankment above a water filled ditch; calling associates observed were *Physalaemus pustulosus* and *Leptodactylus fuscus;* males call in April at the height of the dry season as well as after heavy rains in June and July; reproduction to occur year round where water is available; in savanna areas it reproduces only in the rainy

season; eggs float for 24 hours and then sink; metamorphosis occurs at about 3 months (Kenny; 1969; field notes, JCM). Field notes (JCM, RH) report metamorphosis occurs at SVL of 15–17 mm; new metamorphs look quite different than the adults, and were found in the forest, more than 30 m from water.

Material: Trinidad—FMNH 49690 Brickfield; 219602, Lower Guanapo Valley. USNM 16653 near Maracas Village; 167599–600 Asa Wright, Arima Valley. Tobago—USMN 167497–99 Roxborough-Parlaturier Rd., vicinity of Bloody Bay.

Hyla geographica Spix

Map 8. Plates 19, 20.

> *Hyla geographica* Spix, 1824b:39. Type locality: Rio Tefe, Amazonas, Brazil. *Hyla appendiculata:* Werner, 1899:483. *Hyla spectrum:* Lutz, 1927:49. *Hyla punctatissima appendiculata:* Parker, 1933:10. *Hyla geographica geographica:* Rivero, 1961:102. *Hyla hyla geographica* [sic] MacLean et al., 1977:45.

Distribution: *H. geographica* has an Amazonian distribution. On Trinidad it occurs in the lower and middle elevations of mountian ranges and in the Northern and Southern Basins. Locations reported in the literature for Trinidad: Carlisle River of the southwestern peninsula (Alkins-Koo, 1990); Bamboo Grove, Cedros, Maracas, and Valencia (Kenny (1969); near Port of Spain on Churchill-Roosevelt Highway (Lutz, 1973); schools of tadpoles of this frog in the Arima River at Simla (Dowling, 1960). Field notes (JCM) list the Caroni River, Waller Field, and south of Rio Claro.

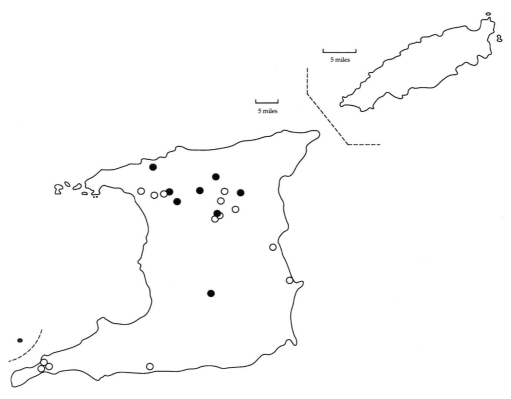

Map 9. *Hyla microcephala misera*

Localities based upon museum material include: Morne Bleu Ridge at 549 m; the Arima Valley; Churchill-Roosevelt Hwy. vic. of 12.25 and 14.25 mileposts; Guanapo Valley; Grande Riviere River at Paria Main Road; Maracas; Santa Cruz; Tabaquite; Centeno; El Socorro; Valencia and Las Cuevas.

Description: Males 58 mm, females 67 mm SVL; on the mainland males reach 62 mm and females 83 mm. Snout rounded in dorsal view, blunt in profile; eye diameter about equal to the eye-nostril distance; tympanum about three-fourths eye diameter; the canthus rostralis rounded. Dorsal skin smooth, ventral skin granulated. First finger shorter than second; all fingers webbed, but webbing between fingers 1 and 2 reduced; toes completely webbed. *H. boans* has extensive webbing between fingers 1 and 2 and it lacks the distinct vertical bars on the flanks and thighs, which are present in this species. Limbs attenuated; a triangular flap of skin (calcar) on heel of adults, this is a small bulb in young individuals. Dorsum yellow or brown, a dark blotch in the sacral region may be present; flanks with transverse bars that usually occur in pairs. Male's vocal sac yellow-orange and webbing yellow or orange. Lower eyelid with gold reticulations, a characteristic that will readily separate it from *H. crepitans*. Young black with cream-tan flecks; as the frog matures, the black is replaced with brown.

Voice: "A low pitched and very muted rattle" (Kenny, 1969). Field notes (JCM) describe the call of this species as a subtle bird-like trill.

Natural History: A savanna and forest-edge frog associated with streams, ponds, gravel pits, marshes, and swamps; and it is tolerant of brackish water (Kenny, 1969; Lutz, 1973; Hoogmoed and Gorzula, 1979; field notes, JCM). Reproduction in Trinidad may occur only during the dry season (Kenny, 1969), but Duellman (1978) found Ecuadorian populations breeding sporadically throughout the year after heavy rains. Males mature at, or before reaching 40 mm SVL (Lutz, 1973). Eggs are deposited in a film on the water's surface (Duellman, 1978; Kenny, 1969) and hatch within 48 hours (Kenny, 1969). Dowling (1960) found schools of black tadpoles containing 65–177 individuals in the Arima River that undoubtedly belong to this species. Tadpoles school in large numbers; field notes (JCM) report these aggregations in the Guanapo and Caroni Rivers as well as the ponds at Waller Field. In Brazil, Caldwell (1989) found 2000–3000 tadpoles per school; of 27 schools she sampled, 48% contained tadpoles in one or two developmental stages, and larger schools had larger numbers of stages represented; tadpoles swam toward the center of school whether it was stationary or moving, suggesting the large dark, moving mass deters potential predators; antipredator experiments show *H. geographica* tadpoles unpalatable to fish, while the same fish readily consume the cryptically colored *H. boans* tadpoles. Handling causes frogs to be motionless with limbs drawn close to the body and to feign death (Cochran, 1955; field notes, JCM).

Material: Trinidad—CM 5498, 56925–27 Maracas. FMNH 49694 Morne Bleu Ridge; USNM 16656 near Arima, 16657 Churchill-Roosevelt Hwy. AMNH 55697–703 Churchill-Roosevelt Hwy., 109269–72 San Antonio Estate, Guanapo Valley.

Hyla microcephala misera Fouquette

Map 9. Plates 21, 24.

Hyla goughi: Boulenger, 1911:1082. *Hyla misera:* Lutz, 1927:66. *Hyla microcephala misera* Fouquette, 1968:324. Type locality: " . . . 17 km NE of Acarigua, Portuguesa . . . ," Venezeula. *Hyla miisera* [*sic*] MacLean, et al. 1977:45.

Distribution: *H. microcephala* is a widespread species, ranging from southern Veracruz and northern Oaxaca, Mexico, southward through Central America to the Amazon Basin. *H. m. misera* inhabits the Venezuelan and Colombian llanos and is best considered an Orinoco Basin form. On Trinidad *H. m. misera* is found throughout the lower elevations. Published Trinidad locations include: Aripo Savannas (Schwab, 1988); Bamboo Grove, Cedros, Icacos, Maracas, Nariva, and Valencia (Kenny, 1969). Field notes (JCM) list Bowen Trace and Coco Trace Ext. in the southwestern peninsula; and Cumoto Road, about 1 mile south of the Churchill-Roosevelt Rd; near Quinam Beach. Museum material documents: Arima Valley; St. Augustine; Brickfield; near Caroni; Cumoto Rd. near milepost 2.5; on Cumoto Rd. 2.1 km south of junction with Churchill-Roosevelt Rd.; Churchill-Roosevelt Rd. near mileposts 11, 14 and 15; on Waller Field Rd. 1.3 km E of junction of Churchill-Roosevelt Rd. and Antigua Rd.; near asphalt plant on Antigua Rd.; along road to Waller Field and the airfield; O'Mera Rd. 0.5 mi N of Churchill-Roosevelt Rd.; milepost 78 on Icacos Rd.; Maracas; Nariva Swamp on Manzanilla-Mayaro Rd. near 45.5 milepost; near Piarco Airport; Valencia Rd. at the 4 milepost.

Description: Males 20 mm, females 25 mm SVL. Snout rounded from above, blunt in profile. Eye diameter greater than the eye-nostril distance; tympanum about one-half the eye diameter; canthus forms a distinct ridge, distinguishing it from *H. minuta.* Dorsal skin smooth, ventral skin granulated. Fingers with reduced webbing, toes moderately webbed. Dorsum orange-yellow with brown lateral stripes that may be connected by transverse markings; ventral skin yellow-brown. Dark dorsolateral stripe, bordered by an upper lighter stripe, extends from nostril to above tympanum. Dorsum with irregular dark markings, interorbital blotch often present; iris bronze. Calling males solid, bright yellow. Size of calling males will distinguish this species from smaller *H. minuscula,* less than 15 mm; as will the "scratchy-notes" of the call (*H. minuscula* has a tick-like call). This species lacks a lateral enamel stripe present in live *Hyla minuscula.*

Voice: "A loud metallic squeak repeated at short intervals, changing to a series of rapid buzzing squeaks to the rhythm of ti-ti-ti . . . " (Kenny, 1969). See comments on call above.

Natural History: A savanna and forest-edge frog associated with swamps, ponds, marshes, and temporary pools (Lutz, 1927; Hoogmoed and Gorzula, 1979; field notes, JCM), Males calling from emergent grasses and sedges in flooded areas between 0.05–1 m above the water. At three localities they were associated with *Hyla minuta,* and at two locations in the southwestern peninsula all three small yellow *Hyla* (*minuta, minuscula,* and *microcephala*) call together, within 2–3 meters of each other; at other sites males call with *Leptodactylus validus, Scinax rubra, Hyla punctata,* and *Phyllomedusa trinitatis.* Kenny (1969) reported amplexing pairs in bushes and at the water's edge, with spawning throughout the rainy season; metamorphosis occurs at about 6 weeks.

Material: Trinidad—FMNH 49622, 8 mi north of Aripo; 49633 Brickfield; 217243 at milepost 78 on Icacos Rd. (=Southern Main Rd.); 219603 at the 4 milepost on Valencia Rd. USNM 166577, 166001–2 Arima Valley; 166578 trail to Maracas waterfall; 166579–84 Piarco, vicinity of airport and Bel Air Hotel grounds; 166585–98 Cumoto Rd., milestone 2.5; 166599–600, 166002–6 Churchill-Roosevelt Hwy. between milestones 14 and 15.

Hyla minuscula Rivero

Map 10. Plates 22, 24.

Hyla minuscula Rivero, 1971:1. Type locality: Nirgua, Estado Yaracay, Venezuela.

Distribution: *H. minuscula* ranges from the Venezuelan llanos eastward through the Guianas to Belem, Brazil, and occurs in the Icacos peninsula of southwestern Trinidad. Hoogmoed (1979b) considered this frog to be a lowland Guiana endemic, I am reassigning it to the Orinoco Basin considering its extensive distribution in the Orinco Basin and its savanna habitat. The distribution on Trinidad appears to be restricted to the southwest peninsula, near Bonasse (Read, 1986b). Field notes (RIC) report this frog 6.7 km east of Bonasse on the Southern Main Road (4.6 km east of the junction with Austin Rd. South). Field notes (JCM) report this frog in the same area, along Bowen Trace and Coco Trace Extension.

Description: Males 12–17 mm SVL; hind limbs 1.5–1.6 times the SVL. Snout blunted from above and sloping in profile; eye diameter about twice the eye-nostril distance; tympanum almost invisible, and less than one-fourth eye diameter. Canthus forms a distinct ridge, with light line from anterior of eye to nostril. Dorsal skin smooth, ventral skin and skin under thighs granular. Fingers with some webbing, most reduced to bases of digits and lateral fringe; toes moderately webbed. Dorsal surface yellow with scattered, darker pigmentation; a lateral enamel stripe on each side from posterior of eye, over tympanum, to cloaca in calling males (not present in preserved specimens). *H. minuta* has a rounded canthus and lacks a lateral cream or enamel stripe. To distinguish it from *H. m. misera:* both species have a canthal ridge, but *H. minuscula* is much smaller, calling males tan and red, with side stripe that make this species unique, and readily identified in the field. Preserved specimens can be separated from *H. m. misera* by the upper jaw which protrudes slightly over the lower jaw. Preserved specimens of *H. m. misera* and *H. minuscula* look almost identical.

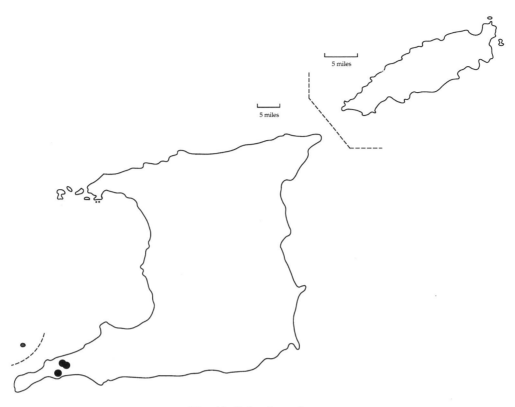

Map 10. *Hyla minuscula*

Voice: Read (1986b) described the call as a high-pitched tick. This is repeated at least four or five times. The call is subtle and difficult to detect among the calls of other frogs.

Natural History: A savanna and forest-edge frog. Males call from emergent vegetation as well as vegetation along the margins of ponds, swamps, and rice paddies; and they are 10–150 cm above the substrate (Hoogmoed and Gorzula, 1979; Read, 1986; field notes, JCM). Field notes (JCM) describe calling associates as *Hyla minuta, H. m. misera,* and *Scinax rubra.* At both locations where *H. minuscula* was found it was present in smaller numbers, (two specimens at one site and one specimen at another, while 20–30 individuals of the other species call at each of these sites). Habitat at the Bowen Trace site is a small (0.5 m wide) intermittent stream, with emergent vegetation in small pools, and a dense canopy. The Coco Trace Extension site was a roadside pool at forest edge. Housing construction was occurring within a few hundred meters of both these locations.

Material: Trinidad—FMNH Bowen Trace and Coco Trace. USNM 248788–91, Southern Main Road near Bonasse, between mileposts 71.5 and 71.75. Suriname—FMNH 121093, 128943.

Hyla minuta Peters

Map 11. Plates 23, 24.

Hyla minuta Peters, 1872:680. Type locality: Nova Friburgo, Rio de Janerio, Brazil.

Comment: Kaplan (1994) suggested several species are currently masquerading under the name *Hyla minuta;* and named the new species *Hyla stingi* from the Cordillera Oriental of central Colombia. The new species is distinguished from *Hyla minuta* on the basis of several osteological characters; the only distinguishing external feature he noted is the arrangement of chromatophores in the gular area of the male. *H. stingi* has the chromatophores concentrated near the anterior and lateral edges of the chin, while *H. minuta* from Meta, Colombia has the pigment scattered laterally, with some chromatophores in the central region of the vocal sac. A Trinidad male (FMNH 251238) has the chromatophores restricted to two very distinct lateral stripes with an area uniform in color near the mental gland. Thus, the Trinidad and Tobago populations of this species may eventually be shown to be distinct from at least some of the mainland populations, currently recognized as *H. minuta.*

Distribution: *H. minuta* has an Amazonian distribution; and it occurs on both Trinidad and Tobago. Published Trinidad localities include: Arima Valley (Beebe, 1952); Cedros, Icacos, Maracas, Nariva, Valencia (Kenny, 1969); Aripo Savanna (Schwab, 1988). Field notes (JCM) add Arena Dam Road west of Cumuto; and Bowen Trace and Coco Trace Ext. in the southwestern peninsula. Museum material documents the following Trinidad localities: Arima Valley; Chatham Beach on Erin Bay; Mt. St. Benedict; O'Mera Rd.; 5 mi north of Churchill-Roosevelt Rd;

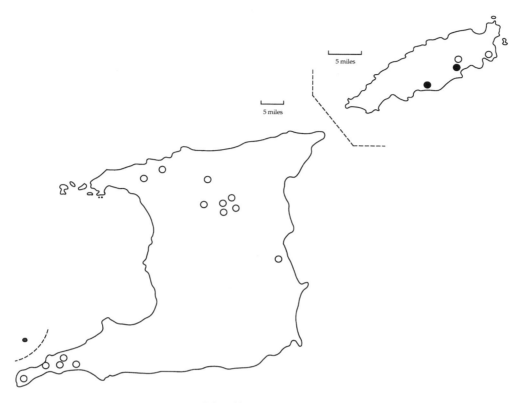

Map 11. *Hyla minuta*

Waller Field. Field notes (JCM) for Tobago report this frog to be abundant along the Windward Road between Speyside and Roxborough, and on Roxborough-Parlatuvier Rd. between Roxborough and Bloody Bay. Tobago museum specimens document the Windward Rd. near mileposts 7 and 16.

Description: Males 24 mm, females 26 mm SVL. Snout rounded from above and in profile. Eye diameter greater than the eye-nostril distance; tympanum about one half the eye diameter; canthus rounded, a character that distinguish this frog from *H. microcephala misera* and *Hyla minuscula*. Dorsal skin smooth; ventral skin granular. Fingers with reduced webbing; toes heavily webbed. Dorsal coloration yellow-brown with blotches, stripes or hourglass-shaped markings; a dark interorbital bar may be present; venter white. Calling males bright yellow and lack enamel lateral stripe present in *H. minuscula*. Males have a single, large, yellow vocal sac, and a well-developed mental gland. Size of calling males will separate this frog from the smaller *H. minuscula* (15 mm or less), as will the call, the lack of an enamel lateral stripe, and the snout's protrusion over the lower jaw in *H. minuscula*.

Voice: A short, quarrelsome squeaking. Kenny (1969) described it as " . . . a loud metallic squeak, but the call is longer sustained than in *H. [m.] misera*. When calling in chorus, the period of the call may be reduced and a running series of short squeaks."

Natural History: This is a forest and forest-edge species inhabiting vegetation at the margins of forest ponds. It is relatively abundant in the Arima Valley, hiding between leaves of plants during the day, calling almost every night during the rainy season (June-July). Males call in vegetation 5 cm above the ground, in secondary forest where there was no standing water, in vegetation over-hanging ponds, on emergent vegetation, in bushes 2 m above the ground near a pond, and on grasses and herbs; calling associates are *Hyla microcephala, Hyla punctata, Hyla minuscula,* and *Scinax rubra.* Vocalizing males were often accompanied by satellite males, similar to the situation described by Haddad (1991) for a Brazilian population. A roadside pool adjacent to a forest along the Arena Dam Road contained a chorus of this species and about two crabs per square meter; the crustaceans are probably important predators on these frogs and their eggs (field notes, JCM). Kenny (1969) reported rainy season reproduction peaks with heavy rains in May or June, eggs are deposited on submerged objects and hatch within 36 hours, and metamorphosis occurs at about 8 weeks. Field notes (JCM) describe an amplexing pair laying several hundred eggs; most hatched within 48 hours.

Material: Trinidad—AMNH 53289 no data. Tobago—USNM 244444 Windward Rd. near its junction with Hillsborough Dam Rd., milepost 7; 24445 Roxborough ca. 1.5 mi west of Windward Rd. at milepost 16.

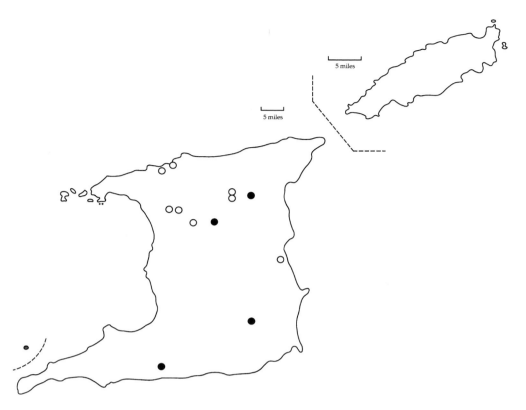

Map 12. *Hyla punctata*

Hyla punctata (Schneider)

Map 12. Plates 25, 26.

Calamita punctata Schneider, 1799:120. Type locality: "America." *Hyla punctata:* Daudin, 1802:41. *Hyla punctata punctata:* Lutz, 1973:67.

Distribution: *H. punctata* has an Amazonian distribution; on Trinidad, Kenny (1969) presumed it to be found through-out lower elevations in isolated pockets of suitable habitat. Literature records for Trinidad include: Maracas Bay, Las Cuevas, and St. Augustine (Parker, 1934); Tacarigua (Brongersma, 1956b); Maracas, Valencia, and Nariva (Kenny, 1969); and 9 mi west of Port of Spain on Churchill-Roosevelt Highway (Lutz, 1973). Locations based on museum specimens include: Cumuto Rd., milepost 2.5; below the Hollis Reservoir Dam; Pinal-Coora Rd. within 1 mile of Quinam Bay; 3 miles south of Rio Claro on Guayaguayare Rd.; and Valenica Rd. at the 3 milepost.

Description: Males 38 mm, females 35 mm SVL. Snout flattened from above, and truncated in profile; eye diameter about equal to the eye-nostril distance; tympanum about two-thirds of eye diameter; supratympanic fold continuous with dorsolateral fold; eyes oriented dorsally; canthus a rounded ridge. Dorsal skin finely granular; ventral skin granular. Fingers depressed, with reduced webbing; third finger disk covers about one third of tympanum; the feet heavily webbed. Color varies dramatically from day to night; apple-green dorsum with longitudinal yellow lines from canthus to

the flanks with a line of purple pigment below it during the day; this pattern will readily distinguish this species from *Sphaenorhynchus lacteus,* the only other medium-sized adult green tree frog (newly metamorphosed *Hyla crepitans* are green); purple or yellow flecks may be present on the dorsum. At night the green dorsum becomes a deep red. Venter white. Male's subgular vocal sac is green. Breeding males with slightly thickened forearm, and callosity under first finger.

Voice: Kenny (1969) noted both sexes call, and compared the voice of this frog to the sound made by stroking the teeth of a comb, only much amplified. Hoogmoed (1979a) described the call as a high-pitched, short purring sound that cannot be heard from a distance.

Natural History: A savanna-dwelling frog. Twelve specimens were collected in grasses or sedges 10–30 cm above the substrate. These observations agree with Kenny (1969), Lutz (1973), and Hoogmoed (1979a) who reported this species from open habitats with grasses and bushes at low elevations, including ditches and adjacent marshy ground. Males may call from a vertical position, and satellite males were present at one location. Reproduction may occur year round; Kenny (1969) described captives breeding in January, and reported the presence of tadpoles in March-April, the middle of the dry season; all of my observations were made in June-July. Hoogmoed (1979a) reported calls in all months of the year in Suriname, and Duellman (1978) found breeding sporadic after heavy rains in Ecuador. Associates at

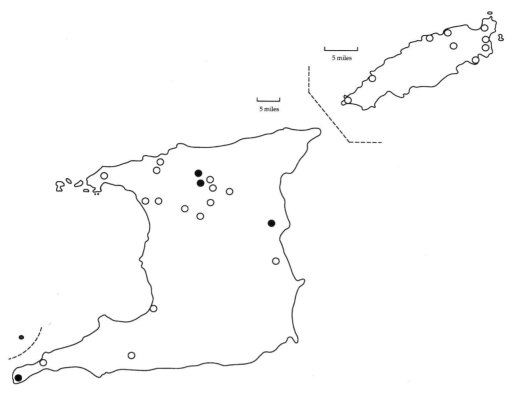

Map 13. *Phrynohyas venulosa*

calling sites include: *Sphaenorhynchus lacteus, Hyla minuta,* and *Hyla microcephala;* hatchling *Caiman c. crocodilus* and *Rhinoclemmys punctularia* (field notes, JCM).

Material: Trinidad—FMNH 216456, 3 mi S of Rio Claro; 219586–8 on Pinal-Coora Rd., within 1 mile of Quinam Bay; 218990–2, on Valencia Rd., about the 3 milepost. USNM 166607–14, 166708, Cumuto Rd., vicinity of milepost 2.5

Phrynohyas venulosa (Laurenti)

Map 13. Plate 27.

Rana venulosa Laurenti, 1768:31 (based on a plate in Seba, 1734). Type locality: "Indiis," restricted by Duellman (1956) to Lago Tefé, at the mouth of Rio Tefé where it enters into the Rio Solimoes, Amazonas, Brazil. *Hyla pardalis:* Garman, 1887b:16. *Hyla coriacea:* Mole and Urich, 1894a:90. *Hyla venulosa:* Roux, 1926:292. *Phrynohyas zonata:* Duellman, 1956:35. *Phrynohyas venulosa:* Hemming, 1958:172. *Hyla tibiatrix tibiatrix:* Rivero, 1961:128.

Distribution: *P. venulosa* is widespread, ranging from Tamaulipas and Sinaloa, Mexico, southward to Amazonia, and Trinidad and Tobago. Trinidad localities based upon the literature include: Arima Valley (Beebe, 1952); and Bamboo Grove, Cedros, Icacos, Maracas, Nariva, Valenica (Kenny, 1969). Field notes (JCM) add Bonasse in the southwest peninsula; the eastern end of Churchill-Roosevelt Highway; and the Guanapo Valley. Trinidad localities based upon museum material include: Aripo; St. Augustine; Los Bajos; Churchill-Roosevelt Rd. at the 11.5 milepost; San Fernando; Morne Bleu Ridge; Grande Riviere, Mt. Plaisir Beach; Pi-

arco Bel Air Hotel; Mt. Tabor; and Tucker Valley. Tobago locations based upon the literature include: the Louis D'Or Settlement and Orange Hill Ranch (Mertens, 1972). Field notes (JCM) add 0.5 mile west of the Blood Bay River on the Northside Road; Roxborough-Parlatuvier and the Windward Rd. between Speyside and Kings Bay Rd. Tobago locations based upon museum material are: Charlotteville; Northside Road at the 27.75 milepost; Milford Bay; and Bird of Paradise Inn, Speyside.

Description: Males 100 mm SVL, and females 113 mm. Snout rounded from above and in profile; canthus rounded; eye diameter equal to, or slightly greater, than the eye-nostril distance; tympanum about two-thirds of the eye diameter. Pupil horizontal; iris gold with black flecks. Dorsum with thick glandular skin studded with scattered tubercles; this and its dark brown–light brown mottled color readily distinguish it from other tree frogs found on these islands; venter very granular. Fingers with reduced webbing and large disks, the disk on the third finger covers tympanum; toes heavily webbed. Dorsal color light to dark brown, with highly variable pattern that may consist of blotches, spots, and mottling; often a dark brown stripe extends from the tympanum to the large gland in front of the forelegs; digits frequently with blue-green tint. Males with two lateral vocal sacs at the angle of mouth, and inner surface of prepollex with a nuptial pad when in breeding condition. Duellman (1971a) noted the high degree of variation in this species is responsible for it receiving 19 scientific names in 200 years.

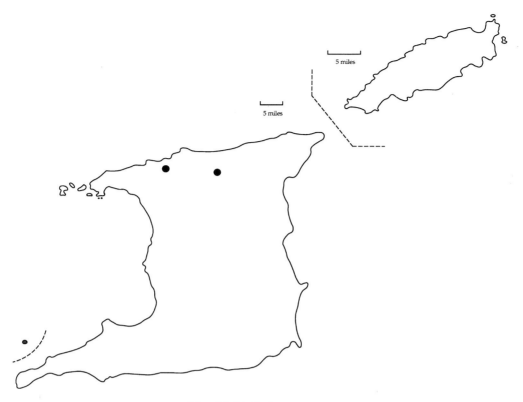

Map 14. *Phyllodytes auratus*

Voice: A nasal squawking, or honking sound; a large chorus is an impressive auditory display. Kenny (1969) described it as a "loud low pitched sawing noise repeated at short intervals."

Natural History: A forest and forest-edge frog that may use savanna, edificarian environs, secondary growth, citrus orchards, cacao plantations, and primary forest (Kenny, 1969; Hoogmoed and Gorzula, 1979; Toft and Duellman, 1979). Field notes (JCM) report specimens dropping out of trees onto the car on two occasions, and Cott (1926) described parachuting behavior for lower Amazonian populations of this frog. Field notes (JCM) describe a single individual basking at 1030 hours in a cacao tree, 2.5 m above the ground, in direct sunlight. Choruses occur after exceptionally heavy rains, and occurred in flooded gallery forests where males called from trees and bushes over water, as well as from the water; in another chorus, frogs migrated across a road from a forested area to an open pasture to join a chorus of about 50 animals, calling associates at this site are *Hyla minuta* and *Physalaemus pustulosus* (field notes, JCM). Kenny (1969) noted choruses from June to December. Handling this frog stimulates it to secrete a sticky latex-like material that is difficult to remove from human skin; it also triggers uncontrolled sneezing in some individuals (Altig, 1979; field notes, JCM); W. W. Lamar (personal communication) observed swelling and numbness in humans exposed to skin secretions, and observed a cat with permanent paralysis after feeding on this species.

Material: Trinidad: FMNH 216455, 2.4 mi north of Simla on Arima Rd.; 49775, 8 mi north of Aripo; 49777, Morne Bleu Ridge; 49778, Mt. Harris; 218532, near Icacos.

Phyllodytes auratus (Boulenger)

Map 14. Plates 28, 29.

Amphodus auratus Boulenger, 1917:184. Type locality: "above 3000 feet on Mt. Tucuche, in a bromeliad," Trinidad. *Phyllodytes auratus:* Bokermann, 1968:157.

Common Name: "El Tucuche golden frog" (Murphy and Humbert, 1983).

Distribution: *P. auratus* is known from the type locality, the summit of Aripo and probably Morne Bleu Ridge. The other species in this genus are restricted to the Atlantic Forests of eastern Brazil. *Phyllodytes auratus* is a Trinidad endemic.

Description: Males 29 mm, females 35 mm SVL. Snout pointed from above, and protruding in profile. Canthus rounded and slopes upward toward nostril; eye diameter about three-fourths of eye-nostril distance; tympanum indistinct, and one-third diameter of eye. Lower jaw with medial pair of fang-like projections with tooth-like serrations on each side of jaw's edge (a 23 mm individual, FMNH 40449, has much shorter fangs than do larger adults). The inner upper jaw also has tooth-like serrations, with a medial projection that fits between lower fangs for complete mouth closure. Teeth-like serrations readily distinguish this species from all other Trinidad and Tobago frogs. Head and body

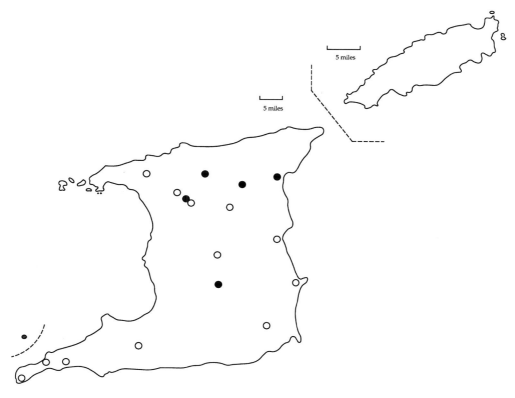

Map 15. *Phyllomedusa trinitatis*

very depressed; *Scinax rubra* is the only other tree frog with depressed body and dorsal stripes, it is common and widespread, and olive brown or brown-yellow; but it lacks a serrated jaw, and does not occur in the specialized bromeliad microhabitat with this species. Dorsal skin smooth, venter and thigh skin granular. First finger shorter than second and fingers free; toes slightly webbed. Dorsum brown with two stripes extending from eyes to cloaca; stripes may be joined just posterior to snout and enclose upper orbit of eye, and contain a brown blotch posterior to orbit. Stripes iridescent yellow or yellow-green; limbs cream. Males have a subgular vocal sac, but this species is apparently voiceless.

Natural History: The macrohabitat for *P. auratus* is montane rainforest above 800 m and elfin woodland; the microhabitat is highly specific, and the frog appears to be associated with the giant epiphytic bromeliad, *Glomeropitcairnia erectiflora,* in the Northern Range. Kenny (1969) found tadpoles throughout the year and as many as five tadpoles in different stages of development in a single plant. Field notes (JCM) report two adults in a single plant, each plant is divided into numerous compartments by layered leaves, and adults and tadpoles living in a single plant can easily avoid each other. Kenny speculated that the tadpoles may be carnivorous, but are more likely omnivorous, feeding on debris accumulating in the bromeliad pool as well as on siblings. Murphy and Humbert (1983) discussed the habitat and history of this highly specialized, poorly known species. It is interesting to note that fang-like projections and

voicelessness are also linked in a group of southeast Asian ranid frogs and that they may be the product of sexual selection (Emerson and Berrigan, 1993; Emerson, 1994).

Material: Trinidad—FMNH 40449, 218982, 218984–6, 219606 from near summit of El Tucuche. USNM 166629–34, 166709–10, near summit of El Tucuche; 244419 near summit of Mt. Aripo.

Phyllomedusa trinitatis Mertens

Map 15. Plates 30, 31, 32.

Hyla viridis: Court, 1858:441. *Phyllomedusa burmeisteri:* Mole and Urich, 1894a:90. *Phyllomedusa trinitatis* Mertens, 1926:145. Type locality: "Port of Spain, Island of Trinidad." *Phyllomedusa burmeisteri burmeisteri:* Beebe, 1952:174. *Phyllomedusa burmeisteri trinitatis:* Rivero, 1961:149. *Phyllomedusa trinitatus* [*sic*]: MacLean et al. 1977:45.

Comment: Duellman (1974) suggested that *P. trinitatis* resembles *P. tarsius,* a species of the Upper Amazon Basin; these two may be conspecific.

Distribution: *P. trinitatis* inhabits Trinidad and coastal northern Venezuela, and is a species of the Caribbean Coastal Range. Literature records for Trinidad localities include: Arima Valley (Beebe, 1952); Cedros, Icacos, Maracas, Nariva, and Valencia (Kenny, 1969). Field notes (JCM) add: Arena Dam Road; Guayaguayare Rd., south of Rio Claro; and near Siparia on Coora Road. Locations based upon museum material add the following localities: Arima Valley, numerous locations; Mt. St. Benedict; Brickfield; Catham Beach on Erin Bay; St. Joseph; Mayaro; Navet; Orange Grove Rd. and Churchill-Roosevelt Rd., near Piarco Airport; and Tunapuna.

Description: Males 80 mm, females 90 mm SVL. Snout blunted in dorsal view, sloping in profile, eye diameter about 1.2 times the eye-nostril distance; tympanum is about one-half the eye diameter. Dorsal skin finely granular with scattered tubercles; sides and belly are very granular. First finger shorter than second and opposable; fingers and toes free; distal end of each digit dark bronze in color; hind legs very long. Dorsum green with some white and pink mottling or spots laterally; lower lip white in preserved material and yellow-brown in life; gular and chest purple-lavender with white spots; belly is white in preserved material and peach in life. Coloration in juveniles olive-green with orange patches on flanks which become enclosed with black markings, these disappear with age; froglets turn a deep red-purple at night, turning green with sunrise. Males do not have an external vocal sac. The only large bright green frog with an iris with orange reticulations on Trinidad.

Voice: A short, subtle nasal "quank." Kenny (1969) stated both sexes call, the male has a mating call that is a soft "huh-huh-huh."

Natural History: A lowland, arboreal frog inhabiting secondary forest and savannas. Kenny (1969) considered it to be bush-dwelling, noting it, "is most common in clearings at the edges of forests, in proximity to some standing water, and rarely above elevations of 100 m above sea level." In Venezuela, Rivero and Esteves (1969) described a breeding site as a plant thicket of *Dieffenbachia*-Marantacea. Field notes (JCM) report *P. trinitatis* active on evenings preceded by afternoon rain, a requirement stated by Kenny (1966) for amplexus to occur. Kenny (1966) described reproductive behavior in this species: amplexus occurs after 2100 hours, and it may be initiated on the ground, at the edge of a pond, or in a bush; the female climbs through the vegetation in search of a nest site, one pair moving 7 m. [Field notes (JCM) describe a pair moving at least 20 m over a period of 2 hours before laying eggs.] Nest site selection often in a shaded area where a branch of a bush or small tree overhangs the water. The female hangs from a branch by her front limbs and grasps one to six leaves with her hind feet. A single leaf may be rolled into a tube, or a cluster of leaves may be held close together and placed near her cloaca so that they will be glued together by the egg mass and associated secretions; egg laying often starts after 2400 hours. The female moves slowly up the branch, depositing clumps of 30–40 eggs; the male fertilizes them; and the pair may remain motionless for 5 minutes before the next clump is released. When fertilization is completed the male leaves; the female may stay with the nest for 30 minutes. A gelatinous substance deposited with the eggs acts as an adhesive to hold the eggs in the leaf nest; as the substance hardens it reduces water loss from the eggs. Nests reported by Kenny (1966) ranged from 0.5–7 m above the water; field notes (JCM) report several nests in the Arima Valley located over

ground that was well drained, and Kenny (1966) described several exposed nests in grass; as well as some nests parasitized by dipteran and hymenopteran larvae. He found a female depositing eggs three times (in June, July, and October) in one year, and one male was observed in amplexus on 2 successive nights. Kenny (1966) stated that during reproduction these frogs turn a dull brown color, and turn bright green when reproduction has ended [field notes and photographs of 10 amplexing pairs (JCM, MB) do not support an amplexus color change]. Field notes (JCM, RHH) describe two frogs, presumably both males, in combat for about 2 minutes; the aggressive encounter occurred in a face-to-face posture with front legs together; the frogs pushed and grappled with each other while standing on their hind legs. An individual was observed with numerous lacerations on the dorsum that may have resulted from biting during an intraspecific encounter, or from a predator (field notes, JCM). Hatching occurs about day 7 or 8 and metamorphosis takes place about 12 weeks later (Kenny, 1969). Field notes (JCM) report individuals metamorphosing on 20 April, the height of the dry season, next to artificial ponds. *P. trinitatis*, like all phyllomedusines, moves with a slow deliberate action, similar to that of a slow loris or sloth; this may be useful in avoiding detection by both prey and predators.

Material: Trinidad—FMNH 49702–4, Brickfield; 219611–2, Valencia Rd., between Valencia and Toco. USNM 167519, Piarco, junction of Orange Grove Rd. and Churchill-Roosevelt Hwy. 197427 Spring Hill Estate, Arima Valley.

Scinax rubra (Laurenti)

Map 16. Plates 33, 34.

Hyla rubra Laurenti, 1768:35. Type locality: "America," a lectotype selected by Fouquett and Delahoussaye (1977) is from Suriname. *Hyla lineomaculata:* Werner, 1899:483. *Ololygon rubra:* Fouquett and Delahoussaye, 1977:387. *Ololygon rubra rubra:* Harding, 1983: 234. *Scinax rubra:* Duellman and Wiens, 1992:1.

Distribution: *S. rubra* is widespread, ranging from the Panama Canal through the lowlands of northern South America and to Trinidad, Tobago, and St. Lucia. Trinidad localities in the literature include: Arima Valley (Beebe, 1952); Arima (Werner, 1899); Aripo Savannas (Schwab, 1988); Bamboo Grove, Cedros, Icacos, Maracas, Nariva, Valencia (Kenny, 1969). Field notes (JCM) add: Arena Dam Road; Arima By-Pass; Coco Trace Extension, in the southwestern peninsula; Cumuto Rd.; Guanapo Valley; and Mexico Rd. between the Eastern Main Road and Churchill-Roosevelt Highway. Trinidad localities based upon museum material include: Arima Valley; Brickfield; Guanapo Valley; Mayaro; Morne Diablo, Siparia District; Nariva Swamp on Manzanilla-Mayaro Rd. near the 45.5 milepost; Piarco on Orange Grove Rd.; 5 miles south of Rio Claro on Guayaguayare Rd; Carenage west of Port of Spain; San Rafael; Tucuche; Valseyn Park; and Waller Field. Tobago locations based on the literature include: Grafton Estate and Prospect

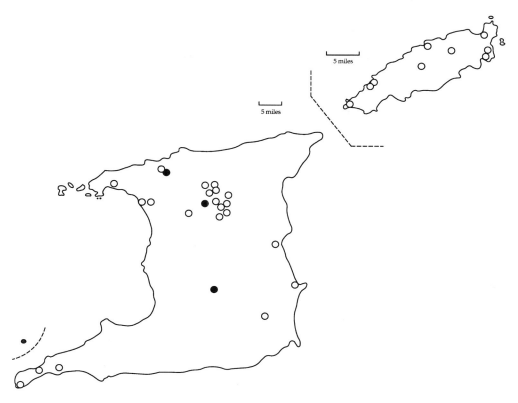

Map 16. *Scinax rubra*

Estate (Mertens, 1972). Field notes (JCM) report it along the Windward Rd. between Speyside and Roxborough at numerous locations, and on Roxborough-Parlatuvier Rd. between Roxborough and Bloody Bay at numerous locations. Tobago locations based on museum material include: Bon Accord near Store Bay; Bacolet; Charlotteville; Bloody Bay River; and Hillsborough Dam; and Windward Rd. near Lambeau Hill Crown Trace, vicinity of 22.5 milepost.

Description: Males 33 mm, females 39 mm SVL. Snout pointed from above, rounded in profile; protruding over mouth in profile; eye diameter less than eye-nostril distance; tympanum about one-half diameter of eye; canthus a rounded ridge. Body very depressed. Fingers with reduced webbing, some individuals may only have lateral fringe present; finger disks wider than long; toes moderately webbed. Dorsal skin finely to coarsely granular, ventral skin coarsely granular; a transverse fold of skin extends across chest. Dorsum with two brown streaks running posteriorly from interorbital blotch. *Phyllodytes auratus* has a similar pattern, but it is iridescent yellow, and has serrated jaws. A canthal streak extends through and past eye, over the tympanum, and onto sides of body. Upper margin of iris red-gold. Kenny (1969) suggested males are yellow-brown above, while females are brown; field notes (JCM) report calling males turn very yellow. Concealed surfaces of hind limbs mottled with yellow; chest yellow, and abdomen white. Ventral surfaces of limbs pink or flesh colored in life. Males with a subgular vocal sac.

Voice: A continuous squeaking but erratic; sounds almost mechanical. Kenny (1969) described it as, "A soft 'eh-eh' repeated at intervals of a few seconds, occasionally interspersed with a softer and more abbreviated chuck-chuck-chuck." Schwartz and Henderson (1991) describe the voice as a series of up to 10 notes that sound like "aah, aah, aah."

Natural History: *S. rubra* is a savanna frog, and a human commensal. Kenny (1969) notes it in open country near standing water; Duellman (1978) suggested that lumbering allows it to expand its range in Ecuador; and in Venezuela, Hoogmoed and Gorzula (1979) found it restricted to edificarian environments. Field notes (JCM) suggest this frog thrives in human modified environments, and it will enter buildings; along roadsides, calling in bushes; and in agricultural fields; calling from bushes as high as 2 m above the water; calling associates include *Hyla minuta, H. microcephala,* and *H. minuscula.* Field notes (JCM) report an amplexing pair in a cavity in a road embankment about 2 m above a water-filled ditch; erratic, long leaps are characteristic and make capture difficult, and members of this genus tend to run, or scurry over surfaces. Reproduction occurs throughout the rainy season, as late as January; eggs are deposited in shallow, turbid roadside pools, choked with vegetation (Kenny, 1969).

Material: Trinidad—FMNH 4372 Tucuche; 49695–8 Brickfield; 49699–70 San Rafael.

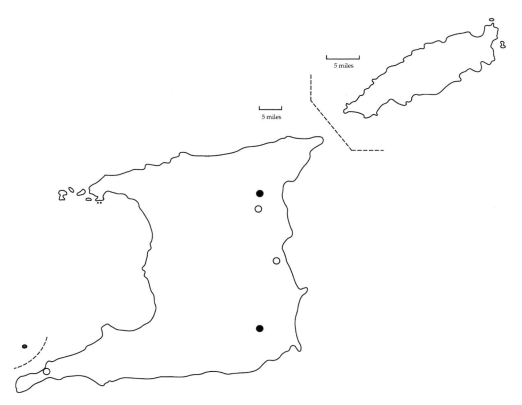

Map 17. *Sphaenorhynchus lacteus*

Sphaenorhynchus lacteus (Daudin)

Map 17. Plates 35, 36.

Hyla lactea Daudin, 1802:20. Type locality: "Brazil." *Hyla orophila:* Boos and Quesnel, 1968:32. *Sphaenorhynchus lactea:* Duellman and Lynch, 1981:238. *Sphaenorhynchus lacteus:* Duellman, *In* Frost 1985:175.

Distribution: *S. lacteus* has an Amazonian distribution, occurring in the Amazon and Orinoco basins, the Guianas, and on Trinidad. On Trinidad it occurs at lower elevations. Kenny (1969) stated that it is found throughout Trinidad in every drainage system, but cites only Cedros and Nariva as locations. Field notes (JCM) and museum specimens add the following locations: Sangre Grande Rd.; milepost 20 on the Southern Main Rd. near Cedros; on Valencia Rd. between Valencia and Toco; and south of Rio Claro on Guayaguayare Rd.

Description: Males 32 mm, females 40 mm SVL (Kenny, 1969). Snout pointed from above with a blunt, angular tip, and protruding over mouth; eye diameter equal to eye-nostril distance; canthus distinct and slightly rounded; tympanum is not distinct and about one-half eye diameter. Dorsal skin very finely granulated; ventral skin smooth, except for granulated thighs. Fingers moderately webbed; toes heavily webbed. In life the disks of the fingers and toes are translucent blue-green (white to yellow in preservative); in life a yellow canthal streak (brown in preservative) passes through eye and fades on flank. Posterior margin of vent trimmed with a narrow flap of yellow skin, a character that will distinguish this species from all other Trinidad and Tobago frogs. Venter translucent white tinted with green. It can be distinguished from *Hyalinobatrachium* by the presence of an intercalary cartilage, claw-like digits, and circular toe disks. Males have a huge subgular vocal sac. *Hyla punctata* may be confused with this species; however *H. punctata* lacks extensive webbing between fingers 2–3 and 3–4, and the narrow flap of skin trimming vent.

Voice: Kenny (1969) described the voice as a "sharp loud croak," repeated at irregular, but long intervals; and noted that it is rarely heard in massive choruses. Field notes (JCM) report chorus containing 3–20 adult males; and describe the call of this species as "quacking."

Natural History: A savanna and forest-edge frog: Kenny (1969) reported it in low bushes over water, at the edge of forest clearings, and in swampy terrain; in Venezuela, Hoogmoed and Gorzula (1979) found it in open vegetation (swamps and savanna lagoons), where the vegetation is well developed; field notes (JCM) describe flooded roadside ditches surrounded by dense vegetation, males call 5–45 cm above the water; Rivero (1971) reports males in Venezuela calling from the surface of the water.

Material: Trinidad—FMNH 215967, Guayaguayare Rd., south of Rio Claro.

Order Anura
Family Leptodactylidae: Leptodactylid Frogs

Leptodactylid frogs range from Texas and Florida in the southern United States southward through the Neotropics

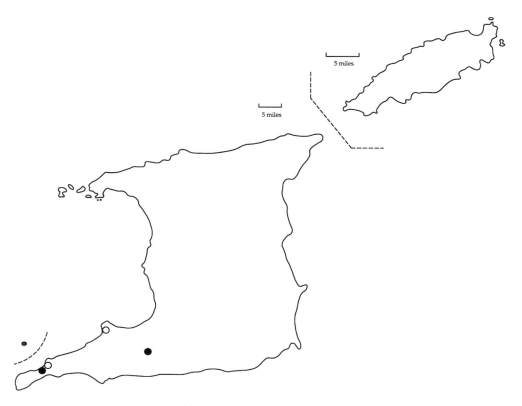

Map 18. *Adenomera hylaedactyla*

and in the West Indies. The family contains at least 51 genera holding more than 720 species, which are diverse in structure and habits and difficult to characterize based upon external structure and life histories. Some of these are typical in appearance while others are bizarre; many lay eggs in foam nests with an aquatic tadpole; others deposit eggs on land and have direct development. Five genera are represented on Trinidad and Tobago by 14 species. Four of these species are known from one to three specimens; one species, *Eleutherodactylus johnstonei,* is a recent introduction to Trinidad by man; and one species may have been pushed to extinction because of its edibility. Many of these frogs have a discoidal fold on the belly, a flap of loose skin, circular in shape, that allows the ventral skin direct contact with the substrate. The *Eleutherodactylus* are tree-frog-like and may be confused with members of that family, but they lack an intercalary cartilage and the claw-like end of each finger, and have a snout that protrudes beyond the mouth. Lynch (1971) commented on the lack of knowledge about these frogs.

Three factors have contributed to our current deplorable lack of general knowledge concerning this large family: 1) the most recent synopsis of a revisionary nature is that of Boulenger, 1882; 2) the bewildering number of generic names and the indiscriminant application of family and subfamily names of numerous authors; and 3) the problem of dealing with *Eleutherodactylus,* one of the largest vertebrate genera known.

A note on *Eleutherodactylus* identification is in order. Within all major taxa of organisms there are groups that become notoriously difficult to divided into species. *Eleutherodactylus* is such a group. Lynch and LaMarca (1993) have summarized the reasons for this: (1) pattern polymorphism, with individuals of the same species having stripes, uniform patterns, vertebral raphes, and interorbital bars; (2) subtle sexual dimorphism, making it all but impossible to determine the sex of an individual without dissection; (3) direct development, producing populations with great diversity in size; and (4) males do not congregate at breeding sites; instead they call from dispersed locations, making them difficult to sample. Thus, when presented with a collection of these interesting frogs, it is very tempting to give up on identification, and believe that if you have seen one you have seen them all.

Leptodactylids are the most commonly encountered frogs on the islands, and even the casual visitor to Port of Spain is like to hear them calling or see their foam nests in streetside gutters and puddles.

Adenomera hylaedactyla (Cope)

Map 18. Plate 37.

Cystignathus hylaedactylus Cope, 1868:115. Type locality: "From the Napo or upper Maranon" River, Peru. *Adenomera hylaedactylus:* Heyer, 1974:42. *Adenomera hylaedactyla:* La Marca, 1992:11.

Distribution: *A. hylaedactyla* has an Amazonian distribution; it also occurs on the southwest peninsula of Trinidad.

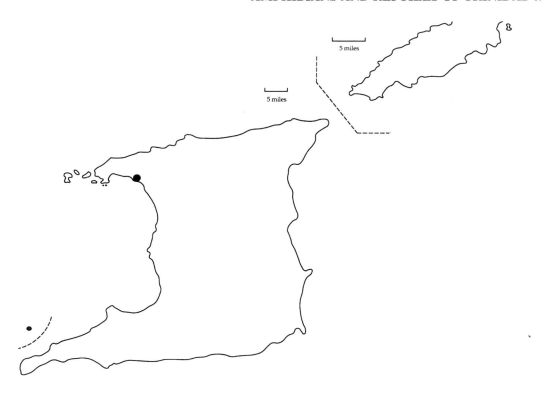

Map 19. *Eleutherodactylus charlottevillensis*

Read (1986b) reported it calling along a 30 km stretch of highway between Bonasse and San Fernando. Museum material documents localities near Siparia and Cedros.

Description: Males 26 mm, females 31 mm SVL. Snout rounded in profile and pointed from above; tympanum distinct and about one-half diameter of eye; tympanic fold present; nostrils located closer to snout than to eye. Dorsal skin mostly smooth, but small tubercles or dorsolateral folds may be present; ventral skin smooth. First finger shorter than second (almost equal), this will distinguish it from all Trinidad *Leptodactylus;* hind feet not webbed. Dorsal color gray to brown with numerous dorsal and lateral dark spots; a dark, triangular interorbital blotch and mid-dorsal stripe may be present. Seven of seven Trinidad specimens have a V-shaped blotch with apex pointing anterior, in scapular region. Venter uniform white. Males with small tubercles on posterior of dorsum with white tips; females lack these.

Natural History: A savanna and forest-edge frog in Trinidad, although mainland populations have been found in secondary forests, flooded forests, rain forests, and river-edge habitats (Heyer and Peters, 1971; Toft and Duellman, 1979). Read (1986b) collected a specimen during the day on swampy ground, noted the species appears to be common, and reported diurnal, chorusing frogs in roadside marshes, often in very dense vegetation near streams or ditches; and noted chorusing may occur at night when the weather is unseasonally wet in January. Field notes (JCM) describe calling throughout the afternoon of 29 June in the vicinity of

Pitch Lake; the area is a mosaic of villages, industrial complexes, agriculture, and small patches of forest; and this species uses many wet, heavily vegetated terrestrial microhabitats present here; it also moves actively over roads at night. Heyer and Silverstone (1969) described this species in French Guiana in a marsh that had been developed into a landing strip; the tadpoles were in thin foam, cup-shaped nests with a distinct rim, about 35 mm in diameter, under a metal and wood marker. Eggs are large (3 mm) and relatively few (9–14) in number (La Riva, 1995). The tadpoles complete metamorphosis in the foam chamber, feeding on yolk.

Material: Trinidad—FMNH 218785–6 Laurier Pond, near Siparia. USNM 248792, just east of Bonasse, on the Southern Main Road.

Eleutherodactylus charlottevillensis

Map 19. Plate 38.

Eleutherodactylus terraebolivaris Hardy, 1982:68. *Eleutherodactylus charlottevillensis* Kaiser, Dwyer, Feichtinger, and Schmidt 1996: 153. Type locality: 7 km Roxborough along the Roxborough-Bloody Bay road, St. John Parish, Tobago, West Indies.

Distribution: Known only from the island of Tobago. Field notes (JCM) report it from several localities along Roxborough-Parlatuvier Rd., the Northside Rd. at the 33.25 milepost in Charlotteville, and in the vicinity of the 32 milepost. On Tobago all of the museum specimens are from the northeastern end of the island: the Northside Road between

Errata Sheet

Murphy, AMPHIBIANS AND REPTILES OF TRINIDAD AND TOBAGO

Please substitute this map for the one on page 80.

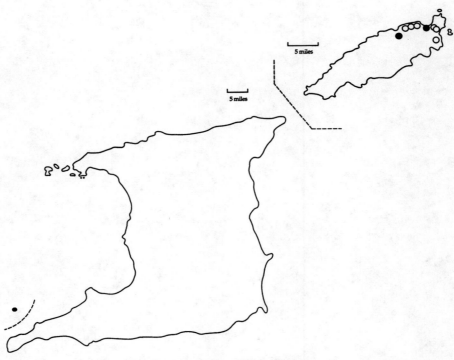

Map 19. *Eleutherodactylus charlottevillensis*

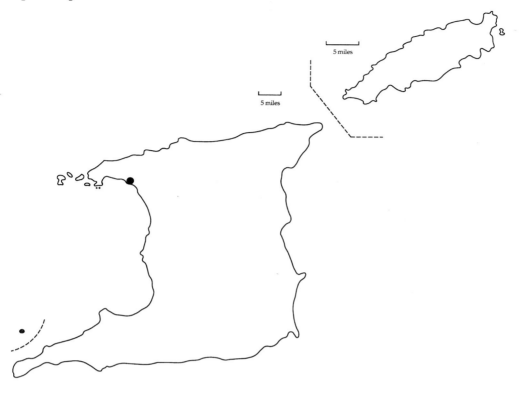

Map 20. *Eleutherodactylus johnstonei*

mileposts 22.5–30; and SW of Speyside on Lambeau Crown Trace.

Description: Males 31 mm, females 47 mm SVL. Snout rounded in profile and blunted in dorsal view. Eye diameter slightly less than eye-nostril distance; tympanum distinct and about two-thirds diameter of eye; supratympanic fold present. First finger equal in length to second, or slightly shorter; this may confuse it with *Adenomera*. However *Adenomera* is unknown from Tobago and has numerous dorsal spots and blotches as well as dorso-lateral folds or tubercles, and live specimens are dark brown or grey; this species lacks these and is red-brown. No webbing on fingers or toes. Dorsal skin of adults smooth; small individuals (<25 mm) have scattered tubercles with a small cresent of red-orange colored glands above and posterior to tympanum; ventral skin smooth with some granulations on posterior belly. Dorsum red-brown with mottling; dark spot between the eyes; vertical bars on upper lip; front and hind limbs have dark crossbars; adults have a small black spot on each side of dorsum in scapular region; venter cream or white in preserved material, in life posterior belly yellow, with some intrusion of pigment on the limbs from dorsal surface. *E. charlottevillensis* readily distinguished from other Trinidad and Tobago *Eleutherodactylus* by its wide head and mostly smooth ventral skin.

Voice: "jivit, jivit, jivit."

Natural History: A frog of forest leaf litter and streambeds. We found this frog moving across the road between Bloody Bay and Roxborough on rainy nights. In 1994, dur-

ing a very dry week, this frog was calling and active around streams, when almost all other anuran activity had ceased. Small (20–25 mm SVL) individuals were sitting on leaves 10–15 cm above streambed; one individual was feeding on flies and beetles while sitting on a white shelf fungus (Basidiomycoeta) growing on a log over a stream; the insects may have been drawn to the fungus. This species presumably has direct development like other members of the genus.

Material: Tobago—AMNH 87407–33, hills above Man of War Bay, 1.5–3.5 km ENE of Charlotteville. FMNH 251224–26 Bloody Bay Road.

Eleutherodactylus johnstonei Barbour

Map 20.

Eleutherodactylus johnstonei Barbour, 1914:249. Type locality: "St. George Parish, Grenada. *Eleutherodactylus martinicensis:* Kenny, 1979b:27.

Distribution: *E. johnstonei* has a Lesser Antilles distribution, and it has been introduced into Jamaica, Bermuda, coastal Venezuela, Curacao, Guyana, and Trinidad. In Trinidad it occurs in the Port of Spain dock area in the vicinity of the Port of Spain Holiday Inn.

Description: The single Trinidad specimen 20 mm SVL. Elsewhere males are known to reach 24 mm and females to 31 mm SVL. Snout blunted in dorsal view, truncated profile. Eyes relatively large, diameter about equal to eye-nostril distance; tympanum distinct, about one-half diameter of eye; canthus distinct, with a broad streak that extends through

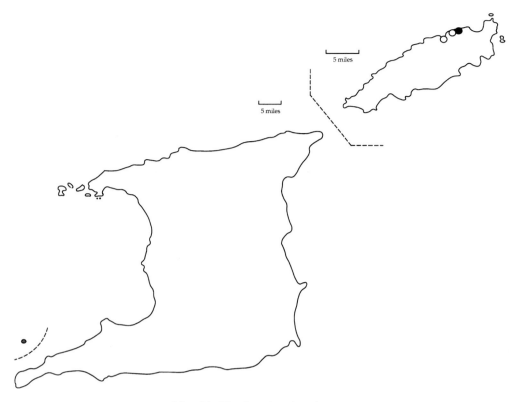

Map 21. *Eleutherodactylus* cf. *rozei*

eye, over the tympanum and into a lateral stripe. Dorsal skin and upper eyelids with numerous (>4–5) tubercles; ventral skin posterior to front legs granular and cream colored (these characters will separate this species from all other Trinidad and Tobago *Eleutherodactylus*); chin speckled with chromatophores. Dorsum with a dark brown blotch from interorbital region to the vent, and a thin vertebral stripe. Limbs with crossbars and tubercles. First finger shorter than second; all digits lack webbing; all digits with expanded toe disks, but lack the claw-shaped distal phalange present in hylid frogs. Two individuals from Barbados lack the medial dorsal stripe, but have a chevron in the scapular region.

Voice: A high pitched "bleep, bleep, bleep."

Natural History: Field notes (JCM) report this frog calling along the runways at the Barbados Airport; no experience with it in Trinidad. Schwartz and Henderson (1991) reported it from rainforests, yards, gardens, sugarcane fields, coconut trash, arboreal and fallen bromeliads, under rocks, logs in forests, walls of ruins, trash piles and rock piles in the Lesser Antilles; and, the diet includes ants (44%), arachnids (19%), leafhoppers (11%) with springtails and termites making up the rest of the diet. Calling sites range from ground level to 3 m above the ground; males in the Barbados population exhibit call site fidelity; females select mates based upon body size and guard eggs (Ovaska, 1991a, 1991b).

Material: Barbados—FMNH 195561–4. Trinidad—USNM 244420 Wrightson Road, across from the Holiday Inn.

Eleutherodactylus cf. *rozei*

Map 21.

Eleutherodactylus cf *rozei:* Hardy, 1982:102.

Comment: Lynch and La Marca (1993) review the *Eleutherodactyus* associated with *E. bicumulus* from Venezuela's Coastal Range and described the holotype of *E. rozei* as a juvenile female, distinct from *E. bicumulus,* but suggest that it may be a juvenile *E. reticulatus,* and that it be kept as a separate species pending further study.

Distribution: Northeastern Tobago. Along Northside Road in the vicinity of milestones 27.5 and 28; also in the vicinity of Windward Road milepost 22.5 near Lambeau Hill Crown Trace.

Description: Both sexes 14–18.5 mm SVL. Eye diameter about 1.25 times eye-nostril distance; canthus distinct, but slightly rounded, canthal streak extends from nostril through eye, over tympanum to shoulder; tympanum small, about one-third eye diameter, and about same size as disk on third finger (and second toe); supratympanic fold weak to moderate. Cluster of tubercles located between tympanum and anterior edge of front leg. Large gland present above tympanum. One specimen (USNM 227827) with cluster of tubercles and gland better developed than in smaller specimens. Hands and feet lack webbing. Dorsal skin mostly smooth, with a few tubercles on dorsum of hind legs; venter smooth to granular. The

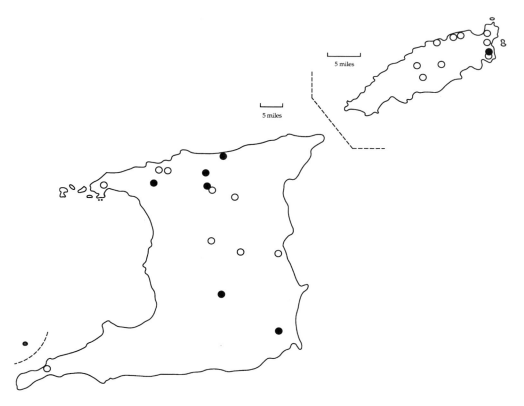

Map 22. *Eleutherodactylus urichi*

tibia/SVL ratio for this species ranges from 45.5 to 56.6 ($\bar{x}$ = 53.7). Head width/SVL ratio ranges from 33.1 to 40.1 ($\bar{x}$ = 36.4). Dorsal pattern variable: three specimens with distinctive vertebral cream stripe extending from snout to vent; three specimens with midline stripe expanded to large dorsal blotch that extends to waist; five specimens with interorbital crossbar and hour-glass-shaped dorsal marking, that may be well defined or barely visible. Venter appears uniform to unaided eye, but with magnification chromatophores are scattered over venter. Front and back legs have cross bars. In overall appearance difficult to distinguish from *E. urichi;* however in life this species has a gold iris, while *E. urichi* has a blue iris. *E.* cf. *rozei* has a tympanum which is about the same size as the disk on the third finger and the disk on the second toe. *E. urich* has a tympanum that is larger than the disk on the third finger. [See color photo of *E.* cf. *rozei* on page 17 in Hardy, 1983b.]

Natural History: Information about habitat accompanies some museum specimens. Males call from the ground or on vegetation, above the ground. It has also been found along the edges of streams and in leaf litter.

Material: Tobago—MCZ 86950 Northside Rd. in vicinity of milepost 27.75; 86952–53 near Hermitage, above Corvo Point; USNM 192758–9 Northside Rd. vic. of milestone 27.75, near Hermitage, above Corvo Point; 227820–28 on Northside Rd. at milepost 27.5.

Eleutherodactylus urichi (Boettger)

Map 22. Plate 39.

Hylodes urichi Boettger, 1894b:88. Type locality: "St. Annes, Trinidad." *Eleutherodactylus urichi:* Barbour, 1914:251. *Eleutherodactylus urichi urichi:* Schwartz, 1967:10 (Trinidad). *Eleutherodactylus u. urichi* x *euphronides:* Schwartz, 1967:11 (Tobago).

Distribution: *E. urichi* is a Trinidad and Tobago endemic (Kaiser et al. 1994). On Trinidad and Tobago it is widespread in forested areas. Literature reports the following localities: Arima Valley (Beebe, 1952); Tucuche, Maracas, Valencia, Oropuche River Valley near Vallencia, Nariva, Cedros, and Tamana Caves (Kenny, 1969; 1979a). Museum material documents the following localities: Arima Valley, numerous locations; Aripo; the Guayaguayare Forest; Mt. St. Benedict; Morne Bleu Ridge; Brickfield; Tucker Valley; near Talparo; Mt. Tamana; Tucker Valley; and the summit of Mt. Tucuche. Literature records from Tobago include: Hillsborough Dam; 4.8 km north of Mt. St. George; 6.4 km north of Pembroke; and Speyside (Schwartz, 1967). On Tobago museum material documents the following localities: Windward Rd. at milepost 22.5; Northside Rd. at mileposts 23.75, 27.5, 27.75; Charlotteville cacao plantation.

Description: Males 21 mm, females 24 mm, the smallest individual measured was 12 mm. A highly variable frog with a snout rounded in profile and blunted in dorsal view. Tympanum distinct, about one-third eye diameter, and larger than

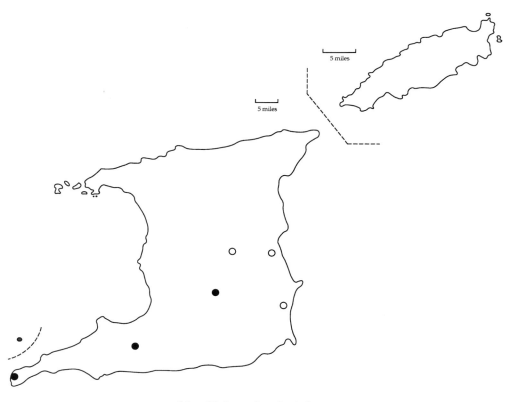

Map 23. *Leptodactylus bolivianus*

disk on third finger; eye diameter larger than eye-nostril distance; canthus distinct. Dorsal skin smooth with some scattered tubercles, mostly toward posterior body, and on upper eyelids; belly skin very granular. All digits lack webbing. Dorsal coloration brown to yellow-brown and pink; often uniform, but blotches, partial stripes, and flecks in some individuals. Many with a dark brown supratympanic stripe extending posteriorly for short distance. Ventral skin off-white in the gular region, blue to purple on the chest and belly. Upper portion of iris bright blue or turquoise, a characteristic that will distinguish it from *Eleutherodactylus* cf. *rozei* (known from Tobago). Hind legs with crossbars, vertical bars on the upper lip; posterior surfaces of thighs red.

Voice: Schwartz (1967) described the call as " . . . a 2-note call, the second note higher than the the first, first note fainter and less accented than the second."

Natural History: A forest and forest-edge frog. Driving around the islands on a wet night its call is ever present in wooded areas (field notes, JCM); Johnson (1946) and Kenny (1969) reported it in open habitats, but my experience suggests these are most likely forest-edge situations, and this frog probably does not occur in savanna habitats. Wells (1981) found males have a high degree of site fidelity; 75% of 168 recaptures were made at the previous capture site; male combat started with a series of clicks by two individuals at close range, followed by one male charging the other and knocking it off its perch; frogs grappled with each other for several minutes at a time, sometimes kicking with the

backlegs; males called within 1.5 m of the ground. Field notes (JCM) describe nine calling males within 0.6 m of the ground, and two within 2 meters of each other. Oviposition is usually terrestrial in leaf litter, but Read (1986a) found nests, probably belonging to this species, on Mt. Aripo 2 meters above the ground in moss covered aerial roots. Eggs undergo direct development.

Material: Trinidad—FMNH 22503, Mt. St. Benedict; 43668–70 Guayaguayare Forest; 49609–21, 8 miles north of Aripo; 49627–32 Brickfield; 49667–89, 218793, 218796–7 Morne Bleu Ridge; 172490–502, 174336–7 Arima Valley. USNM 146356–8, 166493–508, 166509–12, 195064–71, 195101–2, 195050–1, 227702 Arima Valley (various locations). Tobago—FMNH 217151, Merchiston Rd.

Leptodactylus bolivianus Boulenger

Map 23. Plate 40.

Leptodactylus bolivianus Boulenger, 1898:131. Type locality: "Barranca and Missiones Mosetenes," Bolivia. *Leptodactylus pentadactylus pentadactylus:* Kenny, 1969:72. *Leptodactylus p. pentadactylus:* MacLean, et al., 1977:45.

Common Names: "Edible frog, mountain chicken" (Copper and Bacon, 1981).

Distribution: *L. bolivianus* is a widespread species ranging from Panama, through Amazonia. On Trinidad it is known from scattered localities at low elevations. Literature records for Trinidad include: Nariva, Tamana Cave (Kenny, 1969; 1979a); Icacos (White, 1988); Mayaro (Cooper and Bacon, 1981). Museum specimens document Brickfield,

Siparia, and the Icacos peninsula. Heyer (1994) wrote about tadpoles presumed to be *L. validus* which is in the *podicipinus-wagneri* group from Tobago, "The larvae [presumably USNM 306098] from Tobago correspond in total size and proportions (particularly the oral disk) with the *L. bolivianus-ocellatus* group larvae on the mainland of South America rather than with the *podicipinus-wagneri* complex. As far as is known, no member of the *L. bolivianus-ocellatus* group occurs on Tobago." Thus, there is excellent evidence that this species does occur on Tobago.

Description: Males 90 mm, females 115 mm. Snout truncated in profile and blunted from above. Tympanum distinct; about three-fourths eye diameter; supratympanum fold from posterior edge of eye to shoulder; canthus distinct. Dorsal skin smooth with a slight texture; dorsolateral folds extend from upper eyelid to groin; second pair of lateral folds rarely present. The single pair of folds will distinguish it from all other *Leptodactylus* in the area except *L. kundseni*, and *L. knudseni* lacks the mottling on the posterior surface of the thigh, present in this species. Ventral skin smooth, with a discoidal fold on belly. First finger shorter than the second; fingers free; toes with webbing reduced to lateral fringe. Dorsum brown, venter white or cream; dark triangular blotch between eyes pointing posteriorly; dark supratympanic and canthal streak; dark blotches on upper and lower lips separated by light spots; visible surfaces of thighs barred. Breeding males have enlarged forearms and one or two tubercles on inner side of each digit.

Voice: Kenny (1969) described the voice as a "bloop" or multiple "bloops," with a chorus producing a sound similar to that of bubbling porridge.

Natural History: A lowland forest and savanna frog that uses ponds and stream margins (Kenny, 1969; Hoogmoed and Gorzula, 1979; field notes, JCM). Anuran associates at an artificial pond were *L. fuscus, Adenomera hylaedactlya, Bufo marinus,* and *Bufo beebei.* Staton and Dixon (1977a) suggested this species is more tolerant of dry conditions than *L. macrosternum,* a species *L. bolivianus* associates with the Venezuelan llanos. Reproduction commences with the rainy season in temporary pools and swamps, amplexus occurs in the water, eggs are deposited in foam nests 6 x 30 cm, eggs hatch within 24 hours, metamorphosis occurs at 4 weeks (Kenny, 1969). An unusal case of parental interaction with the tadpoles was described from a Panama population of this frog by Wells and Bard (1988). They observed a female pumping her posterior end in the water to generate a wave which attracts her school of tadpoles; the larvae followed her down a water-filled ditch. Cooper and Bacon (1981) stated this species is eaten by man.

Material: Trinidad—FMNH 49661–63 Brickfield; 218782–83 Laurier Pond, near Siparia. USNM 287010 Erin Beach at Icacos Point; 306180 Icacos Peninsula.

Leptodactylus fuscus (Schneider)

Map 24. Plate 41.

Rana fusca Schneider, 1799:130. Type locality: None given. *Leptodactylus longirostris:* Garman, 1887b:14. *Leptodactylus typhormis* [sic.]: Hart, 1890:25. *Leptodactylus typhonius:* Mole and Urich, 1894a:89. *Leptodactylus sibilatrix:* Lynn, 1959:115. *Leptodactylus fuscus:* Heyer, 1968:162.

Common Name: "Whistling frog" (Boos and Quesnel, 1968).

Distribution: *L. fuscus* is widespread, ranging from Panama through Amazonia in areas of savanna. Trinidad localities reported in the literature include: Arima Valley (Beebe, 1952); Maracas, Bamboo Grove, Valencia, Nariva, Cedros, Icacos (Kenny, 1969). Field notes (JCM) report it from Valencia Road; and the road to Arena Dam, west of Cumuto. Trinidad localities documented by museum material include: Arena Dam Rd 2.35 km from junction with Cumoto-Tunapuna Rd; Brickfield; Port of Spain; La Veronica; Piarco, Bel Air Hotel; 4 mi south of Chaguanas; Cuare River; lower Guanapo Valley; Manzanilla-Mayaro Rd. in the vicinity of the 44 and 45.5 mileposts; on Icacos Rd. vicinity of the 78.5 milepost; in a marsh off Icacos Rd.; Laurier Pond near Siparia; along Coora Rd. near Quinam Beach; Tunapuna Rd. at Churchill-Roosevelt Rd.; Tucker Valley; and Waller Field. Literature records for Tobago include: Scarborough (Mertens, 1972). Tobago localities based upon museum material include: Bacolet Rd.; Bloody Bay River at Bloody Bay; Charlotteville; Crown Point Airport; Roxborough-Parlatuvier Rd. numerous localities; Northside Rd. at the 27.75 milepost; SW of Speyside on Lambeau Crown Trace; Louis D'Or Settlement; Scarborough Botanical Gardens; Windward Rd. at the 25.25, 27.75 milepost. It also occurs on Little Tobago Island.

Description: Males 42 mm, females 50 mm SVL. Snout pointed in dorsal view, protruding over mouth in profile; eye diameter equal to, or greater than, eye-nostril distance; tympanum distinct, about two-thirds of eye diameter; supratympanic fold extends from lower eyelid to shoulder. Dorsal skin smooth with five or more folds. Ventral skin smooth with a discoidal fold. First finger longer than second; fingers free; toes have lateral fringe, but lack webbing. Dorsum brown, tan or red, frequently with spots and/or stripes that may be cream, orange, or red. Usually a yellow or red middorsal stripe extends length of body, with a row of spots or dark stripes bordering it; upper and lower lips mottled; belly uniform off-white. Males have black, paired, external vocal sacs. Five or more longitudinal folds, pointed snout and black external vocal sacs in the male, separate this species from all other Trinidad and Tobago frogs.

Voice: A melodious whistling, "week, week."

Natural History: It is terrestrial in forest and savanna, and associated with large temporary and permanent lagoons (Kenny, 1969; Hoogmoed and Gorzula, 1979). Field notes (JCM) describe calling sites in a variety of locations at low elevations, including: roadside ditches; in dense secondary growth in the foothills of the Northern Range; and in the flat and rolling forests of the Northern and Southern Basins. This frog was very abundant at some locations; hundreds were present on Valencia Rd. during a heavy rain on 5 July 1984; and hundreds were observed

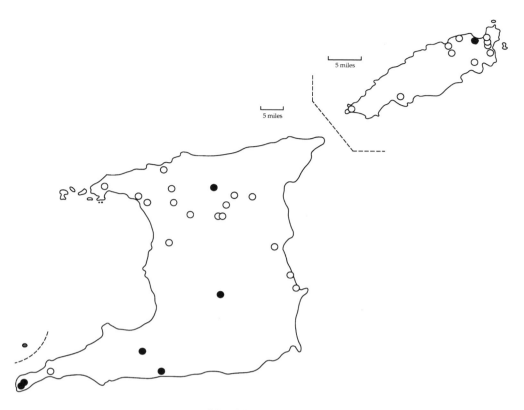

Map 24. *Leptodactylus fuscus*

sitting on the road during a rain on the road to Arena Dam on 2 July 1993. On Tobago this frog was observed calling within 15 m of ocean surf. Kenny (1969) found males call throughout the rainy season; Heyer (1969) described frogs excavating chambers for use as oviposition sites, after rain has softened soil. Reports of similar behavior in mainland populations are found in Lescure (1972), Lamotte and Lescure (1977), Staton and Dixon (1977a), and Hoogmoed and Gorzula (1979). Hoogmoed and Gorzula (1979) wrote, "The males excavate small cavities from the mouth of which they call. The caves are made in depressions which are liable to flood shortly after the rains start." Eggs are surrounded by foam nest within the cavity, when the cavity floods the larvae escape to open water. Metamorphosis occurs at about 6 weeks (Kenny, 1969). Downie (1984; 1989; 1990) demonstrated that *L. fuscus* tadpoles can generate foam after the nest foam has dissipated. He suggested that the foam is used to prevent desiccation and found that the ability to produce foam decreases with development past Gosner stage 27–28. Individual *L. fuscus* tadpoles made foam by spitting mucus bubbles, but as they age, foam occurs only in groups of five or more individuals. Laboratory experiments documented *L. fuscus* tadpoles feed on the eggs and embryos of *Physalaemus pustulosus,* but not on their free swimming tadpoles. He (Downie, 1994a,b) also found tadpoles capable of going into an arrested state of development after 4 days if no rain has fallen, noting that the arrested state can be maintained

to about day 20 after egg laying; and he hypothehsized that the arrested development may be mediated by *Candida* or *Prototheca* infections.

Material: Trinidad—FMNH 41684–5 no data; 49666 Brickfield; 217244 Icacos Rd., between mileposts 78–78.5; 217247–50 marsh off Icacos Rd., Icacos; 218781 Laurier Pond, near Siparia; 219613 Coora Rd., near Quinam Beach; 219614 Lower Guanapo Valley. Tobago—FMNH 217244 Cambelton.

Leptodactylus knudseni Heyer

Plate 42.

?*Leptodactylus pentadactylus:* Mole and Urich, 1894a:89. *Leptodactylus pentadactylus pentadactylus* (in part): Rivero, 1961:36. *Leptodactylus knudseni* Heyer, 1972:3. Type locality: Limoncocha, Napo, Ecuador. ?*Leptodactylus* cf. *pentadactylus:* Hardy, 1982:68. (Tobago).

Distribution: *L. knudseni* inhabits the greater Amazonian area. Its occurrence on Trinidad is based on a single specimen, MCZ 8663. R. R. Mole collected, or presented the specimen to the MCZ, in May 1915. It is in the *pentadactylus* Group and early references to *L. pentadactylus* on Trinidad may refer to this species. Barbour (1914) suggested that *L. pentadactylus* may have been exterminated on Trinidad because of its culinary value. The species has been reported only once from the island (Mole and Urich, 1894a) and they suggested it may have been exterminated by the introduction of the mongoose. Hardy (1982) suggested a member of the *pentadactylus* Group may also occur on Tobago, recounting Ober's (1898) description of

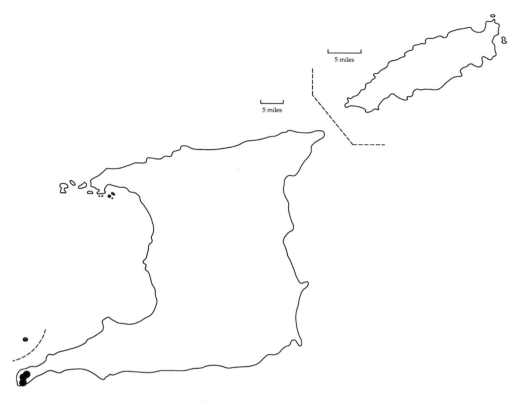

Map 25. *Leptodactylus macrosternum*

a gourmet frog dinner on Tobago and a subfossil frog femur from a cave. The presence of an extant population of this frog on either island is not substantiated in this work.

Description: Males 165 mm, females 147 mm SVL. Snout ovoid in dorsal view and rounded in profile; eye diameter greater than eye-nostril distance; tympanum distinct, almost equal to eye diameter; well-developed supratympanic fold from posterior edge of eye to angle of jaw. One pair of dorsolateral folds extend from eyes to sacral region; *L. fuscus* and *L. macrosternum* have five or more dorsolateral folds; and these folds are poorly developed and incomplete in *L. nesiotus*. Dorsal skin smooth with some white tipped tubercles on tibia; ventral skin smooth, with distinct discoidal fold on belly. First finger longer than second; fingers free; toes with a visible fringe, but no webbing. Dorsum red-brown and barred, spotted or uniform; lip with dark triangular bars. Ventral surface of thighs uniformly black with light orange markings, a characteristic that will distinguish it from all other leptodactylids in the area. Juveniles have a yellow-green head with green-yellow bands enclosing black-edged brown areas. Sexually active males possess a spine on each thumb and chest spines.

Natural History: A forest frog. In Amazonian Brazil Hero and Galatti (1990) found this species constructed large foam nests in excavated bowls or depressions in the ground adjacent to, but rarely connected with, isolated forest ponds or streamside pools. Nesting there occurs August-March, calling is from July-March. Tadpoles escape the ponds when they flood with rain and overflow into nearby permanent water.

Material: Trinidad—MCZ 8662, no data.

Leptodactylus macrosternum Miranda-Rivero

Map 25. Plate 43.

Leptodactylus ocellatus macrosternum Miranda-Rivero, 1926:147. Type locality: Bahia, Brazil. *Leptodactylus macrosternum:* Gallardo, 1964:379.

Distribution: *L. macrosternum* has an Amazonian distribution. On Trinidad it is known from Icacos Swamp in the southwest peninsula (Kenny, 1977; White, 1988). Other Trinidad locations are in the same area based upon museum material collected between mileposts 77.5 and 78.5 on Icacos Rd. Kenny (1977) hypothesized this species has recently arrived in Trinidad by rafting on floating vegetation from the Orinoco.

Description: Males 75 mm, females 80 mm. Snout rounded from above, mildly truncated in profile, it barely extends past the mouth which will help distinguish it from *Leptodactylus fuscus;* canthus indistinct. Eye diameter equal to eye-nostril distance; tympanum distinct, and about three-fourths eye diameter; supratympanic fold extends from lower eyelid to shoulder. Dorsal skin smooth with longitudinal folds numbering five or more; ventral skin smooth with a discoidal fold present. First toe longer than second; fingers free; toes slightly webbed. Dorsum light brown with a row

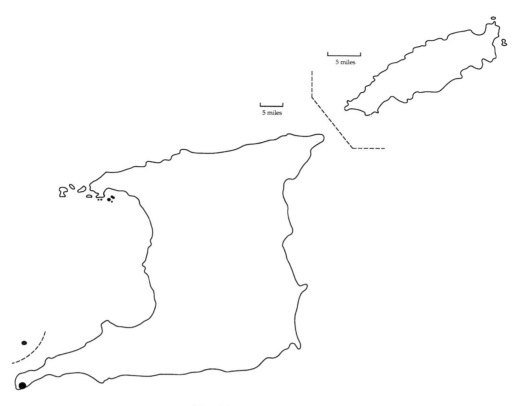

Map 26. *Leptodactylus nesiotus*

of large medial spots and dorsolateral rows (one or more on each side) of spots; venter uniform, with some mottling on the throat. *Leptodactylus fuscus* often has a wide yellow, orange, or red middorsal stripe. *L. macrosternum* has a large triangular blotch between the eyes pointing posteriorly; a dark tympanic and canthal streak; visible surface of hind limbs spotted, concealed surfaces of thighs uniform; venter white or cream. Males have two spines on each thumb, males in breeding condition with enlarged forearms; male *L. fuscus* lack thumb spines.

Natural History: A savanna frog. Field notes (JCM) describe this frog as common in the vicinity of Icacos from the following habitats: a coconut plantation, a cattle pasture, and the edge of a stream. In Venezuela, Hoogmoed and Gorzula (1979) recorded it in vegetation along the margins of large lagoons. Dixon and Staton (1976) conducted a mark-recapture study of this species in the llanos and found a home range for 10 individuals ranges from 9.4–133.9 square meters; home ranges were abandoned with the onset of the dry season; an 810 square meter study plot contained 255 frogs of this species (3.8 m square per individual); 94% of recaptures were in the immediate vicinity of the first capture; juveniles and adults appeared at twilight (10–15 minutes before total darkness) and remained above ground until dawn; frogs fed for the first 3 hours and then remained motionless for another 3 hours; reproduction occurs early in the wet season, young of the year attain sexual maturity at about 54 mm, second year

adults apparently died, and estivation is in deep cracks left in dried mud of ponds and lagoons.

> **Material:** Trinidad—FMNH 219582 and 219584 between mileposts 77.5 and 78.5 on Icacos Rd. (= Southern Main Road); 217247–50, Icacos.

Leptodactylus nesiotus Heyer

Map 26. Plate 44.

> *Leptodactylus nesiotus* Heyer, 1994:91. Type locality: "Trinidad, St. Patrick; Icacos Peninsula, Icacos."

Distribution: Known only from the type locality, Icacos Swamp, the southwestern peninsula, Trinidad.

Description: A single male 33 mm SVL. Snout rounded from above and slightly protruding over lower jaw; canthus indistinct; eye diameter equal to eye nostril distance. Tympanum distinct, about three-fourths of eye diameter; tympanic fold stops a very short distance posterior to the tympanum, a character that should distinguish this frog from *L. validus*. Dorsal skin smooth anteriorly, studded with tubercles posteriorly. First finger longer than second, and the single specimen has two thumb spines; no webbing between the fingers, slight webbing between toes 1–2 and 3–4. Dorsum uniform brown, with a large interorbital triangular blotch and two small dark brown sacral blotches; a white side blotch extends from axillary region to groin bordered by a dark brown stripe anteriorly; light stripe extends to a point above groin where it diffuses into a mottled pattern. This stripe should readily separate this frog from *L.*

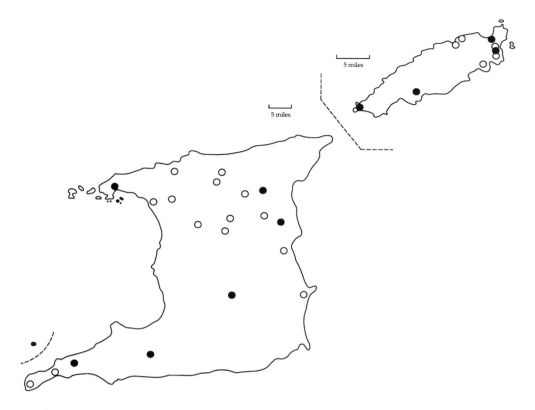

Map 27. *Leptodactylus validus*

validus; also this species has a white lip stripe under the eye, while specimens of *validus* with a lip stripe have it starting at the corner of the eye and extending posteriorly. Lower jaw with light upper margin around the mouth. Upper surface of thighs mottled; venter white with scattered chromatophores concentrated in gular region and widely separated on belly.

Voice: Heyer (1994) described the call rate at " . . . about 3.8 calls per s; call duration 0.03 s; calls partially pulsed with 4–5 partial pulses; calls frequency modulated with fast rise times; broadcast frequency 1500–2000 Hz, maximum energy 1800–2000 Hz."

Natural History: One specimen was found calling at night in a burrow under a mass of fern roots in a stagnant swamp.

Material: Trinidad: USNM 306179, Icacos Peninsula. Two other specimens not seen for this study are in the British Museum (BMNH 1992.147–148).

Leptodactylus validus Garman

Map 27. Plate 45.

Leptodactylus validus Garman: 1887b:14. Type locality: Kingston, St. Vincent. *Leptodactylus caliginous:* Mole and Urich, 1894a:89. *Leptodactylus petersi:* Parker, 1933:12. *Leptodactylus podicipinus petersi:* Rivero, 1961:48. *Leptodactylus wagneri:* Johnson, 1946:108.

Comment: Heyer (1994) wrote,

The larval type described by Kenny from Trindad is unique for all other known *Leptodactylus* in having a ventral papillary gap in the oral disk, suggesting either that the larvae described and figured are abnormal or that the larvae in fact are not *Leptodactylus,* but represent some other genus. The larvae described by Kenny further differ from the Tobago and St. Vincent larvae in that the A-2 labial tooth row is split in the stage 29 Trinidad larvae (stage based upon published figure), whereas for all similar stage (and greater) larvae from Tobago and St. Vincent, the A-2 labial tooth row is entire.

Thus, the tadpole of this frog is in need of description.

Distribution: Trinidad and Tobago. I considered it to be a Caribbean Coastal Range form endemic to Trinidad and Tobago, and secondarily dispersed into the Lesser Antilles (St. Vincent, Bequia, and Grenada). Its distribution on Trinidad and Tobago is widespread, ranging from sea level to near 730 meters. Trinidad literature records include: Arima Valley (Beebe, 1952); Bamboo Grove, Cedros, Icacos, Maracas, Nariva, Valencia, and "throughout Trinidad at lower elevations" (Kenny, 1969). Museum material from Trinidad document the following localities: Arena; Arima Valley-numerous locations; St. Augustine; 1.5 km W of Brasso Seco Village on Paria Morne Bleu Rd.; Brickfield; Mt. Harris; St. Joseph; Manzanilla-Mayaro Rd.; along Naparima-Mayaro Rd. on floodplain of Balata River; San Rafael; Tucker Valley; Sangre Grande; Lauier Pond, Siparia; Southern Main Rd. about the 67 mile-post; Valencia Rd.; Waller Field. Tobago museum material documents: Buccoo Bay; Bacolet River; Bacolet; Louis D'Or Settlement; Northside Rd. at milepost 27.75; Roxborough-Parlatuvier Rd. at Bloody Bay River; SW of Speyside on Lambeau Hill Crown Trace; Windward Rd. at milestones 22.5, 27.5, and 29.5. See comment in the Zoogeography section.

Description: Males 46 mm, females 51 mm SVL. Snout rounded from above and truncated in profile, and shape variable, eye diameter equal to eye-nostril distance. Tympanum distinct, one-half to three-fourths eye diameter; tympanic fold extends from posterior edge of eye to the shoulder. Dorsal skin usually with small black tubercles on posterior of body, and upper surface of thighs; a large gland present just anterior to front leg; longitudinal folds absent; ventral skin smooth. First finger slightly longer than second; fingers free of webbing; toes have a lateral fringe (*L. nesiotus* and *L. bolivianus* also have fringed toes) and slight webbing. Dorsum gray-brown with occasional spots; light spots on tip of snout and upper lips. Venter off-white with occasional mottling on throat and hind limbs. The only Trinidad and Tobago *Leptodactylus* lacking longitudinal dorsal skin folds and having a tympanic fold extending to the shoulder. Males with single gular vocal sac, two spines per thumb, forearm slightly enlarged in breeding individuals. Note that this frog is highly variable.

Voice: A metallic, high pitched rattle, "oit, oit, oit." Heyer fisement call at a

Call rate of 1.1–1.9 calls per s; call duration 0.03–0.06 s; call usually two notes, first note a single pulse occasionally weak or apparently absent, second note with 2–6 partial pulses; calls frequency modulated with very fast rise times; broadcast frequency range 1300–3500 Hz, with maximum energy in 2300–3500 Hz range; harmonic structure equivocal, but second note perhaps representing a shift to a harmonic of the first note . . .

Natural History: *L. validus* is a forest and forest-edge frog; roadsides, parks, and yards may occasionally be used, but forested stream banks, heavily shaded gullies, and caves are more likely habitats (Johnson, 1946; Kenny, 1969; field notes, JCM)). Reproduction occurs throughout the rainy season; males call from drainage ditches in towns, flooded roadsides, and wet forests (Kenny, 1969; field notes, JCM). The foam nests may be partially covered with sticks or leaves; larvae left the nest in 5 days, and metamorphosis occurred at about 8 weeks (Kenny, 1969). Predators include the snakes *Leptodeira annulata* and *Liophis reginae zweifeli* (field notes, JCM).

Material: Trinidad—FMNH 49654–5 Mt. Harris, Coal Mine River; 49656–60 Brickfield; 49664–5 San Rafael; 218785 Laurier Pond near Siparia; 219596–7 Valencia Road; 219598 near the 67 milepost on the Southern Main Road; USNM 119055–60 Upper Tucker Valley; 166622–4, Arima Valley. Tobago: AMNH 87403–6 Man of War Bay; 55863–5 Bucco Bay; 55873 Bacolet River. MCZ 27788–9 Speyside.

Lithodytes lineatus (Schneider)

Plate 46.

Rana lineatus Schneider, 1799:138. Type locality: Guiana. *Lithodytes lineatus:* Fitzinger, 1843:31.

Distribution: *L. lineatus* has an Amazonian distribution.

Its occurrence on Trinidad is based on one specimen, MCZ 6033, collected by Richard Decker, probably in 1919.

Description: The single Trinidad specimen 44 mm SVL; elsewhere males 45 mm, females 56 mm SVL. Snout pointed from above and truncated in profile. Canthus rounded, not distinct. Eye diameter greater than eye-nostril distance; tympanum distinct, and about three-fourths eye diameter. Dorsal skin with scattered tubercles; ventral skin smooth. First finger longer than second; tips of digits T-shaped. Fingers free of webbing; toes fringed, but lack other webbing. Dorsal color black with yellow dorsolateral stripes starting at nostrils, passing over the orbits to groin; this color and pattern will readily distinguish it from all other Trinidad and Tobago frogs. The only other black frogs in the islands are the vocalizing male *Mannophryne,* and they quickly change to brown when they are not calling, and are only 25 mm SVL. Red blotches occur in the inguinal area, and on the concealed surfaces of the thighs and tibia. Venter gray with scattered white spots.

Natural History: *L. lineatus* is terrestrial in primary, secondary, and forest-edge situations (Rivero, 1961; Duellman, 1978). Schluter and Regos (1981) found this frog in primary rainforest as well as logged forest, and associated with the leaf-cutting ant *Atta cephalotes;* the frog calls from within the ants' nest. Schluter and Regos (1981) and Duellman (1978) suggested that *Lithodytes* is a mimic of *Epipedobates femoralis, E. pictus,* and *Phyllobates* sp. None of these species is known to occur on Trinidad. Despite attempts to locate it by excavating leaf-cutting ant nests, the presence of an extant population of this frog on Trinidad cannot be substantiated.

Material: Trinidad—MCZ 6033.

Physalaemus pustulosus (Cope)

Map 28. Plates 47, 48, 49.

Paludicola pustulosa Cope, 1864:180. Type locality: "New Grenada, on the River Truando," Colombia. *Eupemphix trinitatis:* Boulenger, 1889b:307. *Eupemphix pustulosus* Boettger, 1892:40. *Bufo atrigularis:* Werner, 1899:482. *Eupemphix pustulosa:* Lutz, 1927:49. *Eupemphix pustulosus trinitatis:* Parker, 1933:8. *Eupemphyx pustulosus:* Boos and Quesnel, 1968:39. *Physalaemus pustulosus:* Lynch, 1970:489. *Eupemphix pustulosus trinitatus* [*sic*] MacLean, et al., 1977:45. *Physalaemus pustulosus trinitatis:* Harding, 1983:234.

Common Names: "Coong-la" (Netting, 1930); "canal frog, pung-la-la" (Boos and Quesnel, 1968).

Distribution: *P. pustulosus* is widespread, ranging from Veracruz and Oaxaca, Mexico, southward through Panama and into Amazonia. It is widespread on Trinidad and Tobago, occurring from sea level to at least 365 m. Published Trinidad localities: Arima (Werner, 1899); Tucker Valley (Johnson, 1946); Arima Valley (Beebe, 1952); southwest of Caura on Tucuche Rd. (Brongersma, 1956b); Maracas, Bamboo Grove, Valencia, Nariva, Cedros, and Icacos (Kenny, 1969). Trinidad localities supported by museum material include: Simla Research Station, 6 mi north of Arima; St. Augustine; Mt. St. Benedict; Trinidad Botanical Gardens, Port of Spain; Cuare River; San Fernando; Guayaguayare; Maracas; Mayaro; San Rafael; Churchill-Roosevelt Highway at the 11.5 milepost; Siparia; Icacos Rd. at the 75.75 milepost; Tucker Valley; Tunapuna; Waller Field. Tobago localities based upon museum

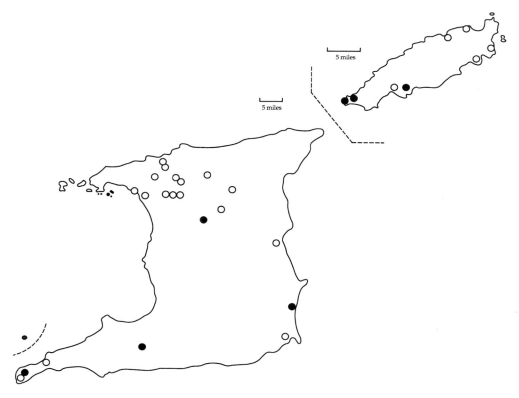

Map 28. *Physalaemus pustulosus*

material include: Bacolet River; Buccoo Bay; Milford Bay; Roxborough-Parlatuvier Rd. at Bloody Bay River; and Louis D'Or Settlement; Merchiston; Scarborough; Windward Rd. at the 22.5 milepost

Description: Males 28 mm, females 32 mm SVL. Snout pointed in dorsal view, rounded in profile; eye diameter equal to eye-nostril distance; tympanum indistinct; small, triangular parotid present. Dorsal skin with tubercles arranged, more or less, in longitudinal rows; lateral skin with numerous tubercles and glands; ventral skin granular. Fingers and toes lack webbing, but toes have some lateral fringe. Dorsum brown to gray with darker pigment following rows of warts; venter tan to yellow. Dorsal surface of hind limbs with crossbars. Absence of cranial crests and ridges will distinguish this species from the true toads which it superficially resembles. Males have a prominent subgular vocal sac.

Natural History: *P. pustulosus* is a savanna frog and human commensal. Netting (1930) described the habitat in Trinidad as follows,

> I collected specimens in foul sewers, in roadside drainage ditches, in ditches of muddy water about construction projects, and in kitchen and laundry drains which were full of soapy water . . . I never found individuals in a natural pool or stream, although frequently such habitats were separated by only a few feet from the artificial pools which were in use.

Forest floors, cleared jungle, secondary forest, roadsides, artificial ponds, and agricultural areas are used by this species (Johnson, 1946; Kenny, 1969; Hoogmoed and Gorzula, 1979; field notes, JCM). It quickly colonizes environments disturbed by human activity; field notes (JCM) suggest this frog is ubiquitous in agricultural areas and other sites disturbed by human activity, including some of the busiest sections of downtown Port of Spain; males call from the water's edge as well as from the surface of temporary pools and puddles; foam nests present along highways, in yards and drainage ditches. Spawning sites are frequently in pools resulting from water collecting in ruts made by passing motor vehicles. Brattstrom and Yarnell (1968) found the call order to be a hierarchy maintained by spacing and agonistic behavior, that includes kicks and aggressive notes. Heyer and Rand (1977) found foam nest construction results from a secretion that is beaten, or whipped into a foam by kicking the hindlegs. Clutch size about 300 eggs per nest (Lynn, 1959); eggs hatch in 72 hours, with tadpoles remaining in the nest for as long as 7 days; metamorphosis occurs at about 6 weeks (Kenny, 1969). Field notes (JCM) describe amplexing pairs being preyed upon by the large, terrestrial manicou crab, *Pseudothelphusa garmani* (Pseudothelphusidae). Downie (1988; 1990) found foam nests offer no temperature regulation abilities, but have some ability to protect the eggs from desiccation; nests subject to predation by *Leptodactylus fuscus* tadpoles, although they apparently do not feed on free-swimming *Physalaemus* tadpoles; *L. fuscus* tadpoles eat a much higher proportion of free-floating *P. pustulosus* eggs than groups of eggs embedded in foam nests; and free-swimming tadpoles preyed on by

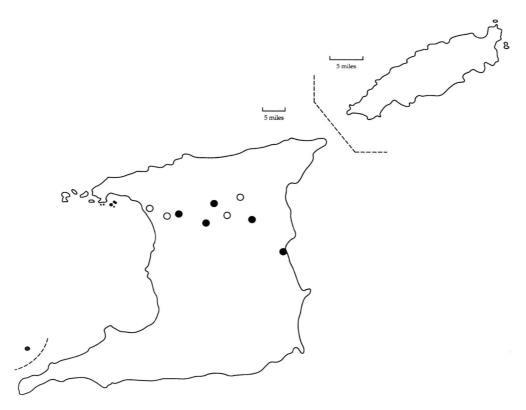

Map 29. *Elachistocleis ovalis*

dragonfly nymphs. Later Downie (1993) demonstrated that at 28°C isolated eggs hatch after 40 hours of incubation, but noted few tadpoles leave the nest at this time; instead they remain in the nest until they reach Gosner stages 23–24. The late emergence may allow for more advanced development in a protected environment, but tadpoles leaving the nest early can attain Gosner stage 25, by the time their siblings exit the nest. Ryan (1985) studied sexual selection and communication in this species on Barro Colorado Island, Panama, and the impact of predation by the bat *Trachops cirrhosus;* this bat also occurs on Trinidad.

> **Material:** Trinidad—FMNH 35103–4 Mayaro Bay; 49608 San Rafael; 218794 Quarry Rest House, Siparia; 219616 Icacos Rd. about milepost 75.75. Tobago—AMNH 55866 Bacolet River; 55867 Buccoo Bay. MCZ 4080–86 Milford Bay.

Order Anura
Family Microhylidae: Narrow-mouthed Frogs

Narrow-mouthed frogs are pantropical amphibians that have invaded temperate latitudes in North America and Eurasia. The family contains terrestrial and arboreal species in 61 genera, with at least 285 species. The Neotropical genera appear to have evolved in isolation in South America and then spread into Central and North America after the closure of the Panamanian Portal. These small (less than 100 mm) frogs have a stout body with a small head and narrow, slit-like mouth. The digits usually lack webbing. Instead of hopping, these frogs tend to raise themselves up and walk on all four legs. Most microhylids have small, pigmented eggs and free-swimming tadpoles without beaks or denticles. The Trinidad species have a fold of skin across the back of the head which will distinguish them from all other frogs in the area. Two species occur on Trinidad; both are members of the genus *Elachistocleis* which has a confused taxonomic history. Cochran and Goin (1970) commented on the confusion generated by the frogs in this group.

Since the recent monographer of this group in South America (Carvalho, 1954) saw fit to place this species in the genus *Relictivomer* and since we have had very little first-hand experience with the other genera in South America, we follow him in the generic assignment. We must say, however, that to us, *ovalis* and *pearsei* seem to be rather closely related, and in fact we must agree with Dunn (1949, p. 13): "I would take them for vicarious races save for the statement of Ruthven that the two occur together at Fundación."

Elachistocleis ovalis (Schneider)

Map 29. Plate 50. Figure A.

> *Rana ovalis* Schneider, 1799:131. Type locality: none given. *Engystoma ovale:* Boulenger 1882:163. *Elachistocleis ovalis:* Mertens, 1930:163. *Elachistocleis ovale:* Parker, 1933:12.

Distribution: *E. ovalis* has an Amazonian distribution. On Trinidad it occurs throughout lower elevations. Literature records for Trinidad localities: Bamboo Grove, Valencia, Nariva, Cedros, and throughout the Caroni drainage (Kenny, 1969); Aripo savannas (Schwab, 1988). Beebe (1952) recorded this frog in the Arima Valley, and field notes (JCM) describe it in the lower portion of this valley. Additional localities based on museum material include: Manzanilla Bay; Churchill-Roosevelt Highway at various localities between mileposts 6 and 10.5; and on an unnamed road between the Eastern Main Road and Churchill-Roosevelt Highway, and Guaico.

Description: Males 32 mm, females 40 mm SVL. Snout very pointed in lateral and dorsal views; mouth is inferior, with snout projecting 1–2 mm beyond opening. Eyes small, approximately the same size as the tympanum which is indistinct. Transverse fold of skin behind eyes, a character that separates it from all other Trinidad and Tobago frogs except *E. surinamensis*. *E. surinamensis* has a large orange patch on groin, which this species lacks. Dorsal and ventral skin is smooth. First finger shorter than second; all digits lack webbing. In Trinidad specimens there is a well-defined white line on the concealed surface of thigh [Figure A], and a distinct white vertebral stripe; *E. surinamensis* lacks these. The dorsum black overall, with scattered white flecks. Venter uniform off-white, but males have a black vocal sac and the female's gular region is mottled.

Voice: A sharp "eeee."

Natural History: *E. ovalis* is a savanna frog, but it also occurs under coconut palm litter at Cocos and Manzanilla Bay. In Venezuela, Hoogmoed and Gorzula (1979) found this frog in aggregations under boards and buried in sand about 4 cm below the surface during the dry season. Spawning occurrs throughout the rainy season in Trinidad; however, in Venezuela, Hoogmoed and Gorzula (1979) reported males call about 2 weeks after the rains start. Field

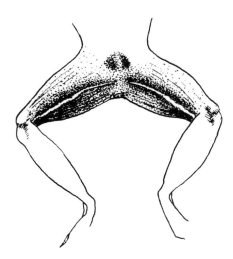

Figure A

notes (JCM) describe choruses from flooded agricultural land in late June and early July. Eggs hatched within 48 hours and metamorphosis occurred at 8 weeks (Kenny, 1969).

Material: Trinidad—AMNH 55852–4, 113281–88 6–8 mileposts on Churchill-Roosevelt Highway; 55855–6 Churchill-Roosevelt Highway 10.5 milepost; 55857 Churchill-Roosevelt Highway near junction with Freeman Rd. FMNH 215964 Arima Valley; 215965–6 Manzanilla Bay; 218987–9 between the Eastern Main Road and Churchill-Roosevelt Highway, east of Arima. MCZ 4089 and 6085 Guaico. Venezuela—FMNH 175141–95 Puerto Ayacucho.

Elachistocleis surinamensis (Daudin)

Map 30. Plate 51.

Bufo surinamensis Daudin 1802:91. Type locality: "Surinam." *Elachistocleis surinamensis:* Kenny, 1969:66. *Relictovomer* sp.: Harding, 1983:232.

Comment: M. S. Hoogmoed and C. E. Nelson discussed the complex history of the forms of *Elachistocleis* and *Relictovomer* in Frost (1985). Field observations (JCM) suggest these two species of *Elachistocleis* appear quite different in life, have distinctive calls and separate habitats, and therefore, are most likely distinct species.

Distribution: *E. surinamensis,* as currently known, is widespread, occuring on both sides of the Andes and Trinidad. Published Trinidad localities: Mayora, Valencia and Charuma forests (Kenny, 1969); Aripo savannas (Schwab, 1988). Field notes (JCM) report it about 1 mile west of Cumuto off of Tumapuna Road; and on the road to Arena Dam, just west of Cumuto.

Description: Males 35 mm, females 48 mm (Kenny, 1969). Snout sharply pointed from above and rounded in profile, it projects well beyond the mouth; transverse fold of skin immediately behind the eyes; tympanum not visible. Body short and squat. First finger shorter than second; no webbing between fingers; webbing between the toes reduced to a lateral fringe. Dorsum mottled with grey and black; no middorsal stripe, which will distinguish it from *E. ovalis* which has a middorsal stripe. Venter mottled with grey, black, and yellow; male's vocal sac black; orange spots on sides of groin and thigh, orange spots on concealed surfaces of calf and upper thighs. The orange spots and lack of vertebral stripe will distinguish this frog from *E. ovalis,* the only species on the islands with which it could be confused.

Voice: A high-pitched "eeee." A chorus resembles a siren circling the observer, with a distinct Doppler effect; it is much louder and higher pitched than the call of *E. ovalis.*

Natural History: A terrestrial, forest frog. Field notes (JCM) report a small chorus of these frogs in dense secondary forest with a closed canopy; males called from small water-filled stump holes, 0.5 to 1.0 m in diameter, with dead leaves covering the bottom making them extremely difficult to locate. Spawning occurs throughout the first 3 months of the rainy season; eggs float and are nonadhesive; eggs hatch

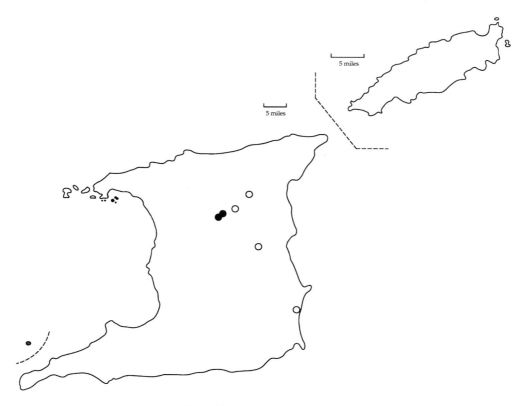

Map 30. *Elachistocleis surinamensis*

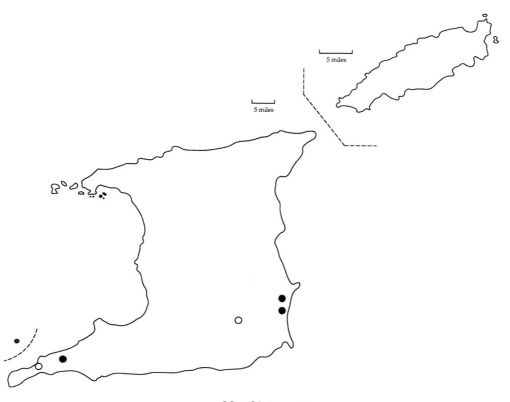

Map 31. *Pipa pipa*

in 48 hours, and metamorphosis occurs at about 8 weeks (Kenny, 1969).

Material: FMNH 251230 about 1 mile west of Cumuto on Tunapuna Road; 251231 on road to Arena Dam, west of Cumuto.

Order Anura
Family Pipidae: Tongueless Frogs

Living pipids are distributed in sub-Saharan Africa and the Neotropics. The family is ancient, with fossil representatives in the lower Cretaceous; the distribution pattern of living and fossil forms points to a Gondwanaland origin (Estes, 1975). A single, highly aquatic, and very distinctive species occurs on Trinidad. The genus *Pipa* is composed of seven species; *Pipa pipa* occurs on Trinidad and has an unsual reproductive mode with the eggs embedded in the dorsal skin of the female; *P. pipa* eggs hatch from their mother's skin into miniature froglets. DeVerteuil (1858) described the unusual method of reproduction in this frog.

The pipa is a large batrachin, very remarkable on account of its singular form, but more, and chiefly so from its mode of generation. The female carries on its back the eggs or semina which the male has placed there; a sort of inflammation is the consequence of such application, and each egg becomes as imprisoned in a cell, which gradually increases in size, so as to accommodate the growth of the semen. When hatched, the young escape from the cells, the back of the mother remaining for some time as if honey-combed.

Pipa pipa (Linnaeus)

Map 31. Plate 52.

Rana pipa Linnaeus, 1758:210. Type locality: Suriname. *Pipa americana:* Court, 1858:441. *Pipa pipa:* Barbour, 1923:3.

Distribution: *P. pipa* has an Amazonian distribution, and occurs at scattered localities in southern and eastern Trinidad. Localities reported in the literature include: Nariva Swamp, Rio Claro, Mayaro, and Cedros (Kenny, 1969). Museum specimens add Plaisance-Mayaro, and a small stream that crosses the Southern Main Road at Bridge 1/71.

Description: 200 mm SVL. Head and body extremely depressed, so much so that it will readily distinguish this species from all others in the area. Snout pointed from above and protruding in profile; eyes minute; tympanum hidden; mouth wide, with small flap at angle of jaw. Dorsal and ventral skin studded with small, evenly distributed tubercles, with larger tubercles scattered in between smaller ones. Lateral line organs present on dorsum. Each finger tipped with four small projections, each subdivided into two or three smaller projections. Fingers lack webbing, toes heavily webbed. Dorsum dark brown, venter cream to tan, with an occasional dark midventral line and scattered dark spots. The distinctive shape of this animal will immediately identify it.

Voice: The call of this species is a subtle clicking sound made underwater.

Natural History: An aquatic frog in ponds, slow moving streams, marshes, and swamp forests. Field notes (JCM) describe it in isolated pools in a streambed during the dry season (April) in the southwest peninsula, where the water is heavily shaded by trees and very turbid; a dead specimen chewed upon by a predator or scavenger was found approximately 10 m from the water; the pools contained large fish populations, including *Cichlasoma* and *Erythrinus*. DeVerteuil (1858) described reproduction (see quote in the family description); Rabb and Rabb (1960; 1963), and Rabb and Snedigar (1960) have more scientific descriptions of reproduction.

Material: Trinidad—FMNH 49601–2 Plaisance, Mayaro; 218773 Southern Main Road at Bridge B1/71.

Order Anura
Family Pseudidae: Pseudid Frogs

Pseudid frogs are distributed in the tropical lowlands of South America east of the Andes. They are best known for their aquatic habits and giant tadpoles which may reach 25 cm in length. Muscular legs, long digits with an extra phalange bone, and heavily webbed feet distinguish them from other frogs. There are two genera with at least four species; *Pseudis paradoxa caribensis* occurs on Trinidad. DeVerteuil (1858) commented on *Pseudis*

Of real frogs I know but one, the paradoxal or fish-frog, so remarkable for the size of the tadpole, which is several inches long, and has some resemblance to the cascaradura; its body which is smooth and not scaly—exhibiting oblique bands exactly like those of that fish. It still retains the tail sometime after the four limbs have grown, which gives it the grotesque appearence of a fish provided with a toad's feet; hence the erroneous impression, among the vulgar, that the cascaradura is ultimately metamorphosed into a toad.

Pseudis paradoxa caribensis Gallardo

Map 32. Plates 53, 54.

Pseudis merianea: Court, 1858:441. *Pseudis paradoxus:* Parker, 1933:10. *Pseudis paradoxus caribensis* Gallardo, 1961:116. Type locality: "Mayaro Bay, Trinidad, B.W.I." *Pseudis paradoxa caribensis:* La Marca, 1992:75.

Common Names: "Frog-fish, paradoxal frog" (DeVerteuil, 1858).

Distribution: *P. paradoxa* has an Amazonian distribution. *P. p. caribensis* is an Orinoco Basin-Trinidad taxon. Literature records for Trinidad include: St. Joseph, in Mayaro Ward (Ditmars and Bridges, 1935); ponds a few miles southeast of the Arima Valley (Beebe, 1952). Bamboo Grove, Nariva, Cedros, Icacos throughout the lower elevations of the southern and western portions of the island; its occurrence in the Caroni drainage is the result of escaped captives; and, it is present on the north side of Beetham highway on reclaimed lands with saline water (Kenny, 1969,

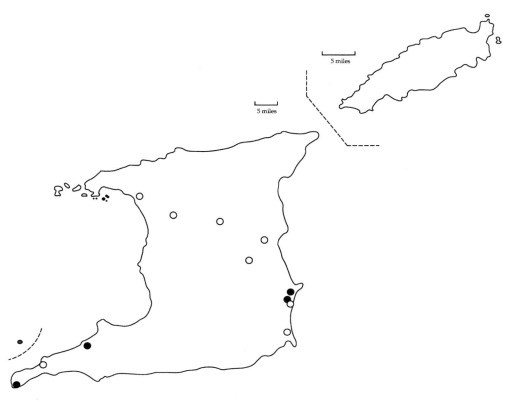

Map 32. *Pseudis paradoxa caribensis*

1971). Museum material documents the following Trinidad locations: Arena Dam; Biche; Cedros; Arepero Dam, Point Fortin; Icacos Rd. at the 78 milepost; Manzanilla Bay; Plaisance, Mayaro; St. Bernard's Estate, Mayaro Bay.

Description: Males 65 mm, females 73 mm SVL. Snout rounded in dorsal view and truncated in profile; canthus flattened and indistinct; eye diameter equal to the eye-nostril distance; tympanum about three-fourths eye diameter. Dorsal skin smooth with a few glands on the flanks; this will separate it from *Rana palmipes,* which has dorsolateral folds; ventral skin smooth. Fingers long, tips are slightly expanded; first finger opposable to others and longer than second; fingers lack webbing; toes are heavily webbed. Dorsal skin brown and green with mottled pattern; canthal streak and tympanic streak brown. Concealed surfaces of the thighs mottled with yellow, two "eyespots" or contrasting stripes of yellow and brown-black on the proximal ends of thighs below cloaca; this pattern will distinguish this frog from all other Trinidad and Tobago frogs, including *Rana palmipes* with which it might easily be confused. The ventral surface of thighs and tibia mottled.

Voice: "A single sharp croak, repeated at irregular intervals, made both by night and day throughout the rainy season. Calls in chorus several times during any 24 hour period at commencement of spawning season" (Kenny, 1969). This species calls from the water and the resulting sound is often highly magnified.

Natural History: An aquatic, savanna frog; inhabiting edges of ponds, swamps, reservoirs and rice fields, including brackish water (Kenny, 1969; Hoogmoed and Gorzula, 1979). Adults highly aquatic, rarely leave the water; choruses in June and July from flooded areas near Manzanilla Bay and along the Princess Margaret Highway; males call from the surface of the water, frequently anchored to vegetation with their opposable digits clasping stems; diurnal vocalization does occur, but they are extremely wary; after sunset they are much easier to approach (field notes, JCM). Kenny (1969) suggested a single, explosive spawning in June or July in Trinidad, while Hoogmoed and Gorzula (1979) found reproduction occurs throughout most of the rainy season on the mainland. Kenny's (1969) data suggested that metamorphosis occurs at 6 months of age. Emerson (1988) found tadpoles reach 220.5 mm (Kenny reports 230 mm tadpoles), and suggested the giant larva may result from prolonged exposure to prolactin; she proposed sexual maturity occurs at about 56 mm SVL.

Material: Trinidad—CM 33787 Mayaro. FMNH 49705–6 Plaisance, Mayaro; Icacos Rd. at the 78 milepost. USNM 145426 Point Fortin, Arepero Dam.

Order Anura
Family Ranidae: True Frogs

True frogs are widespread, occurring on most tropical and temperate landmasses, except for Greenland, Australia, New Guinea, and New Zealand. Most ranids are small, less than 50 mm, but some of the largest frogs, including the African

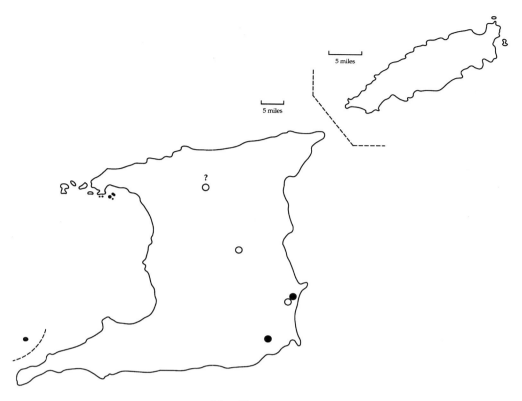

Map 33. *Rana palmipes*

goliath frog, *Conraua goliath,* belong to the family. Again, this is a diverse group in structure and life history and very difficult to characterize on the basis of external features. Africa was probably the center of origin for the family, and the family's radiation presumably occurred after Africa and South America broke apart in the Cretaceous. A group with three species has invaded South America from the north; one species, *Rana palmipes,* occurs on Trinidad and it is known from relatively few specimens. Lutz (1927) wrote about this frog's habits

> It is easily recognized by its size, the green back and the large webs of the feet. It could only be confounded with some species of *Pseudis* but those are smaller . . . its rather characteristic croak is often heard [in Venezuela]. This frog is aquatic but may be found even in day time on the margins of the rivulets and ditches with running water where also the tadpoles are found. Those near to the metamorphosis are quite large.

Rana palmipes Spix

Map 33. Plate 55.

Rana palmipes Spix, 1824a:5. Type locality: "Amazonenfluss." (= Amazon River, Brazil).

Distribution: *R. palmipes* has an Amazonian distribution, occurring in the lowlands of northern South America east of the Andes (Hillis and de Sa, 1988). It is known from rela-

tively few Trinidad specimens. All the specimens are from the Central Range and the southeast corner of the island. Published Trinidad localities include: Arima Valley (Beebe, 1952); Mayaro and Tamana Caves (Kenny, 1969; 1979). Museum material documents the following localities: Plaisance, Mayaro, and Guayaguayare Road south of Rio Claro. Krintler (1982) reports this species from Tobago; Hardy (1984b) questioned the record and noted the absence of Tobago specimens.

Description: Males 126 mm, females 101 mm SVL. The largest Trinidad specimen we have examined was 91 mm SVL. Snout rounded in dorsal and lateral views; canthus a distinct ridge; eye diameter about equal to eye-nostril distance; tympanum equal to or larger than the eye diameter. Dorsal skin studded with small tubercles, each with a white tip; dorsolateral fold on each side from the posterior of eye to cloaca; two large glands between tympanum and shoulder; ventral skin granular. Fingers free of webbing, toes heavily webbed. Dorsum olive green, with the head a slightly brighter green; forearms and concealed surfaces of thighs and groin marbled with black and yellow; venter cream or white. *Pseudis paradoxus* similar in size and color, but has eye spots or stripes on the concealed surface of the thighs, and opposable thumbs. Distinguished from *Leptodactylus* by the extensive webbing between the toes; leptodactylids have reduced to minimal webbing on their feet.

Voice: The call is described by Duellman (1978) as a " series of guttural chuckling sounds produced in the water."

Natural History: A forest frog, poorly known on Trinidad. Field notes (JCM) report this frog active at night on a road running through secondary forest. In southern Venezuela, Hoogmoed and Gorzula (1979) encountered it in pools, but more frequently found it in gallery forests. In Ecuador, Duellman (1978) found it to be nocturnal, in jungle clearings water, and noted gravid females occur throughout the year. Egg masses are laid in stagnant or slow moving water.

Material: Trinidad—CM 5495–6 Guayaguayare, Rio Claro, Nariva Co. FMNH 49773 Plaisance, Mayaro.

Order Gymnophiona

Caecilians are unusual, poorly known, legless amphibians that inhabit the soils, leaf litter, and aquatic environs of the tropics. They are seldom encountered, even in areas where they are abundant. The eyes have degenerated into small dark spots under the skin, there are no vestiages of limbs, and while they may have dermal scales buried in their skin, they lack the epidermal scales of reptiles. Eggs are fertilized internally, and may be deposited in a nest or retained in the female's body; and the young may be hatched or born in a larval form, or they may undergo direct development and look like miniature adults at hatching or birth.

Order Gymnophiona
Family Typhlonectidae: Aquatic Caecilians

These are aquatic, worm-like amphibians that lack a tail. Species in this family are both oviparous and viviparous. The family contains four genera and about 20 species, and is distributed in cis-Andean South America. One individual specimen of the genus *Typhlonectes* has been reported from Trinidad; the specimen was apparently destroyed along with the Dresden Museum during WW II, and confirmation of this family on Trinidad awaits additional specimens. A discussion is included here because it is possible that representatives of this family will eventually be rediscovered on the island. The aquatic caecilian *Potomotyphlus kaupii*

(Typhlonectidae) also occurs in the Orinoco drainage and thus may show up as a waif, or an established population in the Trinidad area.

Typhlonectes sp.

Plate 56.

Typhlonectes compressicauda natans: Dunn, 1942:535. *Typhlonectes natans:* Cochran, 1961:15.

Comment: Dunn (1942) listed the sole Trinidad specimen as "Dresden 639" but does not give any measurements, thus he may not have seen the specimen. Several other authors (Cochran, 1961; Gorham, 1962; Roze and Solano, 1963) have reported this caecilian from Trinidad but their reports are apparently all based upon Dunn's citation. Taylor (1968) does not list any specimens of *Typhlonectes,* or any other caecilian from Trinidad. The Dresden specimen was apparently destroyed during the Second World War, on 13 February 1945, by Allied bombing (Obst, 1977). *Typhlonectes* is aquatic and is present in the Orinoco drainage. There is no reason to suspect that it could not be on Trinidad, existing in one of the coastal freshwater swamps, or rivers. However, there are no specimens to document an extant population.

Description: Total length may be 615 mm. A black, legless, worm-like amphibian with a recessed mouth. It lacks the dermal scales and secondary grooves found in many caecilians. Primary grooves number 86–105 and are poorly developed. Eyes are visible; there are two rows of teeth in the lower jaw; no tail; and anal disk well developed, white in color and 6–7 mm in diameter. Tentacle in a horseshoe-shaped groove on the side of the head, very close to the posterior edge of the nostril. Body laterally compressed with a dorsal keel and fin on the posterior of the body.

Natural History: Little is known about this aquatic caecilian's habits. Dunn (1942) cited an earlier paper reporting a litter of four young born on 16 January. The young measured 190–200 mm, and the sheet-like gills are resorbed before birth.

Material: None

Plate 1. The Arima Valley of Trinidad's Northern Range is inhabited by 75 (64%) of the species of amphibians and reptiles found on the island. The mosaic of forest and agriculture supports a diverse and relatively well-known herpetofauna. This valley is inhabited by 16 species of frogs, 1 species of crocodilian, 4 species of turtles, 2 species of amphisbaenids, 17 species of lizards, and 35 species of snakes.

Plate 2. The St. Patrick's Estate area of the Arima Valley is wet and lush with old growth secondary forest and transitional forest between deciduous seasonal and lower montane rainforest. *Mannophryne trinitatis, Gonatodes humeralis,* and *Erythrolamprus a. aesculapii* are known to occur in this area.

Plate 3. The cocal, along Manzanilla and Cocos Bays on Trinidad's east coast, is dominated by coconut palms. The trees and fallen palm fronds cover a sandy soil. The area supports a herpetofauna containing the following species: *Bufo marinus, Phrynohyas venulosa, Physalaemus pustulosus, Elachistocleis ovalis, Amphisbaena f. fuliginosa, Gonatodes vittatus vittatus, Thecadactylus rapicauda, Mabuya bistriata, Ameiva ameiva, Cnemidophorus lemniscatus, Oxybelis aeneus, Pseudoboa neuwiedii,* and *Tantilla melanocephala.*

Plate 4. A small stream near Charlotteville, Tobago. Species inhabiting this area include *Hyalinobatrachium orientale tobagoensis, Mannophryne olmonae, Gonatodes ocellatus,* and *Tupinambis teguixin.*

Plate 5. *Bufo beebei.* Note the small, angular head. Near Cumuto in the Northern Basin, Trinidad.

Plate 6. *Bufo marinus.* Locally called the crapaud, this ubiquitous bufonid has large parotoid glands and a more rounded head than the other toad species in the area. Simla, the Arima Valley, Trinidad.

Plate 7. *Bufo marinus.* Metamorph. Charlotteville, Tobago.

Plate 8. *Hyalinobatrachium orientale tobagoensis.* A male collected along a stream crossing Roxborough-Parlatuvier Road about 1 kilometer south of Northside Road, Tobago.

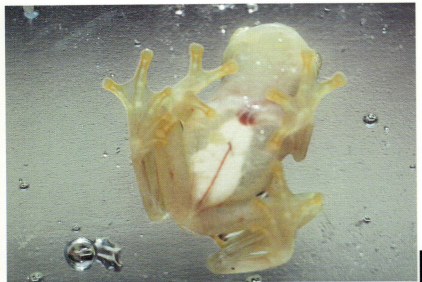

Plate 9. *Hyalinobatrachium orientale tobagoensis.* The ventral view explains why this frog and its relatives are called glass frogs. Specimen from a stream off Roxborough-Parlatuvier Road, about 1 kilometer south of Bloody Bay Road, Tobago.

Plate 10. *Mannophryne olmonae.* A female from Charlotteville, Tobago. Note the yellow throat and distinctive black collar. Males have a gray-black throat.

Plate 11. *Mannophryne trinitatis.* Calling males turn jet black. The color quickly changes to brown if they are disturbed. From a trail at the Asa Wright Nature Centre, Arima Valley, Trinidad.

Plate 12. *Mannophryne trinitatis.* A male transporting tadpoles on its back. From a trail at the Asa Wright Nature Centre, Arima Valley, Trinidad.

Plate 13. *Flectonotus fitzgeraldi.* A female dwarf marsupial frog with three eggs in its dorsal pouch. From the road to Arena Dam, just west of Cumuto, Trinidad.

Plate 14. *Hyla boans.* Trinidad's largest tree frog, red-brown color. Arima Valley.

Plate 15. *Hyla boans.* Trinidad's largest tree frog, gray-green color. Arima Valley.

Plate 16. *Hyla crepitans.* Newly metamorphosed individuals do not resemble adults. Simla, Arima Valley, Trinidad.

Plate 17. *Hyla crepitans.* Color change from white to brown. An adult from the upper Guanapo Valley, Trinidad. See Plate 18.

Plate 18. *Hyla crepitans.* Color change from white to brown. An adult from the upper Guanapo Valley, Trinidad.

Plate 19. *Hyla geographica.* Metamorphosing individuals and young have few external features or colors in common with the adults. Guanapo River, Trinidad. William B. Montgomery.

Plate 20. *Hyla geographica.* An adult from about 10 km south of Rio Claro, Trinidad. The triangular calcar on the heel is one characteristic that will help separate it from other Trinidad and Tobago tree frogs.

Plate 21. *Hyla microcephala misera.* An abundant tree frog in Trinidad's roadside ditches and flooded fields.

Plate 22. *Hyla minuscula.* This frog is known from a few localities in Trinidad's southwestern peninsula. The enamel side stripe, readily seen in calling males, will distinguish it from other small yellow hylids. From a roadside pool along Coco Trace Extension east of Bonasse, Trinidad.

Plate 23. *Hyla minuta.* This species occurs on both Trinidad and Tobago. Calling males are bright yellow; other individuals are yellow-brown. Simla, Arima Valley, Trinidad.

Plate 24. *Hyla microcephala misera* (left); *Hyla minuscula* (center); *Hyla minuta* (right). Adults of three small yellow hylid frogs that may be easily confused with each other. All three species occur together at Bowen Trace and Coco Trace Extension in southwestern Trinidad.

Plate 25. *Hyla punctata.* A male from the Rio Claro area, Trinidad. A lowland, savanna-dwelling frog with a subtle call.

Plate 26. *Hyla punctata.* Adults change color from day to night; daytime coloration is an apple-green (Plate 25). They turn dark red at night.

Plate 27. *Phrynohyas venulosa.* A large tree frog with very glandular skin. It occurs on both islands. This animal is from a flooded pasture near Bloody Bay, Tobago.

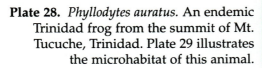

Plate 28. *Phyllodytes auratus.* An endemic Trinidad frog from the summit of Mt. Tucuche, Trinidad. Plate 29 illustrates the microhabitat of this animal.

Plate 30. *Phyllomedusa trinitatis.* Amplexus. Simla, Arima Valley, Trinidad.

Plate 29. The giant bromeliad *Glomeropitcairnia erectiflora* on the summit of Mt. Tucuche, Trinidad, is the microhabitat for *Phyllodytes auratus*.

Plate 31. *Phyllomedusa trinitatis.* Oviposition. Simla, Arima Valley, Trinidad. Melvin R. Bruns.

Plate 32. *Phyllomedusa trinitatis.* Newly metamorphosed individual. Note the color difference between these and the adults. Simla, Arima Valley, Trinidad. Ron Humbert.

Plate 33. *Scinax rubra.* Calling male. Coco Trace Extension, east of Bonasse, Trinidad.

Plate 34. *Scinax rubra.* Simla, Arima Valley, Trinidad.

Plate 35. *Sphaenorhynchus lacteus.* Calling male, in a swamp off Valencia Road, near the Turure River, Trinidad.

Plate 36. *Sphaenorhynchus lacteus.* About 8 km south of Rio Claro, Trinidad. Michael Dloogatch.

Plate 37. *Adenomera hylaedactyla.* Austin South Branch Road, in the southwestern peninsula of Trinidad.

Plate 38. *Eleutherodactylus charlottevillensis.* An adult and juvenile from near Charlotteville, Tobago.

Plate 39. *Eleutherodactylus urichi.* Simla, Arima Valley, Trinidad.

Plate 40. *Leptodactylus bolivianus.* Near Icacos, Trinidad. V. M. St. J. Read.

Plate 41. *Leptodactylus fuscus.* Northern Basin, near Waller Field, at the eastern end of Churchill-Roosevelt Highway, Trinidad.

Plate 42. *Leptodactylus knudseni.* Known from a single specimen on Trinidad, it is relatively well known from mainland populations. William W. Lamar.

Plate 43. *Leptodactylus macrosternum.* From the 77.5 mile marker on Icacos Road (Southern Main Road) in south-western Trinidad.

Plate 44. *Leptodactylus nesiotus.* Type specimen from Icacos Swamp, Trinidad. V. M. St. J. Read.

Plate 45. *Leptodactylus validus.*
The Guanapo Valley, Trinidad.

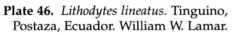

Plate 46. *Lithodytes lineatus.* Tinguino,
Postaza, Ecuador. William W. Lamar.

Plate 47. *Physalaemus pustulosus.*
Near Arima, Trinidad.

Plate 48. *Physalaemus pustulosus.* Amplexus.
Simla, Arima Valley, Trinidad.

Plate 49. *Physalaemus pustulosus.*
Foam nest. Near Arima, Trinidad.

Plate 50. *Elachistocleis ovalis.*
Manzanilla-Cocos Bay
cocal, Trinidad.

Plate 51. *Elachistocleis surinamensis.*
Female from the road to Arena
Dam, west of Cumuto, Trinidad.

Plate 52. *Pipa pipa.* A highly specialized
aquatic anuran from the stream flowing
under Bridge 1/71 on the Southern
Main Road, Trinidad.

Plate 53. *Pseudis paradoxa caribensis.* From the road to Arena Dam, west of Cumuto, Trinidad.

Plate 54. *Pseudis paradoxa caribensis.* Posterior view, showing eyespot markings. Melvin R. Bruns.

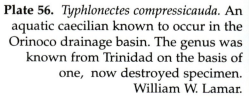

Plate 55. *Rana palmipes.* From Guayaguayare Road, near the junction with the Lizard River in southeastern Trinidad.

Plate 56. *Typhlonectes compressicauda.* An aquatic caecilian known to occur in the Orinoco drainage basin. The genus was known from Trinidad on the basis of one, now destroyed specimen. William W. Lamar.

Plate 57. *Chelus fimbriatus.* A hatchling from a captive reproduction. Ron Humbert.

Plate 58. *Chelus fimbriatus.* An adult from Nariva Swamp. William B. Montgomery.

Plate 59. *Phrynops gibbus.* V. M. St. J. Read.

Plate 60. *Phrynops gibbus.*
Juvenile from Meta, Colombia.
William W. Lamar.

Plate 61. *Caretta caretta.*
G. R. Zug. USNM.

Plate 62. *Chelonia mydas.*
Florida.

Plate 63. *Eretmochelys imbricata
imbricata.* R. Barbour.

Plate 64. *Lepidochelys olivacea.*
David Owens.

Plate 65. *Dermochelys coriacea.* A female
nesting on Matura Beach, east coast of
Trinidad. Katherine F. Murphy.

Plate 66. *Dermochelys coriacea.*
A recently emerged hatchling
on its way to the sea. Matura
Beach, Trinidad. Steve Barten.

Plate 67. *Dermochelys coriacea.* Profile. Note
characteristic pink blotch on dorsum of head.

Plate 68. *Rhinoclemmys punctularia punctularia.* From a pond off Guayaguayare Road about 8 kilometers south of Rio Claro, Trinidad.

Plate 69. *Kinosternon scorpioides scorpioides.* Near the Erin River, vicinity of Los Bajos, Trinidad.

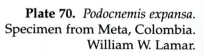

Plate 70. *Podocnemis expansa.* Specimen from Meta, Colombia. William W. Lamar.

Plate 71. *Podocnemis unifilis.* A juvenile from Meta, Colombia. William W. Lamar.

Plate 72. *Geochelone carbonaria.* Copulating. Emperor Valley Zoo, Trinidad. Melvin R. Bruns.

Plate 73. *Geochelone denticulata.* A captive living at Simla, Arima Valley, Trinidad.

Plate 74. *Caiman crocodilus crocodilus.* Hatchling from Hollis Reservoir, Trinidad. Ron Humbert.

Plate 75. *Caiman crocodilus crocodilus.* Female on a nest at Hollis Reservoir, Trinidad. Melvin R. Bruns.

Plate 76. *Crocodylus acutus.* Specimen from Tuxtla, Gutierrez, Mexico. William W. Lamar.

Plate 77. *Crocodylus intermedius.*
Juvenile from Río Ele, Casanare,
Colombia. William W. Lamar.

Plate 78. *Amphisbaena alba.*
A captive Trinidad specimen.

Plate 79. *Amphisbaena fuliginosa
fuliginosa.* From the cocal,
Manzanilla Bay, Trinidad.

Plate 80. *Gonatodes albogularis.* Specimen from Limón, Costa Rica. William W. Lamar.

Plate 81. *Gonatodes ceciliae.* A male from Simla, Arima Valley, Trinidad.

Plate 82. *Gonatodes humeralis.* A male from Simla, Arima Valley, Trinidad.

Plate 83. *Gonatodes ocellatus.* A male from near Charlotteville, Tobago.

Plate 84. *Gonatodes vittatus vittatus.* A male from Simla, Arima Valley, Trinidad.

Plate 85. *Gonatodes vittatus vittatus.* A female from Simla, Arima Valley, Trinidad.

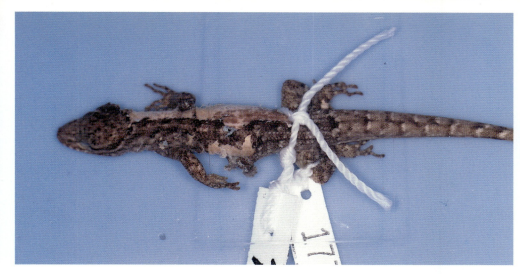

Plate 86. *Gymnodactylus geckoides.* The only Trinidad specimen known. Collected by E. H. Taylor in 1962.

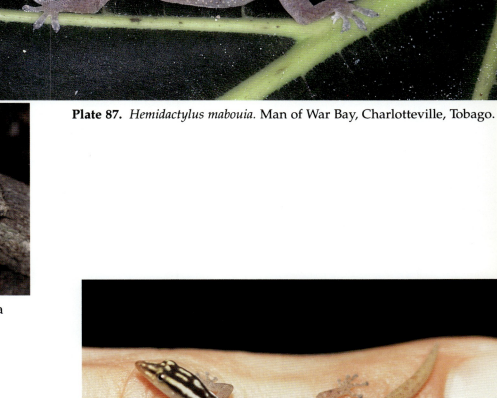

Plate 87. *Hemidactylus mabouia.* Man of War Bay, Charlotteville, Tobago.

Plate 88. *Hemidactylus palaichthus.* From a derelict building on Little Tobago Island.

Plate 89. *Sphaerodactylus molei.* A male from Simla, Arima Valley, showing breeding coloration. William B. Montgomery.

Plate 90. *Sphaerodactylus molei.*
A female from the Arima Valley.

Plate 91. *Thecadactylus rapicauda.*
Cryptic coloration. Charlotteville,
Tobago.

Plate 92. *Thecadactylus rapicauda.* Tail
breaking. Simla, Arima Valley, Trinidad.

Plate 93. *Bachia heteropa trinitatis.*
Simla, Arima Valley, Trinidad.

Plate 94. *Gymnophthalmus underwoodi.*
Simla, Arima Valley, Trinidad.

Plate 95. *Proctoporus shrevei.* A juvenile
from the Arima Valley, Trinidad.

Plate 96. *Proctoporus shrevei.* An adult male
from Aripo. Ocelli visible. BM specimen.

Plate 97. *Anolis aeneus.* From the
grounds of the Forestry Division
offices on Long Circle Road.

Plate 98. *Anolis chrysolepis planiceps.*
From Bowen Trace, just east of Bonasse
in Trinidad's southwestern peninsula.

Plate 99. *Anolis extremus.* George Gorman.

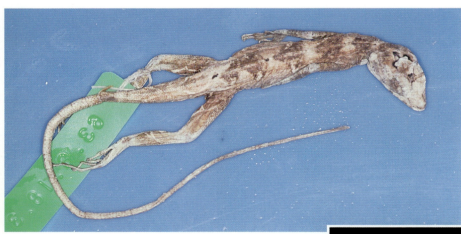

Plate 100. *Anolis* cf. *lemurinus.*
BM specimen.

Plate 101. *Anolis richardii.*
Charlotteville, Tobago.

Plate 102. *Anolis trinitatis.* George Gorman.

Plate 104. *Iguana iguana.* A young animal from the Arima River, Trinidad.

Plate 103. *Iguana iguana.* A young male from near Icacos, southwestern Trinidad.

Plate 105. *Polychrus marmoratus.* Simla, Arima Valley, Trinidad.

Plate 106. *Tropidurus plica.*
Simla, Arima Valley, Trinidad.

Plate 107. *Tropidurus plica.* A juvenile on a lichen-covered tree trunk. Simla, Arima Valley, Trinidad.

Plate 108. *Mabuya bistriata.*
Simla, Arima Valley, Trinidad.

Plate 109. *Ameiva ameiva.*
Simla, Arima Valley,
Trinidad.

Plate 110. *Cnemidophorus lemniscatus.* From the cocal, Manzanilla Bay, Trinidad.

Plate 111. *Kentropyx striatus.* Nariva Swamp, Trinidad. V. M. St. J. Read.

Plate 112. *Tupinambis teguixin.* A captive Trinidad specimen. Melvin R. Bruns.

Plate 113. *Boa constrictor constrictor.*
Arima Valley, Trinidad.

Plate 114. *Boa constrictor constrictor.*
Near Kings Bay, Tobago.

Plate 115. *Corallus hortulanus
cookii.* Arima Valley, Trinidad.
Melvin R. Bruns.

Plate 116. *Epicrates cenchria maurus.* Juvenile from Simla, Arima Valley, Trinidad.

Plate 117. *Epicrates cenchria maurus.* Juvenile from Simla, Arima Valley, Trinidad.

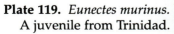

Plate 118. *Epicrates cenchria maurus.* An adult from Trinidad. © J. Ellen Marsden.

Plate 119. *Eunectes murinus.* A juvenile from Trinidad.

Plate 120. *Atractus trilineatus.* Arima Valley, Trinidad.

Plate 121. *Chironius carinatus.* Arima Valley, Trinidad.

Plate 122. *Chironius carinatus.* Note kinked body posture that serves a cryptic function when the snake is on the forest floor in leaves and twigs. Arima Valley, Trinidad.

Plate 123. *Clelia clelia clelia.* Juvenile coloration. Arima Valley, Trinidad. William B. Montgomery.

Plate 124. *Clelia clelia clelia.* Adult from Guatemala. William W. Lamar.

Plate 125. *Dipsas variegata trinitatis.* Arima Valley, Trinidad.

Plate 126. *Drymarchon corais corais.* A male, 1500 mm in total length. From the vicinity of Hato el Frio, Apure, Venezuela. William W. Lamar.

Plate 127. *Erythrolamprus aesculapii aesculapii.* Specimen from Suriname. William W. Lamar.

Plate 128. *Erythrolamprus bizona.* Female, 700 mm total length. Lomalinda, Meta, Colombia. William W. Lamar.

Plate 129. *Helicops angulatus.* An adult from a roadside ditch along the east end of Churchill-Roosevelt Highway, Trinidad.

Plate 130. *Helicops angulatus.* A juvenile from a pasture pond near St. Joseph, Mayaro, Trinidad. Steve Barten.

Plate 131. *Hydrops triangularis neglectus.* Sangre Grande, Trinidad. William B. Montgomery.

Plate 132. *Imantodes cenchoa cenchoa.* Arima Valley, Trinidad.

Plate 133. *Imantodes cenchoa cenchoa.* Arima Valley, Trinidad.

Plate 134. *Leptodeira annulata ashmeadi.* Near Charlotteville, Tobago.

Plate 135. *Leptophis ahaetulla coeruleodorsus.* Arima Valley, Trinidad.

Plate 136. *Leptophis ahaetulla coeruleodorsus.* Arima Valley, Trinidad.

Plate 137. *Liophis cobella cobella.* Nariva Swamp, Trinidad. V. M. St. J. Read.

Plate 138. *Liophis melanotus nesos.* An adult from near Charlotteville, Tobago.

Plate 139. *Liophis reginae* ssp. Gilpin Trail, Tobago. UFMNH specimen.

Plate 140. *Liophis reginae zweifeli.* Arima Valley, Trinidad.

Plate 142. *Mastigodryas boddaerti boddaerti.* A juvenile from Simla, Arima Valley, Trinidad.

Plate 141. *Liophis reginae zweifeli.* Note flattened neck in defense display. Arima Valley, Trinidad.

Plate 143. *Mastigodryas boddaerti boddaerti.* An adult from the Arima Valley. William B. Montgomery.

Plate 144. *Mastigodryas boddaerti dunni.* An adult from Cambelton, Tobago.

Plate 145. *Ninia atrata.* Arima Valley, Trinidad.

Plate 146. *Oxybelis aeneus.* Simla, Arima Valley, Trinidad.

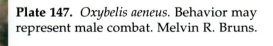

Plate 147. *Oxybelis aeneus.* Behavior may represent male combat. Melvin R. Bruns.

Plate 148. *Oxyrhopus petola petola.* Piarco Airport, Trinidad.

Plate 149. *Oxyrhopus petola petola.* Black morph. Upper Guanapo Valley.

Plate 150. *Pseudoboa neuwiedii.* Siparia, Trinidad.

Plate 151. *Pseudoboa neuwiedii.* Arima Valley, Trinidad.

Plate 152. *Pseustes poecilonotus polylepis.* Juvenile. Arima Valley, Trinidad. William B. Montgomery.

Plate 153. *Pseustes poecilonotus polylepis.* Defensive posture. An adult from Simla, Arima Valley, Trinidad.

Plate 154. *Pseustes sulphureus sulphureus.* Waller Field, Trinidad. William B. Montgomery.

Plate 155. *Sibon nebulata nebulata.* Arima Valley, Trinidad.

Plate 156. *Siphlophis cervinus.* Specimen from La Florida, Loreto, Peru. William W. Lamar.

Plate 157. *Spilotes pullatus pullatus.* Total length 2311 mm. This animal had been killed by blows from a machete. From the Arima Valley, Trinidad, about 4 km north of the Asa Wright Nature Centre.

Plate 158. *Spilotes pullatus pullatus.* Defense display. Sangre Grande, Trinidad. William B. Montgomery.

Plate 159. *Tantilla melanocephala.* Arima Valley, Trinidad. V. M. St. J. Read.

Plate 160. *Thamnodynastes* sp. Road kill, from southwestern Trinidad.

Plate 161. *Tripanurgos compressus.* Hatchling from the 4.0 milepost on Valencia Road, Trinidad.

Plate 162. *Tripanurgos compressus.*
Simla, Arima Valley, Trinidad.

Plate 163. *Micrurus circinalis.* From the
Arima Valley, about 3.2 km north of Simla.

Plate 164. *Micrurus lemniscatus diutius.*
From the lower Arima Valley, at about
the 1.5 milepost on the Arima-
Blanchesseuse Road.

Plate 165. *Leptotyphlops albifrons.*
Simla, Arima Valley Trinidad.

Plate 166. *Typhlops brongersmianus.* From near Formosa, Argentina. James R. Dixon.

Plate 167. *Typhlops trinitatus.* From near the 6.4 milepost off Roxborough-Parlatuvier Road, Tobago.

Plate 168. *Bothrops asper.* From Valencia Road about 3.2 km east of its junction with Cumaca Road.

Plate 169. *Bothrops asper.* Near the summit of Mt. Tucuche.

Plate 170. *Lachesis muta muta.* A juvenile. Sangre Grande, Trinidad. William B. Montgomery.

Plate 171. *Lachesis muta muta.* An adult. Sangre Grande, Trinidad. William B. Montgomery.

Plate 172. *Lachesis muta muta.* Habitat, about 7.75 miles north of Arima on the Arima-Blanchesseuse Road, Trinidad. William B. Montgomery.

PART 4

Reptilia Species Accounts

Class Reptilia

Living orders of reptiles are a collection of diverse animals, and while species within the major groups share a common ancestor, the relationships between some of these groups are not as clear. Reptiles are best known for their scale-covered skin that retards water loss in terrestrial environments, but more importantly they have evolved the amniotic egg, an egg that can be placed on land or carried within the female's body, an egg that has allowed reptiles to escape the reproductive dependence on water seen in the amphibians. All reptiles have internal fertilization; and while most show no postnatal care, some do. Reptile growth appears dependent on shedding the outer layer of epidermal tissue, and growth continues throughout life. Humans often show a loathing for these animals, a loathing that is quite undeserved. The cold blooded nature of reptiles is a misunderstanding. Most of these animals have active body temperatures that approach those in mammals; the heat source however is external, since they usually do not use food as a source of heat energy. Reptiles (and amphibians) should not be considered primitive life forms, but the results of different evolutionary pathways. Trinidad and Tobago have 93 species and subspecies of reptiles in 22 families.

Order Chelonia

Turtles and tortoises are highly distinctive reptiles with a shell of dermal bone fused to the vertebrae and ribs in the carapace or upper shell; the plastron, or lower shell is fused to the clavicle and sternum, elements of the pectoral girdle; the carapace and plastron are joined by a bridge. These are long-lived, egg-laying vertebrates that lack teeth. The shell is often attributed as the reason for turtles' success, but are turtles successful? There are relatively few species, only about 260 in 13 families, but within these relatively few species are a plethora of adaptations to diverse lifestyles and habitats. Turtles are the end of an early evolutionary pathway, the anapsids, and living species show specializations to varied environments. A very large number of turtle species are currently considered endangered, usually as a result of human alteration of the environment. Even if turtles were not being overexploited by man, they appear to be a group of reptiles with a greatly reduced number of species after a 200 million year history. However, humans have accelerated the extinction rate with habitat destruction and predation, and the fate of many turtles seems near at hand. Sadly, an IUCN report (1989) documented 41% of the world's turtle species as being in trouble. Thirteen species in seven families are suspected to inhabit Trinidad and Tobago. Two species in one family, Pelomedusidae, may visit the area only as waifs washed down the Orinoco.

Order Chelonia
Family Chelidae: The Austro-American Side-necked Turtles

Living species in this family are restricted to South America east of the Andes, Australia, and New Guinea. These freshwater turtles have a neck that is incompletely retractile and thus lays to one side, and an unusual jaw-closing mechanism, placing this family and the Pelomedusidae in the suborder Pleurodira. The family contains 37 species in nine genera; four genera are endemic to cis-Andean South America; two species occur on Trinidad, *Chelus fimbriatus* and *Phrynops gibbus*. The family is unknown on Tobago.

Pritchard and Trebbau (1984) described prey detection mechanisms in *Chelus,*

The waters frequented by *C. fimbriatus* are almost invariably turbid, and the remarkably small eyes suggest a trivial role for vision in prey location . . . the animal is apparently detected by vibrations sensed by the numerous fringes and skin flaps on the ventral and lateral surfaces of the head . . . The large size of the tympana suggest extreme sensitivity, and their wide separation may correspond to to a refined "binocular" effect in detecting the direction and distance of stimulus.

Chelus fimbriatus (Schneider)

Map 34. Plates 57, 58.

Testudo Fimbriata Schneider, 1782:349. Type locality: Uprouague and Rémire Island, French Guiana. *Chelus fimbriatus:* Mertens and Muller, in Rust, 1934:65. *Chelys fimbriatus:* Underwood, 1962:173. *Chelys fimbriata:* MacLean et al. 1977:45.

Comment: Zug (1977) investigated the spelling of the generic name and points out that Duméril used the following ". . . *Chelys* (chelus) . . ." and thus it would appear that *Chelys* is the first usage. However, when examination of other accounts in this work are considered, it appears that Duméril used the italics to indicate an informal group name and the genus was not placed in italics and was in parentheses and lowercase. Thus, *Chelus* is the first name assigned to the matamata.

Common Names: Pritchard and Trebbau (1984) reported "doctor galap" is used to distinguish this species from *Rhinoclemmys punctularia,* the "galap," in Trinidad. Outside Venezuela the name "matamata" is often applied to this species.

Distribution: *C. fimbriatus* has an Amazonian distribution, occurring in the Orinoco and Amazon drainage systems, and in the Essequibo, Tahuta, and Rupununi rivers of the Guianas. Boos (1984c) commented that one was taken by Mary Alkins-Koo from Chatham Beach on the south coast of Trinidad. Underwood (1962) speculated that Nariva Swamp would seem to be a likely locality; and an Emperor Valley Zoo specimen apparently came from this locality. Kearny (1972)

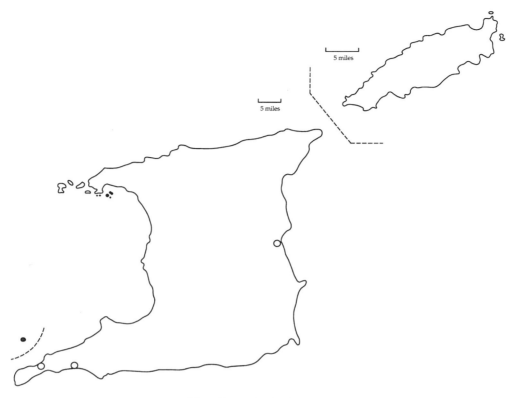

Map 34. *Chelus fimbriatus*

quoted a checklist of Trinidad turtles by Ray Shingler, former curator of the Emperor Valley Zoo, which stated, it was uncommon, and confined to a small colony in Nariva swamp. Kearny also recounted a story by Shingler of a matamata crawling out of the surf onto a beach. Pritchard and Trebbau (1984) listed three Trinidad localities: Nariva Swamp, Cedros, and near Blanquizales Swamp; and provide a photo of an individual with small barnacles attached to its shell, indicating time spent in brackish or salt water. The three localities were given to Pritchard by H. Boos and P. R. Bacon and are undoubtedly valid, but do they represent established populations or waifs? Long-lived animals occasionally turning up on Trinidad could be present without actually starting a population. A natural population of these turtles on Trinidad is likely, but not yet documented with museum specimens.

Description: Carapace length 311–404 mm, may reach 441 mm. A distinctive aquatic turtle that cannot be confused with any other chelonian. Carapace depressed and broad with three knobby keels, one medial, two lateral; posterior carapace margin with large serrations; bridge narrow, equal in width to two marginals; plastron long and narrow, with deep anal notch. Head flat and wide, with dorsal surface tuberculate; nostrils at end of narrow, fleshy, tube-like snout. Triangular flaps extend laterally above the large tympanum. Mouth wide; eyes minute; neck extremely long and muscular with numerous fleshy appendages. Legs and feet relatively small with webbing; tail short. Overall adult coloration red-brown with dark brown lines on head and carapace; juveniles tan-cream color.

Males have a slightly larger tail than females, and a plastral concavity.

Natural History: An aquatic turtle, known from a variety of lake and river environments. Food probably includes most species of appropriately sized fishes that are sympatric with the turtle. Fish are captured by ambush, although, Holmstrom (1978) described fish herding by captive specimens. Formanowicz et al. (1989) did not confirm Holmstrom's herding behavior, but did show that prey density influences search behavior; the turtles changed ambush sites frequently when prey density is low. When the prey is within range, the mouth is opened rapidly and the prey is drawn in by the vacuum that forms in the mouth and throat of the turtle. Drajeske (1983) described courtship and reproduction in captives, with 10 clutches laid between January and April (from 1976–1983); the mean clutch size was 7.3 (range 2–12). He found hatching occurred 208 days after oviposition; and proposed egg shell degradation may be necessary for successful hatching. Pritchard (1979) described nesting from October to December, and clutch sizes of 12–18.

Material: Colombia—FMNH 73410. No data 34776.

Phrynops gibbus (Schweigger)

Map 35. Plates 59, 60.

Emys gibba Schweigger, 1812:299. Type locality: unknown. *Phrynops gibbus:* Diesing, 1850:406. *Hydrapsis Gordoni* Gray, 1868:563, pl. 42. *Hydrapsis gibba:* Mole and Urich, 1894a:79. *Mesoclemmys gibba:* Underwood, 1962:172. *Phrynops (Mesoclemmys) gibbus:* Pritchard and Trebbau, 1984:119.

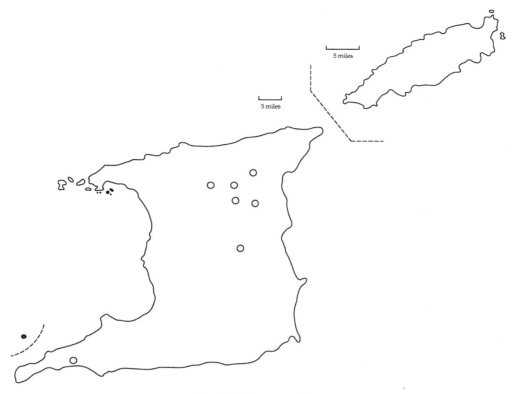

Map 35. *Phrynops gibbus*

Common Name: "Gibba turtle" (Kearney, 1972).

Distribution: *P. gibbus* has a disjunct, Amazonian distribution. Literature records from Trinidad include: Sangre Grande (Underwood, 1962); Valencia, Sangre Grande, Cumaca River, Arima, near Tamana Hill, and several miles east of Arima (Pritchard and Trebbau, 1984); Aripo savannas (Schwab, 1988); and the Carlisle and Quarahoon Rivers in the southwest peninsula (Alkins-Koo, 1990).

Description: Adult carapace length 235 mm. Head wide and flat; tympanum large; two small barbels on chin. Depressed carapace in adults; young with a medial keel on carapace, lost with age; bridge relatively small, equal to width of three marginals; marginals in bridge region flare upward; plastron long and relatively wide with a deep anal notch. Fingers and toes extensively webbed. Dorsum of head olive-brown, jaws yellow; carapace dark brown or black lacking a pattern; plastron dark or light brown to yellow. Males have longer, thicker tail than females, and show a slight plastral concavity; and females most likely attain a greater size than males. The inability of this turtle to withdraw its head directly back into the shell, instead laying it off to the side, will distinguish it from all other turtles in the area except *Chelus* and *Podocnemis;* it can be distinguished from *Chelus* by the absence of the three dorsal keels and from *Podocnemis* by the lack of wrinkled skin on the top of its head.

Natural History: An aquatic turtle inhabiting still and moving bodies of waters; Kearney (1972) reported it to be nocturnal and inhabit streams. Pritchard and Trebbau (1984) observed captives basking early in the morning and late af-

ternoon. Its diet is omnivorous. Mittermeier et al. (1978) reported five clutches with 2–4 eggs; incubation ranges from 178–200 days; hatchlings are 43–48 mm, and show a preference for terrestrial rather than aquatic habitats. Goode (1988) presented data on captive reproduction involving four clutches, with 2–7 eggs ($\bar{x}$ = 3.92), and incubation periods of 140–248 days.

Material: Colombia—FMNH 73430, no specific data.

Order Chelonia
Family Cheloniidae: Sea Turtles

Sea turtles are circumglobal; some overwinter in the muddy bottoms of cold coastal areas, while others migrate into warmer water, but most are tropical. They have paddle-like limbs and compressed, streamlined shells; are 75–150 cm in length; and may attain weights of 450 kilograms. These animals mature slowly; some may not reach sexual maturity until they are 20–25 years old. Only females of these species leave the water, and only then to lay eggs. Sea turtles are the most economically important reptiles because of the demand for their meat, eggs, and shells; and this demand has pushed all of these large turtles to the brink of extinction. Five living genera contain six species, four of which nest on the beaches of Trinidad and Tobago. DeVerteuil (1858) recounted sea turtle capture techniques used during the last century.

They are caught either in nets, or on the beach when crawling ashore to deposit their eggs. For this purpose, they

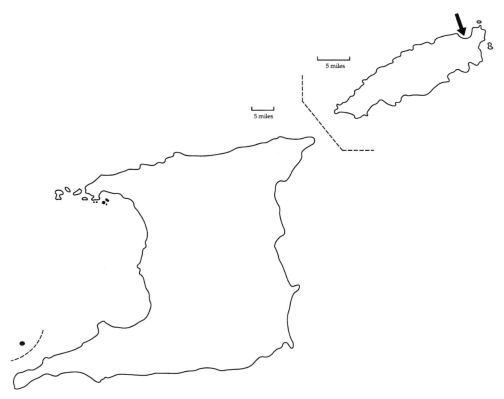

Map 36. *Caretta caretta*

come forth at night, and are watched by the catchers. As soon as a turtle is aware of any danger it immediately takes to the sea. The safest plan in that case, is to gain the seaward of the animal, and seize it by the foreflaps; it then continues to urge against the catcher, and is, with its own aid, easily turned up. If approached and held by the side, it makes a powerful resistance, and in the struggle throws up a cloud of fine sand, which almost blinding its antagonist, causes him to lose his hold. A very ingenious contrivance is sometimes adopted to bring a turtle of the largest size from a distance. One of the fore-flaps is secured to the carapace, or shell, with a line, and the animal placed in the sea, the bound flipper shoreward, so that it is thus easily led along the beach to any distance. The turtle may also be harpooned whilst rising to, or laying on, the surface, and sometimes it may even be taken asleep in that position.

Legislation has tried to protect sea turtles in many countries, but it has rarely been successful. Section 3(1) (c) of the Trinidad and Tobago Fisheries Ordinance, Chapter 25, No. 9, 21 August 1951 makes it illegal to take turtle eggs, sell turtle eggs, catch or kill a female turtle within 1000 yards of the high water mark on any reef, or sell turtle meat or turtles between 1 June and 13 September. Niddrie (1980) commented on the exploitation of sea turtles.

The days have long since gone when ships could sail from Tobago for Europe, their decks covered with live turtles, lying helpless on their backs to be sold in European mar-

kets. This does not prevent the islands from keeping an eye open for the arrival of Green and Hawksbill females, and raiding the nests for eggs from which a cake is made. And should the visitor be in a boat he will be able to photograph a local "kraal" off Sheerbirds Point, knowing it to be the relic of a once profitable trade when turtles could be captured and corralled until wanted . . . It would be a bold official however who arrested a citizen for such an offense. The Tobagonian looks upon such harvest as his birthright . . .

Kenny and Bacon (1981) described human use sea turtle use in the islands. All species were caught at sea by fishermen using harpoons or nets and find a ready sale at the fishing depot. Only a small number of these pass through the official markets, where annual meat sales were in excess of 25,000 kilos. Many of the females were killed on beaches while nesting and their meat and eggs taken because, even though there was a closed from April to September, there was little enforcement of the Turtle Protection regulations.

Caretta caretta (Linnaeus)

Map 36. Plate 61.

Testudo caretta Linnaeus, 1758:197. Type locality: "insulus Americanas," restricted to Bermuda by Smith and Taylor (1950); and to Bimini, British Bahamas by Schmidt (1953). *Testudo marina:* Court, 1858:440. *Thalassochelys caretta:* Mole and Urich, 1894a:78. *Caretta caretta:* Stejneger, 1904:715.

Common Names: DeVerteuil (1858) used the name "Caouane" for this species and the name Caret, or tortoise for

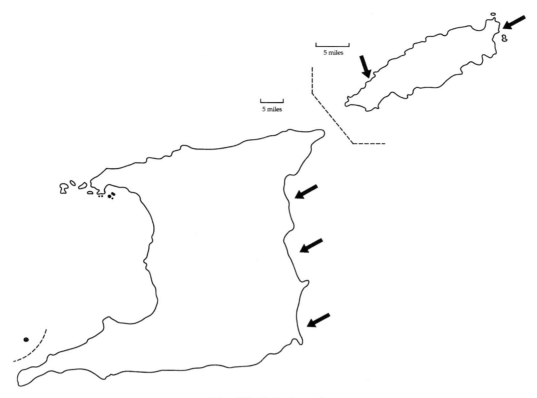

Map 37. *Chelonia mydas*

Testudo Imbricata (= *Eretmochelys imbricata*). Loggerhead is used in most English-speaking New World countries. Kenny and Bacon (1981) gave the names loggerhead and carey for this species.

Distribution: *C. caretta* is distributed throughout the world's oceans. Pritchard (1979) considered its breeding range to be "antitropical" except for sites in the western Caribbean. Nesting areas are north of the Tropic of Cancer or south of the Tropic of Capricorn. Bacon and Maliphant (1971) reported this turtle to nest on Trinidad, but Pritchard and Trebbau (1984) pointed out this record is for *Eretmochelys*, not *Caretta*. Bacon (1981) stated that this species is known to forage in the waters off Trinidad's northern coast and reports the species nesting at Charlotteville, Tobago. On the basis of this information it is regarded as an occasional nesting species in the Trinidad and Tobago area by Pritchard and Trebbau (1984). However, this turtle's presence in the islands has been clearly known since the mid-19th century based upon comments in DeVerteuil (1858).

Description: Carapaces of nesting females ranged from 700–1149 mm (Pritchard and Trebbau, 1984). Carapace heart-shaped, elongate and depressed; hatchlings have three longitudinal keels on carapace that disappear with growth; posterior marginals bluntly serrate; bridge is relatively wide, equal in distance to about four marginals. Hatchlings have two plastral keels that disappear with age; anterior lobe of plastron broad, and continuous with scutes on shoulder; posterior lobe narrow, more well defined with bluntly point spines at posterior margins. Head large, as are the eyes. Fore-limbs modified into paddles; each with two claws; hind limbs shorter and also with two claws. Carapace color variable, but usually red-brown. Skin of limbs red-brown with lighter or darker margins. Males have much longer tails than females, and males have strongly curved claws on each front limb. Five pairs of costal scutes, and an elongate, red-brown shell distinguish this species from all other sea turtles. Hatchlings have a dark brown carapace, and flippers with a light margin and underside.

Natural History: A carnivorous sea turtle, feeding on many kinds of animals including sponges, coelenterates, molluscs, crabs, and fishes, but occasionally feeding on marine turtle grasses and algae. Stomach contents for a Trinidad-Tobago specimen is the mollusc *Conus ermius* (Márquez M., 1990). Reproduction is mostly in temperate latitudes, and nesting usually occurs on continental margins, rarely nesting on oceanic islands (Pritchard and Trebbau, 1984). Underwood (1962) stated that its flesh does not have much commercial value, but that it is often eaten. And Niddrie (1980) agreed, ". . . its meat is held to be very rank and therefore inferior to the two other turtles."

Material: Egypt—FMNH 142637. No data—FMNH 121932.

Chelonia mydas (Linnaeus)

Map 37. Plate 62.

Testudo mydas Linnaeus, 1758:197. Type locality: "Insulas pelagi: insulam Adscension." Mertens and Muller (1928) restricted it to Ascension Island, in the South Atlantic. *Chelonia Mydas:* Schweigger, 1812:291. *Chelone mydas:* Mole and Urich, 1894a:78.

Common Names: DeVerteuil (1858) called it "Common turtle"; Mole and Urich (1894a) used the name green turtle; Kenny and Bacon (1981) listed the names: "Green, Greenback, Green turtle, green sea turtle, edible turtle, and greenback turtle." Soup made using calipee is green, thus "green turtle soup" is green soup from a turtle (Lazell, 1989).

Distribution: *C. mydas* inhabits the tropical, and to a lesser extent, the subtropical seas of the world. Bacon and Maliphant (1971) reported fishermen caught many off the coast of Toco, Trinidad. Bacon (1970) stated that nesting on Trinidad does occur but is rare; and later (Bacon, 1981) listed Trinidad nesting beaches for this species as Manzanilla, Matura, and Mayaro; and Tobago nesting beaches as Batteaux Bay and Grafton Estate. Ingle and Smith (1949) also reported this turtle nesting on Tobago but give no specific localities.

Description: Carapaces of nesting females 831–1175 mm (Pritchard and Trebbau, 1984). Size of nesting females geographically variable, with the largest females nesting in the Comoro Islands, and the smallest nesting in Guyana (Márquez M., 1990). Carapace depressed and streamlined; medial keel present in hatchlings, but disappears in adults; slight nuchal notch present; posterior marginals rounded; plastron large; two longitudinal keels in young specimens; bridge wide, equal to four or five marginals. Head relatively small, with a well-developed beak containing the nasal and first supralabial; eyes relatively large; neck cannot be retracted because of its thickness. Front legs paddle-shaped, each with a single claw on the anterior edge. Hind limbs small, digits more obvious. Carapace of hatchlings black, with brown growth streaks on each scute; these form radiating streaks from center of each scute, eventually replaced with spots. Adult carapace brown, green, or black in color; dorsal surface of head black, brown, or green; lower portion of head, throat, and neck white; upper surface of limbs brown, lower surface yellow-brown. Males have a longer, thicker, prehensile tail ending in a hard process; more depressed shell; and stronger recurved claws. Four pairs of costal scutes, one pair of prefrontals, and a relatively smooth posterior margin on the carapace will distinguish *C. mydas* from other sea turtles.

Natural History: A huge herbivorous sea turtle; although first year hatchlings are thought to be more carnivorous. After the second year the diet shifts and the turtle becomes more herbivorous, grazing on the turtle grasses and algae, but they may still take prey. Research indicates this species is capable of digesting cellulose as efficiently as any mammalian ruminant. No nesting data available for Trinidad and Tobago, although Ingle and Smith (1949) wrote this species "comes into sandy bays during November to lay their eggs [on Tobago]." Green turtles are the most economically important reptile in the world, and were apparently economically important in Trinidad at one time. Ingle and Smith (1949) state that green turtles are taken in nets, and that nearly half those taken at Matelot on Trinidad's north coast in 1947 were half grown. One man in a boat reportedly caught 10,000 pounds of sea turtle during 1946, valued at $1,000, and represented a return of $0.89 per man-hour; they also describe 60,000 pounds of turtle meat sold in the Port of Spain market in 1947. Bacon and Maliphant (1971) also commented of the volume of meat, "About 10,000 lbs of turtle meat was sold through the Carenage, Port of Spain, and San Fernando markets and most of this was green and hawksbill turtle meat. This is only a small percentage of the meat sold as most of it does not pass through the larger markets where statistical records are kept." Niddrie (1980) stated, "Ecological changes and uncontrolled hunting have been enough to drive the green turtle from the island [Tobago]"; and Kenny and Bacon (1981) described this species being used for meat, eggs, calipee (fat used for soup), shell, skin, and oil (used in cosmetics). Literature on this species is extensive, see Pritchard and Trebbau (1984) and Márquez M. (1990), but literature on the Trinidad and Tobago population is scant.

Material: No data—FMNH 207912.

Eretmochelys imbricata imbricata (Linnaeus)

Map 38. Plate 63.

Testudo imbricata Linnaeus 1766:350. Type locality: "Mari Americano, Asiatico," restricted by Smith and Taylor (1950:16) to the Bermuda Islands; and by Schmidt (1953:106) to Belize, British Honduras. *Chelone imbricata*: Mole and Urich, 1894a:78. *Eretmochelys imbricata imbricata*: Mertens and Muller, 1928:23.

Comment: Lazell (1989) considered the genus *Eretmochelys* invalid because this species and *Chelonia mydas* hybridize in captivity and in the wild, and he placed this species in the genus *Chelonia*.

Common Name: DeVerteuil (1858) applied the names "Caret, or tortoise" to this species. Kenny and Bacon (1981) listed the names "Hawksbill" and "oxbill". "Carey" is used in non-English speaking regions of the New World (Pritchard and Trebbau, 1984).

Distribution: *E. i. imbricata* inhabits the world's tropical oceans. Nesting on Trinidad and Tobago was reported by Ingle and Smith (1949), but they provided no locality data; however, Caldwell and Rathjen (1969) suggested it does not nest on Trinidad and Tobago. Bacon (1970) and Bacon and Maliphant (1971) stated it does so occasionally, that scuba divers see sleeping hawksbills on rock ledges off Trinidad's northwest coast, and that nesting occurs at Las Cuevas Beach. Bacon (1973, 1981) listed nesting sites at: Mayaro; Big Bay; San Souci; Matelot; Monos Island; Huevos Island; Chacachacare Island; Maracas; Matura; Manzanilla; Bird of Paradise Bay, Tobago. Carr et al. (1982) added: Brigand Hill, Trinidad, and confirmed Tobago nesting sites. Courtland Bay has a rocky promontory and a volcanic rock near Plymouth, Tobago, that share the name Hawksbill, an indication that the area may have been used by this species in the past (Niddrie, 1980). Meylan (1989) considered nesting on Trinidad and Tobago to be possible, but the population of nesting females was estimated to be very small.

Description: Carapace length for nesting females 62–88

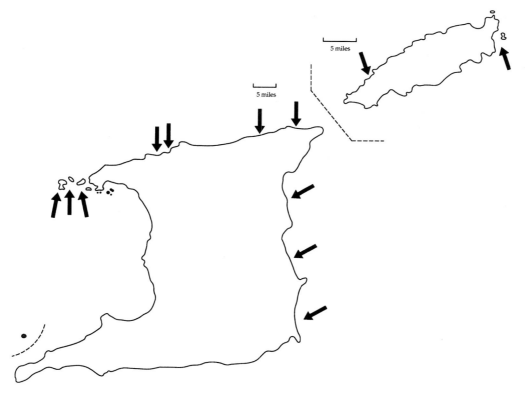

Map 38. *Eretmochelys imbricata imbricata*

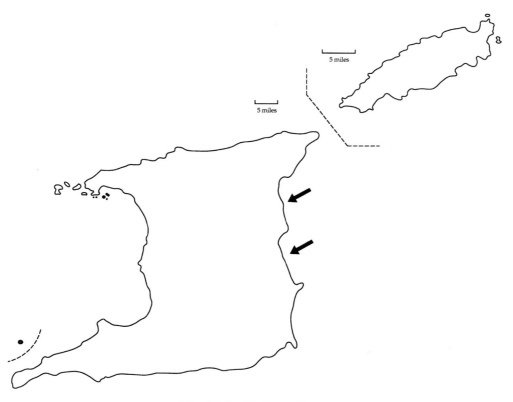

Map 39. *Lepidochelys olivacea*

cm. A relatively small turtle with a depressed, streamlined carapace; young have a well-defined median keel that becomes a ridge in adults; nuchal notch present; posterior margin strongly serrate. Bridge wide, equal to four or five marginals; plastron large, scutes juxataposed in hatchlings, overlapping in young and become juxataposed in adults. Head narrow and covered with large scales, rounded beak prominent; eyes small. Paddle-like front limbs each have two claws; hind limbs shorter, each with two claws. Hatchling carapace brown; adult carapace red, brown or black with dark streaks. Head yellow with brown-black blotches on each scale. Upper surface of limbs heavily pigmented; the lower surface lightly pigmented. Males with a plastral concavity and narrower carapace than females. The four pairs of costal scutes and four prefrontals (one pair divided transversely) combine with the narrow head, beak-like snout and relatively small size to readily distinguish this species from other marine turtles.

Natural History: A carnivorous sea turtle, feeding mostly on benthic invertebrates, including sponges and tunicates. Meylan (1988) found this species to feed almost exclusively on sponges in the orders Astrophorida and Hadromerida which include species that produce toxic secondary compounds and have abundant siliceous spicules. It occurs mainly in shallow tropical waters with rock or coral substrates. Juveniles reportedly feed on sargassum, contrary to the belief that all young turtles are carnivorous (Pritchard and Trebbau, 1984). In Venezuela, it is known to nest from May to December, with most activity occurring from July to October. Hawksbills were hunted on Trinidad during the nesting season (June-July). Evidence suggests the meat may be toxic in some populations, but the species is reportedly eaten in the Caribbean (Ingle and Smith, 1949; Kenny and Bacon, 1981; Pritchard and Trebbau, 1984).

Material: No data: FMNH 208323–4

Lepidochelys olivacea (Eschscholtz)

Map 39. Plate 64.

Chelonia olivacea Eschscholtz, 1829:3. Type locality: "China sea, Monila Bay, and Sumatra." *Lepidochelys olivacea:* Fitzinger, 1843:30.

Common Names: "Olive Ridley" is the preferred English name (Pritchard and Trebbau, 1984). Bacon and Maliphant (1971) noted that the presence of this turtle on Trinidad was suggested by fishermen talking about a small turtle called "Batali." Pritchard and Trebbau (1984) suggested that the Trinidad name "batali" is not of English origin and may be used on both sides of the Golfo de Paria.

Distribution: *L. olivacea* inhabits tropical oceans of the world. Bacon and Maliphant (1971) reported the first known nesting of this species in Trinidad and later (Bacon, 1973) recorded nesting on Matura and Manzanilla beaches. Pritchard and Trebbau (1984) also listed recaptures of tagged specimens taken in Trinidad waters and considered these waters to be foraging grounds for this species. The principal nesting sites of this species on mainland South America are in the Guianas.

Description: Maximum carapace length 750 mm. Carapace almost circular; with a flat top; young with three dorsal keels which disappear with maturity; a slight nuchal notch; bridge wide, equal to about four marginals in width; plastron with two longitudinal keels; the anterior lobe is broader than the posterior lobe. Head medium in size and triangular from above; neck partially retractable; short and thick. Front limbs paddle-like; each with two claws on the anterior edge; hind limbs shorter with two claws. Hatchlings uniform grey in color; plastron lightens in the months after hatching. Adults olive-green above; yellow to white on ventral surface. Males with only one claw on each front limb; and longer, thicker tail than females. The triangular head and wide, olive green shell with six or more pairs of costal scutes will readily distinguish this sea turtle from others.

Natural History: The olive ridley is a tropical species that nests on continental shorelines and avoids oceanic islands. Individuals seen at sea are usually within 100 km of shore. Feeding habits are described as indiscriminant, but no detailed study has been done; crustaceans and other invertebrates have been reported as food (Pritchard and Trebbau, 1984). Trinidad nesting occurs between March and August (Bacon and Maliphant, 1971). This species may be the most abundant of the world's sea turtles (Márquez M., 1990)

Material: Mexico—Chiapas, FMNH 73664.

Order Chelonia
Family Dermochelyidae: Leatherback Turtle

This family contains one living species, which is the world's largest turtle. It exceeds 2 m in shell length and reaches weights exceeding 900 kg. It is the most frequently seen sea turtle on the beaches of Trinidad and Tobago, and attracts the attention of the ecotourist. Lindblad (1968) described encountering poachers with a leatherback on Trinidad beaches:

She fell over on her back, and her big, sweeping fin-like paddles forced the men to retire rapidly. They were dancing backwards and forwards, the moonlight glinting on their knife blades, ready to aim the first blow. I let out a yell and rushed forwards. I tried to convince them that this particular animal had long since been reserved for filming purposes and that I had been sent there by the government. The government was always a good wicket in a number of different situations. I spoke of how strictly the authorities were now punishing offences against the protection laws, and laid a trail of other white lies.

Dermochelys coriacea (Linnaeus)

Map 40. Plates 65, 66, 67.

Testudo coriacea Linnaeus, 1766:350. Type locality: "Mari mediterraneo, Adriatico various," Smith and Taylor (1950:13) restricted it to Palermo, Sicily. Based upon data with the type specimen Fretey and Bour (1980) corrected the type locality to: "Tyrrhenian coast near Rome, Italy." [See the note on this in Pritchard and Trebbau, 1984:

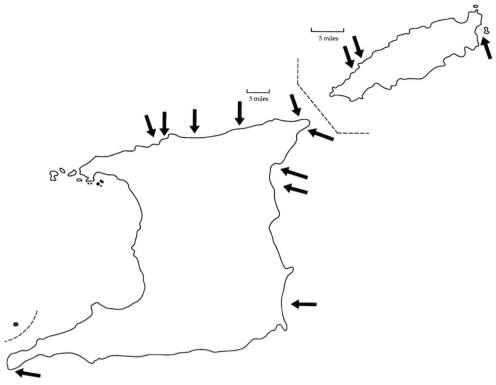

Map 40. *Dermochelys coriacea*

266–267.] *Testudo Marina:* Court, 1858:440. *Dermochelys coriacea:* Blainville, 1816:119.

Common Names: "Leather back, Caldon, Leather Turtle" (Boos and Quesnel, 1968). Pritchard and Trebbau (1984) stated that the names, "Orinook turtle" and "coffin-back turtle" are also used on Trinidad; they also listed other English names: "leatherback (preferred), leatherneck turtle, leathery turtle, trunkback turtle, trunk turtle, coriaceous turtle, and luth." Carr (1956) stated that the Trinidadians believe this turtle comes via the flooding Orinoco and thus call it the "Orinook turtle."

Distribution: *D. coriacea* is widespread in the world's oceans; and Trinidad is considered a major nesting area for this species by Sternberg (1981). Bacon (1981) listed nesting at Paria Bay, Matura Bay, Valentines Bay, Gran Tacaribe, Petit Tacaribe, Gran Murphy, Madamas, Cachipa, Las Cuevas, Maracas Blanchisseuse, Big Bay Toco, Cuman Bay, Salibia, Mayaro, and the mouth of the Oritorie River; White (1988) reported nesting at Icacos; and on Tobago Sternberg (1981) reported nesting at Bird of Paradise Bay, Grafton Estate, Turtle Beach, Courtland Beach, and Plymouth.

Description: Carapace length about 1.5 m in nesting females on Trinidad, but maximum carapace size may exceed 2 meters. Márquez M. (1990) gave a range of 135–185 cm CCL with a mean of 156.5 cm for Trinidad females and notes that this turtle grows faster than any other sea turtle. Eckert and Luginbuhl (1988) reported the record sized specimen washed ashore on 23 September 1988 at Harlech Beach,

Gwyneed, Wales, had a carapace length of 2.56 m; a weight of 916 kg; and a flipper span of 2.77 m. A huge marine turtle, immediately recognizable by its barrel-shaped body and flexible, leather-like shell. Twelve tuberculate ridges around a scuteless body; the anterior edge fuses with the skin of the neck; posterior tip of carapace pointed. Head cannot be withdrawn. Hatchling's carapace and plastron covered with small, polygonal bead-like scales; adult carapace composed of thick, oil-soaked connective tissue; most plastral bones present as remnants; scutes lacking. Head triangular with a blunt snout; neck short and thick. Dorsal surface of head covered with scales in juveniles only; upper jaw strongly notched. Front legs long, paddle-like and covered with small, polygonal scales in hatchlings; hind limbs short and broad. Tail long; connected to the rear paddles by a flap of skin. Limbs lack claws. Dorsum mostly black with white-yellow spots; juveniles with spots restricted to the tuberculate ridges. Pigment present on the plastron between the longitudinal ridges. Males with narrow, more depressed shell and longer tail than females; females often with a pink blotch on dorsum of head.

Natural History: *D. coriacea,* the largest living turtle, nests more frequently on Trinidad beaches than any other turtle. It is the most migratory of any reptile, visiting all of the world's oceans including arctic waters. Food is mostly cnidarians, which are usually uncommon in Trinidad waters, probably due to low salinity, but in February and March there are dramatic increases of *Physalia* and *Stomolophus*

(Bacon, 1969). Off the North Carolina coast, Grant and Ferrell (1993) report observations of leatherbacks feeding on cabbagehead or cannonball jellyfish (*Stomolophus meleagris*), noting that the turtle blows out air just before ingesting a jellyfish; and they noted cobia were often associated with the leatherbacks. The maximum diving depth reported by Eckert et al. (1986) was 475 m, and the maxium dive time was 37.4 minutes; these authors suggested the dives were for feeding purposes, but hypothesize that thermoregulation and predator avoidance may also be motives for diving. Bacon (1969; 1970b, 1975) and Bacon and Maliphant (1971) studied this species in Trinidad, and include data gathered by members of the Trinidad and Tobago Field Naturalist's Club; the patrols were most frequently on Matura Beach. These reports suggested nesting extends from March to August, with activity peaking in April and May; emergence often occurs between 2000 and 0200 hours; the population of nesting female leatherbacks estimated at 150–200, and later revised to 400–500; clutch size 65–130 eggs, however many females deposited eggs three to four times per season. Many nests are lost at Matura to changing tides submerging the nests. Field notes (JCM, RHH, MB) report: four nesting females in April, all were close to 160 cm in carapace length; two recently butchered turtles, only carapace and plastrons remain; nesting process 85 minutes from female's emergence from the water to her return to the ocean; nest construction required about 20 minutes; egg laying required about 35 minutes; remaining time spent searching for a nesting site, covering nest, and returning to the water. James (1983) commented the Protection of Turtles and Turtle Eggs Regulations of 1975 under the Fisheries Ordinance provides for the prosecution of anyone who captures, kills, or mutilates any marine turtle, or removes their eggs from beaches. She wrote "Every year scores of rotting carcasses could be observed along beaches of Trinidad as a result of illicit slaughter by poachers who are unable to carry away all of the meat, and the major portion is left to rot. Nests of eggs are dug up." The situation has been been slowed by conservation groups patroling beaches. As of 1991 a permit is required to visit the turtle beaches (Anon., 1991), and the leatherback now seems to be playing a role in ecotourism on Trinidad. A small fee is charged for the permit and a per person charge of about US $1.00–1993. Turtle patrol volunteers report the beaches are visited almost every night by tourists (field notes, JCM).

Material: No data—FMNH 190256–306. Trinidad—MCZ 10094, Blanchisseuse Bay.

Order Chelonia
Family Emydidae: Pond and River Turtles

Emydids are mostly Holarctic in distribution with some species invading the tropics. Most species have aquatic and terrestrial habits and are omnivorous; about 90 species in more than 31 genera comprise this family. One species oc-

curs naturally on Trinidad and it may occur as an occasional waif on Tobago. The presence of a feral population of North American *Trachemys scripta* is a possibility on Trinidad; captive adults living under seminatural conditions were seen during this investigation, and hatchlings were sold in local pet shops. Pritchard and Trebbau (1984) commented on the eggs of the galap, *Rhinoclemmys punctularia*.

The eggs of this species are brittle-shelled and elongate. The former characteristic doubtless helps retard dehydration in the exposed nesting sites characteristically utilized, and the latter is an essential characteristic if such voluminous eggs are to be successfully laid by turtles of such small size and with such narrow posterior shell openings.

Rhinoclemmys punctularia punctularia (Daudin)

Map 41. Plate 68.

Testudo punctularia Daudin, 1801:249. Type locality: "Cayenne." ?*Emys:* Court, 1858:440. *Nicoria punctularia:* Boulenger, 1889a: 124. *Geomyda punctularia:* Beebe, 1952:175. *Geomyda punctariola:* Underwood, 1962:172. *Rhinoclemmys punctularia punctularia:* Ernst, 1981:1.

Common Names: "Galap" (DeVerteuil, 1858). Pritchard and Trebbau (1984) listed a variety of names used for this species in various parts of its range and suggest the name "Guiana wood turtle."

Distribution: *R. punctularia* has an Amazonian distribution, inhabiting the Orinoco River basin, the Guianas and the northern and central Amazon. *R. p. punctularia* inhabits most of the area noted above, except southwestern Venezuela. Many of these populations are disjunct. Trinidad localities reported in the literature: Arima Valley (Beebe, 1952); Aripo Savanna (Underwood, 1962 and Schwab, 1988); the Carlisle River of the southwest peninsula (Alkins-Koo, 1990). Field notes (JCM) give localities: about 5 miles south of Rio Claro; and, 3 miles east of Sangre Grande. Museum material documents the following Trinidad locations: Arena; Cedros; Guayguayare, Mayaro County; San Rafael; and the La Seiva River, north of Sangre Grande. The only evidence this turtle occurs on Tobago comes from Hardy (1982) who reported it from Tobago at Bloody Bay (an apparent waif), and near Hillsborough Dam. Hardy (1982) quoted Poyntz (1683, 1695) that there are two kinds of "land tortoises" on Tobago, and that one lives on land, the other in water; and suggested the water turtle may be this species. He further stated, "Occasional specimens of *Rhinoclemmys punctularia punctularia* are captured on Tobago. These may be escaped captives, or may have drifted to Tobago on the Orinoco current."

Description: Carapace length 180–190 mm; maximum size 260 mm. Carapace slightly depressed; annuli present, except in very old animals. Plastron large and broad; bridge wide, equal to four or five marginals; anal notch well developed. Head small and elongated, with a projecting snout; indistinct tympanum; upper jaw serrated. Limbs relatively

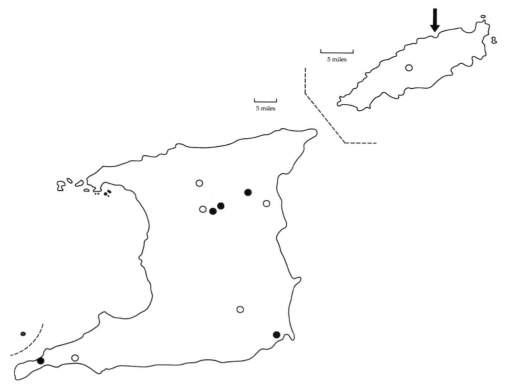

Map 41. *Rhinoclemmys punctularia punctularia*

long; front feet with four digits, hind feet with five webbed digits. Tail small and pointed. Head black with yellow, orange, or red spots and/or stripes, a character that will readily distinguish this species from all other Trinidad and Tobago chelonians. Sides of head with black and yellow mottling that extends onto the neck; throat yellow. Carapace brownblack, plastron with a dark central region with light margins. Males smaller than females, with a thicker tail, and a plastral concavity.

Natural History: A semi-aquatic turtle using ponds, streams, and swamps; Underwood (1962) reports it from Aripo Savanna, a sedge savanna; field notes (JCM) describe one in a shallow pond at the edge of lowland rainforest, and another in a wet grassy area surrounded by houses. *R. punctularia* is omnivorous, feeding on vegetation, fruits, and invertebrates (Pritchard and Trebbau, 1984). Eggs not laid in nests, but in partially open situations, where they are loosely concealed by leaf litter, bark or other debris; oviposition may correspond to the rainy season, Pritchard and Trebbau (1984) mentioned 30 eggs were made available to them by the Emperor Valley Zoo between June and September; eggs laid singly or in pairs, and communal egg deposition does occur in captivity. Kenny and Bacon (1981) wrote, "Small numbers of the freshwater turtle or galap, *Geomyda punctularia,* are collected for the aquarium or pet trade. This is on a casual basis and its potential for expansion is not known." Chadee et

al. (1984) found the tick *Amblyomma dissimile* parasitizing Trinidad specimens.

Material: Trinidad—AMNH 73142 Cedros, 73143 Arena, 78963 La Seiva River, north of Sangre Grande. FMNH 53657–9, 53662 San Rafael. USNM 166103 vicinity of Guayguayare, Mayaro Co.

Order Chelonia
Family Kinosternidae:
American Mud and Musk Turtles

Three genera and about 22 living species make up this family; all are restricted to the New World, ranging from the northeastern United States to Bolivia and Argentina. The greatest diversity is in Mexico and Central America. These are small, less than 250 mm, carnivorous, aquatic turtles that walk the bottom of ponds and streams in search of food and mates, but they may occasionally forage on land and use terrestrial retreats. Only one species enters South America; it also occurs on Trinidad. Kearney (1972) observed *Kinosternon* on Trinidad.

As we played our beams into the clear water, I was amazed to see it fairly teeming with bizarre life. There were six inch fish barely able to keep their backs wet, giant snails with shells as big as conches, some kind of eel, several large marine toads, and assorted small crabs, crayfish and other invertebrates. . . . Incredibly, after another two minutes of search a mud turtle appeared in the beam, actively

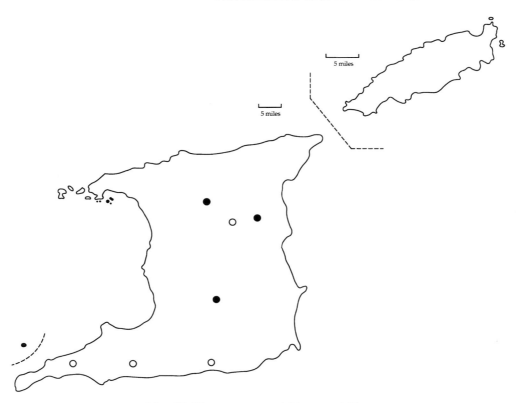

Map 42. *Kinosternon scorpioides scorpioides*

foraging along the bottom! Not a stunted, emaciated survivor, mind you, but a beautiful specimen with a flawless five-inch shell.

Kinosternon scorpioides scorpioides (Linnaeus)

Map 42. Plate 69.

Testudo scorpioides Linnaeus, 1766:352. Type locality: Suriname. *Kinosternon scorpioides:* Gray, 1831a:34. *Cinosternum scorpioides:* Roux, 1926:292. *Kinosternon scorpioides scorpioides:* Mertens and Wermuth, 1955:337

Common Names: There appears to be no local name for this species on Trinidad. Pritchard and Trebbau (1984) suggested that it is commonly called the "scorpion mud turtle" because of the scientific name. Linnaeus apparently based its name on the sharp-pointed spur at the tip of the male's tail.

Distribution: *K. scorpioides* is widespread, occurring from southern Tamaulipas, Mexico southward through Central America to Peru and Brazil. *K. s. scorpioides* has an Amazonian distribution. On Trinidad it is widespread in the lower elevations. Trinidad literature localities are: Carlisle River in the southwestern peninsula (Alkins-Koo, 1990); and Aripo savannas (Schwab, 1988). Field notes (JCM and RH) report this species in the Los Bajos area of the southwestern peninsula and in the Moriquite River near Moruga. Trinidad localities supported by museum material: Arima, Brickfield, and Sangre Grande.

Description: Carapace length of males 175 mm, females 159 mm. Carapace high domed, elongated with three dorsal keels, the medial keel extending the length of the carapace. Bridge moderate in size, equal in width to three marginals; plastron long and broad, and hinged at the humeral scutes; anal notch small. Head large and wide with a pointed snout; barbels present on the chin in varying number and arrangements. Legs and feet relatively small, the front feet with five digits, the hind feet with four digits. Male's tail with a small terminal spur. Carapace yellow; plastron yellow-brown with a dark central region with light edges. Mature males with a longer, thicker tail, a strongly hooked upper jaw, larger head, longer chin barbels, and a larger size than females. The high domed, yellow carapace; 11 plastral scutes; and pectoral scutes not forming part of the bridge, will distinguish this turtle from all other Trinidad and Tobago turtles.

Natural History: *K. scorpioides* inhabits ponds and slow moving bodies of water: Underwood (1962) believed them to be common in freshwater swamps. Kearney (1972) found one in a stagnant ditch. Field notes (JCM) describe six individuals foraging for food after dark in small streams heavily overgrown with vegetation; Pritchard and Trebbau (1984) described captives feeding on worms, insects, and other animal matter. Clutch size is 1–3 for Venezuelan animals (Sexton, 1960).

Material: Trinidad—AMNH 118650 Sangre Grande; 119845 Arima. FMNH 53654–6, Brickfield.

Order Chelonia
Family Pelomedusidae:
Afro-American Side-necked Turtles

Living pelomedusids comprise 5 genera and about 19 species that inhabit South America, Africa, and Madagascar. Two species may occur on Trinidad, but it is most likely that they occur only as occasional waifs that have been washed down the Orinoco. There is no evidence that established populations of these turtles currently live on the island. However, Ingle and Smith (1949) made the following statement in their account of Trinidad's sea turtle industry, "River turtles, known as the Orinoco or coffinback turtles are caught as they lay their eggs on the beaches." And, in their Tobago account they write, "A few Orinoco or River Turtles weighing from 400 pounds are caught but are not considered good eating." Two explanations exist, and they are not mutually exclusive: (1) one of these turtles has nested on Trinidad, and possibly Tobago, beaches in the recent historical past, and may have inhabited the streams that they could navigate, but are now extirpated; and (2) these authors have confused *Podocnemis expansa* with the leatherback, *Dermochelys coriacea*. The last possibility is based upon the fact that Carr (1956), and later Pritchard and Trebbau (1984), reported that *D. coriacea* is locally known as the 'Orinook turtle' and Carr suggested that afro this is because the local people erroneously believe the flooding Orinoco brings the turtle to Trinidad. Additional evidence is the size reported for these turtles. It is unlikely that *P. expansa* reaches 400 pounds; half that weight would be an exceptionally large individual; while *D. coriacea* could easily weigh well in excess of 400 pounds. These species are discussed here because they may be found as waifs.

Podocnemis expansa (Schweigger)

Plate 70.

Emys expansa Schweigger, 1812. Type locality: South America.
Podocnemis expansa: Wagler, 1830: plate 4.

Common Names: This species is apparently only an occasional visitor to Trinidad and Tobago waters, and does not have a local name. Pritchard and Trebbau review the vernacular names for this species and suggest the preferred English name "arrau sideneck."

Distribution: This huge freshwater turtle has an Amazonian distribution and occurs in the Orinoco and Amazon River basins. Carr (1956) reported seeing this species in coastal waters of Trinidad; and Ditmars and Bridges (1935) bought four turtles, imported from the mainland, from the Union Club manager in Port of Spain. Underwood (1962) wrote it ". . . sometimes turns up on the east coast of Trinidad washed down by floods in the Orinoco." Iverson (1992) has a range map with a Trinidad locality for this species, and King and Burke (1989) include Trinidad as part of its distribution. It is included here based upon these literature records and a single museum specimen, (a carapace and plastron, AMNH 5290) which was given to the museum by R. R.

Mole, author of early Trinidad herpetofauna checklists and correspondent with R. L. Ditmars. Cooper and Bacon (1981), in their Appendix II, conclude that "*Podocnemis* ssp." or the "Orinoco turtle" occurs in the south and east coastal rivers, but that it is an occasional visitor from the mainland, and that it is used for food.

Description: Carapace of males 500 mm, female carapace length 890 mm. A sideneck turtle, the neck cannot be retracted into the shell, instead it lays to one side. This characteristic will readily distinguish it from *Rhinoclemmys*. And, it can readily be distinguished from the other, more common sideneck turtle, *Phrynops* because skin on the crown of the head is smooth in *Podocnemis*, while wrinkled in *Phrynops*. A pair of chin barbels usually present. *Podocnemis expansa* has a broad, flattened carapace that widens posteriorly, while *P. unifilis* has a slight keel on the carapace that is highest on the third scute; this species lacks the keel. Juveniles have large yellow head spots, including a yellow line that extends from the nostril, over the eye, and along the posterior edge of the orbit. The yellow spots disappear with age, with males retaining them longer than females. Carapace gray-brown to black; plastron tan in hatchlings, becomes darker with age. Hind feet heavily webbed.

Natural History: Large lowland rivers and their banks are the expected habitat; and on the mainland it is known to nest on sandbanks in huge aggregations. Food is mostly fruit, but also includes freshwater sponges, insects, and it may scavenge fish carcasses (Pritchard and Trebbau, 1984).

Material: Trinidad—AMNH 5290.

Podocnemis unifilis Troschel

Plate 71.

Podocnemis unifilis Troschel, 1848 in Schomburgk, 1848:647. Type locality: Rupununi and Takutu Rivers, British Guiana.

Common Name: This turtle does not have a common name on Trinidad and Tobago, because it is probably not found on the islands. "Yellow-headed sideneck" is the preferred English name for this species (Pritchard and Trebbau, 1984).

Distribution: The comment made by Kearney (1972) claiming the species occurs in Nariva Swamp is the reason for including it here. H. Boos and P. Bacon denied its presence on Trinidad (Pritchard and Trebbau, 1984). In the absence of specimens it seems unlikely that this species occurs on Trinidad; it has an Amazonian distribution and is widespread in the Amazon and Orinoco basins.

Description: Maximum carapace length 680 mm, most specimens less than 465 mm, males usually less than 330 mm. A sideneck turtle with an oval carapace; a low keel on second and third vertebral scutes; and a single chin barbel. Juveniles with orange-yellow spots on the head. All of these characteristics will distinguish it from *P. expansa*. Distinguished from *Phrynops* by the smooth skin on top of the head; *Phrynops* has wrinkled skin on the crown of the head. Carapace brown to black in adults, females usually dark brown; males often with a blotched carapace, head spots, and a thick tail.

Natural History: Expected habitat includes small streams and flooded forest. It nests earlier in the season than *P. expansa,* and does not form the large nesting aggregations that its congener does. Its diet is mostly herbivorous, but molluscs and dead fish may also be consumed (Pritchard and Trebbau, 1984).

Order Chelonia
Family Testudinidae: Tortoises

These are terrestrial turtles with an almost cosmopolitan distribution (being absent from the Australian-New Guinea region); and Cracraft (1974) proposed the family had its initial radiation in Laurasia. *Geochelone* is the only genus to reach South America, and it is represented in Africa, India, and southeastern Asia. Ten genera with more than 40 species comprise the family; one species is currently found on Trinidad; a second occurs on at least one offshore island and may have been present on Trinidad and Tobago in the past, introduced by man or naturally occurring, or possibly both at various times. It is now difficult, if not impossible, to determine the cycles of tortoise populations on these islands. Tortoises are economically important because of their food value. Garman (1887c) discusses *Testudo tabulata* in Trinidad; this name has been applied to both *Geochelone carbonaria* and *Geochelone denticulata* and from his discussion it is not possible to determine what species he was observing. He wrote, "Abundant in the market at Port of Spain, Trinidad. Secured also at St. Vincent and St. Lucia. It feeds readily in captivity and is kept about the houses and carried from place to place much as the more common domestic animals." Andre (1904) reported regular trade prior to 1860 between Trinidad and Ciudad-Bolivar, Venezuela by schooners and sloops carrying mail, goods, and passengers. Certainly there is a high probability that food items, including tortoises, were involved in this commerce. He also commented on their value as food.

Morocoy, as the tortoise is called in Venezuela and Trinidad, is a favourite dish when well prepared. These reptiles can remain a considerable length of time without food. The liver of the tortoise is large compared with its body, and it shrinks in proportion to the length of time during which its owner has been deprived of nourishment, and this has given rise to the belief among the people that the animal eats its liver when it is unable to obtain any other food.

Hardy (1982) discussed the Tobago tortoise situation, quoting Poyntz (1683, 1695), mentioning land tortoises on Tobago; he also interviewed older Tobago citizens who recognized the name morocoy, and described tortoises as once abundant. Additionally, hunters informed him that tortoises are extant in remote parts of the island. He also described the release of a captive population which contained both *G. car-*

bonaria and *G. denticulata* near Speyside, and the subsequent location of tortoise shells in the nearby forest. He commented that Tobago specimens have always been found in or near villages and are probably escaped pets. Noting the Quaternary remains of *Geochelone* on other Caribbean islands, Hardy concluded tortoises may have become extinct and then reintroduced. Censky (1988) reviewed the distribution of *Geochelone carbonaria* in the West Indies and suggested four hypotheses for its distribution: (1) natural dispersal; (2) introduction by prehistoric humans; (3) introduction by early European settlers; and (4) recent introduction as pets. She noted that none of these are irrefutable, and none are mutually exclusive. Lazell (1993) further complicated the issue by documenting pre-Columbian remains probably belonging to *Geochelone carbonaria* on Anguilla, in the Windward Islands.

Geochelone carbonaria (Spix)

Plate 72.

Testudo carbonaria Spix, 1824a:22. Type locality: "Capitary." *Geochelone carbonaria:* Williams, 1960:10.

Common Names: In Venezuela this species, as well as *G. denticulata,* is known as the "morrocoy." The preferred English name for this species is "red-footed tortoise" (Pritchard and Trebbau, 1984).

Distribution: *G. carbonaria* has an Amazonian distribution. The presence of this turtle on Trinidad is highly questionable. Underwood (1962) suggested it is absent, at least in natural populations. Pritchard (1979) believed it to occur naturally on Trinidad, noting its presence on other West Indies islands is due to human activity; but later (Pritchard and Trebbau, 1984) wrote, "It is a familiar species on Trinidad, but is probably introduced there, although, *G. denticulata* is native." USNM 084702 is cataloged as being from Trinidad, but an attached NZP specimen tag reads, "Guyana, 70 mi. from Georgetown." USNM 15882 is cataloged as, "St. George, County, Port of Spain" but it was hatched in the Emperor Valley Zoo from a female caught in July 1963. Boos (1990) reported remains of a shell from Monos Island, off the northwest peninsula. Boos and Quesnel (1994) followed up: Tommy Griffith, a watchman at Siegert house, had two subadult females and believed the Monos Island tortoises (presumably the ancestors of these subadults) were brought to the island by illegal Grenadian immigrants between 1939 and 1950. Pritchard and Trebbau's (1984) distribution map (their Figure 36) shows this species as widespread in much of northern Venezuela, and when human commerce is taken into consideration it seems highly probable that it was introduced to Trinidad and Tobago.

Description: Carapace exceeds 500 mm in length when measured in a straight line. However, most specimens probably don't exceed 400 mm (Pritchard and Trebbau, 1984). Carapace oval in juveniles, becoming elongate in adults; shield of carapace usually sculptured with growth rings.

Plastron elongate and thick with gular shield extending beyond anterior edge of carapace, and anal notch; bridge wide, equal to width of 7–8 marginals. Forelimbs flattened, with large scales on the anterior surface, and five digits. Hindlimbs columnar with four digits. Tail flattened. Carapace black with yellow centers on each shield, but specimens with yellow carapaces are known. Plastron yellow-tan with dark diamond-shaped marking at mid-abdomen. Yellow postorbital stripe on an otherwise black head. Large scales on front limbs usually red, but may be orange or yellow. Males have a long tail with vent located at midpoint; females with a shorter tail. Mature males from northern populations with constricted shell at midbody. A large, terrestrial turtle that can be distinguished from all other forms found on Trinidad and Tobago, with the exception of *G. denticulata* by its columnar legs. It can be distinguished from *G. denticulata* by its black carapace with small, yellow area around the areola of each scute; its black forelimbs with red-tipped scales; and adult males, from at least some populations, have a lateral constriction of the carapace at the bridge.

Natural History: This species inhabits forests, forest-savanna edges, and savannas; and at some localities co-exists with *G. denticulata* (Moskovits, 1988). Food includes a variety of plant and animal material, and preferred foods are those easily fermented with a high concentration of minerals (Moskovits and Bjorndal, 1990).

Geochelone denticulata (Linnaeus)

Plate 73.

> *Testudo denticulata* Linnaeus, 1766:325. Type locality: "Virginia," in error. *Testudo tabulata:* Court, 1858:400. *Geochelone denticulata:* Williams, 1960:10.

Common Names: "Morocoy" (Deverteuil, 1858). Pritchard and Trebbau (1984) spelled this "morrocoy"; and commented that English names for this species include, "yellow-footed tortoise, South American forest tortoise, and Brazilian giant tortoise."

Distribution: *G. denticulata* has an Amazonian distribution, ranging from western Colombia (east of the Andes) southward to Bolivia and Brazil. In Trinidad it probably existed in the lower elevations throughout most of the island, and now may be restricted to localized areas. Literature records for Trinidad localities: Arima Valley (Beebe, 1952); Aripo savannas (Schwab, 1988). All Trinidad museum material lacks specific locality data.

Description: Males 442 mm, females 400 mm; specimens that attain giant size are known; Pritchard and Trebbau (1984) give measurements of 20 specimens between 490 and 820 mm, but none are from Trinidad. Carapace oval in juveniles, elongates with age; nuchal notch present; posterior carapace margin finely notched in juveniles, and disappears with age. Plastron large, small anal notch; bridges wide, equal to about four marginals. Head small, slightly elongate; eyes large, greater in diameter than tympanum. Limbs columnar, front feet with five poorly defined digits;

back feet with four poorly defined digits. Tail short. Skin on head black with orange dorsal scales; skin on neck brown; limbs brown except for large orange to yellow scales on anterior surface of forelimbs. Carapace yellow-brown at center of each scute, with darker coloration toward the edge of its margins. It can be distinguished from *G. carbonaria* [which may occur on Trinidad as feral animals] by its brown carapace; center of each shield lighter in color than outer part of shield; orange-yellow coloration on head and forelimbs. Adult males will not have lateral constriction of carapace at bridge. Males smaller than females; with lower, narrower shells, a plastral concavity, and a larger, thicker tail carried to one side.

Natural History: A rainforest and forest-edge species, that will use more open habitats including treefalls in forested areas (Moskovits, 1988; Moskovits and Bjorndal, 1990). DeVerteuil (1858) commented on their omnivorous diet: they, ". . . live on soft plants, fruits and insects; the morocoy seems to be particularly partial to the wild plum, which it swallows entire; during the ripening season, several of them may be met with under one tree . . ." Captives readily take a variety of plant matter and its natural diet has been investigated in northwestern Brazil (Moskovits and Bjorndal, 1990). Trinidad specimens are difficult to find, and Underwood (1962) considered it to be scarce due to human predation. DeVerteuil (1858) states, " . . . the liver of the morocoy (*Testudo tabulata*) is as delicate, or even much richer and choicer than the foie gras; it requires the condiments of lime juice, salt, and pepper, and must be dressed in the frying pan. Morocoys are sometimes kept in pens, and fattened upon the ripe plantains and guavas for the table." Wing and Reitz (1982) reported remains from Trinidad archeological sites and it may still be present at some locations in the southern part of the island (John Bindernagle, personal communication). DeVerteuil (1858) states, "Dogs often detect the morocoy by barking at it; also when coupling, they emit a peculiar grunt which likewise serves to discover them." Auffenberg (1965) reported males make a "clucking" sound during copulation. Pritchard and Trebbau (1984) discussed the wide discrepancy of clutch sizes reported for this species; numbers as high as 15–20 eggs have been reported, but clutches of 1–8 with an average of 4–5 eggs are more probable.

Material: FMNH 190748 Port of Spain. USNM 073932, all data questionable.

Order Crocodylia

Twenty-two species in eight genera and three families comprise this order. They are large, 1.5 to 7.5 m, long-lived, aquatic carnivores inhabiting the subtropics and tropics. They have a number of features that allow them to feed underwater, and retreat to submerged locations if the air temperature becomes too cold. Parental care is present in many crocodilians, and one or both parents may be involved in nest guarding; hatchlings may also be protected by adults for a

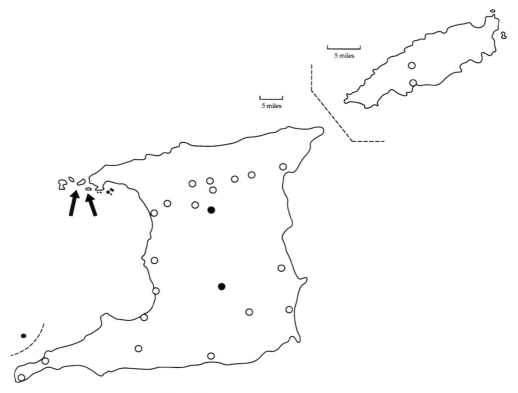

Map 43. *Caiman crocodilus crocodilus*

short period of time after emergence from the nest. The leather industry has created a demand for the skins of these animals, threatening almost all of the extant species. One species is known to inhabit Trinidad and Tobago; two others may occur as waifs.

Order Crocodylia
Family Alligatoridae: Alligators and Caimans

Alligatorids occur in the southern United States, Central and South America, and China; and caimans may have entered South America from North America prior to the closure of the Panamanian Portal. Mandibular teeth that fit inside the upper jaw so that no teeth are visible when the mouth is closed will distinguish members of this family from other crocodilian families. Members of this family have been extensively hunted for their skins; and while they are protected in Trinidad and Tobago, they are still taken on the mainland. Four living genera hold about eight species. The American alligator and black caiman probably both exceed 4.5 meters; a smaller species occurs in Trinidad and Tobago. The Amazonian race of one widespread species, *Caiman crocodilus*, occurs in Trinidad and Tobago. Worth (1967) commented on the caimans' economic value.

It is a cayman's good fortune to possess a hide that can be tanned only by a process that leads also to its virtual disintegration. The Latin name, *Caiman sclerops*, refers to a

sclerotic plaque within each scale, a calcified center that must be dissolved out chemically before leather becomes pliable. By that time the skin too, has reached a friable state approaching liquefaction. Therefore caymans have escaped "alligator" purse and shoe markets that would otherwise surely have been their destiny.

Worth's comment is in error; many thousands, if not hundreds of thousands, of these animals are harvested annually on mainland South America. The osteoderms pose only minor problems for the hide industry and as more desirable species such as the black caiman and crocodiles are depleted, hide hunters have turned to this species (Groombridge, 1982).

Caiman crocodilus crocodilus (Linnaeus)

Map 43. Plate 74, 75.

> *Lacerta crocodilus* Linnaeus 1758:200. Type locality: Guyana. *Alligator sclerops:* Court, 1858:440. *Alligator punctulatus:* Reinhardt and Lutken, 1862:22. *Caiman sclerops:* Boettger, 1893:20. *Caiman crocodilus crocodilus:* Muller, 1923:315. *Caiman c. crocodilus:* Mertens, 1970:43.

Common Names: "Alligator or babiche" (DeVerteuil, 1858). Medem (1981; 1983) and Murphy (1986) discuss the meaning of the name babiche, noting that its probable origin is derived from the Spanish "babillas" meaning thin skin, usually on a horse's flank.

Distribution: *C. crocodilus* is a widespread species

ranging from Oaxaca, Mexico, southward to the Paraguay River in Paraguay. *C. c. crocodilus* has an Amazonian distribution. It occurs on Trinidad and Tobago, and possibly other near shore islands. On both islands it is found at lower elevations, although it will follow streams into hills and colonize man-made reservoirs. Trinidad localities in the literature: Caroni Swamp (Mole 1892b; Bacon 1970a); in Nariva Swamp (Underwood, 1962; Worth, 1967); Arima River (Beebe, 1952); "particularly numerous at Mayaro and in the county of Caroni" (DeVerteuil, 1858); La Blanquizales Lagoon, Caroni Swamp, Cedros, Cumana River, Couva, near Gaspar Island, Godineau Swamp, Hollis Reservoir, Icacos, Mayaro Bay, Monos Island, Moruga, Navet Reserve, Negra Point, Pointe-à-Pierre, Point Fortrin, Salibea River, Tacarigua (Medem, 1983). Field notes (JCM) add: Laurier Pond near Siparia; Guanapo River; Tunapuna Rd.; east of Piarco Airport; Churchill-Roosevelt Highway south of St. Augustine; the Hollis Reservoir; and about 5 miles south of Rio Claro. Museum material from Trinidad documents: Brickfield and San Rafael. It should be noted that Woodcock (1867) provided ancedotal evidence of this species on Tobago; its presence there was not recognized by herpetologists until 1970. Literature records for Tobago documents: " . . . rivers, mostly on the northwest side of the island." (DeVerteuil, 1968); Hillsborough Dam (Mertens, 1970); Powell (1971) erroneously stated the species is not present on Tobago. Hardy (1982) provided photographic documentation of a caiman killed in the ocean 3 miles off northeast Tobago.

Description: Urich (1892) described an individual 8 feet 9 inches (about 258 cm) from the Caroni River. Medem (1983) listed sizes for other Trinidad specimens between 30.1 and 244 cm; and gives measurements for five Tobago specimens between 86 and 136.5 cm. The fourth tooth of the lower jaw enters a socket in the upper jaw; this immediately distinguishes it from all members of the genus *Crocodylus*. Snout relatively slender; head length 1.5–2.0 times its width; a bony, transverse ridge just in front of the eyes, giving it the appearance of having spectacles; post-occipital scutes in 2–3 transverse rows; mandibular symphysis extending to the level of the fourth or fifth mandibular tooth. Nuchal scutes (neck plates) in four closely juxtaposed rows. The trunk scutes in orderly transverse and longitudinal rows. Fingers free, toes webbed. Cloacal opening transverse. Dorsum dull brown or olive with black transverse marks; flanks yellow-brown; venter cream-white.

Natural History: Caimans inhabit brackish and freshwater environments in Trinidad. Field notes (JCM) report it in small, grass-edged streams; in floodplain pools of the Ortoire River; in a man-made pond; in the Guanapo River; and in water-filled quarries off Tunapuna Road east of Piarco Airport. Bacon (1978) observed caimans colonizing gravel pits where fish, frogs, and birds are abundant. Underwood (1962) listed fish, crabs, snails, and other animals as food. Staton and Dixon (1977b) studied the reproduction of a Venezuelan llanos pop-

ulation: courtship occurs in the dry season and early wet season; nests are made of grass in grassland habitats, and leaves, twigs, and soil are used in forest habitats; vegetation is formed into a mound, a nest chamber is excavated, and eggs deposited; the sequence requires 2–7 days; mean clutch size is 28.6; nests are visited and repaired by females. The matte, *Tupinambis teguixin,* is the major nest predator; Worth (1967) also noted *Tupinambis* preying upon Trinidad caiman nests. Field notes (MB, RHH, JCM) describe nesting females in April, and juveniles present in April as well as June-July; a female on a nest composed mostly of leaves. Wing and Reitz (1982) reported remains from Trinidad Indian middens suggesting humans have been historic predators of caiman. Joseph (1838) commented on eating caiman eggs, "I have eaten them (without knowing what eggs they were) and found them good." Caimans are probably not a serious threat to humans, but they may chase people; Worth (1967) reported one of his employees being chased by a caiman that he hypothesized was a nesting female. Powell (1971), cited J. Boos and J. Kenny, and commented, "There is nominal legal protection for six months of the year, but this is not enforced. However, there is relatively little hunting and no significant market for hides. A few are killed to be stuffed as curios, or whenever a farmer feels they are threatening his livestock." Bowman and Bowman (1939) related a story about a Trinidadian witch using alligator teeth as part of her trade. Kenny and Bacon (1981) wrote that it

". . . is hunted for sport and small numbers of young animals are caught and stuffed for sale as tourist items. No accurate data available. This once abundant reptile has been reduced in numbers by uncontrolled hunting . . . The export of turtle skins is a lucrative trade in Trinidad at present, and the same markets would open to accept alligator skins, if these could be guaranteed in reasonable amounts."

Material: Trinidad—FMNH 53650 Brickfield; 53653 San Rafael.

Order Crocodylia
Family Crocodylidae: Crocodiles

Crocodiles are circumtropical in freshwater and many species will readily enter the marine habitats; three genera with about 14 species comprise the family. The first and fourth madibular teeth are displayed outside the closed mouth in members of this family, distinguishing these species from other crocodilian families. Two species may occur on Trinidad and Tobago as waifs; there are no known established populations of these large animals on Trinidad or Tobago. They are, however, known from Venezuela, and apparently move into Trinidad and Tobago waters on occasion; and the possibility that an established population may be found should not be ruled out.

A brief note in Woodcock (1867) suggested a member of this genus was present on Tobago.

In the rivers in the windward part of the island the alligator is often seen; one has been taken seventeen feet long;

it was killed in the Betsey's Hope River, where it had attacked a man who was crossing the stream, but who fortunately escaped the monster. It has always been considered that this animal was a stranger, brought by the current from one of the continental rivers; the native alligators do not measure much over six feet, and I have not heard of any injury done by them to man.

Wing and Reitz (1982) reported the remains of *Crocodylus acutus* from an archeological site at St. John's, Trinidad. Urich (1893) described a skin of crocodile 390 cm long that was presumably taken near Port of Spain. Rousseau (1895) stated that Kernaham harpooned a crocodile near Cedros, and commented that sharks destroyed most of the tail. Medem (1983) summarized three reports of *Crocodylus* taken near Trinidad from Julius Boos: in 1954 or 1955 one was killed by Paul dé Meilao at Mayaro Beach; a second was found floating in the Boca Grande near the island of Chacachacare in 1962 or 1964 by Bobbie, a fisherman and resident of Staubles Bay; and a third was shot in 1966 or 1967 by Cuthbert Thavenot at Balandra Bay. Medem differentiated between *C. acutus* and *C. intermedius* taken on Trinidad but does not explain the basis for determining which records go with which species. In 1984 Canadian zoologist John Bindernagle described seeing a large crocodilian while doing an aerial survey for manatee in Nariva Swamp.

Crocodylus acutus (Cuvier)

Plate 76.

> *Crocodilus acutus* Cuvier, 1807:55. Type locality: "La grande ile de Saint-Domingue, Antilles, Amerique" (= Hispaniola, probably the French portion, which is now Haiti); restricted to "Santo Domingo, Puerto Plata," by Smith and Taylor (1950:364); and further restricted to, "L'Etang, Saumatre, Haiti" by Schmidt (1953:111). *Crocodylus acutus:* Stejneger, 1917:289.

Common Name: This animal has no local name. It is commonly called the "American crocodile" (Groombridge, 1982).

Distribution: A widespread species ranging from central Mexico southward through Central America, present on both coasts; on the Pacific as far south as northern Peru and to at least the mouth of the Orinoco along the northern coast; the Caribbean, and southern Florida. Reinhardt and Lutken (1862) considered this species part of the Trinidad herpetofauna, while Groombridge (1982) suggested Trinidad records represented vagrants. Medem (1983) presented a map with a locality for this species near Chacachacare Island, and his Venezuelan map showed this species on the Península de Paria; Wing and Reitz (1982) reported remains from an archeological site at St. John's, Trinidad. It appears that this large animal was at one time present in Trinidad and is now extirpated, possibly due to human predation, habitat destruction, or some combination of these factors. The species may still occur on the island in small numbers in one or more of the coastal swamps. King et al. (1982) discussed

the presence of crocodiles on Trinidad ". . . none of these specimens was preserved in a museum, so it is impossible to ascertain whether they represent *C. acutus* or *C. intermedius*." Later, King and Burke (1989) did not recognize this species on Trinidad, but they did recognize the presence of *C. intermedius*.

Description: Reported to exceed 7 m, but in recent history large specimens are uncommon (Smith and Smith, 1977; Medem, 1983). Snout elongate and pointed; large adults with preorbital hump. Fingers webbed at the base; toes almost completely webbed. Scutes on the limbs, particularly the hindlimbs strongly keeled. Distinguished from caimans by the fourth tooth in the lower jaw visible, hidden in caiman; lacks the interorbital ridge found in caimans. Distinguished from *C. intermedius* by raised preocular area (a hump) and symphysis of lower jaw extends to fourth or fifth tooth in *C. acutus;* in *C. intermedius* it extends to sixth tooth. In overall appearance *C. acutus* has a shorter snout than *C. intermedius*. Adult *C. acutus* olive-brown or olive-green, smaller individuals darker in color with dorsal flecks and blotches; venter cream.

Natural History: Habitat is usually coastal, including mangroves forests, salt marshes, and brackish creeks, but it also occurs in larger freshwater rivers and freshwater lakes with access to coastal areas. Adults often have a den 3–9 m into a stream bank with the entrance below the waterline. Eggs are deposited in a mound nest (Groombridge, 1982).

Crocodylus intermedius Graves

Plate 77.

> *Crocodilus intermedius* Graves, 1819:344. Type locality: Unknown.

Common Name: This animal has no local name. It is commonly called "Orinoco Crocodile" (Groombridge, 1982).

Distribution: *C. intermedius* is known from the Orinoco drainage of Colombia and Venezuela. King and Burke (1989) stated that it occasionally washes up on the shores of Trinidad and nearby islands. Medem (1983) presented a map of Trinidad showing isolated records for this species at Chacachacare Island, Port of Spain, Cedros Bay, Mayaro Bay, and Balandra Bay, as well as the 1910 record mentioned by Barbour (1914) for Grenada. King et al. (1982) discussed the presence of crocodiles on Trinidad, ". . . none of these specimens was preserved in a museum, so it is impossible to ascertain whether they represent *C. acutus* or *C. intermedius*." The species is considered here because of the literature citations only. There is no evidence that this species occurs on Trinidad or Tobago, but because the Orinoco species may occasionally wander down river to these islands, there is a possibility of its occurrence. Hardy (1982) discussed Woodcock's (1867) report and stated, "The animal involved was probably *Crocodylus intermedius*." He then cited two accounts of animals of this species rafting to other Caribbean islands: Grenada in 1910 (Barbour, 1914) and Barbados in 1886 (Fielden, 1914; King, 1962).

Description: A large, 6.78 m, crocodilian, with an extremely elongated snout. Fourth tooth in the lower jaw visible; this will distinguish it from *Caiman crocodilus.* It can be distinguished from *Crocodylus acutus* by lack of a pre-orbital elevation, and the symphysis in the lower jaw extending to the sixth tooth, instead of the fourth or fifth tooth. Dorsum of adults yellow or yellow-green, with grey or black cross-bands; sides light with some dark spots, these form incomplete bands on the sides of tail; venter cream, dark blotches on subcaudals.

Natural History: During the dry season large, deep sections of rivers are inhabited; during the wet season individuals may move great distances. Juveniles use still water with dense vegetation. Thorbjarnarson and Hernández (1993) reported females mature at 250 cm; nesting occurs early in the dry season and eggs hatch during the initial rise in water level at the start of the wet season; eggs are laid in a hole excavated in either an eroded river bank or a beach. Individual females are known to reuse nesting sites.

Order Squamata: Lizards, Snakes, and Their Relatives

Squamates are the most successful group of modern reptiles with 6300 species in 31 families that have a shared common ancestor. These animals have a transverse cloacal slit; males have a unique, paired hemipenis; and numerous shared internal morphological features place them in this taxa. Three distinct lineages—lizards (Sauria), snakes (Serpentes), and worm lizards (Amphisbaenia)—compose the group; all have representatives in Trinidad and Tobago.

Order Squamata: Suborder Amphisbaenia

Amphisbaenids are burrowing squamates distributed from North America, the Carribbean, South America, Africa, and the Mediterranean area. Approximately 150 species occur in 21 genera and four families. One family (Bipedidae) has remnant legs, and like most elongated vertebrates one lung is reduced—but unlike any other vertebrate, it is the right lung. Invertebrates and vertebrates compose their diet, and prey is recognized by odor and sound. Two species in one family are known from Trinidad; one of these, *Amphisbaena alba,* is the largest member of the suborder.

Order Squamata: Suborder Amphisbaenia Family Amphisbaenidae: Worm Lizards

This family contains 19 genera and about 133 species that are distributed in tropical and subtropical America, Africa,

and southwestern Asia. They have reduced or absent limbs, degenerate eyes, body scales arranged in annuli or rings, blunted tails; they are fossorial, and feed on invertebrates. Most species are oviparous. Two species occur on Trinidad; the suborder is unknown on Tobago.

Sometimes called "two headed snakes," amphisbaenids are neither snakes nor do they have two heads. Ditmars and Bridges (1935) commented on this paradoxical common name for these animals.

> Or, take the case of the "two-headed snake," which undeniably looks like a snake—we picked up a dead one, two feet long, on the road up to the guacharo gorge—but certainly isn't a snake. It is a lizard, and demonstrably has not two heads, but only one.

Amphisbaena alba Linnaeus

Map 44. Plate 78.

Amphisbaena alba Linnaeus, 1758:229. Type locality: America; restricted to the confluence of the Cottica River and the Perica Creek, Suriname, by Hoogmoed (1973).

Common Names: "Double headed serpent, or serpent-a-deux-tetes" (DeVerteuil, 1858); "White legless lizard" (Beebe, 1952); "Red worm lizard, Two-headed snake, Bachac Snake" (Boos, 1979c). The name "bachac snake" apparently comes from its association with the leaf-cutting ant, *Atta cephalotes,* which is commonly called the bacha ant (Boos, 1979c).

Distribution: *A. alba* is widespread, ranging from Panama (although this is questionable) through much of northern South America. On Trinidad it occurs from sea level to at least the foothills of the Northern Range, and probably to higher elevations. Trinidad locations in the literature include: Arima Valley (Beebe, 1952; Underwood, 1962); Tacarigua (Brongersma 1956b); Fondes Amandes, Santa Cruz, Maracas Bay Road, and the Upper Maracas/St. Joseph Valley (Boos, 1979c). Museum material documents: St. Ann's Valley; St. Augustine; Cedros Road; San Rafael; Port of Spain.

Description: Reaches 609 mm SVL, the largest specimen in this study measured 582 mm; tail short, 10% or less of SVL. A blunt-nosed, legless reptile that is tan to brown above and ivory below. Head slightly wider than body; rostral visible from above; dorsal, medial groove on head. Four supralabials; three infralabials; eye set in center of single ocular scale; one to three postoculars present; prefrontals and oculars usually in direct contact with supralabials, a characteristic that will distinguish it from *A. fuliginosa.* Body scales smooth, rectangular, and arranged in annuli; three Trinidad specimens have 220–233 annuli around midbody; 16 to 21 caudal annuli. Tail lacks constriction for autotomy; this and dorsal coloration will distinguish it from *A. fuliginosa.* Preanal pores number 9–10 in three Trinidad specimens. Adults uniform tan, with a cream colored head; juveniles may be blotched.

Natural History: Fossorial in forest and savanna. On the mainland Stahel and Geijskes (1939) found it in refuse pits of the leaf-cutting ant *Atta cephalotes;* Beebe (1945) found it be-

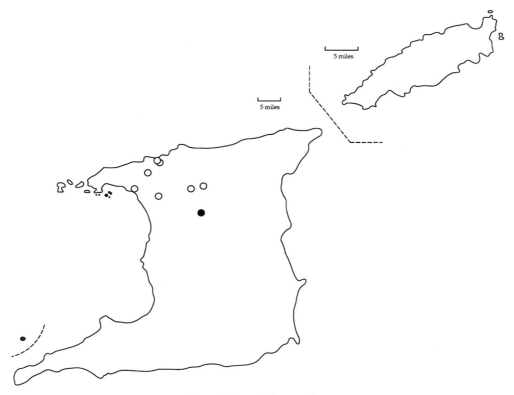

Map 44. *Amphisbaena alba*

neath forest floor debris; and Test et al. (1966) found one in an area of low hills with pastures and savanna. On Trinidad, Brongersma (1956b) reported it in secondary forest, and field notes (JCM) describe a road-killed specimen in an area of secondary forest and agriculture. On the mainland, larvae of the beetle *Coelosis biloba,* which inhabits *Atta* refuse pits were eaten (Stahel and Geijskes, 1939; 1940); also mole crickets, grasshoppers, termites, and mice (Beebe, 1945; Boos, 1979c). Hoogmoed (1973) found a specimen with the snake *Anilius scytale* protruding from its mouth; while W. W. Lamar (personal communication) found an adult *Anilius scytale* eating *A. alba.* In Suriname, Hoogmoed (1973) reported activity centered at dusk and dawn, with more activity at night than during the day; in Venezuela and Guiana, Beebe (1945) found them to be active during heavy rains. Riley et al. (1985) considered the species to have an obligate relationship with ants, laying their eggs only in ant nests, but noted confirmation is needed. Riley (1986) reported excavating seven *Atta cephalotes* nests and found this animal in three nests; ants were present in the digestive systems of seven of eleven specimens, but in low numbers; beetles, particularly the three-horned rhinoceros beetle *Coelosis biloba,* contributed a larger volume to the diet than ants; captives found capable of following ant pheromone trails; and the lung worm *Raillietiella giglionii* may be transmitted through the beetles they eat. W. W. Lamar (personal communication) found both species of *Amphisbaena* occuring on these island to feed on the eggs of the tortoises *Geochelone carbonaria* and *Geochelone dentic-*

ulata which were kept in large captive herds at the Instituto Roberto Franco in Villavicencio, Meta, Colombia. Gans (1962) attributed prominent scars on the tails of this species to predators attacking the tail during the defensive display. Boos (1979c) described defense behavior, including an up-turned tail that quivers and waves, a stiffened body, and strikes with the head; when it bites, the body twists and spins in an effort to tear off a piece of tissue. Boos and Quesnel (1968) have a photograph of this species mislabeled *A. fuliginosa.*

Material: Trinidad—AMNH 38367, 64524 no data. FMNH 49909, San Rafael.

Amphisbaena fuliginosa fuliginosa Linnaeus

Map 45. Plate 79.

Amphisbaena fuliginosa Linnaeus 1758:229. Type locality: America. Restricted to the Guianas by Vanzolini (1951), and further restricted to the confluence of the Cottica River and Perica Creek, Suriname, by Hoogmoed (1973). *Amphisbaena fuliginosa fuliginosa:* Vanzolini, 1951:60.

Common Names: "Double-headed serpent, or serpent-a-deux-tetes" (DeVerteuil, 1858); "Black-and-white legless lizard" (Beebe, 1952); "Two-headed snake, black and white coral, spotted worm snake" (Boos, 1979c).

Comment: Vanzolini (1951) considered the Trinidad population to be intergrades between *A. f. fuliginosa* and *A. f. varia* Laurent.

Distribution: *A. fuliginosa* is a widespread species, ranging

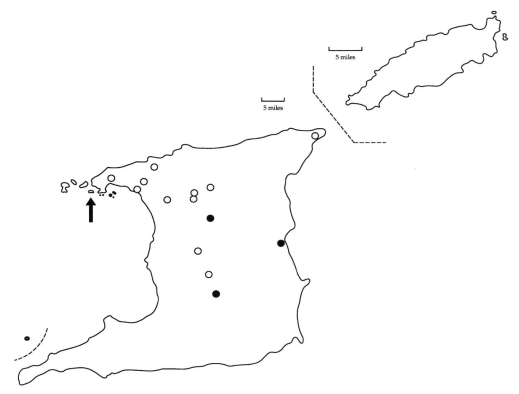

Map 45. *Amphisbaena fuliginosa fuliginosa*

from Panama to Peru and Brazil *A. f. fuliginosa* is a lowland Guiana endemic occurring from central Venezuela and Trinidad eastward to Suriname. Trinidad literature localities: Arima Valley (Beebe, 1952); Gaspar Grande island (Boos, 1984d); Orange Grove Estate and Tacarigua (Brongersma, 1956a); St. Augustine, Capro, and Tabaquite (Underwood, 1962). Field notes (JCM) report it in the Cocal, at Manzanilla Bay. Museum specimens add: Brickfield; Caparo; Southern Main Road between Cedros and Erin; Marval Golf Course, Port of Spain; San Rafael; Santa Cruz Valley; Toco; and Tucker Valley.

Description: Both sexes 425 mm SVL, the largest Trinidad specimen measured in this study is 325 mm; tail relatively long, 11–17% of SVL. Head about the same width as body, with a median groove; small portion of rostral visible from above; three supralabials and three or four infralabials; ocular small, postoculars number one or two; supralabials usually not in contact with prefrontals or oculars. In *A. alba* only the anterior edge of the ocular touches the second labial. Six Trinidad specimens have 186–211 body annuli and 21–28 tail annuli. Preanal pores number 8–11. Body with irregular black blotches on a white ground color on dorsal and ventral surfaces, coloration will separate it from *A. alba*. The ventral surface is mottled.

Natural History: *A. fuliginosa* is fossorial in forest and savanna. Brongersma (1956a) reported it from savanna; and in Suriname, Hoogmoed (1973) noted its presence in agricultural areas, savanna, and primary rainforest. In Trinidad, Boos (1979c) described it in very damp situations. On the mainland, Beebe (1945) suggested it is common and often observed it above ground during the day. Geijske (in Hoogmoed, 1973) found a number of specimens in the leaf-cutting ant *Atta cephalotes* refuse pits; *A. alba* is known from the same microhabitat. Field notes (JCM) report one specimen under coconut husks in the Cocal (coconut plantation along Manzanilla and Cocos Bays). On the mainland, food includes earthworms, crickets, grasshopper nymphs, ants, termites, centipedes, lizard egg shells, and other egg shells (Beebe, 1945; Duellman, 1978). Boos (1979c; 1984d) reported predation by the coral snake *Micrurus circinalis*.

Material: Trinidad—FMNH 49910, Brickfield; 49911–49913 San Rafael; 220620 Manzanilla Bay, The Cocal. USNM 5751 and 5787, no data.

Order Squamata: Suborder Sauria

Lizards have evolved distinct lineages, and current evidence suggests they all had a single ancestor. Today more than 16 families hold 390 genera and almost 3800 species of lizards, with new genera and species being described annually. Lizard diversity is greatest in the tropics, but a few species have been able to colonize high altitudes and latitudes. Most saurians are terrestrial, a few are aquatic, some dwell in the forest canopy, and some of these are adapted for gliding flight. The common green iguana is herbivorous and ferments vegetation in its large intestine; other lizards are insectivorous or carnivorous. Trinidad and Tobago have five families with 17 genera and 30 species and subspecies when questionable records are included.

Order Squamata: Suborder Sauria
Family Gekkonidae: The Geckos

The Gekkonidae is a large, diverse family of lizards containing 85 genera and more than 800 species. The family is circumglobal but uncommon in temperate latitudes. Most of these small lizards feed on invertebrates; produce small clutches of eggs; and have delicate skin covered with tiny scales, some of which have unusual shapes. Five genera and 10 species are represented on Trinidad and Tobago. One of these species, *Gymnodactylus geckoides,* is known from a single specimen from Trinidad and is otherwise known only from Brazil; its presence on Trinidad is questionable. Another species is also represented by a single Trinidad specimen, *Gonatodes albogularis;* while it is widespread elsewhere, its existence on Trinidad and Tobago is also problematic.

Bell (1889) described the turnip-tailed gecko *Thecadactylus rapicauda* in an exaggerated, factually incorrect, but humorous passage.

A much more objectionable reptile is the house lizard or wood-slave. It only comes out at night, and lives in very old wooden buildings. It is a most repulsive object, being a bilious yellowish grey, and covered all over with pimply-looking knobs and excrescences; add to this that it is cold and slimy, and that it has the property of sticking like glue to anything it falls on, and you may guess what a favourite it is with ladies. It makes a loud clucking noise at night, and wages war on cockroaches.

Gonatodes albogularis (Duméril and Bibron)

Plate 80.

Gymnodacatylus albogularis Duméril and Bibron, 1836, 3:415. Type locality: Martinique. *Gonatodes albogularis:* Boulenger, 1885:59.

Common Name: This lizard has no local name; elsewhere it is known as the "yellowhead gecko" (Conant and Collins, 1991).

Distribution: Central America, northern South America and the Antilles. Its presence on Trinidad is based upon material collected at Manzanilla Bay in 1929 by Graham Netting (CM 65526–27), a hatchling and an egg shell, from a dead stump. My examination of this poorly preserved specimen was inconclusive as to its identity, and it may well be a hatchling *G. humeralis.* There is also a note (Anon., 1897) reporting a specimen from Tobago deposited in the ANSP and collected by Dr. Benj. Sharp; Hardy (1984b) commented on this specimen and the fact that it is lost, or nonexistent, and believed the locality data was in error.

Description: Males 40 mm SVL, females 38 mm SVL; tail about 1.38 times greater than the SVL when undamaged; hind leg length/SVL ratio is 0.5. Snout rounded from above and truncated in profile. Canthus rounded and indistinct; eyes large and equal to, or greater than the eye-nostril distance; ear opening large and distinct. Dorsum covered with homogeneous granular scales; ventral scales larger than dorsal scales and overlap. Limbs well developed; each having five digits that are not expanded; dorsal surface of limbs covered by overlapping scales larger than dorsal granular scales on body. Fourth toe with 14–19 lamellae. Tail cylindrical. In preserved material the males are uniform olive-gray, often with a yellow (bright yellow in life) head; females mottled. Both sexes frequently have a bar or stripe in front of humerus, a character that may confuse it with *Gonatodes humeralis.* Adult *G. albogularis* have an eye diameter equal to or greater than the eye-nostril distance; *G. humeralis* has an eye diameter less than eye-nostril distance. *G. albogularis* has digital lamellae that are raised, and not wider than rest of digit, while *G. humeralis* has flattened lamellae that are wider than rest of digit.

Natural History: If this lizard exists on Trinidad and/or Tobago it can be expected to be in coastal areas, on tree trunks and walls of buildings.

Material: Trinidad—CM 65526–7, Manzanilla Bay. Colombia—FMNH 55913, 55918, 61701, 63817, 74936, 165822. El Salvador—FMNH 10981. Panama—FMNH 16715, 170056.

Gonatodes ceciliae Donoso-Barros

Map 46. Plate 81.

Gonatodes ocellatus Boettger, 1893:24 [in error.]. *Gonatodes ceciliae* Donoso-Barros, 1965:5. Type locality: Cerro Azul, Cerca de Macuro, Península de Paria, Estado Sucre, Venezuela. A formal description of this lizard was not published until 1966 (Donoso-Barros, 1966).

Common Name: "Variegated gecko" (Boos, 1977a).

Comment: McBee et al. (1987) reported Trinidad *G. ceciliae* have two different karyotypes; the specimens are from the same locality (Simla, the Arima Valley).

Distribution: *G. ceciliae* is restricted to Trinidad and the Península de Paria, Venezuela. In Trinidad it is known only from the Northern and Central Ranges; and it has a Carribean Coastal Range distribution. Published Trinidad localities include: Chacachacare and Monos islands (Boos, 1984c,d); Arima Valley (Brongersma, 1956a); cliffs of the Blanchissueuse Road (Boos, 1977a); Tamana cave (Kenny, 1979). Field notes (JCM) report it at the following Arima Valley locations: Simla, Asa Wright Nature Centre, Morne Bleu Ridge. Localities documented by museum material: trail to Maracas waterfall; Morne Bleu Ridge; and Tamana Hill.

Description: Males 51 mm, females 39 mm; tail 1.8 times SVL in specimens without damaged tails; size at hatching 15 mm SVL; hind legs about 46–48% of SVL. Snout pointed from above, rounded in profile; eye diameter less than eye-nostril distance; eyes relatively large; eyelids with two to five (usually four) horn-like supraciliary scales; all scales on

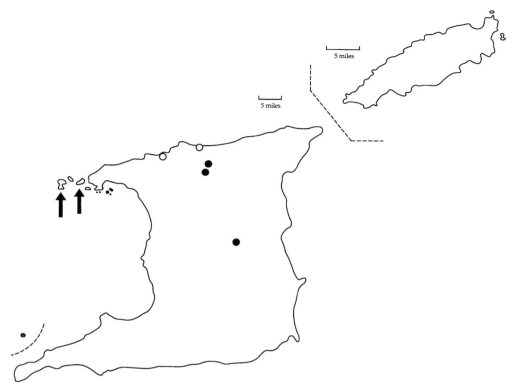

Map 46. *Gonatodes ceciliae*

orbit's anterior margin enlarged. Canthus indistinct and rounded; ear opening small and oval. Dorsum covered with small granular scales; anterior surface of limbs with enlarged scales; ventral scales overlap and are larger than dorsal scales. Limbs well developed, each with five digits; fourth toe with 18–20 lamellae. Male's dorsum brown-red, often with yellow spots and streaks outlined in black on head; yellow collar bordered in black that forms a bar anterior to the front leg in most specimens; gular region with yellow ocelli; sides of body with yellow mottling; belly cinnamon. Female's dorsum mottled with a light middorsal stripe and a light venter.

Natural History: A forest gecko. Field notes (JCM) describe this lizard: under ground cover in secondary forest; on tree trunks in primary and secondary forest; and in buildings at forest edge. Captives eat a variety of small arthropods and snails. J. Price (personal communication) observed this species walking alongside driver ant columns, possibly to eat the ants, or invertebrates flushed by the ants. On at least five occasions male-female pairs observed together on building walls and rafters, or on tree trunks in dense forest shade. The species apparently has a low tolerance for heat; a healthy male placed in direct sunlight for photography, at an air temperature of 27–28°C went into convulsions and died within 4–5 minutes. Another individual was found stuck to a wall that was freshly painted. A gravid female, collected on 1 July, contained a single egg.

Material: Trinidad—AMNH 81485 Simla, Arima Valley; 108712–16 Tamana Hill, Central Range; 108717 Morne Bleu, Northern Range. FMNH 176869, 176872–3, 176868, 176870–1, 215814–5, Arima Valley.

Gonatodes humeralis (Guichenot)

Map 47. Plate 82.

Gymnodactylus humeralis Guichenot, 1855: pl. 3, fig. 1a–1b. Type locality: Rio Ucayali, Mission de Sarayacu, Peru. *Gonatodes ferrugineus* Cope, 1863:102. *Gonatodes humeralis:* Boulenger, 1885:62.

Common Names: "Orange-spotted gecko" (Beebe, 1952); "Spot-nose gecko" (Boos, 1977a).

Distribution: *G. humeralis* has an Amazonian distribution. Trinidad localities in the literature: Monos Island (Boos, 1984c); Tucker Valley (Johnson, 1946); Maracas Valley, St. Augustine and Manzanilla Bay (Underwood, 1962). Trinidad localities based on museum material: Arima Valley; Aripo Savanna; Brickfield; near New Grant, Victoria Co.; 6 mi northwest of Port of Spain; San Fernando; Sangre Grande; San Rafael; Quarry Rest House, Siparia; Toco. Tobago records reported by Underwood (1962) were shown by Hardy (1982) to be misidentified *Gonatodes ocellatus*.

Description: 21–38 mm SVL; tail 1.36 times the SVL when undamaged; hind legs are 38% of SVL. Snout pointed from above and rounded in profile; canthus rounded and indistinct; eye diameter about two-thirds of the eye-nostril dis-

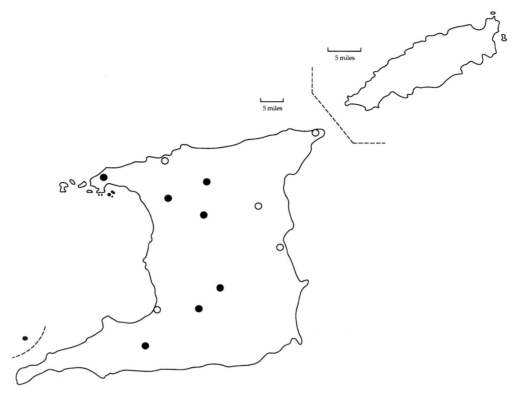

Map 47. *Gonatodes humeralis*

tance, a characteristic that will separate it from *G. albogu-laris*. Ear opening small, but distinct. Supralabials number nine, infralabials number 5–6. Dorsum covered with small granular scales; larger scales on the upper surfaces of limbs; overlapping ventral scales larger than dorsal scales; single row of large overlapping scales present on ventral surface of tail. Fifteen lamellae on the fourth finger, and 16 lamellae on the fourth toe; lamellae are wider than digit. Coloration sexually dimorphic: male's dorsum mostly dark brown, with some black, gray and yellow mottling; flanks with two rows of orange spots that may intrude onto the dorsum; yellow to white streak bordered with red from snout to edge of occipital region; light spot of yellow or grey on tip of snout; dorsum of tail with transverse bands; venter gray with yellow throat and chin; and, venter of tail orange. Female's dorsum brown-tan with indistinct middorsal stripe with scalloped edges; yellow or white bar anterior to front legs; dark brown streaks occur on the head and neck and the lower labials have a dark stripe; venter white, chin with brown spots. The color pattern will distinguish this species from the other common species of Trinidad and Tobago geckos in this genus. *Gonatodes albogularis* has lamellae of digits same width as digits while *G. humeralis* lamellae are wider than digit, at least in adults.

Natural History: *G. humeralis* frequents tree trunks and other vertical surfaces such as rock walls and herbaceous plant stems. On the mainland, stumps, fallen trees, tree trunks, palm leaf spathes, bromeliads, forest, secondary

growth, plantations, back yards, rock outcrops, and treetops (Beebe, 1944a; Underwood 1962; Hoogmoed, 1973) are reported as habitat. Johnson (1946) found one in an abandoned mud hut; Boos (1977a) wrote, ". . . rare in Trinidad, but . . . scattered in cocoa plantations throughout the island. In one large cocoa plantation in South Trinidad there is a fairly large colony. Every tree trunk was the home of a presiding male and several females. On being disturbed they would leap off the tree trunk to disappear into the leaf litter . . ." Field notes (JCM) report it in a forested rock outcrop, in supports of picnic shelters, and around buildings. It does not appear rare, but it is more secretive than its congeners. Food from seven specimens from Suriname examined by Hoogmoed (1973) included: an isopod, spiders, a pseudoscorpion, a scorpion, a millipede, beetles, caterpillars, a butterfly, a wasp, a fly a cicada, a mantis and a land snail. He found gravid females in all months in Suriname, and a clutch size of one egg. In Venezuela, Beebe (1944a) found eggs in debris, palm and bamboo stems, and root cavities. Riley et al. (1985) noted its use of termitaria as egg-laying sites on Trinidad. In Suriname, Hoogmoed (1973) reported 110 days for incubation of an egg kept at 25°C, and suggested incubation is shorter in nature, noting Beebe's (1944a) record of a 52 day incubation period.

Material: Trinidad—FMNH 21581, Simla; 35105, St. Augustine; 49791, 49799 San Rafael; 499800 Brickfield; 218795 Quarry Rest House, Siparia. USNM 16751 Simla; 119071–2 Tucker Valley; 166154 near New Grant, Victoria Co.

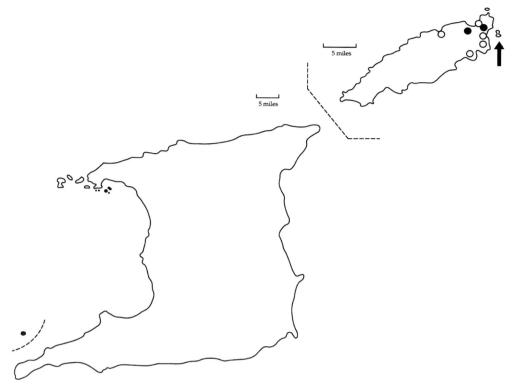

Map 48. *Gonatodes ocellatus*

| *Gonatodes ocellatus* (Gray) |

Map 48. Plate 83.

> *Cyrtodactylus ocellatus* Gray, 1831a:51. Type locality: None given. Restricted to Tobago by Boulenger (1885). *Gonatodes ocellatus:* Boulenger, 1885:60. pl. 15, Fig. 1.

Common Name: "Ocellated gecko" (Boos, 1974).

Distribution: *G. ocellatus* occurs only on Tobago and Little Tobago Islands. Although, Roze (1964) suggested it also occurs on Isla Margarita, and Donoso-Barros (1968) gives its range as, "Estado, Nueva Esparta: Isla Margarita, Cerro El Copey 850 m (Roze, 1964), Trinidad, Tobago and Grenada islands." And, Vanzolini (1968:89, his map 1) shows this species on mainland coastal Venezuela, but does not support it with specimens or data. Boos (1977a) suggested that *G. ocellatus* is restricted to the mesic northeastern end of Tobago. I agree and consider the species to be a Tobago endemic. Published localities include: Robinson Crusoe Hotel, Scarborough (Mertens, 1970); Charlotteville, Bloody Bay, Hermitage, Pigeon Peak Trail, near Roxborough and Merchiston (Hardy, 1982); and Dismore (1970) reported it from Little Tobago. Museum specimens document the species near Speyside, and on Little Tobago Island.

Description: Males 48 mm, females 43 mm SVL; tail 1.2 times the SVL; hind legs 47% of the SVL; hatchlings 19–23 mm SVL. Snout pointed from above, rounded in profile; canthus rounded and indistinct; eye diameter two-thirds of

eye-nostril distance; ear opening a small slit, but distinct. Dorsum covered with small granular scales; scales on the anterior surfaces of thighs much larger than those on the dorsum; ventral scales large and overlapping. Fourth finger with 18–19 lamellae, fourth toe with 25–26 lamellae. Males have a yellow head with red-brown stripes and blotches; dorsal color red-brown with large blue ocelli bordered with black; females with smaller ocelli and mottled dorsum. Yellow shoulder stripes bordered with black meet, or come close to meeting on middorsal line in both sexes. A faint middorsal stripe present in females. The presence of at least one pair of dorsolateral light blue colored ocelli outlined with dark pigment behind the front legs will readily distinguish this species from all other geckos in the area.

Natural History: A lizard of primary and secondary forests. Boos (1974) stated they, ". . . prefer damper regions . . . being found under rocks in river and stream beds, in the cracks of drain culverts, and between the timbers of old bridges on jungle and mountain roads. They have been seen on tree trunks of large trees growing near streams and in deserted buildings . . . " Field notes (JCM) describe *G. ocellatus* in piles of debris along roadsides; in forest bordering stream edges; in abandoned buildings; and roadside drainage tiles. On Little Tobago Island Dinsmore (1970) reported this lizard common in stands of the palm *Coccothrinax australis,* where he observed them on tree trunks and hiding in the root masses of the ground-dwelling aroid *Anthuriuim hookeri.* Captives readily eat termites, other small insects, and land

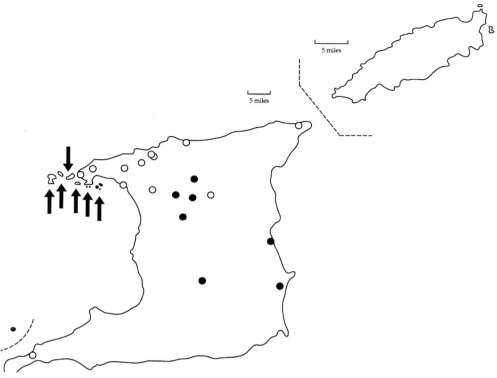

Map 49. *Gonatodes vittatus vittatus*

snails. Boos (1974) suggested males have fixed territories of several square yards that are shared with one or more females; noted a clutch size of one; and found communal nest sites under bark contained 30 eggs in various stages of development. Price and Miller (personal communication) have attempted to hybridize *G. ocellatus* and *G. ceciliae;* all hybrid eggs failed to develop.

Material: Tobago—FMNH 251220–21 near Cambelton. MCZ 55768–70 Charlotteville Rd., 1 km north of Speyside; 79769–70 Little Tobago Island.

Gonatodes vittatus vittatus (Lichtenstein)

Map 49. Plates 84, 85.

Gymnodactylus vittatus Lichtenstein, 1856:6. Type locality: La Guayra, Puerto Cabello and Caracas, Venezuela. *Gonatodes gillii* Cope, 1863:102. *Gonatodes vittatus:* Garman, 1887b:17.*Gonatodes vittatus vittatus* Roze, 1956:81.

Common Names: "White-banded gecko" (Beebe, 1952); "Streak lizard" (Quesnel, 1957).

Distribution: *G. vittatus* ranges from Colombia to Venezuela and occurs on offshore islands. *G. v. vittatus* has a Caribbean Coastal Range distribution, and *G. v. vittatus* is known from Colombia, Venezuela, Aruba, Curaçao(?), Margarita, Coche, Cubagua, Los Frailes, Los Testigos, Tobago and Trinidad. Published localities on Trinidad include: Scotland Bay (Johnson, 1946); Arima Valley (Werner, 1899;

Beebe, 1952; Brongersma, 1956a); Manzanilla Bay (Lynn, 1959); Chacachacare Island, Port of Spain, Maracas Valley, St. Augustine, and Caparo (Underwood, 1962); Chacachacare, Gaspar Grande, Huevos, Monos, and Nelson (Boos, 1984c,d; 1990; Boos and Quesnel, 1994). Museum material documents: Aripo Savanna; St. Augustine; Mt. St. Benedict; Blanchisseuse; Brickfield; Cedros; Marval; Manzanilla-Mayaro Rd. vicinity of milestone 39.5, Mayaro; Piarco; San Rafael; Toco; and Tucker Valley. On Tobago it is known from Scarborough (Underwood, 1962; Mertens, 1972). The relatively few records from Tobago, and the lack of field observations during this study suggest it may be a recent introduction on that island.

Description: Males 34 mm, females 33 mm SVL; the undamaged tail is 1.08 times the SVL; hind legs about 50% of the SVL. Snout pointed from above and in profile; canthus rounded and indistinct; eye diameter about two thirds eye-nostril distance; ear opening small and oval. Dorsal scales small granules, ventral scales large, overlapping and extend onto anterior surface of limbs. Fourth finger has 12–14 lamellae, fourth toe with 19–22 lamellae. Males brown-grey or cinnamon-brown with bright white middorsal stripe bordered with black, and extending to tip of tail; females with white vertebral stripe, and mottling on the sides. Venters of both sexes tend to be white or tan; males sometimes have a white chin with oblique stripes. The white vertebral stripe will readily distinguish this species from all other Trinidad and Tobago geckos; females may be confused with other *Gonatodes* females but the stripe in *G. vittatus* females is relatively well defined and starts in the occipital region.

Natural History: A forest-edge species that occasionally uses more open habitats, and edificarian situations; Lynn (1959) found it under coconut trash along Manzanilla Bay's cocal; Underwood (1962) reported them in open shade, on the trunks of trees with loose bark, and noted them entering houses; and Johnson (1946) found two in a log. Field notes (JCM) report this species to be exceptionally abundant at the base of coconut palms under fallen fronds, the density of these animals was estimated at 3–5 individuals per square meter in this habitat. Mosaics of sunlight around and in buildings at Simla were frequently used and they do not hesitate to use occupied rooms. Captives eat small arthropods. *Gonatodes* frequently curl their tails over their backs in a scorpion-like posture, a female displaying the tail-raised posture toward a male about a meter away, the male then displacing the female from her station. Boos (1977a) suggested this is a threat display in *G. ocellatus;* but Demeter and Marcelini (1981) found tail waving frequent when *G. vittatus* is in a state of high arousal, i.e., during feeding or social contact; this unusual posture needs further study to ascertain its function. Quesnel (1957) reported eggs in every month of the year, females laid eggs about 1 month apart; and fertile eggs were produced for 5–6 months after the last mating. Field notes (JCM) describe eggs of this gecko on the base of palm trees; the eggs are laid on trunks covered with fallen fronds. Demeter and Marcellini (1981) documented behavior associated with courtship and aggression and found female *G. vittatus* to be more aggressive than other lizard behavior studies would predict. *Gonatodes'* skin tears easily and is an excellent predator escape technique; several individuals avoided capture with this mechanism (field notes, JCM).

Material: Trinidad—FMNH 49802–6 Brickfield; 49807–12 San Rafael; 178081 Spring Hill Farm (= Simla), 215812 Simla, Arima Valley. USNM 119074 Tucker Valley; 141569–81 Manzanilla Bay; 166161 Manzanilla-Mayaro Rd., vicinity of milestone 39.25; 166163 Mayaro, Mayaro Co.; 166164 Mayaro-Guayaguayare Rd. vicinity of milestone 5, Mayaro Co.; 1666165–69 Piarco, vicinity of airport and Bel Air Hotel grounds.

Gymnodactylus geckoides Spix

Plate 86.

Gymnodactylus geckoides Spix, 1825: pl. 18, fig. 1. Type locality: Bahia, Brazil.

Distribution: Brazil, and possibly Trinidad's Northern Range. The species is listed here based upon a single specimen (FMNH 177679) labeled "*Gonatodes* sp., British West Indies, Trinidad, Spring Hill Farm." The specimen was collected by E. H. Taylor in 1962. Taylor's field number, 7412, is still on the specimen; other lizards accompanying this specimen are *Gonatodes ceciliae,* they also have field numbers attached, and 7412 is in the middle of the series. *Gonatodes ceciliae* is a near Trinidad endemic and lends support to the accuracy of the locality data. However, Taylor's journal showed he visited Brazil the same year; thus the presence of this species on Trinidad is problematic.

Description: The Trinidad specimen is a female with a SVL of 39 mm, and a 45 mm tail, about 1.15 times SVL, hind limbs about 41% SVL. The skin is damaged on the right side. Snout pointed from above and sloping in profile; canthus rounded and indistinct. Supralabials number six, infralabials number five. Ear opening a small slit, difficult to see. Dorsum covered with small granular scales and 13 longitudinal rows of tubercles, a character that will distinguish it from all species of *Gonatodes*. Ventral scales large and overlapping; scales on upper and anterior surface of limbs are also large and overlapping. Tail cylindrical with transverse dark bands; ventral surface of tail with a row of wide scales. Fourth finger with 16 lamellae; the fourth toe with 12 lamellae; and the proximal 7–10 lamellae are reduced to small scales. Color in alcohol brown. Two postocular stripes, the uppermost continues around the back of the head and connects to the opposite side. There are alternating light and dark spots on the labials. Venter with scattered pigmentation and ventral midline of the tail has a dark spot on each scale.

Natural History: Vanzolini (1972b) observed the three races of this species are associated with three different plant formations: *G. g. geckoides* with the xerophytic caatingas, *G. g. amarali* with the savanna-like cerrados and *G. g. darwinii* with the Atlantic forests. Spring Hill Farm, now the Asa Wright Nature Centre, is located in a secondary forest and was for some time a cocoa estate. The original vegetation was lower montane rainforest. The presence of this lizard on Trinidad is not confirmed by this study.

Material: Trinidad—FMNH 177679 Spring Hill Farm, Arima Valley.

Hemidactylus mabouia (Moreau de Jonnès)

Map 50. Plate 87.

Gekko mabouia Moreau de Jonnès, 1818:138. Type locality: "Antilles"; restricted by Stejneger (1904) and Smith and Taylor (1950) to St. Vincent Island. *Hemidactylus mabouia* Duméril and Bibron, 1836:326. *Hemidactylus mabuia* Court, 1858:440.

Common Names: "Wall mabuia or *mabuia des murailles*" (DeVerteuil, 1858:440); "African woodslave" (Underwood, 1962); "Woodslave, Mabouia, Twenty-Four Hours" (Boos, 1977b). Boos (1977b) found the name "twenty-four hours" commonly applied to this species as well as *Thecadactylus rapicauda, Polychrus marmoratus, Anolis aeneus,* and *Anolis trinitatus*. He asked Trinidadians the reason for the name, answers were: (1) "The lizard jumps onto and 'sticks' irremovable to the victim for 24 hours. Then the victim dies!" (2) "The lizard dies in 24 hours. Also the victim!" and, (3) "No matter how long the lizard stays on, the victim dies. In 24 hours." Boos noted that geckos are considered venomous in

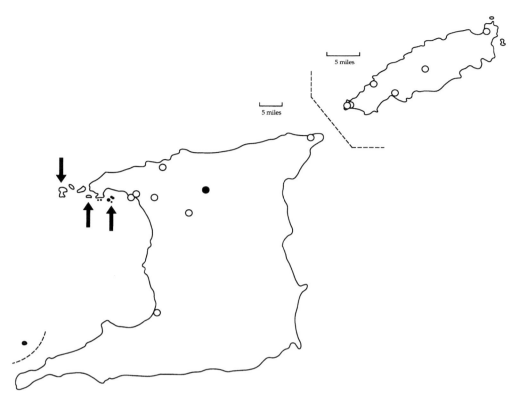

Map 50. *Hemidactylus mabouia*

many parts of the world and the ". . . ethnic pot-pourri in Trinidad and Tobago has perpetuated this myth . . ."

Distribution: Africa, Madagascar, and the islands of the Mozambique Channel; Ascension Island; on the east coast of South America from Uruguay to the Orinoco Delta; the length of the Amazon River; numerous islands in the Antilles, and Trinidad and Tobago. Published Trinidad localities: Arima Valley (Beebe, 1952); Port of Spain, San Juan, and Chacachacare Island (Underwood, 1962); Carrera and Nelson islands (Boos, 1984d) and Gaspar Grande (Boos and Quesnel, 1994). Museum specimens document: Bel Air Hotel at Piarco Airport; Maracas Beach; Toco; Bayshore; and Palmiste Estate, San Fernando. Underwood (1962) stated that on Tobago it is known only from Scarborough; however, Mertens (1972) listed Scarborough (Robinson Crusoe Hotel) and Grafton Estate (south west coast); and field notes (JCM) report it at Charlotteville. Museum specimems document Tobago localities: Store Bay at Crown Point; and Hillsborough Dam. Kluge (1969) made a compelling argument for dispersal of this species from Africa to the New World via natural rafting, instead of the species using the slave trade dispersal route hypothesized by early workers. Subsequently, Vanzolini (1978) suggested this species has had ample opportunity (by both natural and human transport) to test every area in mainland South America where it might survive, and that its current distribution reflects ecological interactions in situ rather than mecha-

nisms of dispersal. It is interesting to note that most of the Trinidad and Tobago localities for this lizard are centers of human activity.

Description: Adults 42–63 mm SVL; hatchlings about 20 mm SVL; tail 1.2 times the SVL; hind legs about 42% of the SVL. Snout pointed from above and rounded in profile; canthus indistinct; eye diameter three-fourths of eye-nostril distance; ear opening oval and small; supralabials number 8–12; infralabials number 7–9. Dorsum covered with small granular scales and studded with trihedral tubercles in 6–14 longitudinal rows. Ventral scales are larger than dorsal scales and the ventrals overlap; large scales on dorsal and anterior surface of the limbs. Lamellae on fourth finger number 7–9, lamellae on fourth toe number 7–8. Femoral and anal pores number 29–33 in males. Tail with granular scales; scattered tubercles on dorsum of tail; ventral surface of tail with double row of scales. Dorsum tan, dark brown, or grey with dark brown middorsal blotches and light and dark alternating spots on labials. This species has some ability to change color, mostly from light to dark brown-grey, and color change may be brought about by background light intensity and temperature. Venter tan to white. This lizard is most readily confused with *H. palaichthus*, which has a more spiny appearance and lamellae on the base of toes four and five that extend to the base of the digit. In this species tuberculate scales are widely separated and lamellae do not extend to base of toes four and five.

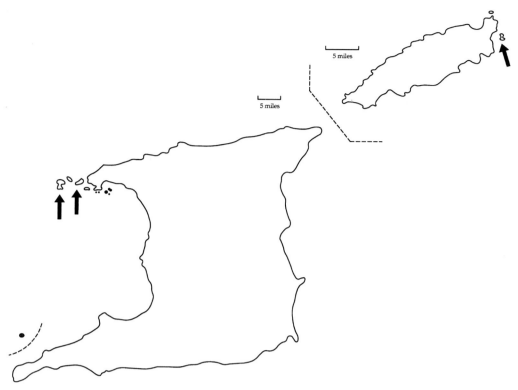

Map 51. *Hemidactylus palaichthus*

Natural History: Frequents edificarian environments—buildings, rock walls, and wooden picnic tables, as well as tree trunks. It may be nocturnal or diurnal: Hoogmoed (1973) reported three specimens during the day; field notes (JCM) describe one specimen active during the early morning (0530 h); and small colonies of 4–5 individuals clustered within 1 m² around outdoor lights to feed and interact socially from sunset to sunrise; Beebe (1944a) considered them nocturnal. The African population probably reproduces year round; Fitch (1970) reported eggs in all months of the year. Food is mostly arthropods.

Material: Trinidad—FMNH 177292–8, Arima Valley.

Hemidactylus palaichthus Kluge

Map 51. Plate 88.

Hemidactylus ?brooki: Underwood, 1962:174. *Hemidactylus palaichthus* Kluge, 1969:39. Type locality: Krupukari, Guyana (4° N, 59° 25′ W). *Hemidactylus brooki haitianus:* Peters and Donoso-Barros 1970:141. *Hemidactylus brooki palaichthus:* Mertens, 1972:9. *Hemidactylus brooki:* Boos, 1977b:29.

Common Name: "Spiny gecko" (Boos, 1981).

Distribution: *H. palaichthus* is a lowland Guiana endemic, known from Brazil, Guyana, Suriname, northeastern and central Venezuela, and Colombia; in the Antilles it is known from Maria Island off St. Lucia; its occurrence on Trinidad and Tobago proper are questionable, but it does occur on small offshore islands and rocks. Localities reported in the literature for the Trinidad and Tobago area include: Monos and Chacachacare islands (Underwood, 1962; Boos 1981, 1984d) and Little Tobago (Tuck, 1972). These locations are supported with museum specimens. The only specimen from Trinidad proper is USNM 146361, collected at Simla, Arima Valley. It seems unlikely this is a valid locality because of the secondary forest habitat; this is a savanna species. Many herpetologists have collected this site before and after the date of the sole specimen's collection; and there is the possibility that the specimen was transported to that site and later found by someone else. Thus, this lizard is probably restricted to small offshore islands and rocks in the eastern Caribbean. The presence of endemic New World *Hemidactylus,* such as this species, raises the question of how it got to the Western Hemisphere—a rafting ancestor from the Old World or a remnant from the breakup of Gondwanaland.

Description: Adults 54–62 mm SVL, tail at least 1.11 times the SVL, based on a regenerated tail; hind legs about 45% SVL. Snout rounded from above, sloping in profile; eye diameter about two-thirds eye-nostril distance; ear opening distinct; canthus rounded and indistinct. Dorsum with small granular scales, and 16–17 longitudinal rows of trihedral tubercles; *H. mabouia* has fewer rows of tubercles. Venter with large overlapping scales; anterior surface of limbs covered with large scales; upper surface of limbs covered with

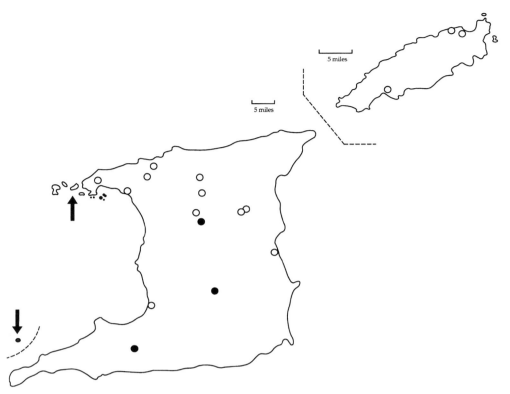

Map 52. *Sphaerodactylus molei*

granules and tubercles. One male has 40 pre-anal and fe-moral pores, another has 36. Tail depressed with six rows of tubercles. Fourth toe with eight lamellae from the base of digit to claw. *H. palaichthus* has three single lamellae at the base of the fourth toe, followed by six paired lamellae; the column terminates with a single lamella. Dorsum tan with brown transverse bands, a brown streak through the loreal re-gion, and some dark brown spots on the head; venter cream-white.

Natural History: A savanna and forest-edge lizard that uses buildings. Underwood (1962) considered the species in-troduced, writing "It is surprising that both these introduced geckos [*mabouia* and *palaichthus*] should have reached Cha-cachacare. They were taken only a few yards apart in adja-cent coconut trees." Boos (1981) reported a sighting at Grand Fond Bay (in a latrine) on Monos Island in 1979; later he (Boos,1984c) stated two specimens were collected on a house, one in 1977 and one in 1979, both were foraging for insects, one during the day, the other at night. Field notes (JCM) report it in a derelict building under a board on the floor; the building is in a transitional littoral woodland-de-ciduous seasonal forest on Little Tobago. Vanzolini (1978) examined the distribution of this lizard on mainland South America and concluded it is primarily nocturnal with a ten-dency toward some diurnal activity; and considered the species an open formation animal with good preadaptations to a perianthropic lifestyle. It seems likely its island distrib-

ution may be restricted to small rocks that lack predators or, more likely, competitors in the form of *H. mabouia*. *H. mabouia* may outcompete *H. palaichthus* and displace it wherever it starts to becomes established within its range; this would account for *H. palaichthus* being found on small, offshore satellites. The island distribution therefore may rep-resent dispersal and attempts to become established that rarely succeed for any length of time.

Material: Trinidad AMNH 64525 Teteron Bay; MCZ 66936 Cha-cachacare; 6066, 127013–17 Trinidad, no data; 159776 Monos Is-land. Little Tobago Island USNM 192763–5.

Sphaerodactylus molei Boettger

Map 52. Plates 89, 90.

Sphaerodactylus molei Boettger, 1894b:80. Type locality: Caparo, Trinidad. *Sphaerodactylus buergeri:* Werner, 1900:264. *Sphaero-dactylus lineolatus molei:* Underwood, 1962:168.

Common Names: "Black-and-white headed gecko" (Beebe, 1952); "Mole's gecko" (Boos, 1977b).

Distribution: *S. molei* is a Caribbean Coastal Range form, distributed from coastal Venezuela to the Guianas and on Trin-idad and Tobago. Published Trinidad localities: Port of Spain (Werner, 1900); Arima Valley (Beebe, 1952); Manzanilla Bay (Lynn, 1959); Arima; Caparo; Maracas Valley; and Sangre Grande (Underwood, 1962); Monos Island and Soldado Rock (Boos, 1984b,c). Field notes (JCM) report it at Simla, in the Arima Valley; the Quarry Rest House in Siparia; and in an abandoned building near Cambleton, Tobago. Museum specimens document the following Trinidad locations: Mt. St. Benedict; Brickfield; Canari Bay east of Moruga; San Fernando; Guaico; Mt. Harris; Manzanilla Bay; grounds of Imperial College, Port of Spain; San Rafael; Siparia; Tucker Valley; and Warneville. Published Tobago localities: Scarborough, Tobago (Underwood, 1962.); Little Tobago Island (Dinsmore, 1970.) Tobago localities documented by museum material are: Anse Fourmi; and the burial ground at Scarborough.

Description: Adults 28 mm SVL, hatchlings about 19 mm SVL; tail about 1.01 times the SVL; hind limbs 34.6% of the SVL. Snout pointed from above and rounded in profile; canthus is rounded and indistinct; rostral strongly notched; eye diameter slightly less than eye-nostril distance; supraciliary (eyelid) spine present; two supranasals separated by 1–3 internasals; supralabials and infralabials number 5–6; ear opening oval and tympanum difficult to see. Dorsolateral scales minute, rhomboid, and strongly keeled; ventral scales overlap and much larger than the dorsals; posterior fourth of venter with a cluster of hypertrophied scales that form an escutcheon. Tail scales become more overlapping distally; ventral side of tail with larger irregular scales. Limbs covered with larger overlapping scales; fourth finger with 7–10 lamellae; fourth toe has 7–8 lamellae. Color variable and sexually dimorphic, Harris (1982) noted females have same color pattern throughout the range, while the males exhibit three color morphs. Females tan above with a pair of yellow, dark bordered dorsolateral stripes extending from eye to tail. Venter lighter in color, chin may be speckled. One gravid female (field notes, JCM) almost uniform tan and the dorsolateral stripes all but invisible, well-developed calcium storage cheek pouches present. Young specimens are brighter in color; pattern similar to the female. Males variable, on Trinidad the upper head can be black with bright white longitudinal stripes, with lower parts tan-yellow, with head pattern ending abruptly at back of head and dorsum of body spotted. Another pattern is dark stripes which edge lighter dorsolateral stripes which break up into spots toward the posterior of the body. The latter pattern is common in Tobago and mainland populations.

Natural History: A minute, diurnal gecko attracted to human dwellings. Beebe (1944a) reported it in buildings; Boos (1977b) described the habitat as unexpected places such as cracks in walls, piles of coconuts, loose dry leaves on banana trees, and later (Boos, 1984c) found it in palm frond leaf axils. Field notes (JCM) describe this lizard in more edificarian environments: a laundry room floor, a bathroom floor, on a brick wall, on drapes in a house, in doorjam, and in abandoned buildings. Dinsmore (1970) also reported it from edificarian structures on Little Tobago. Beebe (1944a) observed it slowly stalking prey, which he described as small-winged wood roaches, ants, and termites; captives readily eat wingless *Drosophila*. In Venezuela, Beebe (1944a) found a 5 x 7 mm egg in a rotten stump

on 30 July; a gravid female on 16 March; and reports predation by the gecko *Thecadactylus rapicauda*. Lazell (1994a) noted *S. molei* belongs in a group with *S. kirbyi* and *S. vincenti* based on morphology and geography, and Haas (1991) has shown that *S. molei* is biochemically remote from the Antillean species.

Material: Trinidad: FMNH 49813–4 Brickfield; 49815 Mt. Harris; 49816–20 San Rafael; 218792 near Siparia, at Quarry Resthouse.

Thecadactylus rapicauda (Houttuyn)

Map 53. Plates 91, 92.

Gekko rapicauda Houttyn, 1782:323. Type locality: West Indies; restricted to Chichén Itzá, Yucatán, Mexico, by Smith and Taylor (1950); and to Paramaribo, Suriname, by Hoogmoed (1973). *Thecadactylus rapicaudus:* Gray, 1845:146. *Platydactylus pheconyx:* Court, 1858:440. *Platydactylus theconyx:* Court, 1884:381. *Thecadactylus rapicauda:* Garman, 1887b:17.

Common Names: "Plantain Mabuia, or *mabouia de bananiers*" (DeVerteuil, 1858); "House gecko" (Beebe, 1952); "Woodslave" (Boos and Quesnel, 1968); "Mabouia, Twenty-Four Hours" (Boos, 1977b). [For a comment on the origin and meaning of the name "Twenty-Four Hours" see the *Hemidactylus mabouia* account.]

Distribution: *T. rapicauda* is widespread, ranging from Mexico into South America and northward into the Lesser Antilles. On Trinidad and Tobago it is widespread, ranging from sea level to at least 305 m in the Northern Range. Published Trinidad localities: Scotland Bay (Johnson, 1946); Arima Valley (Beebe, 1952; Brongersma, 1956a); Port of Spain, St. Augustine, Mayaro Bay (Underwood, 1962); Monos, Chacachacare, Gaspar Grande, Caledonia and Nelson Islands (Boos, 1984b,c). Other Trinidad localities based on museum material: Balandra; Mt. St. Benedict; Brickfield; Mt. Catherine; Diego Martin; San Fernando; Heights of Guanapo; Mt. Harris; Matura-Toco Rd.; Sangre Grande; and San Rafael. Published Tobago localities: Scarborough (Underwood, 1962); Scarborough (Robinson Crusoe Hotel), Grafton Estate, Prospect Estate (Mertens, 1972). Little Tobago Island (Dinsmore, 1970). Tobago localities based upon museum material: Bacolet Estate; Charlotteville; Crown Point Airport; Hillsborough Dam; Man of War Bay; and Speyside.

Description: Maximum SVL 121 mm for both sexes, largest specimen measured in this study 98 mm SVL; tails always appear damaged and less than the SVL; hind legs 33% SVL. Snout pointed from above and sloping in profile; rostral large and rectangular; eye diameter about two-thirds eye-nostril distance; canthus rounded and indistinct; supralabials number 8–13; infralabials number 8–12; ear opening relatively large and oval. Dorsal scales granular and homogeneous; ventral scales larger than dorsals and overlap. Fingers and toes webbed basally; fourth finger with 12–17 lamellae; fourth toe with 13–14 lamellae. Tail usually partially regenerated and turnip-like in shape; tails that have not regenerated do not have this shape. Dorsal coloration

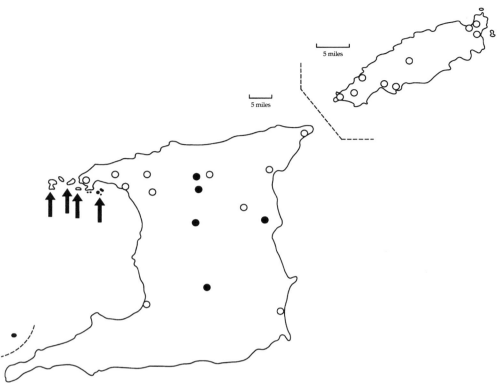

Map 53. *Thecadactylus rapicauda*

dark to light grey, with white labial spots and a white post-ocular streak. Color changes from day to night, and possibly with physiological conditions associated with ambient light, stress, and social conditions. An animal observed on Tobago closely matched the coloration of its tree branch perch (field notes, JCM). Distinguished from the two species of *Hemidactylus* by the webbing that connects the digits and by the uniform, small, granular scales that cover the dorsum of *T. rapicauda*. *Hemidactylus* lacks digital webbing, and has rows of larger, tubercular scales on the dorsum.

Natural History: *T. rapicauda* occurs in a variety of habitats from forests to savanna, and edificarian environments (Field, 1942; Beebe, 1944a; Johnson, 1946; Vanzolini, 1972b; Duellman, 1978). In Suriname, Hoogmoed (1973) reported it in the lower parts of buttresses and observed it basking on tree trunks near openings to tree cavities. Fields notes (JCM) describe it active at night on the ceilings of buildings occupied by humans; and during the day in a decaying coconut palm, and on a concrete drain in cacao. Food is mostly insects but the gecko *Sphaerodactylus molei* has also been listed as prey (Parker 1935b; Beebe, 1944a; Duellman, 1978). Underwood (1962) described the voice of this gecko as, ". . . a diminishing series of chirps;" and, Hoogmoed (1973) suggested vocalizations are used in establishing and maintaining territories. The fragile skin of this species has been noted by several authors (Beebe, 1944a; Johnson, 1946) and this escape technique can be effective;

field notes (JCM) report the loss of several specimens because they literally "crawled" out of their skin. A tail-waving display toward conspecifics and a clutch size of one is reported by Beebe (1944a).

Material: Trinidad—FMNH 49821–2 Brickfield; 49823–5, 49828 Mt. Harris; 49826–7, 49829–31 San Rafael; 177084–5 Simla, Arima Valley; 219604 Arima-Blanchisseusse Rd. at the 1.25 milepost.

Order Squamata: Suborder Sauria
Family Gymnophthalmidae: Microteiids

Gymnophthalmidae contains about 28 genera of small Neotropical lizards with biconodont teeth (teeth with two cusps); hemipenes with folds; nasal plates separated from each other by a frontal; parietals in contact with the supraoccipital in wide suture; well-developed frontal-parietal tabs; and the males smaller than the females (Presch, 1983). Six species are known to occur on Trinidad and Tobago, and I suspect at least one other species in this family occurs on Trinidad but is currently undiscovered. This family is controversial, and many authors retain its subfamily status in the family Teiidae.

Bachia heteropa trinitatis appears to be the animal responsible for the quaint but absurd folk story in Joseph's (1838) *History of Trinidad*.

I have had given to me two specimens, preserved in spirits, of what I believe to be unknown to naturalists: these are intermediate between the serpent and the lizard, hav-

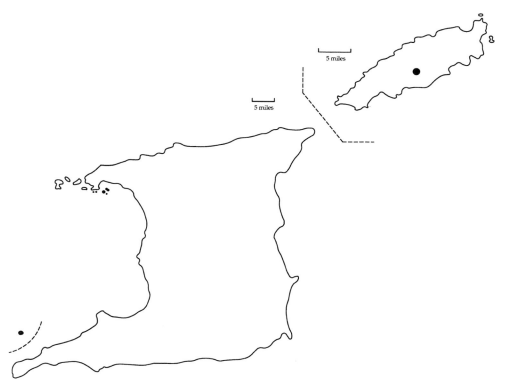

Map 54. *Bachia flavescens*

ing the four legs of the latter, and the body, forked tongue, plantes, and poison tusks of the viper. One of the two specimens I have, stung a fowl, which immediately dropped down and expired. The one is about three, and the other four inches in length; their legs are remarkably small. I should suppose, from the appearance of the specimens, that they glide like serpents, yet never use their legs to aid their progress . . .

Bachia flavescens (Bonnaterre)

Map 54. Figure B.

Chalcides flavescens Bonnaterre 1789:67, pl 12, fig. 4. Type locality: Unknown. *B.[achia] flavescens:* Ruthven, 1922:63. *Bachia* cf. *flavescens:* Hardy, 1982:78.

Distribution: Dixon (1973) described the distribution of this lizard as Kartabo, Moraballi, and the Ireng Valley, Guiana. Hardy (1982) reported collecting three specimens near Hillsborough Dam on Tobago.

Description: The largest Tobago specimen 61 mm SVL, with a 57 mm regenerated tail; maximum SVL for this species 67 mm (Dixon, 1973). A worm-like lizard with greatly reduced limbs, a cylindrical body, and a long tail. Head longer than broad; snout a rounded point from above and protruding in profile. Rostral pentagonal, followed by a hexagonal frontonasal separating the nasals; prefrontals absent; frontal pentagonal and followed by two large parietals and a small, triangular interparietal; nostril on the nasal–first labial seam. One preocular; one postocular; two or three sub-

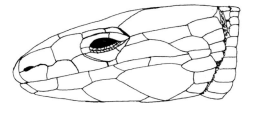

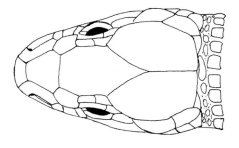

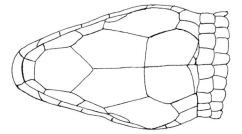

Figure B

oculars; three superciliaries; two supraoculars; six supralabials, four infralabials. Body covered with quadrangular, juxtaposed scales in 47–48 transverse dorsal rows, and 36–37 transverse ventral rows; tail with quadrangular, juxtaposed scales. Limbs covered with large, overlapping, plate-like scales. Front limbs with three digits; hind limbs with two digits. Males with two preanal pores, females lack them. Eight gulars. Scales around midbody number 28–31. Dorsal pattern: three dark stripes, one vertebral and two dorsolateral. Venter yellow-tan. Anal plate divided into three or four scales, and preceded by four or five preanal shields. The scalation of Tobago specimens agrees well with that of the mainland population described by Dixon (1973). The Tobago population has one more gular row, two or three more rows of transverse ventrals, and one or two more preanal shields than mainland specimens.

Natural History: This species is known from five specimens from Guiana and three from Tobago; consequently little is known about its natural history. It is fossorial, undoubtedly feeds on small invertebrates and probably lays one or two eggs, like its congeners.

Material: Tobago—USNM 227942–4 St. Mary Parrish, near Hillsborough Dam.

Bachia heteropa alleni (Barbour)

Map 55.

Scolecosaurus alleni Barbour, 1914:315. Type locality: St. George's, Grenada. [*Bachia*] *alleni:* Vanzolini, 1961:204. *Scolecosaurus trinitatis:* Underwood, 1962:169. *Bachia alleni alleni:* Thomas, 1965: 149. *Bachia heteropa alleni:* Dixon, 1973:34.

Distribution: *B. heteropa* is found on the islands of Grenada, the Grenadines, Tobago, and Trinidad and the arid costal zone of northern Venezuela (Dixon, 1973). *B. h. alleni* is restricted to the islands of Grenada, the Grenadines, Little Tobago, and Tobago. Published Tobago localities include: between Speyside and Charlotteville (Underwood, 1962); Little Tobago (Dinsmore, 1970). Museum material from Tobago adds: Charlotteville cacao plantation; 1–3 mi from Charlotteville on Northside Rd.; Pirate's Cove, Charlotteville; Hillsborough Dam; Kings Bay; near Lambeau Hill; 2.75 milepost on Easterfield Road near Mason Hall; Doctor's River, Speyside. It seems likely this race is autochonotus to Tobago, and introduced in the Lesser Antilles; it has a distribution that parallels that of *Leptodactylus validus.*

Description: Maximum 64 mm SVL; undamaged tail 1.6 times the SVL; hind legs about 12.9% of SVL. A worm-like lizard with greatly reduced limbs, a cylindrical body, and a very long tail. Head longer than broad; snout rounded from above and slightly protruding in profile. Rostral rectangular and followed by pentagonal frontonasal. Frontonasal followed by two prefrontals that contact each other on midline; Trinidad populations of *B. h. trinitatis* have the two prefrontals separated from each other by a frontonasal. In-

terparietal rectangular and smaller in area than parietals. Each nostril on seam between nasal and first supralabial. Supralabials number six, infralabials number five or six. Body with 5–12 longitudinal rows of hexagonal, smooth, overlapping dorsal scales; and 16–22 longitudinal rows of quadrangular, juxtaposed, lateral and ventral scales. Tail scales hexagonal. Limbs covered with large, plate-like, juxtaposed scales. Front limbs with four digits, hind limbs with two to four digits. Scales around the midbody number 27–31. Males with one or two preanal pores, females lack them. Pattern of dark, longitudinal stripes broken into spots and streaks; the light areas stippled with dark brown pigment. The presence of a prefrontal and four digits on the hind legs will readily separate this species from *Bachia flavescens.*

Natural History: Most likely similar to that of *Bachia heteropa trinitatis;* see that account. On Little Tobago, Dinsmore (1970) observed a blue-crowned motmot, *Momotus momota,* feeding this lizard to its young.

Material: Tobago—FMNH 55392 no data.

Bachia heteropa trinitatis (Barbour)

Map 55. Plate 93.

Scolecosaurus trinitatis Barbour, 1914:316. Type locality: Caparo, Trinidad. *Scolecosaurus cuvieri:* Boettger, 1898:76 (Trinidad). *Bachia alleni trinitatis:* Peters and Donoso-Barros, 1970:79. *Bachia heteropa trinitatis:* Dixon, 1973:32. *Bachia heteropus trinitatus* [*sic*]: MacLean et al. 1977:45. *Bachia trinitatis:* Kenny, 1979:9.

Common Names: "Worm lizard" (Beebe, 1952); "ground puppy" (Boos, 1979b).

Distribution: *B. heteropa* has a Caribbean Coastal Range distribution, occuring on the islands of Grenada, the Grenadines, Tobago, and Trinidad and in the arid costal zone of northern Venezuela (Dixon, 1973). *B. h. trinitatis* inhabits Trinidad, Chacachacare and Monos Islands, and Monagas, Venezuela. Published Trinidad localities: Arima (Werner, 1900); Tucker Valley (Johnson, 1946); Tacurigua (Brongersma, 1956b); Arima Valley (Beebe, 1952); near La Veronica (Lynn, 1959); Tamana Caves (Kenny, 1979); Chacachacare and Monos Islands (Boos, 1984c,d). Museum material from Trinidad adds: St. Augustine, Mt. St. Benedict, Blanchissuse; Brickfield; Caparo; Caura Valley; Chacachacare Island; Gaspere Island; St. Joseph; Manzanilla Bay; Maracas Valley; between Princes Town and Moruga; Morne Bleu Ridge; St. Michael's Estate; Pointe-à-Pierre; Port of Spain; Mt. Tucuche; and Tunapuna.

Description: Maximum of 64 mm SVL; undamaged tail 1.6 times the SVL; hind legs about 12.9% of the SVL. A worm-like lizard with greatly reduced limbs, a cylindrical body, and a very long tail; head longer than broad. Snout rounded from above, slightly protruding in profile. Rostral rectangular and followed by hexagonal frontonasal which separates two preoculars in most specimens; in Tobago populations of *B. h. alleni* the frontonasal followed by two pre-

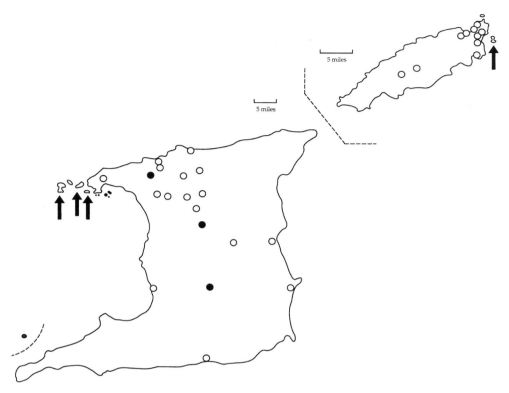

Map 55. *Bachia heteropa alleni* (Tobago)
Bachia heteropa trinitatis (Trinidad)

frontals that contact each other on the midline. Two or three supraoculars. Interparietal scale rectangular, smaller in area than parietals; nostril on seam between nasal and first supralabial. Supralabials number six, infralabials number five or six. Dorsum of body with 5–12 longitudinal rows of hexagonal, smooth, overlapping scales; and 16–22 longitudinal rows of quadrangular, juxtaposed, lateral and ventral scales; tail scales hexagonal. Limbs covered with large, plate-like, juxtaposed scales. Front limbs with four digits, hind limbs with two to four digits. Scales around the midbody number 26–31 for Trinidad animals. Males with one or two preanal pores, females lack them. Dorsal pattern dark, longitudinal lines with four, lighter, wider alternating stripes. Dorsal color brown-black; venter yellow-brown. The Tobago population (*B. h. alleni*) has the stripes obscured by having them broken into spots and streaks. Both races tend to have the light areas stippled with dark brown pigment. The presence of a prefrontal scale and four digits on the hind legs will distinguish this species from *Bachia flavescens*.

Natural History: A leaf litter dwelling lizard of forests and forest-edges; Dixon (1973), on the basis of size and development of limbs, considered *B. h. trinitatis* to be a supraterranean leaf litter inhabitant; Barbour (1914) found them under fallen cacao pods; Lynn (1959) reported one under a stone at roadside and one in coconut trash; Johnson

(1946) found several on the jungle floor. Parker (1935b) listed earwigs, dipteran larva, and mycetophilid larva as stomach contents. Field notes (JCM) report one regurgitated by the coral snake *Micrurus circinalis* (in the same mass was part of a well-digested *Ninia,* and it seems probable that the *Bachia* was not first eaten by the gastropod-eating *Ninia*). Brongersma (1956b) found one in the stomach of the snake *Liophis melanotus;* and field notes (JCM) report 2 of 14 *L. melanotus* stomachs examined contained this lizard. Beebe (1945) noted the superficial resemblance between this lizard and the snake *Atractus trilineatus* which shares the same microhabitat.

Material: Trinidad—FMNH 40000 Mt. St. Benedict; 49872–93 Brickfield; 49896–7 Brickfield; 49898 San Rafael.

Gymnophthalmus speciosus (Hallowell)

Map 56.

Blepharictisis speciosa Hallowell, 1860 [1861]:484. Type locality: Nicaragua. *Gymnophthalmus speciosus:* Stuart, 1939:4. *Gymnophthalmus underwoodi:* Underwood, 1962:178 (Chacachacare Island only).

Comment: The identity of the Chacachacare Island population of this lizard is questioned by Vanzolini and Carvalho (1991); they commented, " . . . what is called *G. speciosus* in Venezuela may well be something else . . . " At the

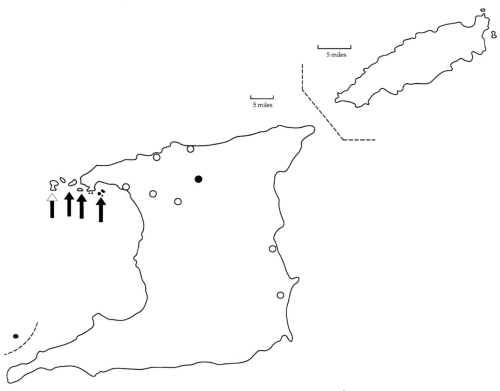

Map 56. *Gymnophthalmus speciosus* ↑
Gymnophthalmus underwoodi

end of their paper in "Note added in proof" they wrote, " . . . the specimens that have been called *G. speciosus* in Venezuela certainly do not belong to this Central American species."

Distribution: A widespread species, *G. speciosus* ranges from southeastern Mexico through Central America into northern Colombia, Venezuela, and Guyana. It also occurs on Chacachacare Island off the northwestern peninsula of Trinidad.

Description: 40 mm SVL; tail about 1.7 times SVL; hind legs 29% of SVL. Body and tail cylindrical; short legs; and a missing first finger. Head longer than wide; rostral hexagonal; undivided nasal scales separated by frontonasal scale; frontal rhomboidal. Interparietal scale elongate, parietal scales pentagonal. Three occipital scales with medial one smaller than laterals. One preocular, two or three postoculars, one supraocular, and one subocular. Ear opening rectangular. Supralabials number eight, infralabials number five. Head scales with numerous pits, otherwise all scales smooth. Three rows of dorsal scales, vertebral row smaller than dorsal scales on either side. The lateral scales are slightly smaller than the dorsals, ventral scales about same size as dorsals. Ventrals arranged in two rows, begin posterior to larger pectoral plates. Thomas (1965) found the only way to distinguish this species from *G. underwoodi,* without looking at chromosomes, was to count the number of ventrals between the pectoral and anal plates. *G. speciosus* has 23–27 ventrals and *G. underwoodi* has 21–24 ventrals. Cole et al. (1990) suggested the light dorsolateral stripe in this species extends onto base of tail, and it may be reduced to a series of spots posteriorly. In *G. underwoodi* this stripe fades at midbody. All body scales overlap. There are 13 scale rows around midbody, and 22–26 transverse scales rows on body. Forelimbs covered with rounded, overlapping scales. Four fingers on each hand. Hind limbs covered with rounded, overlapping scales; feet with five digits. Males have three to five preanal pores.

Natural History: Cole et al. (1990) described the habitat on Chacachacare Island as " . . . open sunny areas around houses and in or at the edges of deciduous forest that was leafless in the dry season, always in sunlit litter." Cole et al. (1993) considered this bisexual species and *G. cryptus* to be ancestral to the unisexual *G. underwoodi.*

Material: Trinidad—AMNH 119744 La Tinta Bay, Chacachacare Is. 128438–45 Chacachacare Is., Venezuela—FMNH 176692.

Gymnophthalmus underwoodi **Grant**

Map 56. Plate 94.

Gymnophthalmus underwoodi Grant, 1958:228. Type locality: Barbados. *Gymnophthalmus lineatus:* Underwood, 1956:25.

Common Name: "Shiny Lizard" (Boos, 1979b).

Comment: Vanzolini and Carvalho (1991) stated, ". . . more than one clone goes under the name *G. underwoodi*. What status to give them is still a moot question." This statement suggests *G. underwoodi* is more than a single taxonomic unit.

Distribution: *G. underwoodi* has an Orinoco Basin distribution known from Venezuela and the Guianas and Trinidad, and has dispersed to the Lesser Antilles, Barbados, St. Vincent, and Guadeloupe. Schwartz and Henderson (1988) suggested that it may be introduced on Guadeloupe and St. Vincent. Hardy (1982) commented on the lack of specimens from Tobago, noting that it occurs on Grenada; however, Vanzolini (1990), using Hardy's specimen (USNM 192965), reported it as *Gymnophthalmus speciosus*. Lazell and Sinclair (1990) report *G. underwoodi* from Bequia Island, Grenadines. Its presence on Tobago remains unconfirmed. Published Trinidad localities include: St. Augustine and Port of Spain (Underwood, 1956); Port of Spain, Maracas Valley, St. Augustine, Piarco Airport, and Manzanilla Bay, (Underwood, 1962). [Note Underwood (1962) also listed Chacachacare Island, but this population has now been shown to be *Gymnophthalmus speciosus*.] Monos, Lenagan and Nelson Islands (Boos, 1984d, 1990) and Gaspar Grande (Boos and Quesnel, 1994). Museum material available from most locations noted above and the Arima Valley, Blanchisseuse, and Mayaro.

Description: 44 mm SVL; tail 1.7 SVL; hind legs 29% SVL. First finger is missing. Head longer than wide; rostral hexagonal; undivided nasals separated by frontonasal; frontal rhomboidal; interparietal elongate; parietals pentagonal; three occipitals, medial one smaller than laterals. One preocular; two or three postoculars; one supraocular, one subocular. Ear opening rectangular. Supralabials number eight; infralabials number five. Head scales with numerous pits, otherwise all scales smooth. Three rows of dorsal scales, vertebral row smaller than the dorsals on either side. Lateral scales slightly smaller than dorsal scales, ventrals about the same size as the dorsal scales; scale arrangement distinguishes this lizard from all other Trinidad and Tobago lizards, except *G. speciosus*. Ventral scales in two rows, counted between pectoral and anal plates. Thomas (1965) finds the only way to distinguish between this lizard and *G. speciosus* is by the number of ventrals. *G. underwoodi* from Trinidad has 21–24 ventrals; South American *G. speciosus* has 23–27 ventrals. Cole et al. (1990) reported the dorsolateral stripe in *G. underwoodi* extends only to midbody, but to base of tail in *G. speciosus* as a row of light spots. Thirteen rows of overlapping scales around midbody; and 22–26 transverse rows of scales on body. Limbs covered with rounded, overlapping scales. Four fingers; fourth finger with 13–16 keeled lamellae. Hind feet with five digits; fourth toe with 16–19 lamellae. Dorsum shiny brown-gray with light dorsolateral stripes, black flanks, venter gray-white. Each ventral scale with patch of brown pigment giving venter an overall dark appearance. Light patch on the throat. This lizard is an all-female species; males if present would be expected to have preanal pores.

Natural History: A savanna lizard, using lawns, gardens, and other human-modified environments (Hoogmoed, 1973; Boos, 1979b). Underwood (1956) wrote, ". . . it is common in Port of Spain. It probably occurs in nearly every yard in the city . . . I found these lizards in fairly dry litter in contrast to the damp situations in which *Scolecosaurus* [= *Bachia*] was found." Field notes (JCM) describe it on the lawn around Simla, in the Arima Valley; they move very fast, darting into burrows and under rocks. Cole et al. (1990) stated, ". . . we found *G. underwoodi* active only on hot, open, sunlit ground, often around buildings. Individuals are best caught in areas of short grass, including lawns, because they are small, they skitter about quickly, and they dive into litter and holes for cover . . . the major activity period for *G. underwoodi* was from about 10:30 AM to 2:00 PM, on clear, sunny days in March, April, June and July." They reported the air temperature in the grass where they found this lizard to be active was 33.4°C. Thomas (1965) first found populations of this lizard consisted of all female populations; and Hoogmoed (1973) later reported parthenogenic reproduction in the Suriname population. However, Cole et al. (1983, 1990) and Hardy et al. (1989) have shown this species is the product of hybridization; they suggested that *G. underwoodi* evolved from *G. speciosus* and a yet undescribed *Gymnopthalmus* during alternating xeric-mesic periods contact when savannas and forests were in flux. Later, Cole et al. (1993) reported the missing ancestor of *G. underwoodi* to be *G. cryptus*, a bisexual species described in 1992 from the Orinoco drainage of Venezuela. The distribution, ecology, morphology, and structural genes at 32 loci all support the idea that *speciosus* and *cryptus* are ancestral to *G. underwoodi*.

Material: Trinidad—FMNH 177041, 218533 Simla, Arima Valley.

Proctoporus shrevei Parker

Map 57. Plates 95, 96.

Proctoporus (Oreosaurus) shrevei Parker, 1935c:283. Type locality: Heaths of the Aripo Northern Range, Trinidad. *Proctoporus shrevei:* Underwood, 1962:178. *Proctoporus shreevei:* MacLean et al. 1977: 46. (typing error).

Common Names: "Luminous Lizard" (Beebe, 1952); "Mountain Teiid" (Boos, 1979b.)

Distribution: *P. shrevei*, a Trinidad endemic, is known only from Trinidad's Northern Range. Literature records include Mt. Aripo, Mt. Tucuche (Uzzell, 1958; Underwood, 1962; Read, 1986a). Museum material supports these two localities. Field notes (JCM) report this lizard at an Arima Valley location, and it is likely that this lizard has other populations in the Northern Range. Donoso-Barros (1968) suggested that it may eventually be found in the Sierra de Paria in Estado Sucre, Venezuela.

Description: 42 mm SVL, but may reach or exceed 50 mm SVL; tail 1.7 times SVL; hind legs 37–42% SVL. Snout pointed from above and in profile; rostral rectangular; frontonasal longer than broad, narrows anteriorly, and is in broad contact with the nasal scales; frontal slightly longer than frontonasal; frontoparietals in broad contact; interparietal longer than parietal and frontoparietal; two occipitals same size as parietals; four supraoculars separated from upper eyelid by four supraciliaries; five supralabials and four infralabials; the nasal is large, with a prenostril ridge that directs the nostril opening posterior and lateral; loreal absent. Pupil round; lower eyelid with translucent disk composed of four large and several smaller scales. Ear opening oval, outlined with two rows of small scales; tympanum visible. Lateral neck scales rugose. Mental scale is a semicircle followed by a postmental and two pairs of chin shields in contact at the midline; three rows of pre-gulars arranged in chevrons with apices pointing anterior; gulars juxtaposed, oval to quadrangular, arranged in seven transverse rows (including the gular fold); gular fold contains eight rectangular scales, each creased. Two to five enlarged, smooth nuchal scales. Dorsal scales hexagonal and moderately keeled; twice as long as broad and slightly overlapping; arranged in 33–41 transverse rows from nuchals to base of the tail; lateral scales 50–75% of dorsal scale size, and make up four to six longitudinal rows. Two lateral scale rows per dorsal row present in axillary and flank region, but at midbody the laterals increase in size, and may equal dorsals. Ventrals are smooth, quadrangular, and juxtaposed; arranged in eight longitudinal rows, with the two most lateral rows on each side much smaller than the middle four rows; in 19 transverse rows with the 19th row forming a semicircle with six scales, the middle two much larger than two laterals on either side. Two to six preanal scales and each has a pore. Anal plate composed of three scales forming a half circle; broader than long. Scales on dorsal surface of tail change from hexagonal to square distally; overlap slightly; and change from keeled to smooth. Ventral tail scales are square, smooth, and in five rows. Scales on upper and anterior surface of the front limbs are large, slightly overlap and plate-like; those on inner surface are large granules. Fingers from shortest to longest are 1, 5, 2, 4, 3; fourth finger with 9–13 lamellae; palm's surface covered with flat granules. Dorsal and posterior surfaces of the hind limbs are rugose; scales of anterior and ventral surface of hindlimbs slightly overlapping and plate-like; toes from shortest to longest 1, 2, 5, 3, 4; fourth toe with 15–18 lamellae, with four most proximal lamellae divided; foot's ventral surface has smooth, flat scales. Femoral and preanal pores number 2–31. In life this lizard has a dark brown dorsum with light flecks; the venter is cream. Light lines on labials. Adult males have a single row of ocelli on each side of the body; center of each ocellus contains a scale or two with red pigment; females and juveniles lack ocelli. In preserved specimens the red-centered ocelli fade to cream. This species can be distinguished from all other microteiids known from the area by the separation of the nasal scales by the frontoparietal scale and the unusual pattern of two lateral scale rows equalling the width of one dorsal row.

Natural History: *P. shrevei* is terrestrial along stream-edge habitat in primary, lower montane rainforest. Field notes (JCM) report three specimens under rocks within 1 meter of a stream; when disturbed they scurry under the nearest cover. Underwood (1962) stated they can be found under logs, in litter, and possibly caves; Read (1986a) observed this species at night, one swimming in a pool of water in the petiole of a fallen palm leaf, and another retreated into a burrow under a fallen tree fern trunk. He found 14 eggs in a moss covered bunch of aerial roots, about 1 meter from ground, 10 eggs adhered in pairs; thus the usual clutch size is two, and this species has communal nesting sites. He also described three other pairs of eggs under moss on branches, and one pair in a bromeliad. Fitch (1970) reviewed the literature on reproduction for other members of this genus and most produce a single egg. There is a remarkable story about this lizard that requires mentioning; Sanderson (1939) stated this species is capable of producing light. He wrote,

> In a crevice beneath a ledge I saw a dim light which promptly went out. I flashed the torch in and there was a small lizard. Putting a net over one end of the cleft, I tickled it, but instead of running out, it turned its head away from me and both its sides lit up for a few seconds like the port holes on a ship. Eventually I got it out with forceps, and as I held it up, it again lit up brilliantly.

Sanderson presented his specimens to H. W. Parker at the British Museum, and Parker (1939) described the ocelli in the males of this species as luminous organs. Roth and Gans (1960) reviewed the situation and concluded there is no evidence to suggest this species generates light, by itself or with the help of symbiotic microorganisms. However, they never actually examined a living adult male, but cite another herpetologists who did. And while it seems highly improbable this species is capable of generating light, Sanderson's claim has not been disproven. Parker (1939) hypothesized that the luminous organs may function as simple reflectors; and W. W. Lamar (personal communication) found sexually active male *Prionodactylus argulus* have stark white lateral ocelli that are highly reflective, and may give the appearance of glowing in the dark.

Material: Trinidad—BMNH 1940.3.11.71–72, 1940.3.11.92–95, Mt. Aripo; FMNH 218993–4 Arima Valley; MCZ 34273, 38659, 62506–07, 160065–67, 100466–71 Mt. Tucuche. USNM 166671 Mt. Tucuche.

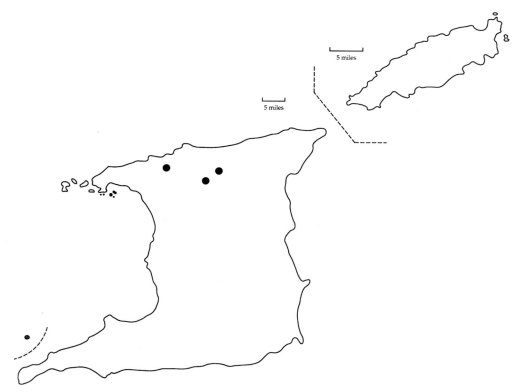

Map 57. *Proctoporus shrevei*

Map 58. *Anolis aeneus*

Order Squamata: Suborder Sauria
Family Iguanidae: Iguanas

The Iguanidae occur in tropical and subtropical America from the southwestern United States and eastern Mexico southward to southern Brazil and Paraguay; the Galapagos Islands; the Antilles; Madagascar, Fiji, and Tonga Islands. The Iguanidae has been recently broken up into several families by Frost and Etheridge (1989), an arrangement that is highly controversial (Lazell, 1992, 1994b; Schwenk, 1994). The more traditional view of this family is retained here, acknowledging the controversy without evaluating the contested character states or the taxonomic philosophies involved. A similar situation exists with the recent changes in *Anolis* (Guyer and Savage, 1986) and considering the critique of Williams (1989b), and others, the more traditional view is retained here. Nine species in four genera inhabit Trinidad and Tobago. One of these, *Anolis* cf. *lemurinus,* is known from a single specimen collected in 1863. Four others have been introduced by humans from elsewhere in Caribbean. Worth (1967) wrote about finding iguanas on Soldado Rock.

On our approach to the Rock we observed large iguana lizards (not a marine species, as in the Galápagos) traversing cliff faces, and here on this scarcely less vertical though lightly vegetated ascent we found their nursury. Numerous babies—green creatures less than a foot long—invited collection, but already they were either fleet or else incredibly knowledgeable about crevices inaccessible to our acquisitive hands.

Anolis aeneus (Gray)

Map 58. Plate 97.

Anolis aeneus Gray, 1840: 114. Type locality: none given. Lazell (1972) restricted it to Pointe Saline, St. George Parrish, Grenada. *Anolius alligator:* Court, 1858:440. *Anolis alligator:* Boulenger, 1885 vol. 2:31. *Anolis roquet aeneus:* Underwood, 1959:209. *Dactyloa aenea:* Schwartz and Henderson, 1988:124.

Common Names: "Grey Speckled Anole, Garden Lizard" (Boos, 1977d).

Distribution: *A. aeneus* has a Lesser Antilles distribution and is autochthonous on the Grenada Island Bank (Lazell, 1972); but it has been introduced into Guyana, Trinidad, and some satellite islands off Trinidad. Published Trinidad localities: Port of Spain (Werner, 1900); St. Augustine and Mayaro (Underwood, 1962); Mayaro coconut plantations, Beetham Highway mangrove swamp, the northwest peninsula, Maracas Bay, the Five Islands, Gasparee (= Gaspar Grande), Gasparillo, Little Centipede, Carrera, Caledonia, Lenagan, and Nelson Islands (Boos, 1977d; 1984c; 1990). Museum specimens document the following localities: Spring Hill Estate in the Arima Valley (= Asa Wright Nature Centre; it is otherwise unknown from there and the data may be in error); the grounds of the Bel Air Hotel, near Piarco Airport; Maracas Beach; St. Augustine; Caparo; Mayaro Beach; San Fernando; Marval; and Rushworth Street, in Queens Park Savanna in Port of Spain. Field notes (JCM) report this anole on the grounds of the Forestry Offices on Long Circle Road in St. James.

Description: Males 80 mm, females 55 mm; hind limbs slightly less than 0.5 SVL. Snout rounded; wide rostral scale, distinguishing this species from *A. extremus* with rostral broken into three separate scales. Canthus a distinct ridge forming outer edge of a trough that slopes to nostril, medial region of snout raised; supraorbital semicircle (a half circle of many tiny scales above the eye) well developed. Ear opening about three-fourths eye diameter. Dorsal scales granular and enlarge laterally; ventral scales and scales on the upper surface of limbs smooth. Distal scales of tail keeled; tail with a middorsal ridge; slight middorsal ridge on body. Males with large gray-green and yellow dewlap. Dorsal color grey-brown with a green tint. Females may have a middorsal pattern: a stripe, transverse bars, or a mottled pattern of gray and brown. Coloration will distinguish it from *Anolis trinitatis,* which is green, and the smooth ventral scales will distinguish it from *Anolis chrysolepis planiceps* which has keeled ventral scales. Underwood (1959) described the color as ". . . a grey lizard; there may be a trace of copper-green. There are fuzzy warm brown transverse bands, five on the trunk, extending onto the tail. The whole lizard is liberally sprinkled with dark spots. The lizard is capable of little color change."

Natural History: A tree trunk dweller in urban areas, ports, coconut plantations, and open woodlands. *A. aeneus* has been the subject of many ecological and systematic studies in Trinidad and Grenada (Gorman, 1969; Gorman and Boos, 1972; Yang et al., 1974; Gorman and Licht, 1975; and Stamps in Grenada, see Schwartz and Henderson, 1991, for a review). Gorman and Atkins (1968), Gorman et al. (1971), Gorman and Boos (1972) suggested this species is forcing *A. trinitatis* toward extinction with competition and hybridization (both species are introduced in Trinidad). They noted the failure of the hybrids to reproduce (*A. trinitatis* has a diploid number of 36, *A. aeneus* has a diploid numer of 34, the hybrids have a diploid number of 35) and the increasing ratio of *A. aeneus* to *A. trinitatis* over an 8 month period. Beebe (1944b) reported that *A. aeneus* feeds on termites and mosquitos, and other insects. Field notes (JCM) describe males displaying about 0.5 m above the ground, on tree trunks; Gorman (1969) noted the hybrids have a territorial display intermediate between those of the parent species. In Grenada, it breeds during the rainy season (Stamps and Crews, 1976). When disturbed, it ascends the tree trunk and keeps the trunk between itself and the intruder in typical anole fashion.

Material: Trinidad—FMNH 176926–8 Spring Hill Farm, Arima Valley. USNM 166640–56, 167602 Piarco, Bel Air Hotel.

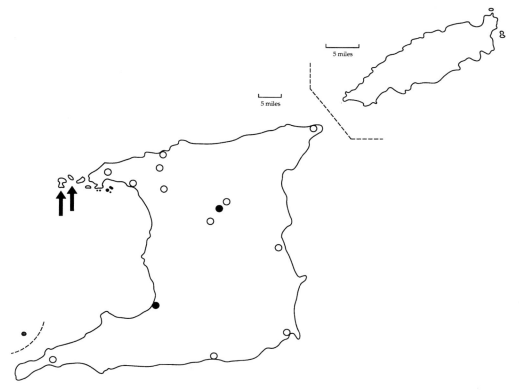

Map 59. *Anolis chrysolepis planiceps*

Anolis chrysolepis planiceps (Troschel)

Map 59. Plate 98.

> *Anolis planiceps* Troschel, 1848:649. Type locality: Caracas, Venezuela. *Anolis chrysolepis:* Mole and Urich, 1894a:81. *Anolis chrysolepis planiceps:* Vanzolini and Williams, 1970:85.

Common Names: "Leaf Lizard" (Field, 1942); "Striped-backed Anolis" (Beebe, 1952); "Jungle Anole" (Boos, 1977d).

Distribution: *A. chrysolepis* has an Amazonian distribution. *A. c. planiceps* occurs in Venezuela, Guyana, and Trinidad; and is a Guiana lowland endemic. Published locality records for Trinidad: Tucker Valley (Johnson, 1946); Port of Spain, Maracas Valley, Nariva Swamp (Underwood, 1962); Chacachacare and Huevos (Boos, 1984b); Aripo savannas (Schwab, 1988). Field notes (JCM): Arena Forest; Aripo savannas; southwestern peninsula just east of Bonasse. Localities documented by museum material: San Rafael; St. Augustine; Mt. St. Benedict; La Seita; Toco; Morgua; Guayaguayare; Mayaro; Chacachacare Island; and Huevos Island.

Description: Males 68 mm, females 54 mm SVL; tail about 2.4 times the SVL; hind limbs long, slightly less or equal to SVL. Snout rounded with single, keeled, elongated rostral with rounded edges; ridge of heavily keeled scales forms canthus; enlarged scales form a supraocular semicircle around each orbit when viewed from above; supralabials number 9–11; infralabials number 10–11. Ear opening small, about half eye diameter. Dorsal scales small and granular;

two rows of vertebral scales enlarged; lower lateral and strongly keeled ventral scales much larger than dorsal scales. Strongly keeled ventral scales will distinguish this species from all other Trinidad and Tobago anoles except *A.* cf. *lemurinus.* This species has a tibia length that is longer than its head, while *A.* cf. *lemurinus* tibia length is equal to, or less than, its head length. All limbs have five digits and are covered with keeled scales that are larger than dorsal scales; tail covered with large keeled scales. Both sexes with scarlet dewlap; females have a light vertebral stripe, males do not; females yellow-brown with light vertebral stripe that widens and narrows on tail; paired dark blotches occur on both sides of the vertebral stripe; pattern missing or poorly developed in males. Venter white or cream, with scattered dark pigment on ventral surface of limbs.

Natural History: A forest dwelling lizard that forages on the ground, uses lower tree trunks for displays, and sleeps in low bushes at night (Beebe, 1944a; Johnson, 1946; and Boos, 1977d); field notes (JCM) report one specimen sleeping on vegetation about 1 meter above a stream. Boos (1977d) reported them present in almost every Trinidad woodland and noted they benefit from cacao cultivation; flowers and rotting fruits attract insects and plantation workers have reduced the number of snakes that would normally prey on them. Diet includes: caterpillars, grasshoppers, wood lice, dipterous larva, termites, spiders, and ants (Parker, 1935b; Beebe, 1944a). In Venezuela, eggs are laid in March, April, May, June, and August (Beebe, 1944b).

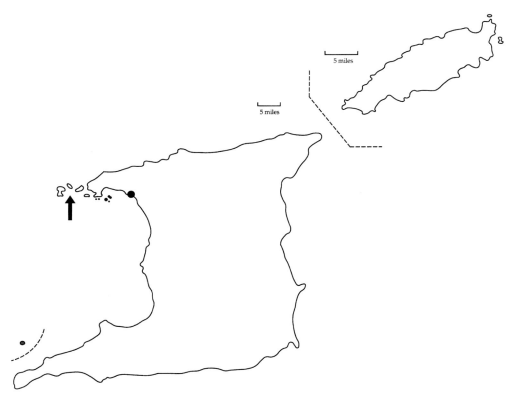

Map 60. *Anolis extremus*

Boos and Urich (1986) reported this species using bipedal locomotion.

Material: Trinidad—FMNH 49831–2 San Rafael. MCZ 81303–05 San Fernando; 100118 Chacachacare Island; 100119 Huevos Island.

Anolis extremus Garman

Map 60. Plate 99.

Anolis extremus Garman 1887a:11. Type locality: Barbados. *Dactyloa extrema:* Schwartz and Henderson, 1988:125.

Common Name: Barbados Anole (Boos, 1977d).

Distribution: A Lesser Antillean species from Barbados; introduced on Bermuda, St. Lucia, Trinidad, Huevos Island off NW Trinidad, and at Caracas, Venezuela. Considered part of the Trinidad herpetofauna based upon a literature record (Boos, 1977d) reporting six pairs of this lizard introduced on Huevos Island in 1965, and noted the species' continued presence in 1976; and, a series of five specimens collected along Wrightson Rd. opposite the Holiday Inn (USNM 244439–244442) in Port of Spain in 1982. In 1993 I spent several hours attempting to confirm its presence at the Wrightson Rd.—Holiday Inn location; the search was inconclusive.

Description: A male 67 mm SVL, with a damaged tail, largest Trinidad specimen examined; elsewhere males are known to reach at least 83 mm SVL, and females reach 60 mm; undamaged tail 1.7 times SVL in a juvenile; hind limbs are about 80% SVL. Snout round with rostral broken into three small granular scales will distinguish it from *Anolis aeneus* with a single rostral scale; canthus concave, forming a trough toward the nostrils; nostrils positioned on outer edges of raised area between the troughs. Trinidad male with 7–8 supralabials and 7–9 infralabials. Ear opening oval, about one-half diameter of eye; semicircles of scales present above orbits. Dorsum covered with keeled, granular scales, a characteristic that will distinguish this species from *A. aeneus,* which has smooth dorsal scales; vertebral ridge present. Ventral scales larger than dorsal scales and smooth. Scales on upper surfaces of limbs larger than dorsal and ventral scales. Fourth finger on a Trinidad male with 33 lamellae, fourth toe with 58 lamellae. Scales on distal three-fourths of tail keeled; tail with distinct dorsal ridge of keeled scales. Dorsum green with blue-gray head; females and juveniles with stripe or middorsal pattern; males with large orange, yellow, and green dewlap.

Natural History: On Trinidad *A. extremus* is an urban lizard. Lazell (1972) reported this species to be very common on Barbados. Gorman (1976) described the introduction of this species on St. Lucia and notes it is common at the Botanic Gardens and suggests it is displacing the native *Anolis luciae* from the area.

Material: Barbados—FMNH 195565; 21087–21100. Trinidad— USNM 244438–42, Port of Spain, along Wrightson Road, opposite Holiday Inn.

Anolis cf. *lemurinus* Cope

Plate 100.

> Anolis (*Gastrotropis*) *lemurinus* Cope, 1861:213. Type locality: Veragua, Panama. *Anolis biporcatus*: Boulenger, 1885, 2:88. *Anolis aeneus*: Barbour (1930b) (in error).

Comment: Boulenger (1885, 2:88) reported *Anolis biporcatus* from Trinidad based upon a British Museum specimen received from a Mr. C. Taylor in 1863. Werner (1900) listed this specimen as being from Port of Spain. Mole and Urich (1894a) retained this species on Trinidad based upon Boulenger's account. Barbour (1930c) considered Mole and Urich's record to be based upon *Anolis aeneus*. Parker (1935b) stated some authors have accepted this as a valid record, but noted that no other specimens have been forthcoming, and the specimen is present in the British Museum is not *A. aeneus,* but that it is closely allied to, if not conspecific with *A. biporcatus*. Parker listed this species in a section titled "Species Probably Incorrectly Reported From Trinidad." Subsequently, someone suggested it be cataloged as *Anolis lemurinus*. My examination confirms this specimen is conspecific with, or very close to, *A. lemurinus*.

Distribution: Veracruz, Mexico, southward to Colombia. It occurs on both the Caribbean and Pacific versants of Central America, and its presence on Trinidad seems unlikely in the absence of additional specimens. But it may have extended along the northern forests of South America to Trinidad in the past and paralleled the distribution of *Leptophis riveti*.

Description: The single Trinidad specimen, BMNH 63.6.18.3, is a male, SVL 69 mm, tail 144 mm. Hind limbs are 26 mm, 38% of the SVL. The snout is rounded, with a single rostral that is about four times wider than high; canthus slightly concave forming a shallow trough toward the nostrils; nostrils separated by 10 scale rows, and directed laterally. Eight large upper labials, 10 lower labials, followed by numerous small granular upper and lower labials; upper labials 4–8 below the orbit, two to three enlarged scale rows between orbit and upper labials. Supraorbital semicircles are separated by two to three scales rows; these and most of the other scales on the crown and upper face keeled. Parietal eye large and distinct. Ear opening large, bordered by granular scales, tympanum recessed. Postorbital ridge, outlined with four rows of enlarged scales, with a posterior projection over ear opening; this projecting crest separated from ear opening by 12 rows of granular scales. Vertebral scale rows slightly enlarged, lateral scales greatly reduced, ventral scales 3 to 10 times larger than laterals. Inner forearm scales, inner thigh scales, and medial ventral scales on tail enlarged and keeled. Infradigital lamellae on fourth finger number 32 (distil 10 not expanded, next 18 expanded and singular, next 4 [proximal] divided; on fourth toe number 30). Scales bordering cloaca granular. The preserved specimen is tan in color with an immaculate cream venter. Interorbital blotch dark and 4–5 scales long; light colored bar behind parietal eye bordered with darker pigment; blotch on neck about 22 scale rows long; blotch on forebody 25 scales long; blotch at midbody 20 scales long; and blotch at postbody 13 scale rows long.

Natural History: A tree trunk and forest floor anole. Stuart (1955) described the Pacific population in Guatemala as a savanna and dry forest inhabitant, while the eastern population attains a higher altitude, to at least 1000 m because of the drier conditions. Duellman (1963) observed specimens on giant tree trunks in Guatemala, and noted that they do not take refuge in the canopy when disturbed, but circle the trunk or jump to the ground; and he observed these lizards foraging on the forest floor. It seems likely that a lizard with these habits would have been discovered on Trinidad if it was present, but there is nothing to indicate the locality data is in error, and it may represent a population extirpated by habitat alteration in the last century.

Material: Trinidad—BMNH 63.6.18.3. FMNH—178088 Costa Rica; 49209 Honduras.

Anolis *richardii* (Duméril and Bibron)

Map 61. Plate 101.

> Anolis *richardii* Duméril and Bibron 1837, 4:141. Type locality: Tortola (in error), revised to Crown Point, Tobago, by Lazell (1972). *Anolis alligator*: Cope, 1879:276. *Anolis richardi*: Boettger, 1894a: 29. *Anolis trossulus*: Barbour, 1916b:222. *Anolis aeneus*: Burt and Burt, 1930:7. *Anolis richardii richardii*: Underwood, 1959:216. *Anolis r. richardii*: DeVerteuil, 1968:103. *Dactyloa richardii*: Schwartz and Henderson, 1988.

Common Names: "Gumangala" (Underwood, 1962); "Richard's Anole" (Boos, 1977d)

Distribution: *A. richardii* has a Lesser Antilles distribution, being native to the Grenadines and Grenada, and introduced on Tobago. This is the only anole known from Tobago. Hoogmoed (1981) described its introduction to Suriname in 1973 and subsequent extinction in 1976. Published localities for Tobago: Crown Point (Brongersma, 1956a; Boos, 1977d); Scarborough and Speyside (Underwood, 1959); Orange Hill Rd., Scarborough, Kings Bay, Grafton Estate, Orange Hill Ranch, Scarborough Botanic Gardens, and Friendship Estate (Mertens, 1972). Field notes (JCM) report this lizard common around Charlotteville, Speyside, and the old sugar mill at Franklyn. Lazell (1972) reported *A. richardii* abundant over all of Tobago suggesting it is native; while Yang et al. (1974) considered it to be a recent introduction to Tobago. Gorman and Kim (1978) provide four pieces of evidence that *A. richardii* is introduced on Tobago: (1) it is morpholologically indistinct from the Grenada population; (2) it is a giant anole, and giant species within this group tend to occur where there is more than one species coexisting; (3) its presence in both disturbed and undisturbed habitats on Grenada, but only in

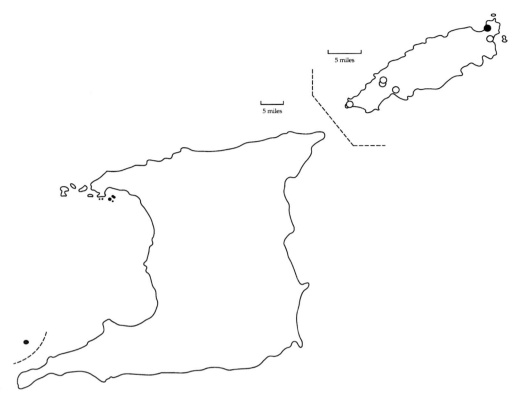

Map 61. *Anolis richardii*

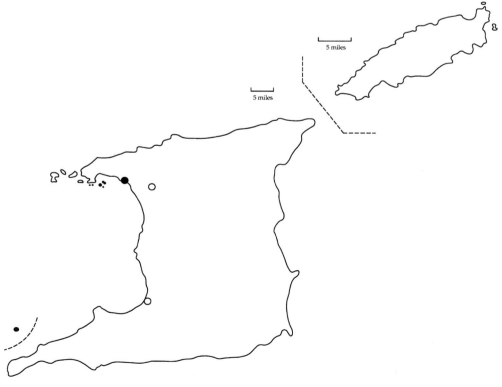

Map 62. *Anolis trinitatis*

disturbed habitats on Tobago, suggest it is a "weed" species, and; (4) the Tobago population shows reduced polymorphism and heterozygosity compared to the Grenada population. But, Hardy (1982) noted remains from the Crusoe Cave system, and suggested the remains could be 1600–2000 years old. Additional evidence supporting an ancient dispersal to Tobago is the larger body size attained by the Tobago population (Lazell, 1972). Surprisingly, it is absent from Little Tobago, an islet that had a land connection with Tobago 10,000 years ago. Dinsmore (1970) lived on this islet for 9 months and did not report it; this study also failed to find museum specimens or document its presence on Little Tobago, further evidence that it is not native to Tobago. Hardy (1982) reported one rafting on a tree trunk about a mile off the mouth of Man of War Bay, Tobago.

Description: Males 70–140 mm SVL, females 56–77 mm SVL; hind limbs are about 88% SVL. Rostral long and narrow; canthus forms a distinct ridge; preocular depression in the middle of the snout; semicircles of large scales above orbit. Ear opening almost equal to eye diameter; postocular ridge extends over and to middle of ear opening. Dorsal scales granular; vertebral ridge slight; ventral scales smooth and larger than dorsal scales. Dorsum dark green to brown above and green-gray to yellow below; some individuals mottled grey-green; light spot often present below eye. Females and young individuals often have a yellow or cream lateral stripe. Both sexes have yellow, orange, and gray-green dewlap. Tail with a serrated middorsal ridge. Large adult males have very sculptured head. This is the only anole known from Tobago, and it can be distinguished from all other anoles in the area with smooth ventral scales by its hind limb/SVL ratio which is about 0.88. The other anoles in the area have a hind limb/SVL ratio of about 0.7 or less.

Natural History: Adults are tree trunk dwellers, but young and juveniles appear more terrestrial, occasionally using low bushes; coconut trees and bushes are commonly used as perches (Underwood, 1962; Boos, 1977d). Field notes (JCM) describe adults basking on tree trunks in a vertical, head down position as high as 7–8 meters, as well as on horizontal branches. Brongersma (1956a) reports a Tobago female collected in October containing a single egg. In Grenada, Wunderele (1981) found the broad-winged hawk, *Buteo platypterus,* preys upon this species. Boos (1977d) described predator avoidance behavior, where the lizard keeps the tree trunk between it and the potential predator.

Material: Tobago USNM 167483–90.

Anolis trinitatis (Reinhardt and Lutken)

Map 62. Plate 102.

Anolis Trinitatis Reinhardt and Lutken, 1862:296. Type locality: Trinidad. Lazell (1972) revised it to Kingston, St. George Parrish, St. Vincent. *Anolis trinitatis trinitatis* Underwood, 1959:212. *Anolis*

trinitatus trinitatus: Peters and Donoso-Barros, 1970:68. *Dactyloa trinitatis:* Schwartz and Henderson, 1988:127.

Common Name: "Green Anole" (Boos, 1977d).

Distribution: A Lesser Antillean species, *A. trinitatis* occurs on the islands of St. Vincent, Young Island, and Chateaubelair Island, and is introduced on Trinidad. Published Trinidad localities illustrate the urban distribution of this species: Port of Spain, St. Augustine, San Fernando, and Usine Ste. Madeleine (Underwood, 1962). Lazell (1972) suggested that *A. trinitatis* reached Trinidad via breadfruit saplings brought from St. Vincent. It is possible this species is now extinct on Trinidad.

Description: Males 74 mm SVL, females 57 mm; a 19 mm specimen possesses an umbilical scar, probably size at hatching; hind limbs about 0.6 SVL Snout pointed from above, rounded in profile. Rostral elongated, with medial posterior extension; canthus forms distinct ridge; ridges slope separated by a raised area. Ear opening about two-thirds eye diameter; semicircles of scales present above orbits. Dorsum covered with granular scales, vertebral line scales slightly enlarged; lateral and ventral scales greatly enlarged. Scales on upper surface of limbs larger than dorsal granules, and keeled, as are scales on upper surfaces of digits; these keeled scales will distinguish this species from *A. aeneus* which has smooth scales on the upper digits. Ventral scales are smooth; scales on distal three-fourths of tail heavily keeled and the middorsal scales form a serrated ridge. Males with dewlap extending well into abdominal region; female's dewlap small and restricted to gular region. Dorsum green to green-blue, with yellow on jaws and venter; females muted in color. Uniform green, dorsal coloration distinguishes it from all other anoles in the area; *A. aeneus* is brown-grey with pattern of bars or stripes on dorsum. Underwood (1959) described the color. "In life *trinitatis* is a bright grass green, and can turn dark brown. The skin around the eye is dark and on the head and anterior trunk is a little fine blue mottling."

Natural History: An urban lizard, inhabiting gardens and yards. Barbour (1914) stated "they are almost always found on the bark of the cocoloba and manchineel trees; indeed Allen found them nowhere else, and never took one in the interior of the island." Underwood (1962) stated they frequent trees and bushes and like shaded areas; and Boos (1977d) found it in gardens and around human habitations and noted that it does not colonize jungle, but urban populations favor wetter, greener bushes. Hybridization and competition with *A. aeneus* may have resulted in its extinction or near extinction on Trinidad; see the *A. aeneus* account.

Material: Trinidad—MCZ 55777–78 Queens Park Savanna, Port of Spain; 55782–84 Tranquility Tennis Club; 55785–86 Port of Spain. *A. aeneus* × *A. trinitatis* hybrids—MCZ 93772–73 Rushworth St., Port of Spain; 96756–59 Queens Park Savanna, Port of Spain.

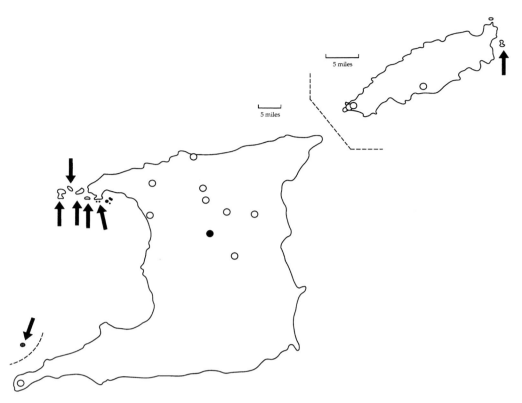

Map 63. *Iguana iguana*

Iguana iguana (Linnaeus)

Map 63. Plates 103, 104.

Lacerta iguana Linnaeus, 1758:206. Type locality: "In Indiis"; restricted by Lazell (1973) to the island of Terre-de-haut, Les Iles des Saintes, Department de la Guadeloupe, French West Indies; and by Hoogmoed (1973) to the confluence of the Cottica River and Perica Creek, Suriname. *Iguana tuberculata*: Court, 1858:440 (Trinidad). *Iguana tuberculata*: Reinhart and Lutken, 1862:23 (Tobago). *Iguana sapidissima*: Mole 1892b:98. *Iguana iguana*: VanDenburgh, 1898: 461. *Iguana iguana iguana*: Underwood, 1962:177.

Common Names: "guana, or lesard" (DeVerteuil, 1858); "iguana" (Beebe, 1952); "gwana" (Boos, 1977c).

Distribution: *Iguana iguana* is widespread, ranging from Mexico through Central America to southern Brazil and Paraguay; in coastal areas it colonizes nearby islands with and without trees; introduced to south Florida. On Trinidad and Tobago it is widespread, using natural and disturbed habitats. Published Trinidad localities: Mt. St. Benedict (Brongersma, 1956a); Chacachacare Island, Saut d' Eau Island, as well as, ". . . all over Trinidad except in the higher parts of the mountains" (Underwood, 1962); Caroni Swamp (Bacon, 1970a); Aripo savannas (Schwab, 1988); Chacachacare, Huevos, Monos, Gaspar Grande, Cronstadt, and Carrera islands (Boos, 1977c, 1984c,d); Soldado Rock, (Worth, 1967). Field note (JCM) localities: Arima Valley, Blanchisseuse, Tamana Caves, near Icacos. Museum material documents Trinidad localities: Arima, St. Augustine; St. Michael Estate, St. George Co.; San Rafael; and Sangre

Grande. Published Tobago locations include: Crown Point, and some offshore islands (Underwood, 1962); Robinson Crusoe Hotel, Scarborough (Mertens, 1972). Little Tobago Island (Dinsmore, 1970). Tobago museum material documents: Milford Bay and Barbados Bay.

Description: The longest New World lizard, SVL approaches, if not exceeds, 500 mm; tail of a juvenile male is 2.75 times the SVL; hind limbs are about 77% of the SVL; a 74 mm SVL juvenile, with a 202 mm tail has an obvious umbilical scar. Snout is blunt from above and in profile; rostral large and triangular; canthus indistinct; eyes relatively large; tympanum large and visible. Supralabials number 10–13, infralabials number 9–10. Scales on ventral margin of jaw increase in size from anterior to posterior, with largest scale three to four scale rows below the tympanum. Dewlap large with triangular scales medially. Dorsolateral portion of neck with 5–7 rows of slightly enlarged spiny scales. Enlarged triangular scales extend from nape onto the tail forming vertebral crest. Dorsal scales small, keeled and rectangular; ventral scales smooth and overlapping; scales around midbody number 190–219. Limbs well developed, each having five digits, longest digits fourth finger and fourth toe. Femoral pores number 12–18, bordered by extremely small scales on the inner surface of the thigh. Color green with white stripe on axilla and humerus; head blue-green to green; tail with black transverse rings, on one specimen these number 15. Dewlap may have black, brown, or red stripes. Males larger than females and have larger heads, longer spines on the dorsal crest, and larger femoral pores. Females and medium to small males are bright to dull green; largest males dull gray, gold, or tan, and breeding males or males holding territories are bright gold to red-orange—in at least some populations (Dugan, 1982).

Natural History: This large herbivorous lizard has been reported from mangrove woodlands (Bacon, 1970a), and in riparian and coastal situations where shrubs and trees overhang the water. Boos (1977c) stated they, ". . . are often seen high up in the jungle trees, especially sandbox, where despite the thorns they feed on blossoms and leaves." Field notes (JCM) report one individual on a coconut tree trunk adjacent to a flooded pasture near Icacos; a juvenile sleeping on grass 1.5 meters above a stream; and frequently moving across roads or leaping from streamside trees into the water. These lizards can also be found in urban parks, including Queens Savanna Park in Port of Spain, and are therefore at least somewhat tolerant of human activity. Within the species range it uses a variety of habitats ranging from arid savannas to rainforest. Juveniles more terrestrial, using lower vegetation than adults (Van Devender, 1982). Primarily a vegetarian, but juveniles are insectivorous. Boos (1984b) reported comments made by ffrench that iguanas eat tern eggs on Soldado Rock; later, ffrench (1990) stated that he has never actually seen iguanas eat bird's eggs. However, Lazell (1973) reported iguanas feeding on bird eggs and carrion. Basking sites are important for adequate digestion; McBee and McBee (1982) demonstrated hind gut fermentation requires temperatures of 30°C, and supplies 30–40% of the lizard's energy; fermentation is carried out by symbiotic bacteria in the genera *Clostridium* and *Leuconostoc*. Reproductive behavior of this species has been studied by Rodda (1992); iguana reproduction is somewhat seasonal and Rand and Greene (1982) correlated reproduction events with latitude and rainfall. Mating occurs during the beginning of the dry season when wind conditions expose display perches, making males more visible; egg deposition occurs so that incubation is in warm, moist, well-drained soil; hatching occurs with the onset of rains, when the soil softens, and new leaves and insects are abundantly available for the young. Using the data for iguana populations at 10° N latitude, the Trinidad iguana population should lay their eggs December–May, with hatching from March–August; however, because the island receives most of its rainfall in June–July it is likely most eggs hatch by May, and that few eggs are deposited after late March. The Tobago iguana population should be expected to have similar timing for its reproduction. Humans have historically been a major predator on the iguana. DeVerteuil (1858) wrote "The common iguana . . . are not to be rejected from the table. Iguanas are either shot on trees, or caught when laying; their fore and hind feet are tied behind, so that they cannot move; they can live many days without food." Wing and Reitz (1981) reported this lizard's remains from Trinidad archeological sites (middens); and Boos (1977c) wrote, "As a gourmets delight, iguana proves a little 'rich'

for the average palate, but it is still eaten in some parts in this country where its vegetarian diet is given as the reason for its preference over the 'matte' [*Tupinambis teguixin*], whose carrion eating makes that lizard's meat for only truly jaded eaters of rare flesh." Cooper and Bacon (1981) stated the iguana is caught throughout the island and that it provides an important supplement to villagers' diets; and David Auth (personal communication) observed local people hunting land crabs and iguanas in northeastern Tobago. On the mainland, Beebe (1944b) listed jaguars and swallow-tailed kites as predators. Wunderle (1981) reported the broad-winged hawk, *Buteo platypterus,* preys upon this species in Grenada.

Material: Trinidad—FMNH 022032 no data; 049851–53 San Rafael.

Polychrus marmoratus (Linnaeus)

Map 64. Plate 105.

Lacerta marmorata Linnaeus, 1758:208. Type locality: "Hispania." Hoogmoed (1973) restricted it to the vicinity of Paramaribo, Suriname. *Polychrus marmoratus:* Merrem, 1820:48. *Polychrus marmoratus marmoratus:* Burt and Burt, 1930:41. *Polychrus marmorta* [*sic*]: Boos and Quesnel, 1968:25.

Common Names: "Chameleon" (DeVerteuil, 1858); "many-colored tree lizard" (Beebe, 1952); "slow lizard" (Boos, 1977c). Bowman and Bowman (1939) described the following belief among the people of Tobago; their reference is almost certainly describing this lizard: "The bright-green lizard we often see and admire about the garden is actually a dangerous beast, according to her. They call it a 'twenty-four-hour' lizard, because it is suppose to clamp itself upon a person's arm with such tenacity that only a hot iron applied to the green back will remove it. The remedy however, is of no avail; within twenty-four hours the victim will die." Thus, several Trinidad and Tobago lizards have the "twenty-four hour" name and legend applied to them. See the *Hemidactylus mabouia* account for more on this name.

Distribution: *P. marmoratus* has an Amazonian distribution, occurring in the greater Amazon Basin, and on Trinidad and Tobago. Published Trinidad localities include: Arima (Werner, 1900); Arima Valley (Beebe, 1952); Mt. St. Benedict (Brongersma, 1956a); Port of Spain, Maracas Valley, St. Augustine, and Guanapo (Underwood, 1962); Aripo savannas (Schwab, 1988); Gaspar Grande, Monos, and Chacachacare Islands (Boos, 1984d, 1990). Museum records add: Arena; Arima Valley, near Asa Wright Nature Centre on Blanchisseuse Rd.; Brickfield; Cascade Rd., Port of Spain; La Romain; St. Michaels Estate, San Fernando; San Rafael; Tucker Valley; and Waller Field. Tobago localities based on museum records include: Charlotteville and Milford Bay.

Description: Maximum 137 mm SVL; 122 mm SVL largest measured; tail twice the SVL; hind legs are relatively short, about 61% of the SVL. Snout pointed from above and in profile; canthus distinct; rostral rectangular; supralabials number 6–9; infralabials number 6–8. Nostrils lateral; eyes

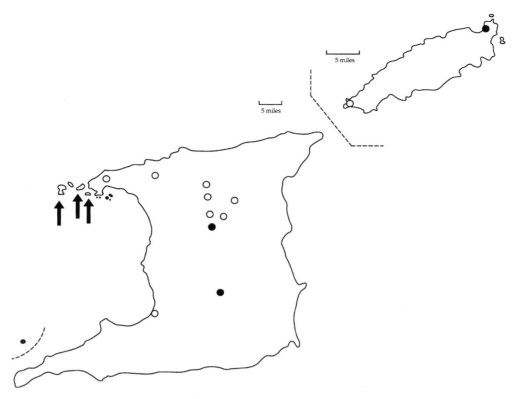

Map 64. *Polychrus marmoratus*

large; tympanum distinct. Dorsal surface of head with pentagonal scales; dorsal scales keeled, larger than ventral scales, and overlap; vertebral scales not enlarged; ventral scales keeled and overlap. Scales on tail larger than other dorsal scales. Limbs well developed, each with five digits. Femoral pores number 12 on each femur; preanal pores are absent. Dorsum green with 5–6 dorsolateral, yellow bands bordered with black; venter white. Both sexes have a dull orange dewlap. Absence of middorsal spines or crests will immediately separate it from *Iguana;* the presence of femoral pores (well-developed in males, present to a lesser degree in females) will distinguish it from *Anolis* and *Tropidurus plica.* Juveniles are uniform green and maybe mistaken for *Anolis.*

Natural History: This is a forest and forest-edge lizard. Field notes (JCM) report four of six specimens in trees (1.5–4 meters above ground); one on the road, most likely blown out of a tree; all six specimens in secondary forest. On the mainland it has been found in bushes and moderately tall trees, in deciduous forests, in bushes near water, on the ground, and in forest clearings (Beebe, 1944a; Test et al., 1966; Hoogmoed, 1973; Dixon and Soini, 1975). Food includes katydids, beetles, roaches, grasshoppers, moths, ants, cicadas, berries, and seeds (Beebe, 1944b; Test et al., 1966; Hoogmoed, 1973; Duellman, 1978). Clutch size is 7–11 eggs; mainland populations contained gravid females in January through April, and hatchlings in November; reproduction is probably year round (Beebe, 1944b; Hoog-

1973; Dixon and Soini, 1975; Rand, 1982). The cryptic nature of this lizard was commented upon by Beebe (1944b) "*Polychrus,* more than any other lizard I know, depends on two factors of safety, change of color to approximate the immediate surroundings, and most remarkable strained and posed attitudes which are maintained for considerable lengths of time." The distal end of the tail may be bent at a 90° angle to a branch and the tail waved back and forth, possibly to distract predators; when handled the body may be inflated with air sacs extending from the lungs and the dewlap displayed (Test et al, 1966; field notes, JCM). White-collared hawks prey upon this lizard (Beebe, 1944b; Test et al., 1966); and field notes (JCM) describe a specimen on Tobago that was being played with by a house cat. The laterally compressed body of this lizard would appear to make it an unlikely candidate for gliding or parachuting, but Boos and Urich (1986) described this lizard depressing its body and using its tail as a rudder when it is tossed into the air. Field notes (JCM) describe an adult missing a right front foot, the limb ending in a stump, which did not appear to inhibit the lizard's climbing ability.

Material: Trinidad—FMNH 049839–46 Brickfield; 049847–50 San Rafael. Tobago—FMNH 217257 Charlottville.

Tropidurus plica (Linnaeus)

Map 65. Plates 106, 107.

Lacerta plica Linnaeus, 1758:208. Type locality: "Indes." Etheridge (1970) restricted it to the vicinity of Paramaribo, Suriname. Hoog-

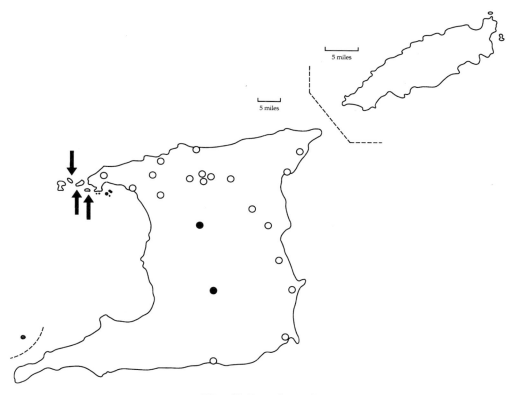

Map 65. *Tropidurus plica*

moed (1973) restricted it to the confluence of the Cottica River and Perica Creek, Suriname. *Plica plica:* Gray, 1831a:41. *Hypsibatus agamoides:* Court, 1858:440. *Uraniscodon plica:* Boulenger, 1885, 2:181. *Tropidurus plica:* Frost, 1992:50.

Common Names: "Spiny Tree Lizard" (Beebe, 1952); "tok-tok, old man" (Boos, 1977c questions the general use of these names.)

Distribution: *T. plica* has an Amazonian distribution occurring east of the Andes in northern South America and Trinidad. On Trinidad it appears to occur over much of the island where forests are present. Published Trinidad localities include: Arima Valley (Beebe, 1952); Port of Spain, Maracas Valley, St. Augustine, Mt. St. Benedict, and 2 miles north of Arima (Underwood, 1962); Monos and Huevos islands (Boos, 1984c,d); Gaspar Grande (Boos and Quesnel, 1994); Moruga on the south coast (Quesnel, 1980). Field notes (RWH) reports one at Hollis Reservoir. Museum localities document: Blanchisseuse, Brickfield, Caura Valley, Guayaguauare, Heights of Guanapo, Matura-Toco Rd., Mayaro, Mt. Harris, Nariva Swamp, Salibea Beach, Sangre Grande, St. Johns, San Rafael, Tucker Valley.

Description: 140 mm SVL can be expected; largest measured 123 mm SVL, tail twice SVL; hind limbs about 81% of SVL. Snout rounded from above; rostral rectangular; canthus short and distinct. Supralabials number 4–5, with shelf dorsal to supralabials; infralabials number 4–5. Supraocular ridges well developed; ear opening has anterior and ventral

tufts of spiny scales, a character that will readily distinguish this lizard from all other Trinidad and Tobago lizards. Mid-dorsal crest starts on posterior head with a few enlarged spines and extends onto tail. Dorsal scales are keeled, overlapping, rhomboidal, and decrease in size laterally. Ventral scales smooth, slightly larger than dorsal scales and overlap. Strong lateral fold of spiny scales from axillary region to base of tail; a character that will separate *T. plica* from all other Trinidad and Tobago lizards. Front limbs well developed with long fingers. Tail laterally compressed. Color green with red-brown transverse bands, each having black spots; limbs and tail banded; red-brown band from eye to ear. Venter orange-yellow in males and orange-brown in females; males with white throat and black gular pouch, females with gray throat and brown gular pouch. Beebe (1944b) commented on the adaptive nature of *Tropidurus plica*'s external morphology for an arboreal life style.

Almost every scale has a sharp protruding spine and a sharp keel. Rubbed the wrong way on its soles, thighs, belly, chin or under tail it feels like razor grass, and these projections must be of great help in sustaining its position on the bark. The fingers are very long and the claws exceedingly long, sharp and bent downward. The exposed dorsal and throat patterns are highly protective, mottled dark and green. In its usual position, upside-down on trunk, the throat patch becomes a shadow and the head an irregular branch stub.

Natural History: On Trinidad *T. plica* is a forest and for-est-edge lizard using vertical surfaces of tree trunks, rock faces, and buildings, and they will use holes at the base of trees for escape; hatchlings are more terrestrial than adults (Underwood, 1962; Hoogmoed, 1973; Dixon and Soini, 1975; field notes, JCM). Mole and Urich (1891) wrote,

> They are found in colonies of six, eight, or even a dozen individuals on the trunks (rarely the branches) of large trees and on rough stone walls of bridges, ruins and old houses, usually head downwards, but in whatever position they may be the head and fore part of the body is raised . . . When on trees . . . they have a habit of placing them-selves on the opposite side to the one in view. They live on spiders, beetles, and caterpillars, and in captivity eat cockroaches with avidity, managing sometimes to swal-low very large one . . .

Bat researcher Jenny Boughman (personal communica-tion) videotaped this species in Caura Cave, and observed them occasionally falling to the cave floor. Food includes ants, beetles and their larvae, true bugs, and bees (Parker, 1935; Beebe, 1944a; Hoogmoed, 1973; Dixon and Soini, 1975.) In Brazil, Vitt (1991) found this lizard a sit-and-wait predator, positioning itself in a head downward posture and eating the insects as they pass by; he also noted that they sit on the trunks of the largest, smooth-barked trees. Mole and Urich (1891) described the eggs as cylindrical, an inch long, covered with tough, white, slightly ribbed, parch-ment-like shells. Beebe (1944a) reported a female taken in May laying two eggs, and Boos (1977c) found two eggs in a fallen palm tree. In Brazil, Vitt (1991) calculated the mean clutch size to be 2.9 eggs, and found clutch size was significantly correlated with the female's SVL, and the re-productive season was extended with females producing two clutches per year. Its aggressive display includes ex-pansion of the black gular area and partial opening of the mouth; it may be used to maintain territories (Debusk and Glidewell, 1972.) Field notes (JCM) report the remains of one of these lizards from the digestive system of the snake *Tripanurgos compressus*.

Material: Trinidad—FMNH 025014 no data; 049834–5 Brickfield; 049836 Mt. Harris.

Order Squamata: Suborder Sauria
Family Scincidae: Skinks

Skinks form the most specious family of lizards, with 85 genera and about 1300 species. The family is cosmopolitan, missing only from subpolar and polar regions. Only four genera inhabit the Western Hemisphere, and only one has entered South America, *Mabuya*. Ten species are currently recognized in the Neotropics, but another 75 species occur in Africa, Madagascar, southern Asia, and the Pacific. North American skinks are most closely allied with Eurasian forms, but the South American *Mabuya* are more likely of African ancestry. The genus is in need of revision and

changes in current names can be expected. The form on Trin-idad and Tobago is currently called *Mabuya bistriata*. Beebe (1945) commented on this skink.

These skinks are occasionally seen or captured but they are so protectively colored that they are probably more common than observations would indicate. They are ter-restrial inhabitants of the jungle floor. Characteristically their scales are smooth and flat. Above they are olive with a bronze sheen and a broad, dark brown lateral band ex-tends from snout to tail, bordered with pink, the under parts vary from sea green to sulphur yellow.

Mabuya bistriata (Spix)

Map 66. Plate 108.

Scincus bistriata Spix, 1825:23, pl. 26, fig. 2. Type locality: Pará, Brazil. *Eumeces spixii:* Court, 1858:441. *Mabuya aenea:* Garman, 1887a:29. *Mabuya agilis:* Boettger, 1893:99. *Mabuia aurata:* Mole and Urich, 1894a:82. *Mabuya aurata aurata:* Roux, 1926:292. *Mabuya mabouya aenea:* Parker, 1935b:69. *Mabuya mabouya mabouya:* Dunn, 1935:544. *Mabuya mabouia mabouia:* DeVerteuil, 1968:105.

Common Names: "Trinidad skink" (Beebe, 1952); "bronze skink" (Boos, 1979c).

Comment: Hoogmoed and Gruber (1983) used the name *Mabuya bistriata* for the populations previously included under the name *Mabuya mabouya mabouya* demonstrating the type specimen of *M. m. mabouya* is not represenative of any neotropical skink, and the oldest available name is *M. bistriata*. It is likely that this lizard is a species complex, composed of more than a single species.

Distribution: *M. bistriata* is widespread, ranging from Mexico to Amazonia and into the Lesser Antilles. Published localities for Trinidad: Arima Valley (Beebe, 1952); Princes Town and Manzanilla Bay (Underwood, 1962); Monos and Huevos islands (Boos, 1984c,d); Gaspar Grande (Boos and Quesnel, 1994); Aripo savannas (Schwab, 1988). Museum material from Trinidad adds: San Rafael; Matura-Toco Rd. vicinity of the 21.75 milepost; Manzanilla Beach; Pluck Rd., La Romain; St. Annes; Chaguaramas; Mt. St. Benedict; Aripo Savanna. Field notes (JCM) describe this species at three previously mentioned localities, as well as near Los Bajos off the Rancho Quemado Road. Published localities for Tobago include: near Speyside (Boos, 1979c); Hotel Robinson Crusoe, Scarborough, and Orange Hill Ranch (Mertens, 1972); between Speyside and Charlotteville, and Scarborough (Underwood, 1962). Tobago museum material adds: Bacolet Estate, and Pirate's Cove outside of Charlot-teville.

Description: 109 mm SVL, largest specimen measured in this study 101 mm SVL; tail about 1.6 times the SVL when undamaged. Head depressed and short; snout rounded from above and in profile; rostral hexagonal, followed by two supranasals in contact with each other. Nostrils directed lat-erally in single nasal scales. Supralabials number 7–8, in-

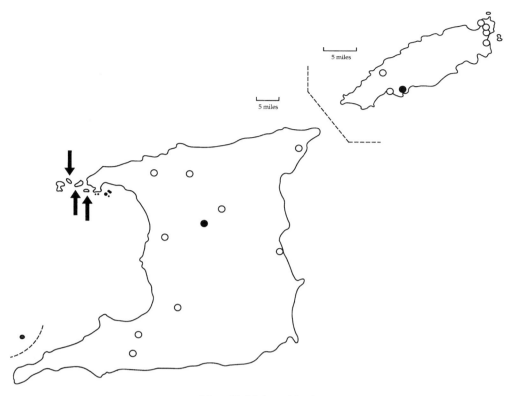

Map 66. *Mabuya bistriata*

fralabials number 7. Ear opening less than half the eye diameter; tympanum deeply set, but visible; lower eyelid with translucent disk. Body and tail covered with smooth, cycloid scales that overlap. Limbs relatively short, but well developed, each with five digits; fourth finger with 13 lamellae; fourth toe with 15 lamellae. Dorsum brown and speckled with darker pigment; lateral, red-brown stripe 2–3 scale rows wide extends from eye onto tail; it is bordered above and below by lighter stripes. Labials and the venter are yellow-orange (white in preserved specimens). The overlapping head scales and scales of equal size on chin will distinguish this lizard from all other species in the area.

Natural History: This is a forest and forest-edge species. Mainland populations have been described using the following habitats: jungle; drier parts of secondary forest, climbing onto vegetation to bask; shaded areas, in forest and forest edge situations, often on fallen tree trunks; trails, roads, clearings, creeks, and rock piles in savanna (Beebe, 1945; Test et al. 1966; Vanzolini and Reboucas-Spieker, 1973; Hoogmoed, 1973.) On Trinidad, Boos (1979c) found it preferred the lighter jungle and cultivated areas, and noted on Tobago they occur on plantations and the walls of old houses. Field notes (JCM) describe this lizard in disturbed habitats, two under coconut trash, and three in junk piles. In Brazil, Vitt and Blackburn (1991) found them active mid to late morning on fallen logs and tree trunks, with an average body temperature of 32.9°C. Prey is mostly arthropods, including grasshoppers, spiders, beetles, roaches, hymenop-

terans, caterpillars, spiders, orthropterans, eruciform larvae, and termites (Vanzolini and Reboucas-Spieker, 1973; Vitt and Blackburn, 1991). In mainland populations litter sizes of 3–7 have been reported; breeding skinks have been reported in July-August, neonates present in August-November (Beebe, 1945; Hoogmoed, 1973; Dixon and Soini, 1975). However, in Brazil, Vitt and Blackburn (1991) found most individuals reach sexual maturity by the end of the first year; most females produce the first brood at the end of their first year, with an extended gestation of 9–12 months; a chorioallantoic placenta between the embryos and the female; and a brood size of 2–9 ($\bar{x}$ = 4.7). Urich (1931) stated that this lizard is ". . . now very rare, if not extinct" due to the mongoose; Underwood (1962) made a similar statement, suggesting it should be expected in all parts of Tobago because of the absence of the mongoose. Clearly, it is not extinct on Trinidad, but it may have undergone a temporary population reduction because of this introduced mammalian predator.

Material: Trinidad—FMNH 49901–08 San Rafael. Tobago—AMNH 73087 Bacolet Estate.

Order Squamata: Suborder Sauria
Family Teiidae: Teiids

The Teiidae is a New World family containing 18 genera of medium to large lizards. They have a variety of tooth shapes; smooth hemipenes; nasal plates that are in contact with each other; the parietals contact the supraoccipital in narrow suture; the fronto-parietal suture is a straight line, with

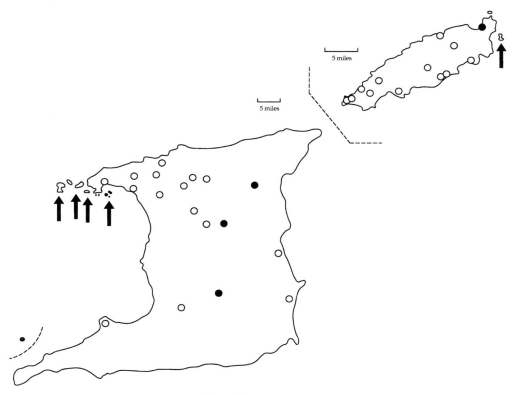

Map 67. *Ameiva ameiva*

no tabs; males are larger that females; and the belly scales are arranged in orderly transverse and longitudinal rows (Presch, 1983). Four species in four genera inhabit Trinidad and Tobago. Worth (1967) wrote about *Tupinambis teguixin,*

> Their thick bodies end in blunted tails; yet with cumbersome forms they could run through the forest at high speed. Often they would wait until one was almost upon them—perhaps they were basking—before taking off with great crashing of leaves and underbrush.

Ameiva ameiva (Linnaeus)

Map 67. Plate 109.

Lacerta ameiva Linnaeus, 1758:202. Type locality: Brazil. Restricted by Hoogmoed (1973) to the confluence of the Cottica River and the Perica Creek, Suriname. *Ameiva vulgaris:* Court, 1858:434. *Ameiva major:* Court, 1858:440. *Ameiva ameiva tobagana:* Cope, 1879:276. *Ameiva atrigularis:* Garman, 1887b:2. *Ameiva surinamensis:* Boettger, 1893:74. *Ameiva ameiva:* Cockerell, 1893:310. [*fide* Peters and Donoso-Barros, 1970]. *Ameiva punctata:* Mole and Urich, 1894a:82. *Ameiva tobagana:* Barbour and Noble, 1915:422. *Ameiva ameiva atrigularis:* Tuck and Hardy, 1973:231.

Comment: Vanzolini (1981) wrote, "The subspecies of *Ameiva ameiva* make no sense." I agree and am not recognizing any subspecies of *Ameiva ameiva.*

Common Names: "Common ground lizard" (Field, 1942); "large jungle runner" (Beebe, 1952); "Zandolie"

(Boos and Quesnel, 1968). Winer and Boos (1991) state that the name "zandoli" is a French Creole ("Patois") name given to this species from the French "les anolis lizard" by the Patois-speaking slaves who came to Trinidad from Haiti, Martinique, and other Caribbean islands after the Spanish cedula of 1793.

Distribution: *A. ameiva* is widespread, ranging from Panama into tropical South America, and it occurs in the southern Antilles as well as Trinidad and Tobago. On Trinidad and Tobago this lizard is widespread. Published Trinidad localities include: Arima Valley (Beebe, 1952); Mt. St. Benedict and the Tacarigua Reserve, La Brea, Carua Valley, and Mayaro (Brongersma, 1956a); Chacachacare Island, Port of Spain, Maracas Valley, St. Augustine, Princes Town, and Nariva Swamp (Underwood, 1962); Monos, Chacachacare, Caledonia, and Nelson islands (Boos, 1984d; 1990); Gaspar Grande, but may be extirpated (Boos and Quesnel, 1994). Museum material adds: Arena, Arima Valley, St. Augustine, Bayshore, Brickfield, Centeno, Marval, Melajotor Reserve 4.5 miles north of Sangre Grande, Maracas Police Station Grounds, Mayaro Beach, San Rafael, and Tucker Beach. Tobago localities in the literature include: Crown Point and Old Grange Tower Road (Brongersma, 1956a); Crown Point, and many points on road from Hillsborough Bay to King's Bay, and Charlotteville (Underwood, 1962); Mt. Irwin, Orange Hill Ranch, Pigeon Point, and Scarborough (Mertens, 1972). Little Tobago Island (Dinsmore, 1970). Museum material for Tobago adds: near Bethel on

Orange Hill Road, Bloody Bay, Milford Bay, 4.25 miles northeast of Scarborough, Crown Point, Store Bay, Crown Point Airport, between Pembroke and Roxborough, vicinity of the 5 milepost on the Roxborough-Parlatuvier Rd., 0.5 mi W of Goldsborough River on Windward Rd., Hillsborough Dam, and Little Tobago Island.

Description: Males 168 mm SVL; females 131 mm SVL; tail 2.4 times SVL; hind legs are 74.5% of SVL. The largest members of this species observed in the field during this study were on Little Tobago Island, and they very likely exceeded the maximum size given here. Body cylindrical, slight depression at base of tail; head is long and narrow. Rostral pentagonal; nostril divides nasal scale; four supraoculars, may be divided in some specimens; one preocular; two or three suboculars; five or six supracillaries. Ear opening large, outlined with small scales; tympanum visible. Supralabials number 5–7, infralabials number 4–7. Lower eyelid with transparent disk. Dorsal and lateral scales granular; number 136 around midbody in one individual. Smooth ventral scales are large, rectangular, overlapped, and arranged in 10–12 longitudinal rows and 28–31 transverse rows. Two striped teiids which this species may be confused with are *Cnemidophorus lemniscatus* with 8 longitudinal rows of ventral scales; and *Kentropyx striatus* with 14 rows of keeled ventral scales. Anal plate with 5–6 enlarged scales. Dorsal surface of front legs with large platelike scales, rest of the leg covered with granular scales. Fingers with 17 lamellae on the fourth finger. Hind legs with large platelike scales on the anterior and ventral surfaces with granular scales dorsal and posterior. Femoral pores number 14–21 per leg; one male (FMNH 49869) with eight preanal pores. Toes long, the fourth toe has 33 lamellae. Juvenile dorsum mostly green, with maturity the head and dorsum become more brown; throat white; venter orange in juveniles, becoming blue or white with age, but retaining some orange in anal region. Three or four rows of lateral blue or white spots may extend onto the hind limbs and tail of adult males.

Natural History: A diurnal, terrestrial lizard of forest, forest-edge, and savanna; it uses areas of forest with open undergrowth where patches of light reach the forest floor, scrub lands, secondary growth, suburban yards and gardens, roadsides, and beaches (Beebe, 1945; Quesnel, 1979; field notes, JCM). On overcast, rainy days this lizard was rarely seen; however, on dry, sunny days its presence was obvious. Beebe (1945) described the rushing and jerking movements of this species; and the frequent scratching with the front legs that often betrays its presence. Food includes a variety of insects, small vertebrates, eggs, and fruits (DeVerteuil, 1884; Beebe, 1945; Boos and Quesnel, 1968). Field notes (JCM) report *Ameiva* carrying figs in their mouths and eating them; and chasing *Cnemidophorus lemniscatus* in the cocal; although they were never observed to catch one of the striped runners, they were persistent, and may have been trying to catch them for food or keeping them out of their territories. Quesnel (1979) described courtship and mating in May, June, October, and November; copulation lasted an average

of 2 minutes and 3 seconds and he observed multiple copulations over a period of a few hours, with 20–52 minutes between events. Field notes (JCM) report lizards mating in June and July and describe copulation lasting only a few minutes; a distinct color change in the head and neck region of both sexes occurs during courting and copulation; the male's head increases its bright green coloration and the female's head, which was brown, turns bright green. On Tobago Brongersma (1956a) reported females collected in October and November contained two eggs. Quesnel (1979) observed fighting males adopting a threat display by arching their neck with their nose to the ground, compressing the body and raising it up on stiffly extended legs; he notes that this did not stop the attacker. Predators on mainland populations included the snakes *Boa constrictor, Clelia, Drymarchon corias, Mastigodryas boddaertii,* the lizard *Tupinambis,* and several species of hawks (Beebe, 1945; Hoogmoed, 1973). On Trinidad, Worth (1967) observed ameivas scattering into adjacent hedges when a hawk appears. Urich (1931) hypothesized this species is ". . . not as common as formerly. They have survived in the vicinity of towns and country houses where their greatest enemy is not the mongoose but the domestic cat." Despite this statement, *Ameiva* continues to be quite common throughout Trinidad and Tobago. Aitkens et al. (1968) found the tick *Amblyomma dissimile* on Trinidad specimens.

Material: Trinidad—FMNH 49854–5 Brickfield; 49856–69, 49872 San Rafael; 49870 Marval; 49871 Sangre Grande. Tobago—FMNH 217258 Charlotteville.

Cnemidophorus lemniscatus (Linnaeus)

Map 68. Plate 110.

Lacerta lemniscata Linnaeus, 1758:209. Type locality: Guinea (= Guyana). Restricted by Hoogmoed (1973) to the confluence of the Cottica River and Perica Creek, Suriname. *Cnemidophorus lemniscatus:* Boulenger, 1885:346. *Cnemidophorus lemniscatus lemniscatus:* Beebe, 1919:212. *Cnemidophorus l. lemniscatus:* Mertens, 1969: 69 (Tobago).

Common Names: "Striped runner, foot-shaker" (Beebe, 1952).

Comment: Vanzolini (1970) found unisexual populations of this species along the Amazon; Hoogmoed (1973) recorded unisexual populations from Suriname; Dessauer and Cole (1989) reported 2N bisexual populations and 3N unisexual populations from Suriname and discussed their possible origins; Peccinini-Seale (1989) found five different diploid cytotypes that vary geographically in Amazonia. Thus, *C. lemniscatus* is a species complex containing several cryptic and sibling species and clones that have been clarified by Cole and Dessauer (1993) for the Guiana region, and they assign Trinidad and Tobago populations to this species.

Distribution: *C. lemniscatus* is widespread, ranging from Guatemala to northern South America east of the Andes; it occurs on the Isla San Andres, Isla de Providencia, Isla Sta. Catalina, Tobago, Trinidad and many of the coastal islands. On Trinidad and Tobago it is found at lower eleva-

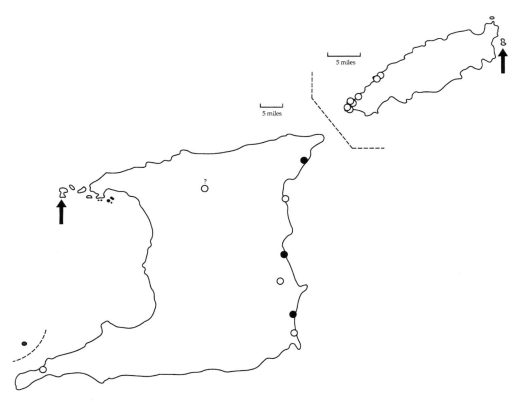

Map 68. *Cnemidophorus lemniscatus*

tions in open habitats. Published Trinidad localities include: Manzanilla Bay, Chacachacare Island (Underwood, 1962); and Bush-Bush Island in Nariva Swamp (Worth, 1967); Chacachacare and Huevos islands (Boos, 1984d). The Arima Valley was listed by Beebe (1952), a site not supported by specimens and seemingly unlikely. Museum material adds: vicinity of the 21.75 milepost on Matura-Toco Rd.; Manzanilla-Mayaro Rd., Manzanilla Beach, Mayaro Beach, Guayaguayare Bay, Las Hermanas, and Cedros. Published Tobago localities include: Crown Point (Brongersma, 1956a), Plymouth (Underwood, 1962), Pigeon Point and Mt. Irwin (Mertens, 1972). Museum material adds: Bucco Bay, Milford Bay, Store Bay, and Little Tobago Island.

Description: Maximum 73 mm SVL female with a 136 mm tail. Four Trinidad specimens examined, all are females; on the mainland, males attain 89 mm SVL; tail about 1.86 times the SVL length. Head longer than broad; narrow snout rounded from above and in profile; rostral pentagonal; nostrils lateral, nasal scales extend dorsally behind rostral and make contact on the midline. Frontonasals scales are hexagonal; the frontoparietals are quadrangular and meet on the midline. Supraoculars number 4–7, separated from the 5–7 supraciliaries by one or two rows of granular scales. Suboculars number 3–5; preoculars absent; postoculars form a row of 3–4 small scales. Ear opening large, tympanum visible. Supralabials number 6–8, infralabials number 7–8. Lower eyelid with transparent disk. Dorsal and lateral scales are

granular; ventral scales smooth, rectangular; in 8 longitudinal rows and about 30 transverse rows. Smooth ventral scales distinguishing it from *Kentropyx,* which has 14 transverse rows of keeled ventral scales. Ten light dorsolateral stripes 3–4 scale rows wide, each separated by a dark stripe 5–9 scales wide. Scales around midbody in two specimens number 123 and 124. Ventral scales in 29 and 31 transverse rows in two specimens. Superficially this lizard may be confused with *Ameiva,* but that species has 10 longitudinal rows of ventral plates, and attains a larger size. Anterior dorsal surface of front legs covered with platelike scales that overlap; granular scales cover the rest of the legs. Hind legs with overlapping platelike scales on the anterior and ventral surfaces, granular scales dorsally and posteriorly. Scales on tail quadrangular, overlapping and keeled. Fingers compressed with 15–17 lamellae on fourth digit; toes compressed with 30–33 lamellae on fourth digit. Live females have a brown back with white stripes and dorsolateral stripes are green on the anterior end; anterior venter of females is white, posteriorly it is green-yellow; females also have a brown tail. Males have lateral stripes that are replaced by 2–3 rows of white spots, posteriorly the dorsolateral region is blue-green, and the tail is blue. Both sexes have the ventral surface of the tail colored blue or green.

Natural History: A beach-savanna lizard that will enter forest and colonize open areas: in Suriname, Hoogmoed (1973) described them using open, sunny places, (e.g., beaches, savannas, gardens, and forest-edge) and stated

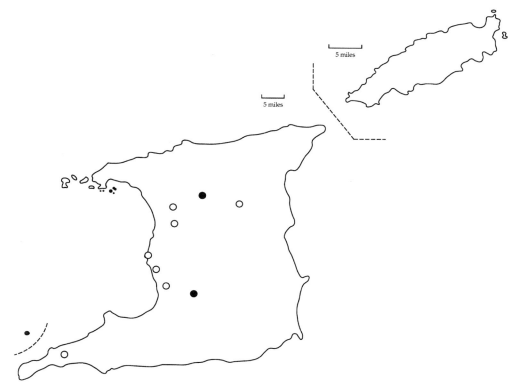

Map 69. *Kentropyx striatus*

that in the Amazon they appear to be strictly perianthropic; Test et al. (1966) found them foraging on open ground and using bushy areas for shelter; Worth (1967) observed them colonizing recently cleared areas on Bush-Bush Island in Nariva Swamp. Field notes (JCM) describe them as abundant along Manzanilla Bay Beach and at Icacos Beach; foraging along the edge of open beach and ground vegetation, rarely venturing onto the open beach; one burrow, 17–20 cm in depth. Arthropods, mostly insects have been reported as food (Parker, 1935; Beebe, 1945; Leon et al. 1970; Hoogmoed, 1973). Although, Test et al. (1966) observed them pulling earthworms from mud where plants had been watered, and eating the small yellow flowers of *Portulaca oleracea*. In Venezuela, Beebe (1925) reported predation by hawks, the snake *Oxybelis aeneus,* and the lizard *Tupinambis.* Urich (1931) considered this lizard rare in Trinidad but common on the Bocas Islands where the there are no mongoose. Field notes (JCM) describe *Ameiva ameiva* chasing *Cnemidophorus;* this may be attempted predation, or competition for territory. These lizards stop abruptly between spurts of rapid, often bipedal, locomotion; they will lift one of their front legs and vibrate or wave their feet; this may represent a territorial display, or have other social significance.

Material: Trinidad—USNM 166657 Matura-Toco Road near the 21.75 milepost; 166658 Manzanilla-Mayaro Road, 5 miles south southeast of Upper Manzanilla; 166659 Manzanilla-Mayaro Road vicinity of 41 milepost; 227725–6 Little Tobago Island.

Kentropyx striatus (Daudin)

Map 69. Plate 111.

Lacerta striata Daudin, 1802:247. Type locality: Suriname. *Centropyx striatus:* Boettger, 1893:73. *Kentropyx intermedius:* Barbour, 1930b:100 (in error). *Kentropyx striatus:* Parker, 1935b:69. *Kentropyx borckianus:* Hoogmoed, 1973:287 (in error). *Kentropyx striatus striatus:* Hoogmoed, 1973:302. *Kentropyx striata:* Gallagher, 1979:165.

Comment: Parker (1935b) wrote,

Boettger, in recording it from the island [Trinidad] for the first time stated that the specimen was coloured like *K. intermedius* Gray, a remark which may have suggested to Barbour (1930b, p. 100) that its identification as *K. striatus* was wrong. But thanks to the courtesy of Dr. Mertens the original specimen, collected by Mole and Urich and reported upon by Boettger has been reexamined: it is an undoubted *K. striatus.*

Unfortunately Parker's comment has been overlooked or ignored for decades. Underwood (1962) considered *Kentropyx intermedius* to be the species inhabiting Trinidad and Barbados, stating that while it has been reported extinct on Barbados, he had seen it on that island but makes no comment as to its actual presence on Trinidad; his Trinidad locality may be based upon Barbour's (1930b) checklist. Hoogmoed (1973) placed *Centropyx intermedius* Cope 1862, *Lacerta striata* Kuhl 1820; and Merrem, 1820; parts of *Centropyx striatus* Duméril and Bibron, 1828 and 1851; and

Acanthopyga striata Gray 1845 in the synonym of *Kentropyx borckianus* and reports *K. borckianus* from "Suriname, Guyana, French Guyana, Venezuela (Bolivar), Trinidad and Barbados." This has stimulated Darevsky et al. (1985), and Schwartz and Henderson (1991) to list *K. borckianus* from Trinidad. During the course of this study nothing has been found to support the presence of *K. borckianus* on Trinidad, except the original error in Barbour's checklist. Gallagher and Dixon (1980) note that *striatus* can be distinguished from *borckianus* by the former having 16 femoral pores or fewer and enlarged middorsal scales in 17 longitudinal rows or fewer, while *K. borckianus* has 23 or more femoral pores and enlarged middorsal scales in 22 or more longitudinal rows. *K. borckianus* is a Barbados endemic.

Common Name: "rain lizard" (Boos and Quesnel, 1971).

Distribution: *K. striatus* is a lowland Guiana endemic, ranging from Colombia eastward to the Guianas and southward to Brazil; it occurs on Trinidad, and possibly Tobago (ANSP 9811 is the only known Tobago specimen). Hardy (1984b) suggested that the Tobago population may have been extirpated by alteration of its habitat. Literature records include O'Meara Savanna (Underwood, 1962), Aripo Savanna, Claxton Bay, Couva Bay, Gasparillo, Warren Rd. and Jerningham Junction, Williamsville (Boos and Quesnel, 1971). Most of these localities are documented with museum specimens; additional museum material is from: 6.7 km east of Bonasse; Victoria, near Eckel Village; and Zanderig.

Description: Males 124 mm, females 84 mm SVL; hatchlings 31–34 mm SVL; tail is at least 2.2 times the SVL; hind legs about 63% SVL. Snout pointed from above, sloping in profile. Rostral scale triangular, nasals in contact on the midline of skull. Scales on crown large plates; eye diameter three-fourths of eye-nostril distance; ear opening slightly less than eye's diameter; tympanum visible. Anterior and lateral neck scales granular and keeled; middorsum with 14 rows of large, overlapping, heavily keeled scales; laterally are 16 rows of small keeled scales. Ventral scales large, heavily keeled, overlapping and arranged in 14 longitudinal rows, distinguishing it from *Cnemidophorus* (with eight longitudinal rows) and *Ameiva* (8–10 longitudinal rows). Tail completely covered with large, keeled scales. Upper surface of the hind limbs with small keeled scales, anterior surface of limbs with very large keeled scales. Forelimbs with large scales on dorsal and anterior surfaces. Fourth finger with 15–19 lamellae, the fourth toe with 24–28 lamellae. Femoral pores number 6–7 in both sexes; males are larger than females and have a pair of preanal spurs on each side of central preanal scales. Dorsum green with tan to white dorsolateral stripes, and blue-white spotting on the flanks; and brown lateral stripes. Orange venter in males, white venter in females. Venter of tail orange in both sexes.

Natural History: An aquatic, savanna lizard that climbs trees and shrubs. Much of its range in Trinidad coincides with sugarcane fields and natural savanna, where it uses streamside (canals and ditches) trees and shrubs. It seeks refuge in water when approached while basking and during the rainy season it occupies small islands of vegetation until the water recedes; activity is centered in early morning, animals not located during hottest portions of the day (Boos and Quesnel, 1971). In northern Brazil it may be more arboreal (Vitt and Carvalho, 1992) but Vanzolini (1972b) also found it restricted to open areas along rivers and swamps. Field notes (RIC) report a Trinidad specimen sleeping on tall grass at 2140 h. Feces of newly captured animals contained remains of insects and arachnids; and captives readily eat grasshoppers and crickets; food also includes frogs, eruciform larvae, spiders, and other lizards (field notes, RIC; Vitt and Carvalho, 1992). On Trinidad, eggs are laid in July and August and hatch in October-November (Boos and Quesnel, 1971). On the mainland, Vitt and Carvalho (1992) reported females reach sexual maturity at 74 mm SVL and produce 3–9 eggs per clutch, and produce more than one clutch per season. In Venezuela, Dixon et al. (1975) found eggs were laid at night in open, short, grassy fields; the nest chamber is about 3.5 cm deep with a 7 cm tunnel leading to a chamber made at a 40° angle dug by 1930 h (full darkness); eggs laid 10 October, hatched between 11–15 February, an incubation period of about 124 days; clutch size 10 eggs. Boos and Quesnel (1971) reported clutch size as eight and nine, with an incubation time of about 3 months. Hoogmoed (1973) listed clutches of 3–5 eggs with an incubation of 90 days in Suriname.

Material: Trinidad—MCZ 58734 O'Meara Savanna, near Arima; 123916–7 Victoria, near Eckel Village. USNM 192389 Caroni Co., Jerningham Junction. [Other material not seen by me. CM 4954 ?Mt. St. Benedict. MCZ 96899 Williamsville; 96030 Williamsville at Guaracara River and Buenitento Rd. 100489–9 Williamsville, San Fernando. UF 41340 Zanderig.]

Tupinambis teguixin (Linnaeus)

Map 70. Plate 112.

Lacerta teguixin Linnaeus, 1758:208. Type locality: "Indiis", restricted by Etheridge (1968) to Paramaribo, Suriname. *Salvator merianae*: Court, 1858:440. *Tupinambis nigropunctatus*: Garman, 1887b:1. *Tejue teguexin*: Mole, 1892:100. *Tupinambis teguixin nigropunctatus*: Mertens, 1969:69 (Tobago) *Tupinambis nigro-punctatus*: Wing and Reitz, 1982:19.

Common Names: "Mato or mate" [also spelled matte], "safeguard" (Court, 1858:440); "Tegu" (Beebe, 1952); "Salimpanter, Salipenta or Salipenter" [on Tobago] (DeVerteuil, 1968; Underwood, 1962; Boos, 1979a).

Comment: Presch (1973) suggested the name *Tupinambis teguixin* for the northern South American species of this genus, formerly recognized as *T. nigropunctatus*.

Distribution: *T. teguixin* has an Amazonian distribution. Published Trinidad localities include: Arima Valley (Beebe, 1952); Bush-Bush Island in Nariva Swamp (Worth, 1967; Everard and Boos, 1975); Bois Neuf in Nariva Swamp (Ramcharan et al. 1979); Chaguaramas, Aripo/Cumoto, Tu-

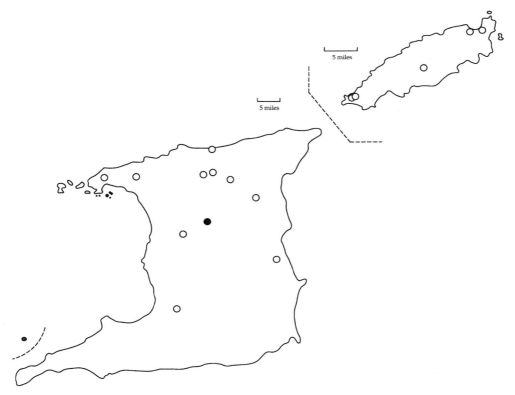

Map 70. *Tupinambis teguixin*

rure Forest (Guaico-Valencia Forest Reserve), Marval Valley (Boos, 1979a); Underwood (1962) suggested that it is restricted to the southern and eastern parts of Trinidad. Field notes (JCM) suggest otherwise, listing: the Arima Valley, Hollis Reservoir, and the north coast road east of Blanchisseuse. Museum material from Trinidad adds: San Rafael, Port of Spain, Tucker Valley; Heights of Guanapo, and Princes Town. Literature records for Tobago include Milford Bay (Barbour 1916b); Crown Point, Buccoo Bay, and widespread on Tobago (Underwood, 1962). Field notes (JCM) record it above Man of War Bay. Museum material adds the following Tobago localities: above Hillsborough Dam and Charlotteville.

Description: Males 253 mm, females 333 mm SVL; tail 1.9 times SVL. Cylindrical body and tail rounded proximally, compressed distally. Head triangular, longer than wide. Rostral triangular or pentagonal; nostrils on seam of a divided nasal; five-sided frontonasal followed by two prefrontals, and irregular octagonal-shaped frontal; paired interparietals followed by three enlarged scales. Supralabials number eight to nine, infralabials number seven to eight, four supraoculars. Ear opening rectangular, at least two-thirds of eye diameter; tympanum visible. Dorsal scales small, ranging in shape from quadrangular with rounded corners to square and circular; arranged in about 86 transverse rows from the nape to anterior edge of the hind limbs; decrease in size laterally. Ventral scales larger than dorsals, rectangular, and arranged in 35 transverse rows and 23 lon-

gitudinal rows; number of longitudinal ventral scale rows will distinguish this species from all other teiids in the area. Tail scales rectangular on all surfaces. Legs well developed, five digits present on each. Fourth finger with 19–21 lamellae, fourth toe with 33–34 lamellae. Young specimens with 10–12 transverse black bands with olive-brown pigment in between. With age, black bands expand and are interrupted by white spots. Lower labials and adjacent scales black, irregular black blotches on an otherwise white or yellow venter. Males with wider head than females and juveniles, appear to have jowls. Males with 12 femoral and preanal pores per side.

Natural History: A large lizard found in every terrestrial habitat, it will enter water to escape predation. Field notes (JCM) describe habitat as savanna, secondary forest, forest-edge, primary forest, coastal areas, and stream margins. In Suriname, Hoogmoed (1973) described similar habitats for this species. Food is catholic, and includes berries, insects, spiders, centipedes, crabs, frogs and their eggs, lizards, caiman eggs, turtle eggs, snakes, mice and rats (Beebe, 1945; Milstead, 1961; Everard and Boos, 1975; Staton and Dixon, 1977b). On the mainland, Beebe (1945) observed copulation on 20 April and states breeding occurs from April to August, with clutch sizes of 4–12; Milstead (1961) found 32 oviductal eggs in a female from southern Brazil. Oviposition occurs in termite nests 2–12 feet above the ground, with eggs hatching during the rains when the nest is softened by water absorption (DeVerteuil, 1858; Beebe, 1945; Everard and

Boos, 1975; Dixon and Soini, 1975), confirming a reason for the Trinidadian folklore story that eggs hatch during thunderstorms (Boos, 1979a). On the mainland, daily activity of captives living in a large seminatural enclosure was monitored by Milstead (1961): activity started about 0830 h and stopped at 1500–1600 h; lizards basked at 23°C (air temperature) and this might last 2 hours; foraging started at 27–30°C (air temperature). Everard and Boos (1975) estimated density of this species at one per 3.2 acres in derived savanna, secondary scrub, and forest-edge. Predators include birds of prey (Hoogmoed, 1973) and humans. Wing and Reitz (1982) identified the remains of this species from an archeological site at St. John's, Trinidad; and Harris (1980) reported remains of this lizard from an archeological site on Tobago. DeVerteuil (1858) described humans hunting this lizard, "Matos are hunted down with dogs, and taken either in holes, or in some hollow tree, wherein they seek a temporary refuge; the best mode, however, is shooting them; they are then watched about mid-day in some copse or bushy spot, whither hens are accustomed to lead their broods, or during the dry season, along the dried beds of ravines, where they lurk for fish." It is also eaten on Tobago (DeVerteuil, 1968), and Copper and Bacon (1981) considered it an important supplement to the diet in some Trinidad villages. Some authors have suggested that *Tupinambis* has been reduced in numbers by competition or predation by the mongoose (Urich, 1931; Greenhall, 1959; Greenhall in Worth, 1967) since both are diurnal foragers, mostly carnivorous, and similar in size. However, Everard and Boos (1975) found the matte coexisting with the mongoose and *Didelphis marsupialis* (opossum) at Waller Field. Aitkens et al. (1968) report the tick *Amblyomma dissimile* on Trinidad specimens.

Material: Trinidad—FMNH 49899–900 San Rafael.

Order Squamata: Suborder Serpentes

Snakes are relatively easy to distinguish from lizards, and almost everyone can readily identify a snake correctly. About 2400 species of snakes in 420 genera and 11 families inhabit the planet, but new species are described annually. These are legless, eyelidless, earless squamates that had a lizard ancestor. Most live on land, but some are highly specialized for life in the trees, soil, or water. All snakes are predators, and most are capable of swallowing relatively large prey. Trinidad and Tobago have representatives of seven families and 45 species and subspecies. Because snakes shed their skin, have a penis divided into two parts, stay coupled together for a relatively long time during mating, have relatively large numbers of offspring or eggs, and are tubular in shape, they make excellent symbols for rebirth, healing, fertility, and sexuality in human cultures. Therefore, snakes have taken on important symbolic roles in human cultures the world over; only in cultures influenced by Christianity does the snake become a symbol of evil.

Order Squamata: Suborder Serpentes
Family Anomalepididae: Dawn Blind Snakes

Dawn blind snakes are restricted to lower Central American and northern South America. They have a toothed maxilla that is movable, one or two teeth in the lower jaw, fused skull bones, and a short tail. They lack the vestigal pelvic bones present in the other families of small, burrowing blind snakes. The family contains about 20 species in four genera. The undescribed Trinidad species is known from a single specimen from the Northern Range. Additionally, the snake *Typhlophis squamosus* has been reported on Trinidad, but there appears to be no specimens to support the literature record (see comment in Species Erroneously Reported or of Questionable Occurrence).

Helminthophis sp.

Map 71.

Distribution: The presence of this genus on Trinidad is based upon a single specimen, USNM 286925, collected 19 August 1984 by Peter Dickson on LaLaja Road, 7.3 km east of the junction with the Arima-Blanchisseuse Rd. and 1.1 km east of the junction with LaLaja Pariah Trace. The specimen represents an undescribed species.

Identification: 140 mm SVL; tail 4 mm, 2.8% of SVL. Rostral visible from above; nasal scale single; one preocular; two postoculars; one supraocular; suboculars absent; three supralabials; one infralabial. Each head plate covered with numerous tubercles. Longitudinal scale count about 401, subcaudals number 12–13. Scale rows around midbody 18. Dorsum and venter brown; head and chin are yellow; a yellow spot on throat on scales 6 and 7. Anal region and six medial, preanal scales are yellow, as well as several of the subcaudals. This animal can be distinguished from *Leptotyphlops albifrons* and *Typhlops trinitatus* by the lack of a striped pattern on the body of this species. Both *L. albifrons* and *T. trinitatus* have yellow tipped heads and tails, as does this species. In overall color it is similar to *Typhlops brongersmianus,* but is much more slender in body build. Diameter at midbody of this species 2 mm (total length/midbody width = 1.4%), while midbody widths for *T. brongersmianus* range between 3.4–12.9 mm (total length/midbody width = 3.21–5.1%, x̄ =4.05%′).

Natural History: The specimen came from an area in the Northern Range that may be best regarded as disturbed lower montane rainforest. The single specimen is an adult female containing one egg.

Order Squamata: Suborder Serpentes
Family Boidae: Boas and Pythons

Boas and pythons comprise about 21 genera with about 66 species, depending upon whose classification is used. Boids

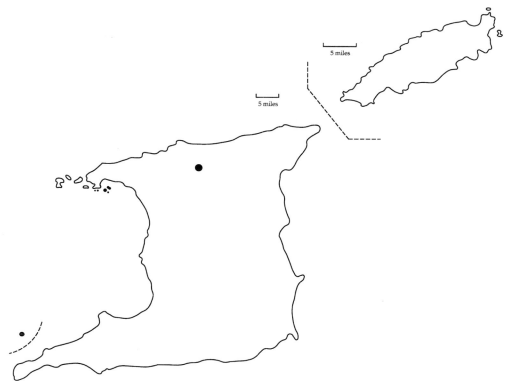

Map 71. *Helminthophis* sp.

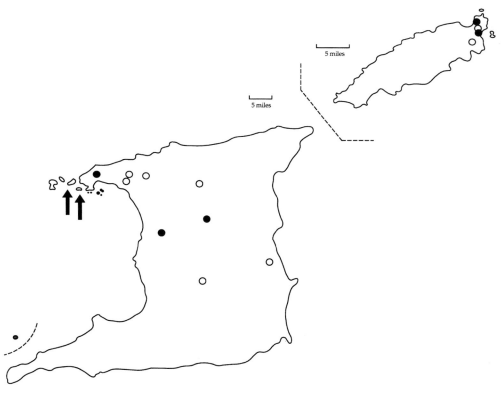

Map 72. *Boa constrictor constrictor*

are distributed mostly in the tropics, with some species ranging into temperate areas. Members of this family are considered to be generalized snakes that have survived from the Upper Cretaceous, and they may have given rise to the Recent snake fauna. Vestiges of hindlimbs are present in these snakes, evidence of a limbed ancestor; the external, claw-like structures tend to be larger in males than females and are used by males of some species during courtship. Four species in four genera occur on Trinidad and Tobago, including the anaconda, the largest boid.

DeVerteuil (1858) wrote "The boa constrictor, or macajuel, seems to prefer low damp places, and the boa—murina, or huilla, never strays far from the river or pond which it has selected as its abode. They are specially plentiful in the Oropuche River, and its affluents, viz., the Cunapo, Sangregrande, and Sangre-chiquito, nor are they scarce at Cedros."

Boa constrictor constrictor Linnaeus

Map 72. Plates 113, 114

Boa constrictor Linnaeus, 1758:215. Type locality: "India" (in error). *Boa imperator:* Reinhardt and Lutken, 1862:12. *Boa diviniloqua:* Boulenger, 1893:118. *Constrictor constrictor:* Barbour, 1916b:223. *Constrictor (Boa) constrictor:* Field, 1942:40. *Boa constrictor constrictor:* Forcart, 1951:199. *Constrictor constrictor constrictor:* Underwood, 1962:179. *Boa c. constrictor:* DeVerteuil, 1968:101.

Common Names: "Macajuel" (DeVerteuil, 1858); "Macacouile" (Mole and Urich, 1894a) "Macaruel" (Wehekind, 1955).

Distribution: *B. constrictor* is widespread, ranging from Sonora and Tamaulipas, Mexico, southward to northern Argentina, the Lesser Antilles, and Trinidad and Tobago. *B. c. constrictor* makes up the Amazonian portion of this range and occurs on Trinidad and Tobago. Published Trinidad localities: Arima Valley (Beebe, 1952); Barataria and Marval (Mole, 1924); Monos Island (Manuel, 1965; Boos, 1984b); Gasparee Grande (Boos, 1984d); Nariva Swamp (Ramcharan et al., 1979). Museum records for Trinidad: near Arima; Mt. St. Benedict; Chaguaramas; Tucker Valley; Maqueripe; San Rafael. Field notes (JCM) add numerous localities in the Arima Valley and, between Tabaquite and Rio Claro. Woodcock (1867) noted its presence on Tobago. Field notes (JCM) record a large (3 m total length), decapitated specimen on the road between Speyside and Charlotteville; and near the 22 milepost marker on the Windward Rd. Museum records for Tobago document: Speyside and Charlotteville.

A Note on Size: *Boa c. constrictor* is a large, well-known snake, but an interesting story involves its maximum size and the island of Trinidad. Dimensions of this species are given by Emsley (1977) as 635 mm at birth (presumed to be total length) to more than 12 feet (3650 mm). This is similar to the comments made by Mole and Urich (1894b) who wrote,

Mr. A. B. Carr of Capro, a very careful observer, who has seen and caught many of these reptiles, says that the largest he has ever seen was a female 11.5 feet long. It contained 41 eggs. We have frequently seen them 6, 8, and

10 feet, and one in our possession now, which came from Chaguaramas, . . . measured from tip of nose to extremity of tail 10 feet 6 inches, but it is probable that it is at least 8 inches longer, as the difficulty of getting it to remain quiet was very great, and it could not be pulled out straight. . . . It is possible that boas (in Trinidad, at any rate) never exceed 12 feet.

Oliver (1958) then reported the following story,

The record for . . . the species is 18 feet 6 inches. This length was obtained from an unusually large individual killed and measured in Trinidad by Collin Pittendrigh while he was on the island doing malaria-control work during World War II. He was working with a crew of men in the thick forest of Trinidad's Central Range. To go from their camp to where they were working, the crew had to cross a swampy area by walking along the trunk of a fallen tree. One morning, they saw a huge snake resting on the tree and, believing it was a giant bushmaster, refused to go out until the snake was killed. Pittendrigh got his gun and went to the spot where the snake had been reported. It was gone. He urged them to go on with their work, but they refused to cross the area until the snake was found and killed. After a careful search the snake was discovered coiled up in the hollow end of the tree trunk. Pittendrigh said it appeared to be a monstrous creature. With long poles it was moved part way out of the log and shot. Then it was dragged out to where its true identity and length could be determined. It was measured in the flesh at 18.5 feet, but the skin after being stretched was much longer. This maximum length for the widely famed Boa places it barely above the maximum of 18 feet 4 inches records for the longest venomous snake, the King Cobra . . .

Boos (1992) contacted Pittendrigh in 1980 and reported his response.

What he wrote was, that on that fateful day, alerted by his field crew he shot what he describes as a "Boa constrictor", which was sunning itself on a felled tree trunk. So heavy that it took two men to carry it back to their camp in the Guico/Tamana area of Eastern Trinidad, where he then stated, he skinned it, so that it stretched completely across the back of their laboratory building which measured 30 feet long. He also said that "The animal was about 18 feet long."

That night the unprotected skin was destroyed and partially eaten by stray dogs and unfortunately no pictures were taken. Apparently, no pieces of skin were preserved either. He ends by saying "However, my memory is clear on it all - it was truly an immense snake!"

In my [Boos] reply to Pittendrigh I pointed out to him the confusion caused by the common use of the name "Boa constrictor" to mean both the Anaconda and Boa in South America . . .

His reply was stunning to me. He admitted that "I certainly cannot exclude the possibility that the snake I shot in Tamana was an Anaconda ('Huilla') because I am no herpetologist." He added that he had assumed that since Anacondas were swamp inhabitants and that there were no swamps in the Guico/Tamana area, that it must have been a Boa constrictor. He ends his letter, "However, there is no doubt that I cannot attest, with any scientific authority, that it was not an Anaconda. Nevertheless, I seriously doubt that."

Boos observed that the location is only a few miles from Nariva Swamp, and that Yussuf Khan, a Trinidad resident, had been with Pittendrigh and positively identified the snake as a "Huille" or "Huillia," the local name for *Eunectes murinus*.

Independently, Joy (1992) also located Pittendrigh and asked him about the boa. Joy writes, "In his reply, Dr. Pittendrigh states that the snake in question was 18.5 feet long, but it was a young anaconda, not a boa constrictor. He says he never published anything on it and has no idea how it ever got into the literature as a boa constrictor. Furthermore, no photos of the animal exist." Thus the maximum size of the boa constrictor is still in question, and undoubtedly much less than 18 feet.

Description: Nasals separated by at least four or five tiny internasals, a character that will readily distinguish it from all other boids in the area. Supralabials number 16–25, infralabials number 20–28; these lack heat sensing pits found in *Epicrates* and *Corallus*. Smooth dorsal scales are in 76–95 rows; ventrals number 214–248; anal plate single; single subcaudals number 49–60. Dorsum tan or gray with dark red-brown transverse marking. Colors change posteriorly, tan areas become cream, or almost white, and brown transverse blotches become red. Brown stripe from snout passes through the eye and extends to first transverse band. Males have larger preanal spurs than females.

Natural History: A habitat generalist, using rainforest, secondary growth, savannas, and cultivated areas; field notes (JCM) describe specimens in close proximity to human habitations; and Mole (1924) considered it common everywhere on the island but seldom seen. Food includes a variety of vertebrates: DeVerteuil (1858) wrote, "Rats and opossums are the great treat of the macajuel; and as many as seven of the latter were once found in the stomach of a boa constrictor"; Urich (1933) reported a mongoose eaten by a boa; Emsley (1977) listed rat, mice, squirrels, agouti, opossum, ducks, chickens, frogs, lizards, and mongoose; Mole (1924) listed stomach contents: ocelot, mongoose, tegu lizard, and *Ameiva,* and noted it occasionally kills dogs. Courtship has been observed in October and copulation reported between December and March, with young born in May (Mole, 1924). Litters of 21–64 are born May through September (Emsley, 1977; Pope 1967); field notes (JCM) describe neonates in June-July. DeVerteuil (1858) wrote, "The macajuel, whenever irritated, inflates its body, and then loudly

emits a fetid and sickening breath, which causes a sort of fainting sensation." Mole (1924) compared the defensive hiss of this snake to the escape of steam from a small boiler. Field notes (JCM) describes hissing when first encountered, but record no evidence that bad smelling noxious gases that cause fainting are expelled with its breath. On the mainland, McGinnis and Moore (1969) monitored a boa over a 3 day period and found body temperature ranges from 22–37°C with a mean of 26.4°C.

Joseph's (1838) *History of Trinidad* discussed the boa, but he may have also confused it with the anaconda, or exaggerated its length.

We have here Boa Constrictors of enormous size. In 1818, I assisted in killing one that measured 22 feet; one was subsequently taken in the mountains above Port of Spain, considerably larger. He was opened in Brunswick Square, and a deer found in his maw. It is astonishing that a creature, which I found on experiment does not move at a quicker rate than four miles an hour, can contrive to catch an animal so active as the deer . . . I never knew of their attacking a man. When torpid, from being overgorged, they are easily killed, and might be easily captured; while in this state, their odour is extremely unwholesome. A planter of Point-a-Pierre sent a Negro to cut down a tree: the man, a few minutes after, returned, dreadfully sick at stomach. He sent a second; after a few strokes of the axe, he also was taken sick. A third Negro went to work: he too began to feel indisposed, and declared he 'smelt snake'; he however succeeded in cutting down the tree, and, like his predecessors, commenced vomiting. When the tree fell, a large boa was found amongst the branches, in a state of torpor. The Negroes shortly after recovered.

It is worth noting that some trees, such as *Rhus* sp., release toxic fumes when cut and that the presence of a boa in the area may have resulted in being linked to the incident.

Material: Trinidad—AMNH 64484, 64484A Tucker Valley. FMNH 49927 San Rafael. MCZ 6105, "Trinidad", 100630–1 born in captivity, mother from Chaguaramas. Tobago—MCZ 32217 (skin). USNM 228015 Speyside; 228016 Charlotteville.

Corallus hortulanus cookii Gray

Map 73. Plate 115.

Corallus cookii Gray, 1842:42. Type locality: unknown. *Xiphosoma hortulanum:* Reinhardt and Lutken, 1862:12. *Corallus cookii* var. *melanea:* Boulenger, 1893:100. *Corallus cookei ruschenbergi:* Boettger, 1898:10. *Corallus cookii* var. C.: Werner, 1900:269. *Boa hortulana:* Barbour, 1930b:108. *Corallus enydris cookii:* Forcart, 1951:197. *Boa enhydris cookii:* Underwood, 1962:179. *Corallus hortulanus cookii:* Roze, 1966:61. *Corallus enydris cooki:* Schwartz and Thomas, 1975:181.

Comment: Recently McDiarmid et al. (1996) showed the correct name for this snake to be *Corallus hortulanus cookii* instead of *C. enydris.* Hedges and Henderson (1995) examined mtDNA from seven widely scattered populations

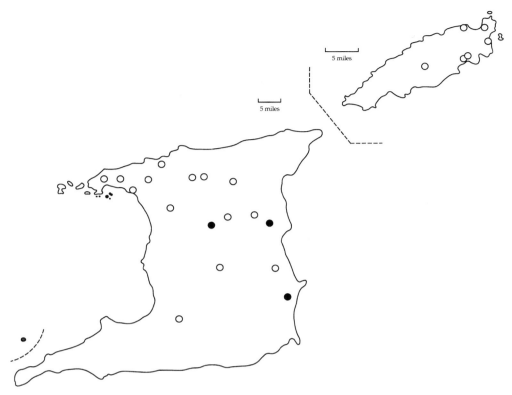

Map 73. *Corallus hortulanus cookii*

including Trinidad and Grenada and found the Grenada populations are most similar to the southern race *C. h. hortulanus,* than the northern race *C. h. cookii.* This was unexpected and suggests that the Trinidad, population and probably the Tobago population, had an ancestry that was proximal, while the Grenada populations had an Amazonian ancestry. Presumably this occurred from a dispersal event involving the rafting of a *C.h. hortulanus* from a population in Guyana or Brazil.

Common Names: "Cascabel Dormillion, which means sleeping rattlesnake" (Mole and Urich, 1891); Mapanare (Mole, 1914); Cascabel (Wehekind, 1955); Cascabel dormillion, Mapanare, Cooks tree boa (Boos and Quesnel, 1968); yellow tree boa, tree boa, doghead, tete chien (Emsley, 1977).

Distribution: *C. hortulanus* is widespread, as is the race *C. h. cookii* as currently defined. It occurs on Tobago and Trinidad; and on the mainland from Costa Rica to Colombia and northern and central Venezuela. Published Trinidad localities: Arima Valley (Beebe, 1952); Bush-Bush Island, Nariva Swamp (Worth, 1967); Caroni River and Botanic Gardens, Port of Spain (Anon., 1926); Port of Spain (Werner, 1900). Museum material from Trinidad documents: Arima, Mt. Harris, San Rafael, Plaisance, Hollis Reservoir, Port of Spain, Mt. St. Benedict, Maracas Valley, Cuare Dam, Diego Martin, Tucker Valley, Sangre Grande, Navet, Waller Field, and Princes Town. Museum material from Tobago documents: Speyside; Man-of-War Bay,

Charlotteville; near Hermitage; above Hillsborough Dam; 0.6 mi W of junction of Windward Rd. on Roxborough-Parlatuvier Rd.

Description: 1870 mm SVL, with a 289 mm damaged tail largest specimen; 1295 mm SVL female with a 340 mm tail (26% SVL). Body laterally compressed; head wide, distinct from neck. Rostral slightly visible from above; nostrils on seam of divided nasal scale; loreal divided; two preoculars; supraoculars and postoculars divided into a series of small scales; 8–13 supralabials, 12–15 infralabials; 252–268 ventrals; anal single; single subcaudals number 100–112. Smooth, dorsal scales in 38–45 rows at midbody. Dorsum khaki-brown to yellow-brown in Trinidad specimens examined; faint rhomboidal pattern may be present; venter uniform cream. Males with larger anal spurs than females. Henderson and Boos (1994) give a detailed description of the variation of Trinidad and Tobago populations. Nasals in contact distinguish it from all other boids in the area.

Natural History: An arboreal, nocturnal, forest and forest-edge boid that occasionally descends to the ground. Field notes (JCM) report three specimens crossing roads in secondary forest after dark. Mole and Urich (1891) commented, "It is invariably found in the daytime rolled up in the loose folds among the twigs of a tree, the branches of which overhang a stream . . . At night these snakes are lively and glide from bough to bough . . ." Later they (Mole and Urich, 1894b) wrote, "The species is frequently found in bamboo

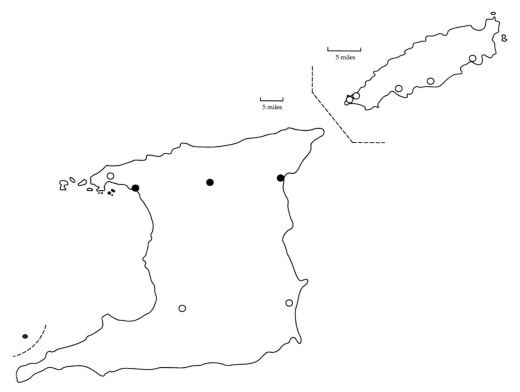

Map 74. *Epicrates cenchria maurus*

clumps, and in bushes in the vicinity of or overhanging streams." Food includes birds, squirrels, bats, mongoose, and porcupine rats (Mole and Urich, 1894b; Mole, 1924; Urich, 1933). Stomachs of five Trinidad specimens empty; one female contained remains of two or three mice of the genus *Akodon* [identified by Philip Hershkovitz, FMNH]; notes with a seventh specimen report a "manicou cros yeux," the small mouse opossum, *Marmosa robinsoni,* as prey. Pendlebury (1974) compared the diet of mainland South American and Carriacou populations and found mainland specimens do not eat ectotherms, while the island population relies on ectotherms. Henderson (1993) reported on 52 prey items from mainland specimens, including Trinidad and Tobago, and found 3 lizards, 17 birds, a minimum of 9 bats, and the remainder were murid rodents. Mole and Urich (1891) reported a secondhand observation of a pair in copula in February with the female giving birth to 20 or 30 the following August. A female contained 15 oviducal eggs (field notes, JCM). Mole (1924) commonly encountered it in February.

Material: Trinidad—FMNH 49918, 49920, 49923–25, San Rafael; 49926 Mayaro; 49921–2 Mt. Harris.

Epicrates cenchria maurus Gray

Map 74. Plates 116, 117, 118.

Epicrates maurus Gray, 1849:96. Type locality: Venezuela. *Epicrates cenchria:* Reinhardt and Lutken, 1862:12. *Epicrates cenchria maurus:* Stull, 1935:396. *Epicrates cenchrus:* Field, 1942:40. *Epicrates cenchris:* Wehekind, 1955:10. *Epicrates maurus:* Chippaux, 1986:37.

Comment: Chippaux (1986) elevated the race *E. c. maurus* to a full species; this is not followed here because the Guiana populations he examined may well be integrades between the forest-dwelling *E. c. cenchria* and the savanna-dwelling *E. c. maurus* (W. W. Lamar, personal communication).

Common Names: "Thick-necked tree boas, Velvet Mapepire" (Mole and Urich, 1894b); "Jack" (Mole, 1914); "rainbow snake" (Boos and Quesnel, 1968); "ringed boa" (Emsley, 1977).

Distribution: *E. cenchria* is widespread; as is the race *E. c. maurus,* which ranges from Costa Rica to the Guianas, and Trinidad and Tobago. Published Trinidad localities include: Arima Valley (Beebe, 1952). Trinidad museum material documents: Valencia-Toco Rd.; Port of Spain; Mayaro; Princes Town; Tucker Valley. Published Tobago localities: Milford Bay (Barbour, 1916b); Studley Park (Mertens, 1972). Tobago museum material documents: near Milford Bay; 0.75 mi east of Buccoo Bay; Scarborough; and Roxborough.

Description: Maximum length about 1700 mm SVL; tail about 16% SVL. Rostral visible from above; nasals divided; loreal elongated; two preoculars; four-five postoculars; 10–12 supralabials; 11–14 infralabials; 225–242 ventrals; anal plate single; 53–63 single subcaudals. Small, smooth dorsal scales in 41–51 rows at midbody. Adults purple-brown with

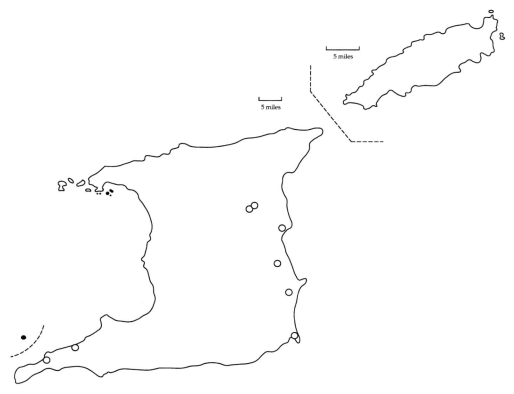

Map 75. *Eunectes murinus*

four or five stripes on head; dark spots or ocelli on body. Iridescent sheen on scales responsible for the names rainbow snake and rainbow boa. Juveniles boldly marked, middorsum with 35–40 bronze-gold spots outlined in black; head with black midline stripe and two black stripes above and behind each eye; sides with three or four rows of black spots; venter uniform off-white. Shallow heat-sensing labial pits, subocular scales, and presence of two internasals will readily distinguish this snake from all other Trinidad and Tobago boids.

Natural History: A snake of forest-edge, savanna, and agricultural areas. Field notes (JCM) report six of eight specimens in agricultural areas or areas of human habitation, others in secondary growth forest; all on road after dark. Mole and Urich (1894b) wrote, " . . . we have only heard of one being caught in a tree, though they can climb well. They are more usually found in holes, and often frequent the palm-thatched roofs of kitchens in the country, under houses, and often in or near water." Food includes frogs, antbirds, chickens, mice, rats, opossums (Mole and Urich, 1894b; Mole, 1924; Beebe, 1946). Copulation has been reported in October and January and birth occurs in March-July (Mole and Urich, 1894b; Mole, 1924; Emsley, 1977). Four of eight specimens collected in July were neonates (field notes, JCM).

Material: Trinidad—FMNH 217224–5 near Arima; 219610 between Valencia and Toco. MCZ 80992 near Emperor Valley Zoo, Port of Spain.

Eunectes murinus (Linnaeus)

Map 75. Plate 119

> *Boa murina* Linnaeus, 1758:215. Type locality: "America." *Boa murina*: Court, 1858:441. *Eunec urnus*: Kingsley, 1890:277. *Eunectes murinus*: Reinhardt and Lutken, 1862:12. *Eunectes murinus gigas*: Dunn and Conant, 1936:503. *Eunectes murinus murinus*: Belluomini, et al., 1976–77:85.

Comment: Strimple (1993) noted that the two races of this snake are distinguished on the basis of size, range, and the color of the postocular stripe; and points out the variability of the postocular stripe's color. Further investigation into the subspecific arrangement of anaconda populations are needed and no race is recognized here.

Common Names: "Huilla" [pronounced 'weel'] (DeVertuil, 1858); "Huilia, Huile" (Mole, 1914); "Water Boa" (Field, 1942); "Anaconda" (Boos and Quesnel, 1968); "Camoudi" (Emsley, 1977).

Distribution: *E. murinus* has an Amazonian distribution, ranging from Trinidad, Venezuela, and Colombia southward to Bolivia. Published Trinidad localities: "It inhabits the rivers and lagoons on the east coast and has been found, but less seldom at Cedros . . ." (Mole and Urich, 1894b). Irois; Guaico; Cunapo; Sangre Grande; Manzanilla; Mayaro; Cedros; "within 10–12 miles of San Fernando" (Mole, 1924). Bush-Bush Island, Nariva Swamp (Kingsley, 1890; Oliver, 1958; Worth, 1967). Point Galeota (Boos, 1984d). Trinidad museum specimens all lack specific locality data.

A Note on Size: Maximum size is controversial. Gilmore and Murphy (1993) suggested that the long accepted record based on Robert Lamon's 37.5 foot specimen reported by E. R. Dunn was, in all probablity, about 25 feet. This is the world's largest snake, possibly in total length and certainly in bulk. *Python reticulatus* may attain a similar or greater length. DeVerteuil (1858) wrote, " . . . a huilla killed in the river Cunapo measured seventeen feet eleven inches; it however attains to twenty and even twenty-four feet." Mole (1924) believed a 32 ft specimen was killed near Iros, Trinidad, in 1810 or 1812, but the largest he measured was 16 feet, 8 inches; it weighed 232 pounds. The smallest neonate examined in this study was 464 mm SVL, 80 mm tail (17% SVL). This snake has been long confused with *Boa constrictor,* and literature references to extremely large boas may refer to this species instead (see the comment from Joseph, 1838 in the *Boa constrictor* account); in many instances it is impossible to determine which species is being discussed.

Description: Rostral visible from above; nasal divided on seam of three scales; loreal single; one preocular; one to four postoculars; usually two, sometimes one or three suboculars; 14–17 supralabials; 15–25 infralabials; 241–269 ventrals; anal plate single; 65–72 single subcaudals. Small, smooth dorsal scales in 53–69 rows at midbody. Dorsum olive-brown with one or two rows of 36–45 dark brown or black blotches, and a lateral row of light-centered ocelli. The lack of labial pits, four symmetrical scales between eyes, and presence of subocular scales (between the eye and upper labials) will distinguish the anaconda from all other Trinidad and Tobago boids.

Natural History: An aquatic snake, restricted to ponds, swamps and riparian habitats. New immigrants, adding to the gene pool, may still be arriving, Boos (1984d) wrote, "I have recently had a young anaconda, . . . brought to me from Pt. Galeota. It was caught in the large mats of vegetation floating in the sea." Bacon (1978) commented on its ability to colonize water-filled quarries. Food of this species is diverse; almost all vertebrates are eaten. Mole (1924) stated it feeds on animals that come to drink at the water's edge, as well as aquatic species. He listed sheep, rodents, dogs, deer, tamandua, caiman, ducks, and turtles. Oddly, fish are rarely reported in its diet, although Beebe (1946) recorded 27 fish from three mainland specimens. Attacks on humans are rare, but Kingsley (1890) gives a secondhand report of a girl attacked by a huilla on Trinidad; it is probable that this was a defensive strike and not an attempt at feeding.

Four young ladies, whose names were mentioned to me, preferred, not wisely, a bathe in the still lagoon to one in the surf outside; and as they disported themselves, one of them felt herself seized from behind. Facing that one of her sisters was playing tricks, she called out to her to let her alone; and looking up, saw, to her astonishment, her three sisters sitting on the bank, and herself alone. She looked back, and shrieked for help; and only just in time;

for the Huilla had her. The other three girls, to their honour, dashed in to her assistance. The brute has luckily got hold, not of her poor little body, but of her bathing-dress, and held on stupidly. The girls pulled; the bathing dress, which was, luckily of thin cotton was torn off; the Huilla slid back again with it in his mouth into the dark labyrinth of the mangrove-roots; and the girl was saved.

Mole (1924) observed copulation in December and January, noted that it could occur on land or in the water, and reported births in July and August. Ditmars and Bridges (1937) discussed a Trinidad anaconda R. R. Mole sent to Ditmars: the snake, "eventually attained a length of eighteen feet and a weight of 138 pounds before she died, and was the casual parent of seventy-four young anacondas. Her offspring are scattered all over the United States in various zoological parks." Pope (1967) mentioned broods between 19–72, the latter coming from a 19 ft female. In Brazil, Belluomini and Hoge (1958) removed 82 young from a female by caesarean. Young tend to be arboreal, while large adults tend to lie coiled on river banks, or rest in the water with only their nostrils exposed (Emsley, 1977). However, even the young are aquatic and Mole and Urich (1894b) wrote, "When in water they often anchored themselves by a turn of the tail round the submerged portion of the branch. At other times they would individually roll themselves into a tight ball and float on the surface."

Material: Trinidad—MCZ 8045–6, born in zoo, female from Trinidad. Colombia—FMNH 45893–99; 45701–20.

Order Squamata: Suborder Serpentes Family Colubridae: Harmless Snakes

Approximately 70% of the world's snake fauna belong to this family, with about 300 genera and 1600 species. The family is composed of typically "harmless" snakes that are the dominant serpents on the planet today. While most species are considered harmless, some have a mild venom, and a few can make humans sick or even kill them, because of secretion from a specialized gland. This oral gland, known as Duvernoy's gland, produces enzymes and other molecules that assist the snake in subduing and digesting prey. Secretions from this gland are released during feeding and are usually not delivered during a defensive bite. Care should be taken when handling these snakes and none of them should be allowed to chew on a human. Trinidad and Tobago species with mild venom and enlarged rear teeth are xenodontine (subfamily Xenodontinae) snakes. Trinidad and Tobago have 30 species of colubrids representing about 24 genera, none of which are known to pose serious danger to humans. DeVerteuil (1858) wrote,

The Clibo or Cribo* haunts inhabited places, and is occasionally seen in houses, where, however, it ought to be welcome as a destroyer of rats. This coluber is very determined, particularly the black kind, and it has been known

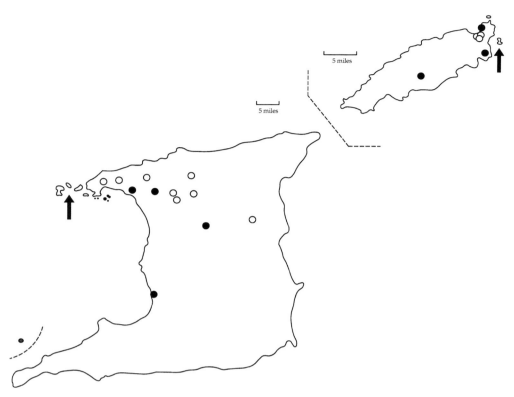

Map 76. *Atractus trilineatus*

to give battle, even chase, to man. When a child, I was once pursued by a clibo, and I also distinctly remember having witnessed one in combat with a gentleman, on which occasion it would stand erect on his tail, and bite at the garments, meanwhile hissing and inflating its neck . . .

*These names are most often applied to *Drymarchon corias,* but they may also apply to *Spilotes pullatus, Clelia clelia,* and possibly *Pseustes sulphureus.*

Atractus trilineatus Wagler

Map 76. Plate 120.

> *Atractus trilineatus* Wagler, 1828:747. Type locality: none given.
> *Rhabdosoma lineatum:* Garman, 1887c:280. *Geophis lineatus:* Mole and Urich, 1894a:84 *Attractus trilineatus:* Barbour, 1916b:224.

Common Names: "Ground snake" (Mole, 1924); "stub-tailed snake, three-lined snake" (Emsley, 1977).

Distribution: *A. trilineatus* is a lowland Guiana endemic, ranging from eastern Venezuela to the Guianas; and occurs on Trinidad, Tobago, and Little Tobago Island. Published Trinidad localities include: Port of Spain (Werner, 1899); Tucker Valley (Johnson, 1946); Arima Valley (Beebe, 1952); Orange Grove Estate, Tacarigua (Brongersma, 1956a); St. Augustine (Lynn, 1959); Port of Spain (Wehekind, 1960); Huevos Island (Emsley, 1977). Trinidad museum material documents: Bayshore, Mt. St. Benedict, near Cheeyou, Caparo, Diego Martin, Marval, Pointe-à-Pierre, San Rafael, and Tunapuna. Tobago locali-

ties based upon museum material are: Charlotteville; Pirate's Cove, north of Charlotteville; cacao plantation near Charlotteville; near Hillsborough Dam; Merchiston; and Little Tobago Island.

Description: 350 mm SVL; tail 7–10% SVL. Snout sharply pointed; rostral slightly visible from above; nasal scale single; loreal and preocular fused into elongated scale; no suboculars; two postoculars; seven or eight supralabials; six or seven infralabials; 121–139 ventrals; single or divided anal plate; 14–17 paired subcaudals. Smooth dorsal scales in 15 rows at midbody. Dorsum brown-gray with three or four longitudinal stripes. Labials and venter yellow or cream. At first glance this snake may be confused with *Leptotyphlops,* but it can be distinguished from it by the lack of cycloid scales, and the lack of yellow spots on the head and tail. *A. trilineatus* is readily distinguished from its close relative, *A. univittatus,* by the presence of 15 dorsal scale rows at midbody, instead of 17.

Natural History: A snake of forest and savanna; field notes (JCM) report 10 specimens, 8 on the road in secondary and primary forests and 2 under debris in secondary growth. Terrestrial urban environments such as gardens, lawns, and rubbish piles, and piles of soil, and logs are frequently used (Wehekind, 1960; Emsley, 1977; Johnson, 1946; Lynn, 1959; Mole, 1924). Field notes (JCM) suggest it to be nocturnal; individuals active on the road after dark. Worms and insects are eaten (Wehekind, 1960). Clutch size is reported as 3–5 (Mole and Urich, 1894b; Mole,

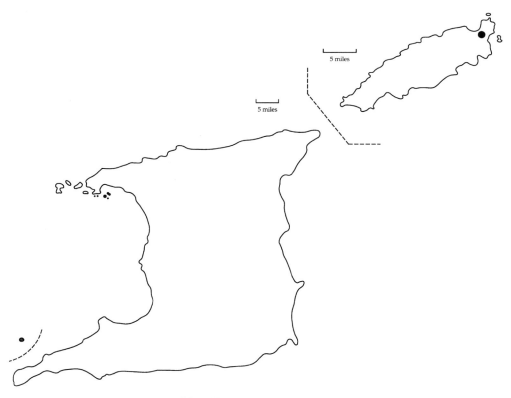

Map 77. *Atractus univittatus*

1924). Egg laying is known in March, April, and August (Emsley, 1977). The tail is used to probe surfaces when it is being handled; scales and caudal vertebrae form a stiff appendage that is continually pushed into the hand holding the snake; this is probably a defense behavior (Mole, 1924; Emsley, 1977); but Beebe (1946) suggested it is used for locomotion. Mole (1924) stated coral snakes prey upon *A. trilineatus;* Beebe (1946) took one from the stomach of an *Erythrolamprus aesculapii;* and field notes (JCM) report one in the stomach of the Tobago snake *E. ocellatus.*

Material: Trinidad—FMNH 41679 Pointe-à-Pierre; 35102, 41678 St. Augustine; 49971 San Rafael. MCZ 89996 Emperor Valley; 49065–6 Pointe-à-Pierre. USNM 141587 St. Augustine; 119079 Tucker Valley; 166675 near Cheeyu; 166676 Arima Valley. Tobago—USNM 228025–26 Charlotteville, above Pirate's Cove; 228045–48 Hillsborough Dam; 228049 Merchiston.

Atractus univittatus **(Jan)**

Map 77. Figure C.

Rabdosoma univittatum Jan, 1862:15. Type locality: Caracas, Distrito Federal, Venezuela. *Atractus univittatus:* Roze, 1961:117. *Atractus univittatum:* Lancini 1979:80. *Atractus* cf. *univittatus:* Hardy, 1982:82.

Distribution: *A. univittatus* has a Caribbean Coastal Range distribution, occurring at Rancho Grande in northern Venezuela, and on the island of Tobago. Roze (1966) and Lancini (1979) described the distribution as the Central de la Cordillera de la Costa (Distrito Federal y Estado Miranda).

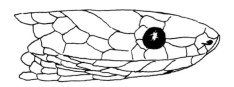

Figure C

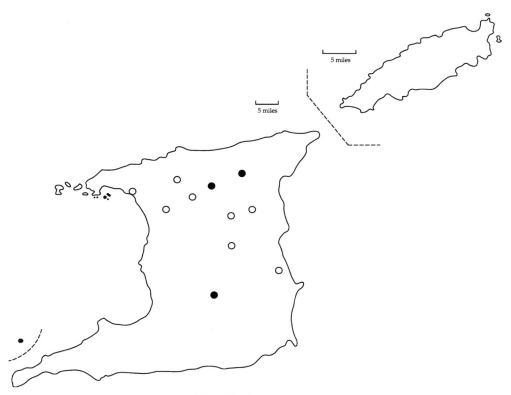

Map 78. *Chironius carinatus*

Hardy (1982) found it along the Main Ridge ca. 1.25 miles SSW of Charlotteville, Tobago. Hoogmoed (1980) tentatively identified a specimen (ANSP 3334) collected by Hering as "*Atractus* cf. *univittatus.*" The specimen is in poor condition, and the Suriname locality is in possible error. Hoogmoed states " . . . the species at the most could be expected to occur eastward to the Paria Peninsula but its endemicity in the area most likely is real." He concluded the collector and data are erroneous and that this species does not occur in Suriname.

Description: 291 mm SVL; 43 mm tail. Lancini (1979) reported the species reaches 40 cm in length. Rostral visible from above; preocular and loreal fused and contact nasal; internasals paired; no suboculars; seven supralabials; six infralabials; there are two anterior and two posterior temporals; 163 ventrals; anal plate single; 32 paired subcaudals. Dorsal scales smooth, each scale in first row with large light spot, scales in second row each contain a slightly smaller spot, all other scale rows with light spot that may be central or shifted to one side; many scales with dark spot on the posterior edge. Dorsal color gray; three indistinct longitudinal lines; venter uniform cream, last two supralabials cream. A small, striped snake distinguished from its relative *A. trilineatus* by its 17 midbody dorsal scale rows and its slightly longer tail.

Natural History: A poorly known, fossorial forest snake.

Material: Tobago—USNM 228024, Charlotteville ca. 1.25 mi SSW, along Main Ridge.

> **Chironius carinatus** (Linnaeus)

Map 78. Plates 121, 122.

> *Coluber carinatus* Linnaeus, 1758:223. Type locality: "Indiis." *Herpetodryas fuscus:* Reinhardt and Lutken, 1862:10. *Herpetodryas carinatus:* Boulenger, 1891:335. *Herpetodryas macrophthalmus:* Mole and Urich, 1894a:85. *Chironius carinatus:* Ruthven, 1922:65.

Common Names: "Known in Trinidad as the Machete or Macheta, because the male's back being rigid [a vertebral ridge] is thought to bear some resemblance to a machete or cutlass." (Mole and Urich, 1891); "Machete savanne" (Mole, 1914); "Yellow Machete" (Wehekind, 1955); "Golden tree snake" (Emsley, 1977).

Distribution: *C. carinatus* a widespread species, ranging from Costa Rica to Ecuador and Amazonian Brazil, and occurs on Trinidad. Published Trinidad localities include: the Botanic Gardens in Port of Spain and the Caroni River (Mole, 1924); Arima Valley (Beebe, 1952); Tacarigua (Brongersma, 1956a); Northern and Southern Ranges (Emsley, 1977); Aripo savannas (Schwab, 1988). Museum material from Trinidad documents the localities: Brickfield; Caura River; 1.6 mi north of Rio Claro; Cumaca; foothills of Guanapo Reserve; Nariva; San Rafael; Sangre Grande; Tamana Hill; and Valencia,.

Description: 1500 mm SVL, tail 58–79% SVL. Rostral visible from above; nasals divided; single loreal; one to three preoculars (one most frequent); no suboculars; two to four postoculars (two most frequent); eight or nine supra-

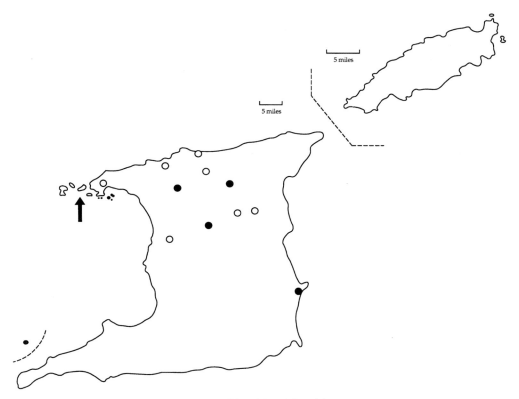

Map 79. *Clelia clelia clelia*

labials; 8–11 infralabials; 158–177 ventrals; anal plate divided; 163–174 subcaudals, (four of eight specimens have damaged tails). Eyes exceptionally large. Dorsal scales in 12 rows, reduced posteriorly to 10 or 8; no other Trinidad or Tobago colubrid snake has so few dorsal scale rows. Smooth scales except those on either side of vertebral line, which are strongly keeled in males and weakly keeled in females; apical pit present on distal edge of each scale (difficult to observe). Each dorsal scale tipped with black. Dorsum olive green, venter yellow, blue or both; chin and labials yellow.

Natural History: A forest and forest-edge snake, descending to the ground to forage during the day; sleeping in bushes and trees; uses primary and secondary forests. Mole and Urich (1891) observed one, "hanging by its tail from the top most branch of a bush on a river bank." In Amazonian Peru, Henderson et al. (1976) radiotracked a 90 cm female for 89 hours in an aguajal swamp and found it highly arboreal, occasionally descending to ground; mean hourly movement was 0.4 m/h, mean daily movement 9.6 m/day; and it had a 119 square meter home range. Food reported includes frogs, lizards, birds, mice (Mole and Urich, 1891; Mole, 1924; Wehekind, 1960); however, the literature suggests frogs may compose the bulk of the diet (Beebe, 1946; Brongersma, 1956b; Test et al., 1960; Dixon and Soini; 1977; Duellman, 1978). Clutch size is 4–5 (Mole and Urich, 1894b; Mole, 1924; Test et al., 1966). Field notes (JCM) describe a juvenile, in secondary forest leaf litter, kinking its body so that it becomes difficult to distinguish it from twigs and leaf peti-

oles; adults will also show this behavior. This snake is easily annoyed and does not hesitate to compress the anterior portion of its body and strike; compression of the body exposes pink skin that contrasts to dark scales. Field (1942) states that it was formerly common, but reduced by the mongoose.

Material: Trinidad—FMNH 49928–30, 49933–35 San Rafael; 49931 Brickfield; 215828–30, 215832, 217242, Arima Valley; 215833 1.6 mi north of Rio Claro. USNM 153836 Valencia, Valencia River.

Clelia clelia clelia (Daudin)

Map 79. Plates 123, 124.

Coluber clelia Daudin, 1803:330. Type locality: Suriname. *Oxyrhopus plumbeus:* Reinhardt and Lutken, 1862:12. *Oxyrrhopus cloelia:* Boettger, 1898:97. *Oxyrhopus cloelia:* Mole, 1914:147. *Clelia cloelia:* Barbour, 1914:341. *Clelia clelia clelia:* Dunn, 1944:201. *Cloelia c. cloellia:* Wehekind, 1955:12. *Cloelia cloelia:* Wehekind, 1960:74. *Pseudoboa cloelia:* Underwood, 1962:179. *Clelia cloelia cloelia:* Roze, 1966:102. *Clelia clelia:* Boos and Quesnel, 1968:7. *Cloelia c. cloelia:* DeVerteuil, 1968:103.

Common Names: "Vidua, Black cribo, Mussurana" (Mole, 1924); "Cribo" (Boos and Quesnel, 1968); "Mustarungua, Vidue" (Emsley, 1977).

Distribution: *C. clelia* is widespread, ranging from Veracruz and Guerrero, Mexico to Uruguay and Argentina. *C. c. clelia* ranges from Guatemala and Honduras to Ecuador and Argentina; and Grenada and Trinidad. Published Trinidad localities include: "the highest point on Saddle Road" and Blanchisseuse (Mole, 1924); Aripo savannas (Schwab, 1988); and

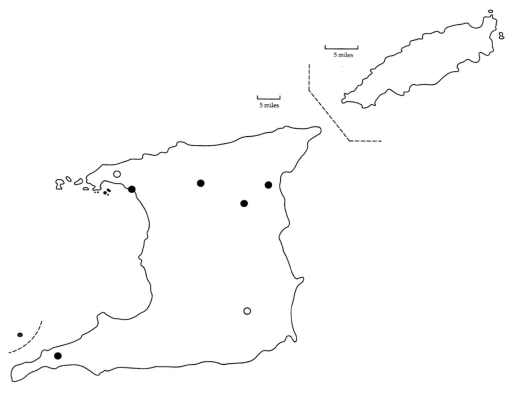

Map 80. *Dipsas variegata trinitatis*

Monos Island, (Anon., 1926). Museum material localities: Plaisance, San Rafael, near Hollis Reservoir, Maqueripie, Tucker Valley, Chaguaramas, Sangre Grande, and Maracas Valley. Field notes (JCM) report it in the Arima Valley. This snake is mentioned as being on Tobago by Barbour (1916b) and this report has apparently led others (Underwood, 1962; DeVerteuil, 1968) to list this species from that island; Hardy (1984b) found all of Barbour's specimens (now in the MCZ) from Tobago are *Pseudoboa neuwiedii*. However, the presence of *Clelia* on Grenada suggests that it may eventually be found, or may have once been present, on Tobago.

Description: Maximum about 2280 mm SVL; tail 24% SVL; largest measured in this study 806 mm SVL and a 188 mm tail. Rostral visible from above; nasals divided; loreal present in two Trinidad specimens; one preocular; no suboculars; two postoculars; seven supralabials; six to eight infralabials; 218–225 ventrals; single anal plate; 62–76 paired subcaudals. Smooth dorsal scales in 19 rows at midbody, reduced posteriorly to 17. Adults usually uniform blue-black above with white or off-white venter. White, cream, or red pigmentation on upper labials. Juveniles have a bright red dorsum with a black crown, followed by a white collar and each red scale in rows 3–13 has a black apical area. Distinguished from its close relative *Pseudoboa neuweidii* by the paired subcaudal scales, *P. neuweidii* has single subcaudals. It is distinguished from its close relative *Oxyrhopus petola* by having an elongated loreal about twice as long as it is high. *Oxyrhopus petola* has a loreal about as wide as it is

high. Most Trinidad *O. petola* have red annuli, but field notes (JCM) report all black specimens that could be easily confused with this species.

Natural History: A terrestrial snake of forests and savannas, often near water; field notes (JCM) report two individuals on road in secondary forest. Mostly nocturnal, with some activity during the day. Food is almost exclusively ectotherms, and includes *Ameiva, Boa constrictor, Bothrops asper, Corallus,* and *Spilotes* (Mole, 1924; Beebe, 1946; Wehekind, 1960). However mammals may also be eaten; Terxeira et al. (1991) report a Brazilian specimen feeding on the opossum *Metachirus nudicaudatus*. In Ecuador, Duellman reported 20 ovarian eggs from a 2070 mm female; and Mole (1924) described a clutch of 16 eggs from a Trinidad specimen.

Material: Trinidad—FMNH 49968 Plaisance Mayaro; 49969 San Rafael. USNM 166682 Cuare Rd., vicinity of milestone 1; near the Hollis Reservoir.

Dipsas variegata trinitatis Parker

Map 80. Plate 125.

Dipsas trinitatis Parker, 1926:205. Type locality: Trinity Hill Reserve. Trinidad. *Dipsas trinitatis:* Wehekind, 1955:11. *Dipsas variegata trinitatis:* Peters, 1960:139.

Comment: This snake may deserve full species status but it will require additional specimens and biochemical data to support this position. USNM 217182 from Altagracia, 15 km NW of Parque Nacional Guatopo, Guarico, Venezuela, looks remarkably like *D. v. trinitatis*. This specimen may represent a mainland population of the species or suggest the race is more widespread.

Common Name: "Snail-eating snake" (Emsley, 1977).

Distribution: *D. variegata* is widespread from Panama, northwestern Ecuador, and the Amazon Basin. *D. variegata trinitatis* is a near Trinidad endemic/Caribbean Coastal Range snake. Foothills of the Northern Range, the Southern Range, the southwestern peninsula, southeastern corner, and probably the Central Range; it may also occur in northern Venezuela (see comment above). Emsley (1977) stated that it is found in the Northern and Southern Ranges. Field notes (JCM) report specimens from the Arima Valley, Valencia Road 1.1 mi east of its junction with Toco Road, and one from Lizard Springs Road south of Rio Claro. Additional localities based upon museum material include: the 20 milepost on the Eastern Main Road, the 68 milepost on the Southern Main Road to Cedros, Diego Martin Valley, and Port of Spain. Thus, it appears absent from the higher elevations of the Northern Range.

Description: 638 mm SVL, 165 mm tail; tail 25–36% SVL. Rostral barely visible from above; nasal divided; single loreal; one preocular (one specimen has two on one side); no suboculars; two postoculars; seven to nine supralabials; 9–12 infralabials; 168–189 ventrals; anal plate single; 81–92 paired subcaudals. Smooth dorsal scales in 15 rows at midbody; vertebral scale row enlarged. Dorsum tan with 17–24 dark blotches on body (26–38 on the body and tail together), each blotch outlined in yellow or white; blotches alternate from one side to next, and extend from vertebral line to outer edge of ventrals. Crown of head dark brown, sides tan, with dark brown pigment on seams of labials. Venter off-white or yellow with flecks of brown pigment. This is the only Trinidad and Tobago colubrid snake lacking a mental groove (a middle chin groove).

Natural History: A forest and forest-edge snake; field notes (JCM) report 25 specimens, most on roads in the Arima Valley, and nearby areas, in early and mid-evenings. The area is a mosaic of secondary forest mixed with some primary forest and areas of human habitation and agriculture. *D. v. trinitatis* feeds on snails lacking an operculum. The snail is extracted from the shell by the snake working its jaws around the body of the snail and removing it from its shell with a ratchet-like motion of its jaws. Emsley (1977) believed that its apparent rarity is due to crepuscular and cryptic habits. Field notes (JCM) report this snake to be one of the more commonly encountered species in the Arima Valley, but sporadic in activity; field work done in the early 1980's produced most of these specimens; in 1993 three weeks in the field produced only one road killed specimen.

Material: Trinidad—FMNH 215835–7, 217215–21, 219609, Arima Valley; 217222 1.1 miles east of Toco Road on Valencia Rd. MCZ 80999 20 milepost on the Eastern Main Road; 100072, 68 milepost on the Southern Road to Cedros; 100479–80 Diego Martin Valley. USNM 166683, 194987 Arima Valley. Venezuela - USNM 22531, 217182.

Drymarchon corais corais (Boie)

Map 81. Plate 126.

Coluber corais Boie, 1827:537. Type locality: America. *Coluber variabilis:* Court, 1858 [in part]. *Spilotes corais:* Reinhardt and Lutken, 1862:8. *Drymarchon corais corais:* Stejneger, 1899:70. *Drymarchon corais:* Barbour, 1916b:224. *Drymarchon c. corais:* DeVerteuil, 1968:101. [Tobago].

Common Names: "Clibo or cribo noir" (DeVerteuil, 1858); "Cribo" (Mole and Urich, 1894a); "Yellow-tailed cribo" (Wehekind, 1960); "Indigo snake" (Emsley, 1977).

Distribution: *D. corais* is widespread, ranging from the southeastern United States through Mexico, Central America, and southward to Argentina. *D. c. corais* occurs on Trinidad and Tobago; on the mainland it ranges from Venezuela to Argentina in the Amazonian and Paraguayan basins. Published Trinidad localities include: Port of Spain (Werner, 1899); the Blanchisseuse Reserve (Brongersma, 1956b); the Turure Forest near Sangre Grande, the Caroni River at Centeno, Monos Island, and St. Ann's Valley (Boos, 1975c; 1984c); north Mayaro, and Manzanilla Bay Road (Boos, 1975c). Trinidad museum material localities: Port of Spain; and the Arima Valley. Field notes (SB and GH) report a road killed specimen from south Speyside on the Windward Road, Tobago. Published Tobago localities include Speyside (Olton in Boos, 1975c). A Tobago location supported by a museum specimen is Milford Bay.

Description: Approaches 3 m total length. A single Trinidad specimen measured, a female, with a 1097 mm SVL, and 271 mm tail; tail 24% SVL. Duellman (1960) described an individual of *D. c. melanurus* from Guatemala that had a SVL of 2450 mm, and a total length of 2950 mm. Rostral visible from above; nasal single; loreal single; one preocular; no suboculars; two postoculars; eight or nine supralabials; 7–10 infralabials; 196 ventrals; single anal plate; 78 paired subcaudals. Dorsal scales with apical pits, otherwise smooth, in 19–17–15 rows. Dorsum grey-brown anteriorly, becoming yellow posteriorly; young may have a very dark anterior body. Scales on the crown outlined in dark pigment and the labial seams outlined with brown; venter yellow. The only Trinidad and Tobago snake with 17 rows of smooth scales at midbody, a single anal plate, and a dark forebody that becomes lighter in color posteriorly.

Natural History: A diurnal, forest snake. Food reported for this species includes any vertebrate (and probably many invertebrates) that can be overpowered. Field notes (JCM) describing observations of North American races of this serpent indicate it does not constrict prey, but seizes the prey with its jaws, may press the prey to the substrate with a loop of its body, and swallows it alive. Mole (1924) relayed a secondhand account of one capturing a grouper in the ocean; Beebe (1946) listed opossums, *Ameiva*, fer-de-lance, *Leptodactylus* frogs, *Bufo marinus,* and spiny rats from five mainland individuals. Clutch size is 9–12 eggs (Mole and Urich, 1894b; Mole, 1924). Mole and Urich (1894b) considered it

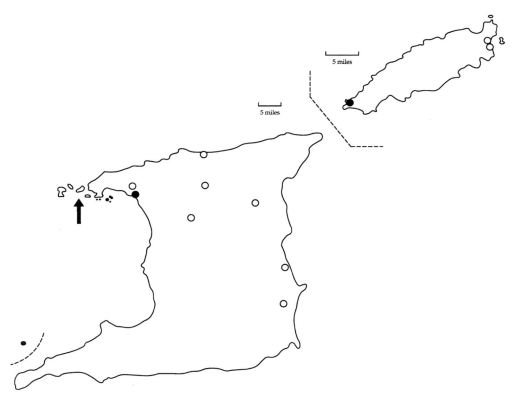

Map 81. *Drymarchon corais corais*

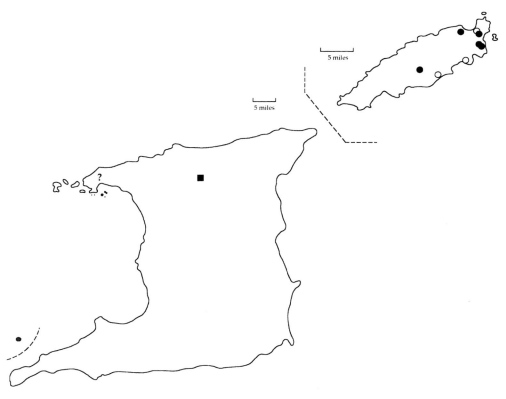

Map 82. *Erythrolamprus aesculapii aesculapii* ■
Erythrolamprus bizona ?
Erythrolamprus ocellatus ● ○

to be "not uncommon" but in 1924 Mole wrote, "Whether the advent of the mongoose has induced it to become almost arboreal in its habits is a matter for conjecture. Country people and others whose business takes them afield, and naturalists, have informed me that they have not seen a cribo for many years." Urich (1931) also considered the Trinidad population of this species reduced in numbers by the mongoose.

Material: Trinidad—MCZ 6673 Port-of-Spain. USNM 5579, 5579b, 12535, 15233 Trinidad. Tobago—MCZ 13194 near Milford Bay.

Erythrolamprus aesculapii aesculapii (Linnaeus)

Map 82. Plate 127.

Coluber aesculapii Linnaeus, 1766:380. Type locality: "Indiis." *Erythrolamprus Aesculapii:* Duméril, Bibron and Duméril, 1854:845. *Erythrolamprus Aesculapii [Aesculapii]:* Jan, 1863:314. *Erythrolamprus aesculapii ocellatus:* Peters and Orejas-Miranda, 1970: 111. (Trinidad and Tobago, Trinidad as a locality for this taxon is in error).

Comment: See the comment in the *Erythrolamprus bizona* account for a short history of *Erythrolamprus* on Trinidad and Tobago.

Distribution: *E. aesculapii* is a widespread species in Amazonia, ranging from Trinidad southward to Argentina and Bolivia. *E. a. aesculapii* makes up most of this range, including the Trinidad population. The presence of this species on Trinidad is based on one specimen, AMNH 75746 from the Arima Valley on a ridge above St. Patrick's Estate. Emsley (1977) also suggested a specimen in the British Museum with accompanying locality data listed as the West Indies is probably from Trinidad.

Description: The Trinidad population of this snake may mimic the coral snake, *Micrurus lemniscatus diutius*. It can be readily distinguished from the coral snake by the presence of a loreal scale, and the paired black annuli, whereas the coral snakes have black annuli in triads (*M. l. diutis*) or single black annuli (*M. circinalis*). The single Trinidad specimen is 640 mm SVL; 88 mm tail. Rostral visible from above; divided nasal; single loreal; one preocular; no suboculars; two postoculars; seven supralabials; nine infralabials; 198 ventrals; divided anal plate; 41 paired subcaudals. Body with 13 triads of black annuli and red annuli seperated by yellow annuli. Tail with two complete triads. Smooth dorsal scales in 15 rows at midbody; each red scale between the black annuli of the triad is tipped with black; yellow scales between the triads are immaculate. The annuli on the body will distinguish it from the Tobago endemic *Erythrolamprus ocellatus* which lacks annuli, but has ocelli. Distinguishing it from *Erythrolamprus bizona* is somewhat more difficult; *E. aesculapii* is likely to have less than 49 subcaudals and no nuchal band, while *E. bizona* is likely to have more than 51 subcaudals and a nuchal band. Subcaudal and ventral counts given by Hardy and Boos (1995) suggest *E. aesculapii* has 31–53 subcaudals and 170–204 ventrals, while *E. bizona* has 39–60 subcaudals and 178–204 ventrals. These numbers are

apparently based upon individuals from widely seperated populations and numbers for the Trinidad populations can probably be expected to have a narrower range that may be useful in separating the two species. However, since the Trinidad populations of these two species are known from only one specimen each, scale count ranges are unavailable.

Natural History: A forest snake, on the mainland Beebe (1946) reports it on and in the forest floor, digging them up a foot or more beneath the surface; in Peru and Ecuador, Dixon and Soini (1977) and Duellman (1978) report finding this species on the forest floor, in or on leaf litter. The Arima Valley specimen (AMNH 75746) is from wet, primary forest that is transitional between seasonal and lower montane rainforest, above a stream. The diet is composed mostly of other snakes; Beebe (1946) recorded the following stomach contents from mainland specimens: *Atractus trilineatus* (150 mm), a very small *Micrurus*, a *Tantilla longifrontale,* two small *Synbranchus* eels, crickets, and an unidentified lizard.

Material: Trinidad—AMNH 75746 Arima Valley on ridge above St. Patrick's Estate.

Erythrolamprus bizona

Map 82. Plate 128.

[*Erythrolamprus Aesculapii*] *bizona* Jan, 1863:314. Type locality: "Bahia, Messico, Popayan, Cayenne, Brasile, Montevideo, Colombia." Restricted to Colombia by Dunn and Bailey, 1939:12. *Erythrolamprus aesculapi:* Schmidt, 1957:61, Figure 9 (upper right). *Erythrolamprus aesoulapii:* Wehekind, 1960:73. *Erythrolamprus aesculapii aesculapii:* Boos, 1975a:25. *Erythrolamprus* [sp.]: Hardy, 1982:86. *Erythrolamprus bizona:* Hardy and Boos, 1995:162.

Common Name: "False coral" (Wehekind, 1960:73).

Comment: The history of *Erythrolamprus* on Trinidad is of interest, unresolved, and adds to the species known from single specimens with apparently valid locality data. The first evidence a member of this genus was present on Trinidad was noted by Schmidt (1957) who wrote, "The venomous *Micrurus* can readily be distinguished from the nonvenomous snakes of Trinidad, that also have a pattern of black, red, and yellow rings, by the fact that the black rings of the harmless *Erythrolamprus* are in pairs, never in threes or single." Schmidt's paper also contains a photograph (his Figure 9, upper right) of a preserved specimen which is labeled "*Erythrolamprus aesculapi.*" Hardy and Boos (1995) point out that the visible portion of museum tag on this specimen shows it to be a specimen (RVIM 112) from the Royal Victorian Institute Museum in Port of Spain. This is undoubtedly the same specimen examined by Mertens (1973) and Emsley (1977) and bears the accompanying data, "Diego Martin, 10.xi.1941." Unfortunately this specimen is now lost, but Mertens (1973), Emsley (1966a), and all other authors since Schmidt (1957) writing about *Erythrolamprus* have called this specimen *E. aesculapii* or *E. a. ocellatus*. Mertens (1973) published scale counts as "189+1/1, 57, 58+ ?"; Hardy and Boos (1995) counted scales on this specimen in 1979 and their numbers agree with Mertens, while scale counts given by Emsley (1977) were 180 ventrals and 43 subcaudals. Based on their scale counts and published photos, they suggest that this specimen is not *E. aesculapii*, but *E. bizona*. and add it to the Trinidad herpetofauna.

Distribution: *E. bizona,* as currently understood, ranges from Costa Rica to northern Colombia and northern Venezuela (coastal ranges), and ranges southward in Colombia along both sides of the Andes, and possibly on Trinidad. From data presented in the Zoogerography section, it is clear that the Trinidad and Tobago herpetofauna is a mixture of Amazonian and more widespread species, including trans-Andean forms; thus the presence of *E. bizona,* a trans-Andean species is not totally surprising. Other snakes showing this same distribution are *Bothrops asper* and *Leptophis riveti.* This species now joins the lost specimen of the caecilian, *Typhlonectes* sp., and other species based upon single specimens from these islands to form a growing enigma. The large number of species represented by single specimens may be due to low collecting effort, but more likely than not it is the result of changing habitats as discussed in the introduction.

Description: Maximum total length about 1.5 m. A tricolored snake which mimics a coral snake. It has a rostral visible from above; a single loreal; divided nasals; one procular, no suboculars; one supracular; two postoculars; seven supralabials with the third and fourth under the orbit; the anal plate is divided; 15 dorsal scale rows. Hardy and Boos' numbers suggest ventral counts of 178–204, and subcaudal counts of 39–62. It has been traditionally (Peters and Orejas-Miranda, 1970) separated from *E. aesculapii* by the number of subcaudal scales; Hardy and Boos (1995) suggest this may not work and suggest that *bizona* and *aesculapii* are in need of revision. *E. bizona* can be distinguished from *E. ocellatus* by its pattern of red, black, and yellow annuli; *E. ocellatus* has 22–29 black ocelli with white centers on red ground color. Using Hardy and Boos' (1995) suggestion, a nuchal band in *E. bizona* and its absence in *E. aesculapii* will work for the two known specimens—but pattern in these animals can be quiet variable and it may not work for other specimens.

Natural History: A rainforest floor snake which is known to occur to at least 2500 m on the mainland. The single specimen is known from the western end of the Northern Range and appears to have come from an area, Diego Martin, that is now relatively well developed.

Erythrolamprus ocellatus Peters

Map 82. Figure D.

> *Erythrolamprus ocellatus* Peters, 1868:642. Type locality: Tobago. *Erythrolamprus aesculapii ocellatus*—Emsley, 1966a:129. *Erythrolamprus aesculapii ocellatus*—Peters and Orejas-Miranda, 1970: 111 (Trinidad and Tobago, Trinidad in error for this race.).

Common Names: Red snake, False coral (DeVerteuil, 1968:101)

Comment: Hardy (1982) considered the Tobago population a distinct species, as described by Peters (1868), that arrangement is followed here. However, this is not supported by scale count data and other external morphology, other than pattern. Scale counts on six of the Tobago specimens are within, or significantly overlap, those scale counts published by Roze (1966), Dixon and Soini (1977), and Lancini (1979) in other parts of its range. However, geographic isolation, a smaller body size, and the striking color pattern imply a distinct species and species status may eventually be supported by internal morphology or biochemical evidence.

Distribution: *E. ocellatus* is known only from Tobago. Published Tobago localities include the Louis D'Or Settlement and Pembroke Estates (Mertens, 1972; 1973). Museum material documents the following localities: Windward Road at Merchiston Road, Charlotteville, Speyside, Cambelton, and 1 mile from Hillsborough Dam on Easterfield Road. All specimens are from the more mesic, and less developed, north end of the island.

Description: 388–445 mm SVL; 72–80 mm tail, 15–19.8% SVL. The smallest individual known is 188 mm in total length. Distinguished from all other snakes in this area by the series of 22–29 dark ocelli present on the dorsum of the body. Rostral visible from above; single loreal; divided nasal; one preocular (one specimen has two on each side); no suboculars; two postoculars; seven supralabials (3–4 enter orbit); eight or nine infralabials (only one specimen has eight on each side); 168–179 ventrals (Emsley, [1966a] gives 168–183 for the British Museum specimens); anal plate divided; 38–44 paired subcaudals (Emsley [1966a] gives 40–49 for the British Museum specimens). Smooth dorsal scales in 15 rows at midbody with no reduciton posteriorly. Anterior chin shields larger or equal in size to posterior pair. The dorsum is red with black ocelli; some invasion of red and black pigment occurs onto the white or cream colored scutes. Ocelli (black, circular blotches, often with open centers) number 22–29 on the dorsum of the body, and form blotches on the tail.

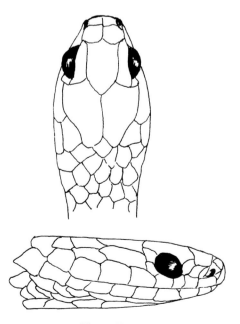

Figure D

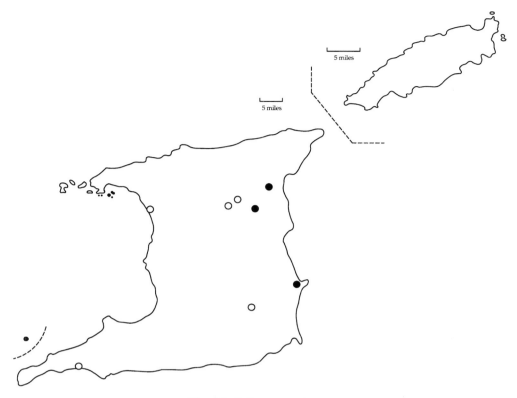

Map 83. *Helicops angulatus*

Natural History: De Verteuil (1968) stated that on Tobago this snake is confined to high forest areas, an assertion not fully supported by museum material localities. It is most likely a forest and forest-edge species. Food includes the snakes *Attractus trilineatus, Tantilla melanocephala,* and the lizard *Hemidactylus mabouia* (field notes, JCM; Hardy and Boos, 1995). *E. ocellatus* has evolutionary significance because it may serve as a model for a tricolor *Erythrolamprus* ancestor that radiated into coral snake mimics in South America; thus its genetics, development, and life history may be important in understanding converging patterns in colubrid and elapid snakes.

Material: Tobago—MCZ 12075 no data. USNM 195111, 228050 Windward Rd. and Merchiston Rd.; 228051–3 Charlotteville; 228054–5 Speyside; 228056 Cambelton; 228058 Hillsborough Dam.

Helicops angulatus (Linnaeus)

Map 83. Plates 129, 130.

Coluber angulatus Linnaeus, 1758:217. Type locality: Asia (in error). *Helicops angulatus:* Wagler, 1830:171. *Helicops angulata:* Underwood, 1962:179.

Common Names: "water mapepire" (Mole, 1914); "banded water snake" (Wehekind, 1960); "water snake, brown banded water snake" (Emsley, 1977).

Distribution: *H. angulatus* has an Amazonian distribution; on Trinidad, it is found over much of the lower elevations of the Northern and Southern basins. Published Trinidad localities include: Caroni Swamp (Bacon, 1970a); Erin Beach (Boos, 1984d); Aripo savannas (Schwab, 1988). Field

notes (JCM) report this snake at the eastern end of Churchill-Roosevelt Highway and south of Rio Claro on Lizard Springs Road. Museum material adds the following locations: Manzanilla-Mayaro Rd. in the vicinity of the 39.75 milepost; 4.2 miles east of Valencia on Valencia Rd.; Rio Grande Forest, Sangre Grande.

Description: 460 mm SVL, with a 202 mm tail; tail 31–43% SVL. Rostral pentagonal and visible from above; nasal divided and separated by two internasals; prefontals paired; loreal single and in contact with the second and third labials; one preocular; no suboculars; two postoculars; two primary temporals and three secondary temporals; seven to nine supralabials, sixth largest, and fourth enters the orbit; 7–10 infralabials; anterior chin shields longer than the second pair and the anterior pair is in contact with the first five lower labials; five gulars; 114–121 ventrals; anal plate divided; 63–72 paired subcaudals. Keeled, striated and elongated dorsal scales in 19 rows at midbody, reduced posteriorly to 17 rows; these characteristics distinguish this snake from all other colubrid snakes found on Trinidad. Dorsum red-brown with 20–27 dark brown crossbands on body and 15–20 blotches on tail; dark blotch on nape may fuse to first crossband. Venter tan or pink with dark brown bands that usually coincide with dorso-lateral bands. Eyes small and directed more dorsally than laterally; crown of head brown, with tan or red-pink areas on labials. Juveniles with dark brown blotches four or five scale rows wide on dorsal midline and separated by light tan bands, one or two scale rows wide on midline. Dark bands narrow toward venter, light bands widen toward venter.

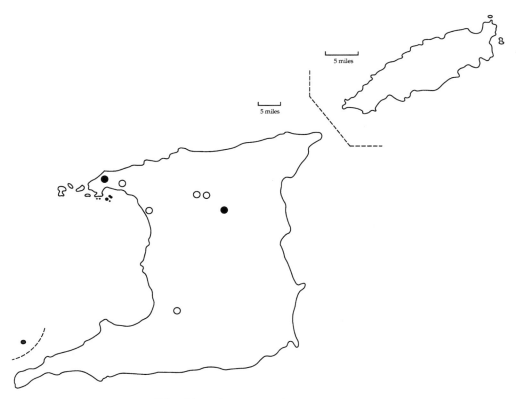

Map 84. *Hydrops triangularis neglectus*

Natural History: A nocturnal, aquatic snake of herbaceous swamps (Bacon, 1970a); ponds, ditches, slow moving streams (Mole, 1924); rice paddies (Wehekind, 1960); and flooded pastures (field notes, JCM). Henderson et al. (1976) radiotracked a 31 cm SVL female in Amazonian Peru for 111.5 hours and found it moved only 17.8 m, spending its time hiding in a water-soaked substrate. Field notes (JCM) describe five of these snakes, two roadkills near streams, two in a water-filled ditch at night, and one in liquid mud in pasture pond. It feeds upon fishes and frogs, including tadpoles (Mole, 1924; Emsley, 1977; Duellman, 1978). Dixon and Soini (1977) reported a specimen from Peru with the aquatic lizard *Neusticurus ecpleopus* in its stomach; they also reported fish and frogs. Clutch sizes are 8–11 (Mole, 1924; Dixon and Soini, 1977; Duellman, 1978.) Rossman (1973, 1984) suggested this snake may be facultatively ovoviviparous; a female imported from Colombia deposits two eggs containing well-developed embryos at deposition; one hatched on 24 August, one day after it was laid. Rossman stated, "It could be highly advantageous to an aquatic snake to bear living young if satisfactory sites for oviposition were unavailable, due perhaps to periods of unusually severe flooding." In 1984 he reported a Peruvian specimen containing seven full term embryos, lacking egg shells and yolk. Defensive behavior includes flattening the body and rapid, side-to-side jerking movements of the head. Field notes (JCM) do not report it launching itself into the air as described by Mole (1924) and Emsley (1977); it does, however, release musk when handled.

Material: Trinidad—AMNH 81458 Rio Grande Forest, Sangre Grande; 117721–22 Manzanilla-Mayaro Rd. FMNH 217241 4.2 mi east of Valencia, on Valencia Rd. USNM 59874 no data; 166686 Manzanilla-Mayaro Rd., vic. milestone 39.75.

Hydrops triangularis neglectus Roze

Map 84. Plate 131.

Hydrops Martii: Reinhardt and Lutken, 1862:7. *Hydrops triangularis:* Mole, 1914:146. *Hydrops triancularis* [sic]: Wehekind, 1955: 11. *Hydrops triangularis triangularis:* Brongersma, 1956b:183. *Hydrops triangularis neglectus* Roze, 1957:18, fig. 13d. Type locality: Trinidad.

Common Names: "Water coral" (Mole, 1914); "red-sided water snake; water snake" (Emsley, 1977).

Distribution: *H. triangularis* has an Amazonian distribution. *H. t. neglectus* is a lowland Guiana endemic, occurring on Trinidad and in Guyana. Published Trinidad localities include: Arima, Caroni Swamp, Princes Town, Four Roads, and Cunupia (Mole, 1924); and Tacarigua (Brongersma, 1956b). Museum material adds Churchill-Roosevelt Highway and Tucker Valley.

Description: 840 mm SVL; 123 mm tail, tail 12.3–14.8% SVL. Rostral visible from above; nasals divided; loreal single and larger than eye; one preocular; no suboculars; one or two (usually two) postoculars; eight supralabials; eight infralabials; 170–176 ventrals; anal plate divided; 45–47 subcaudals. Smooth dorsal scales in 15 rows at midbody with no reduction posteriorly. Dorsum purple-brown with red-brown on sides; off-white on venter. Dorsal annuli number 48–68 on body,

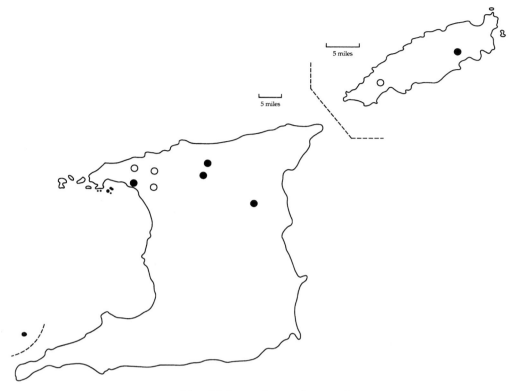

Map 85. *Imantodes cenchoa cenchoa*

most circle the body, some incomplete on middorsum or midventer. Head dark purple-brown, each labial with a light center. The only Trinidad snake with 15 rows of smooth dorsal scales, a loreal (distinguishing it from true coral snakes), and dark purple rings completely encircling the body.

Natural History: A snake of swamps, slow rivers, ponds, and flooded ricefields. Brongersma (1956b) recorded a specimen from a savanna, presumably from an aquatic habitat. Beebe (1946) and Emsley (1977) reported it will burrow in moist situations. Food includes *Synbranchus* eels and other freshwater fishes (Beebe, 1946; Emsley, 1977.) On the mainland, Dixon and Soini (1977) report a different subspecies of this species pursuing a caecilian in a muddy ditch.

Material: Trinidad—AMNH 8372, 73090 Churchill-Roosevelt Highway; 64463 Tucker Valley.

Imantodes cenchoa cenchoa (Linnaeus)

Map 85. Plates 132, 133.

Coluber cenchoa Linnaeus, 1758:226. Type locality: America. *Himantodes cenchoa:* Reinhardt and Lutken, 1862:12. *Dipsas cenchoa:* Garman, 1887c:258. *Imantodes cenchoa cenchoa:* Smith, 1942:384. *Imantodes c. cenchoa:* DeVerteuil, 1968:103.

Common Names: "Mapepire corde violon, fiddlestring mapepire" (Mole and Urich, 1894a); "mapepire corde violon, violin string snake" (Wehekind, 1955); "Fiddlestring snake" (DeVerteuil, 1968).

Distribution: *I. cenchoa* occurs from the Isthmus of Tehuantepec, Mexico, southward through Central America

to Paraguay and Bolivia. *I. c. cenchoa* is also widespread, ranging from Panama and Trinidad and Tobago to the southern edge of the species' range. Published Trinidad localities include: Port of Spain (Werner, 1900); the Colonial Hospital (Mole, 1924); Arima Valley (Beebe, 1952). Trinidad localities documented by museum material include: near Sangre Grande, Mt. St. Benedict, Marval Valley, San Juan, Morne Bleu Ridge, Tucker Valley, and Port of Spain. Literature records for Tobago localities include: Patience Hill (Mertens, 1972). Tobago locations based upon museum material: 2 mi north and 2 mi west of Roxborough; 0.5 mi west of Mt. St. George.

Description: 1050 mm SVL; 450 mm tail, tail 43% SVL. Rostral barely visible from above; nasal divided; loreal small; one preocular; no suboculars; two or three postoculars; seven to nine supralabials; 9–11 infralabials; 234–258 ventrals; divided anal plate; 150–174 paired subcaudals. Smooth dorsal scales in 17 rows at midbody with no reduction; vertebral scale row greatly enlarged. Dorsum tan with dark brown blotches expanded on vertebral line and outlined with dark pigment. In three specimens these blotches number 37–48. Large eyes are bisected horizontally by a light tan stripe, crown of head dark brown; venter off-white to tan with flecks of pigmentation and an occasional incomplete stripe. Very blunt head, presence of a mental groove, enlarged vertebral scale row, and extreme attenuation of the blotched body distinguish it from all other snakes in the area. Myers (1982) noted females from a Central American population have larger heads.

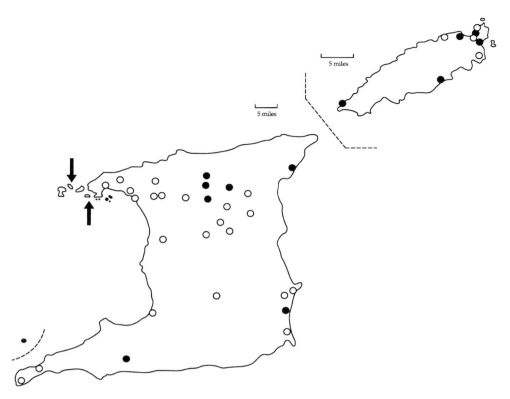

Map 86. *Leptodeira annulata ashmeadi*

Natural History: A nocturnal-crepuscular forest snake. Mole and Urich (1894b) recorded it from, ". . . old walls, trunks of large trees with rough bark, and tree-parasites and orchids"; it coils in epiphytes and between the leaves of other plants during the day (Mole, 1924; Test et al., 1966; Henderson and Nickerson, 1976). *Gonatodes* and *Anolis* lizards are reported as food from Trinidad specimens by Mole (1924.) On the mainland lizards, frogs, birds and their eggs, and invertebrates (may represent secondarily ingested material) have been reported by Beebe (1946) and Duellman (1978); Test et al. (1966) described captives feeding on *Mannophryne trinitatis* and *Eleutherodactylus terraebolivaris,* while refusing insects; and Myers (1982) described a Central American population feeding on *Eleutherodactylus* and *Anolis*. In Central America, Myers (1982) encountered most specimens less than 2 meters above the ground in vine tangles, bushes, small trees, on palm fronds or other broad leaves; and noted they are commonly found prowling on the forest floor or through low herbaceous vegetation. Henderson and Nickerson (1976) observed this snake's activities in a greenhouse, and found they emerge from cover between 0 and 1 footcandles of light; found them to prey upon sleeping anoles; and reported them drinking beads of water from the surface plants and their own bodies. The SVL/weight ratio of this snake allows it to bridge gaps between branches other arboreal snakes cannot; thus it can use smaller branches to support its weight and obtain food unavailable to other species. A laterally projecting shelf between the vertebral

zygopophyses, a lateral compression of the body, wide vertebral scales, and the ability to direct the eyes downward, make this snake the most specialized arboreal species known (Henderson and Nickerson, 1976.) Small clutch size (1–3 eggs) have been reported (Fitch, 1970; Duellman, 1978); but, Emsley (1977) stated that 10 eggs are laid in July or August; and field notes (JCM) describe 5 eggs in one specimen. Myers (1982) reported males have a higher incidence of broken tails than do females. Upon capture this snake does not hesitate to release a large quantity of musk from its anal glands.

Material: Trinidad—AMNH 73115 Morne Bleu; 73116–17 Arima Valley; 81434, Port of Spain; 64477, 64538, 101338–9 Tucker Valley; 101306 Bayshore, Port of Spain; 101307 ca. 5 mi west of Port of Spain. USNM 166712 Eastern Main Rd., environs of Sangre Grande. Tobago—USNM 228059 2 mi N and 2 mi W of Roxborough.

Leptodeira annulata ashmeadi (Hallowell)

Map 86. Plate 134.

Coluber ashmeadi Hallowell, 1845:244. Type locality: 200 miles from Caracas Venezuela. Restricted by Duellman (1958:44) to vicinity of Caracas, Distrito Federal, Venezuela. *Leptodeira annulata:* Garman, 1887c:285. *Leptodeira albofusca:* Boettger, 1889:95. *Leptodeira annulata annulata:* Amaral, 1930a:204. *Leptodira annulata annulata:* Beebe, 1952:175. *Leptodeira annulata ashmeadi:* Duellman, 1958:47.

Common Names: "Mapepire" (Mole, 1914); "Mapepire valsyn, m[apepire] baleyn, m[apepire] barcin" (Mole, 1924);

"annulated night snake" (Wehekind, 1955); "banded night snake, false mapepire, cat eyed night snake" (Boos and Quesnel, 1968); "chunkhead, garden snake, night snake" (Emsley, 1977).

Distribution: *L. annulata* ranges from Tamaulipas and Guerrero, Mexico, to Brazil and Argentina. *L. a. ashmeadi* is an Orinoco Basin form, distributed east of the Santa Marta Mountains, Colombia, through coastal Venezuela and the llanos to the Orinoco; and Isla Margarita, Venezuela; Trinidad and Tobago. Published Trinidad localities include: Port of Spain (Wehekind, 1960); Arima Valley (Beebe, 1952); Tarcarigua (Brongersma, 1956b); Huevos Island (Boos 1984d); and Maris Stella Bay on the north coast of Gaspar Grande Island (Boos, 1990). Trinidad locations based upon museum material include: St. Ann; Arena; St. Augustine; Mt. St. Benedict; 5 milepost Blanchisseusse Rd.; Morne Bleu Ridge; Brickfield; Cedros; Chaguanas; 1.3 mi south of Churchill-Roosevelt Highway on Cumoto Rd.; Rio Grande Forest, Sangre Grande; Guayaguayare; Icacos Rd. at the 79.5 milepost; Plaisance, Mayaro; Petit Valley; the 22.25 milepost on Siparia-Erin Rd., between Los Bajos and Palo Seco; San Rafael; Tucker Valley; San Juan; St. Joseph; Sangre Grande; at the 3.25 milepost on Valencia Rd.; Wallerfield. Tobago locations based upon museum material include: Cambelton; Pirate's Cove, Charlotteville; Charlotteville; Man of War Bay; Northside Rd. at the 28.5 milepost; near Pembroke; Speyside; Windward Rd. vic. of 22.5 milepost.

Description: 1065 mm SVL, 435 mm tail; tail 29–41% of the SVL. Rostral scale visible from above; nasal divided; loreal single; one or two preoculars; no suboculars; one or two postoculars; seven or eight supralabials; 8–10 infralabials; 177–180 ventrals; anal plate divided; 76–90 paired subcaudals. Smooth dorsal scales in 19 or 21 rows at midbody, reduced to 15 posteriorly. Vertebral scale row slightly enlarged. Dorsum tan or brown with a series of 36–38 dark brown or black blotches which may fuse at various points forming a stripe or partial stripe. Three specimens show stripes only, three specimens show only blotches, and three specimens show stripes and blotches, with stripes on neck and anterior body. Crown of head darker than body, and has a dark postocular stripe present. Venter uniform off-white or cream and extends onto the labials and first scale row. The only Trinidad and Tobago snake with 19 (or 21) rows of smooth scales, with a brown ground color and the black blotch/striped pattern.

Natural History: A snake of forest and savanna. Mole (1924) wrote, "It frequents outhouses, old walls, and rubbish-heaps. Once one was taken in the bough of a tree, where it shared its quarters with a large colony of ants." On the mainland, Beebe (1946) reported one in a termitaria. Field notes (JCM) describe 14 specimens active after dark, one foraging in a streambed, another in a tangle of vines 2 meters above a streambed. Food includes lizards, tadpoles, frog eggs, frogs, toads, fish, conspecifics, and their own

eggs (Mole, 1924; Brongersma, 1956b; Wehekind, 1960; Emsley, 1977). Field notes (JCM) report two individuals feeding on *Leptodactylus validus*. Emsley (1977) recorded 3–11 eggs laid in leaf litter between June and November; however, in Ecuador Duellman (1978) found eggs in a bamboo stem cavity 12 m above ground; in Trinidad, Riley and Winch (1985a) described three eggs in the fungus chamber of the leaf-cutter ant *Acromyrmex ostospinosus* on April 25; field notes (JCM) report a female containing three eggs on 12 July. As is the case with many xenodontine snakes, the venom may cause a reaction in humans; in Venezuela, Gorzula (1982) described swelling of a finger and wrist and sensitivity to touch after a bite from this snake.

Material: Trinidad—FMNH 49936 Plaisance, Mayaro; 49937 Morne Bleu Ridge; 215817, 217233, 218581 Arima Valley; 217234 on Toco Rd. 3.1 mi north of junction with Valencia Rd.; 218776 at the 22.5 milepost on Siparia-Erin Rd., between Los Bajos and Palo Seco. USNM 166714, Quare Rd., Hollis Reservoir; 166715, Arima. Tobago—AMNH 110472, near Pembroke. MCZ 11994–5, 12026 Milford Bay. USNM 195127 Cambleton; 195163 Charlotteville; 228056 Speyside.

Leptophis ahaetulla coeruleodorsus Oliver

Map 87. Plates 136.

Ahaetulla liocercus: Reinhardt and Lutken, 1862:10. *Dendrophis liocercus:* Court, 1884:382. *Leptophis liocercus:* Mole and Urich, 1894a:85. *Leptophis coeruleodorsus:* Oliver, 1942:462. Type locality: Trinidad. *Thalerophis richardi coeruleodorsus:* Oliver, 1948:170. *Leptophis ahaetulla coeruleodorsus:* Internat. Comm. Zool. Nom. Op. 1958 (524):270. *Thalarophis richardi coeruleodorsus:* Wehekind, 1960:73. *Leptophis ahaetulla:* Boos and Quesnel, 1968:14. *Leptophis a. ahaetulla:* DeVerteuil, 1968:101.

Common Names: "lora, parrot snake" (Mole, 1914); "Laura" (Wehekind, 1955); "green horse whip" (Boos and Quesnel, 1968); "machete, whiplash" (Emsley, 1977).

Distribution: *L. ahaetulla* ranges from Veracruz and Oaxaca, Mexico, southward to Chile and Brazil. *L. a. coeruleodorsus* has an Orinoco Basin distribution, occurring in coastal Venezuela and the llanos, Trinidad and Tobago. Published Trinidad localities include: Port of Spain (Mole, 1924); Arima Valley (Beebe, 1952); Orange Grove Estate, Tacarigua (Brongersma, 1956a); and Aripo Savannas (Schwab, 1988). Trinidad localities documented with museum specimens include: Arena; 5 milepost on Blanchisseuse Rd.; Diego Martin; Guayaguayare; Hollis Reservoir; Mt. St. Benedict; Palmiste Estate, San Fernando; Plaisance, Mayaro; Rio Grande Forest, Sangre Grande; Santa Cruz Valley; on Siparia-Erin Rd. between Los Bajos and Palo Seco; on Toco Rd. 3.1 mi north of its junction with Valencia Rd.; Tucker Valley; Vega Oropouche. Published Tobago localities include: Scarborough (Mole, 1924); and Mt. Irwin (Mertens, 1972). Tobago locations based upon museum specimens include: Cambleton, Charlotteville, Speyside, Milford Bay; near Pembroke. It also occurs on Little Tobago Island.

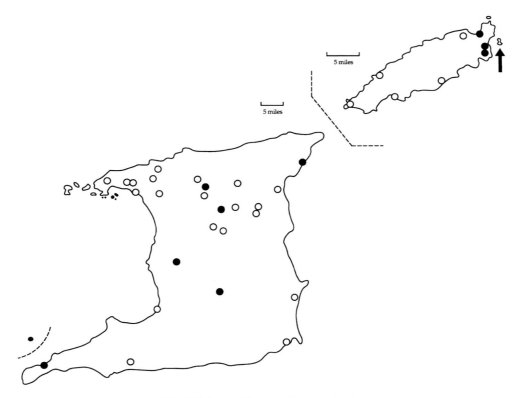

Map 87. *Leptophis ahaetulla coeruleodorsus*

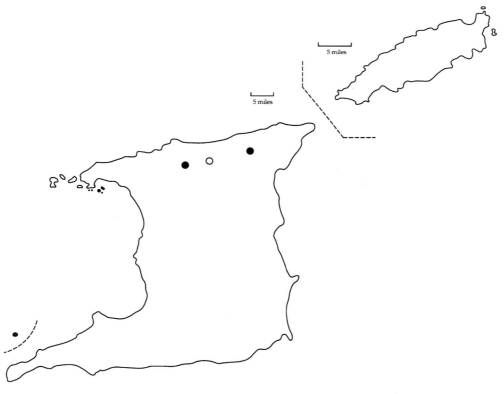

Map 88. *Leptophis riveti*

Description: 1156 mm SVL, 786 mm tail; tail 68% SVL. Rostral visible from above; nasal divided, or not; loreal single; one or two preoculars; no suboculars; two or three postoculars; eight or nine supralabials; 9–11 infralabials; 157–165 ventrals; divided anal plate; 131–163 paired subcaudals. Dorsal scale rows 15 at midbody and reduced posteriorly to 11; most scales keeled, except for those on the first few scale rows, on neck and tail. Dorsum with bright green vertebral stripe about seven scale rows wide; lateral yellow stripe involving scale rows 2–4 and first scale row is white. Crown of head green; face with black postocular stripe; and labials and venter uniform white. Distinguished from its relative *Leptophis riveti* by presence of a loreal scale; *L. riveti* has fewer than 144 ventrals.

Natural History: An arboreal, forest, and forest-edge snake that will use agricultural and urban habitats: Mole (1924) stated the lora used to be common in country gardens in the suburbs of Port of Spain, and Scarborough, Tobago. Using mainland specimens, Beebe (1946) described how this snake is capable of climbing bamboo by putting a half coil around the circumference of the stem and applying pressure to opposite sides of the stem; and noted they often rest with their head and neck erect and gently sway as if in a breeze. Food includes frogs, lizards, birds (Mole, 1924) and other snakes (Emsley, 1977). Using material from Ecuador, Fitch (1970) suggested the Amazonian race has an extended breeding season, possibly year round. Emsley (1977) stated clutches of 3–5 eggs have been found in bromeliads 30–60 feet up in the forest canopy of Panama; and that in Trinidad copulation has been observed in August. Field notes (JCM) report that upon capture it strikes and gapes its mouth. Mole (1924), as well as others, report the venom of this snake to cause a stinging sensation in humans.

Material: Trinidad—FMNH 178495, 215819, 217235 Arima Valley; 49965 Brickfield; 49966, 49990 San Rafael; 77899 Port of Spain; 190747 Bayshore; 218775 Southern Main Rd. at 79.5 milepost; 219599 Cumoto Rd., 1.3 miles S of Churchill-Roosevelt Rd.; 219600–1, Valencia Rd. between Valencia and Toco at the 3.25 milepost. USNM 166731 4 mi south of Chaguanas. Tobago—USNM 195001, 195195 Windward Rd. vic. milepost 22.5; 195004 Charlotteville; 228067–8 Speyside—Bird of Paradise Inn. Little Tobago Island—AMNH 84279.

Leptophis riveti Despax

Map 88. Figure E.

Leptophis Riveti Despax 1910:368. Type locality: Gualaquiza, Ecuador, 730 m.

Distribution: "Higher altitudes to 5000 ft. on both sides of the Andes in Ecuador; Amazonian Peru; western and north central Colombia; Panama. A single record from Trinidad" (Peters and Orejas-Miranda, 1970). W. W. Lamar (personal communication) doubts its presence in the Amazon basin and suggests it is restricted to montane areas. Emsley (1963) wrote, "The inclusion of this species depends upon one specimen, now in the British Museum (Natural History),

taken by Ivan Sanderson from an epiphyte 30 feet above the ground in a tree at the top of Mt. Aripo (3000 ft.) With it is a specimen of *L. ahaetulla coeruleodorsus* from Tobago, so it is probable that both specimens were taken on the same trip." The specimen referred to is BM 1940.3.11.84. Fourteen years later Emsley (1977) considered the locality may be a collector's error and that inclusion of this taxon in the Trinidad herpetofauna should be viewed with caution. However, in 1987 additional specimens were collected. One specimen (USNM 287027) was found in the Arima Valley and another specimen (USNM 287028) was found at Cumaca Cave in the Platanal District. This species is considered here to have a Caribbean Coastal Range distribution, acknowledging that it is more widespread than other taxa in this category.

Description: 352 mm SVL, 240 mm tail, tail 68% SVL. Rostral barely visible from above, and only slightly penetrating the seam between the internasals; nasals single, lateral and separated by two internasals larger than nasals. Prefrontals extend laterally separating preocular from the nasals, and in contact with second and third upper labials. Frontal about 80% length of parietals. Temporals number 1, 2, 3 in primary, secondary, and tertiary rows respectively. Loreal absent, a character distinguishing it from *L. a. coeruleodorsus*. However, in USNM 287027 the upper preocular on right side has divided to form one tiny preocular and what could be considered a small loreal; this same condition is present on both sides of the head in USNM 287028. One large preocular; no suboculars; two postoculars about equal in size; eight supralabials, fourth and fifth enter orbit; 10 infralabials. Second pair of chin shields longer than first and separated by two pairs of small scales; six gulars. Ventrals 141–143; anal plate divided; paired subcaudals 142–145. Keeled dorsal scales, except for the first two to four rows; 15 rows of dorsal scales at midbody; scales elongated and overlapping. Adults have oblique, dark bands on the body, a characteristic that will distinguish it it from *L. a. coeruleodorsus*. Overall this snake has a narrow, elongated head and an extremely gracile body.

Natural History: *L. riveti* is an arboreal forest snake. It probably occurs in seasonal montane forest, lower montane forest, and elfin woodland on Trinidad. Known from few specimens, little is known about its life history and habits, although Oliver (1948) reports a hylid frog in the stomach of one mainland specimen.

Material: Trinidad—USNM 287027 north of Arima; 287028 Cumaca Cave, in Platanal District.

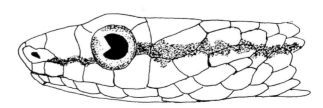

Figure E

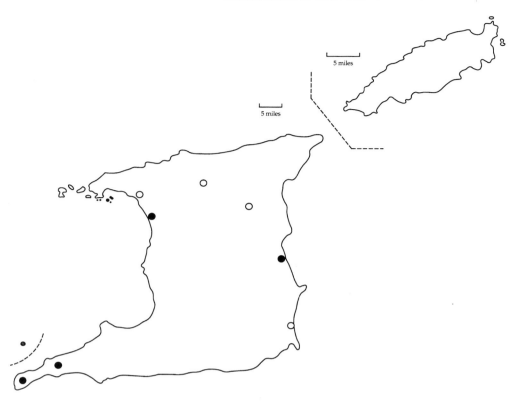

Map 89. *Liophis cobella cobella*

Liophis cobella cobella (Linnaeus)

Map 89. Plate 137.

> *Coluber cobella* Linnaeus, 1758:218. Type locality: America. *Liophis cobella:* Garman, 1887c:280. *Rhadinaea cobella:* Boettger, 1898:66. *Liophis cobella cobella:* Beebe, 1952:175. *Liophis cobellus cobellus:* Dixon, 1989:10.

Common Names: "Mapepiri mangue" (Mole and Urich, 1894a); "Mangrove snake" (Mole, 1914); "Mangrove mapepire" (Mole, 1924).

Distribution: *L. cobella* has an Amazonian distribution, ranges from the eastern flanks of the Andes from near Villavicencio, Colombia, southward to Bolivia; from Trinidad and Venezuela southeastward to Bahia, Brazil. *L. c. cobella* is a lowland Guiana endemic inhabiting the eastern area of the Guiana Shield exclusive of the Venezuelan Tepui system, and Trinidad (Dixon, 1983b). Published Trinidad localities: Arima Valley (Beebe, 1952); and Caroni Swamp (Bacon, 1970a). Trinidad museum material documents the following locations: Barataria; Churchill-Roosevelt Highway; 0.5 mi east of Icacos; Cocal Rd. Manzanilla; Ortoire Hill of Cocal, vic. of 50–51 milepost; Rio Grande Forest, Sangre Grande; the 71.25 milepost on the Southern Main Rd; Caroni Swamp.

Description: 572 mm SVL, tail 222 mm; tail 39% SVL. Rostral visible from above; nasal divided; single loreal; one preocular; no suboculars; two postoculars; seven to nine supralabials; 8–11 infralabials; 130–179 ventrals; divided anal plate; 45–65 subcaudals. Dorsal scales smooth, in 17 rows at midbody reduced to 15 posteriorly, distinguish this species from *Helicops angulatus,* another aquatic snake, which has keeled scales in 19 rows. Dorsum brown to green-black with about 65–70 incomplete white cross bands. Venter red with transverse black bars that may be incomplete; anteriorly the red ventral coloration changes to yellow-pink on the chin extending to the lower labials. Young have a dark nuchal collar with white parietal blotches. This species can be distinguished from the other two Trinidad *Liophis* because it lacks longitudinal stripes.

Natural History: An aquatic snake of fresh and brackish waters; Mole and Urich (1894b) reported it from mangrove swamps, and Bacon (1970a) noted its presence in Caroni's herbaceous swamp. Field notes (JCM) report two diurnal road kills, one close to a small stream, the other adjacent to a flooded, unused rice paddy. On the mainland, Beebe (1946) recorded it in clumps of bamboo and stated that it is diurnal; in Ecuador, Duellman (1978) found two specimens at night. Prey summarized by Michaud and Dixon (1989) included *Mannophryne trinitatis, Thecadactylus rapicauda,* fish, frogs, and other lizards. Mole (1924) stated that they "lay several eggs" and report seeing juveniles in June. In Ecuador, Duellman (1978) collected female in April containing six oviductal eggs.

Material: Trinidad—FMNH 217231 0.5 mi east of Icacos on Icacos Rd. just west of milepost 78.5; 218780 on Southern Main Rd. at the 71.25 milepost. MCZ 6151 no data; 100653 Caroni Swamp; 160072 Manzanilla.

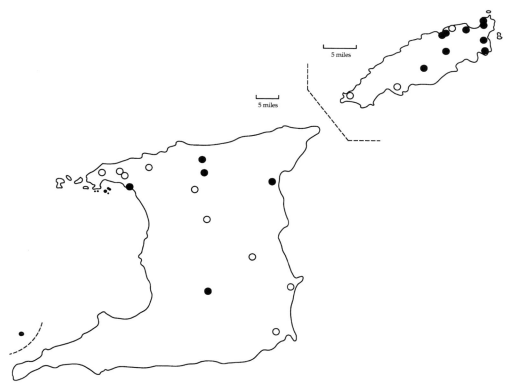

Map 90. *Liophis melanotus nesos*

Liophis melanotus nesos **Dixon and Michaud**

Map 90. Plate 138.

> *Dromicus melanotus:* Gunther, 1858:133. *Liophis melanonotus:* Cope, 1860a:253. *Liophis melanotus:* Boulenger, 1894:134. *Leimadophis melanotus:* Barbour, 1914:304. *Liophis melanurus:* Roux, 1926:291. *Liophis melanotus nesos* Dixon and Michaud, 1992:256. Type locality: ". . . Spring Hill Estate, Arima Valley, Trinidad . . ."

Common Names: "Beh Belle Chemin, Beauty of the Road" (Mole and Urich, 1894b). "Squirrel snake" (Emsley, 1977). On Tobago: "doctor snake" (DeVerteuil, 1968). Shaw's black-backed snake (Dixon and Michaud, 1992)

Comment: Dixon and Michaud (1992) wrote, "The Trinidad and Tobago specimens appear to share a closer affinity to the Colombian sample than to the geographically closer Venezuelan samples. It seems obvious that the Trinidad/Tobago populations should show an affinity to eastern Venezuelan specimens. The eastern tip of the Paria Peninsula is only 16 km from Trinidad, and Tobago is only 30 km north of Trinidad."

Distribution: *L. melanotus* ranges from Colombia to Venezuela and occurs on the islands of Trinidad and Tobago. The subspecies *L. m. nesos* occurs on the islands of Trinidad and Tobago, is a taxon of the Caribbean Coastal Range, and a Trinidad and Tobago endemic. Published Trinidad localities include: Arima Valley (Beebe, 1952); Mt. St. Benedict and Orange Grove Estate, Tacarigua (Brongersma, 1956b). Museum material adds the following localities: Biche, Brick-field, Cascade, Guayaguayare Forest, La Seima Valley, near Matura, Mayaro, Morne Bleu Ridge, Piet Valley near Diego Martin, Plaisance-Mayaro, Port of Spain, River Estate, San Rafael, and Tucker Valley. Tobago literature localities include Orange Hill Ranch and Louis D'Or Settlement (Mertens, 1972). Field notes (JCM) report it from the Windward Road, at the 22.5 milepost near Speyside. Tobago locations based upon museum material include: Anse Fourmi, Bacolet Guest House, Bloody Bay, Bon Accord, Cambelton, Charlotteville, Hillsborough Dam, Merchiston, near the 5 milepost on Roxborough-Parlatuvier Rd., and Speyside.

Description: 604 mm SVL, 150 mm tail; tail 25–29% SVL. Nasal divided; loreal single; one preocular; no suboculars; two postoculars; seven or eight supralabials; seven to nine infralabials; 142–156 ventrals; anal plate divided; 54–63 subcaudals. Dorsum with black vertebral stripe five scale rows wide with two rows of yellow or salmon specks on anterior of body; narrow yellow or salmon stripes on each side; a second black stripe involving scale rows 4 and 5 may form a series of small blotches on anterior body; venter uniform yellow or salmon. Crown of head olive-brown, separated from yellow or salmon labials by black stripe anterior to the eye passing under the orbit and becoming a thick postocular stripe. Black stripe on the occipital region joining the postorbital stripe.

Natural History: A snake of secondary growth and agricultural areas; Mole (1924) and Emsley (1977) considered this one of the more common snakes on Trinidad, but field notes

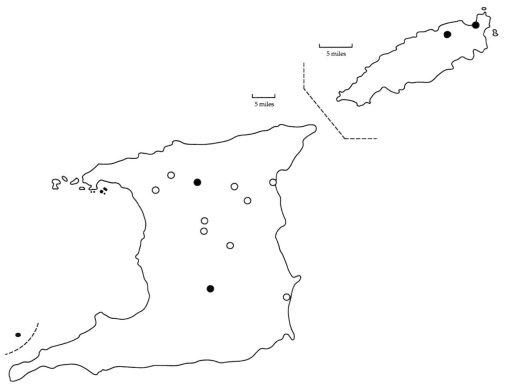

Map 91. *Liophis reginae* ssp. (Tobago)
Liophis reginae zweifeli (Trinidad)

(JCM) report only four specimens from Trinidad and two from Tobago: three road kills in areas of secondary growth, one under tin in secondary forest, one in a cacao plantation, and a juvenile under a rock near a pond in secondary growth. A terrestrial snake with aquatic tendencies that feeds on ectotherms; prey is killed by constriction (Emsley, 1977); Test et al. (1966) found one containing the lizard *Gymnophthalmus speciosus;* Brongersma (1956b) reported one containing a hylid frog and a *Bachia heteropa.* Field notes (JCM) report stomach contents for 16 of 20 specimens (80% contained food), four (25%) with *Bachia heteropa,* three (18.75%) with *Eleutherodactylus urichi,* two (12.5%) with *Gonatodes vittatus,* one (6.25%) with *Physalaemus pustulosus,* one (6.25%) with tadpoles or frog embryos, three (18.75%) containing unidentified frogs, and one (6.25%) contained unidentified fish remains. Clutches of 4–10 eggs laid between January and July (Emsley, 1977; Mole and Urich, 1894b; Mole, 1924.) Field notes (RH) describe a Tobago specimen depositing two extremely elongated eggs the first week of August.

Material: Trinidad—FMNH 5674, 77902–3, 190745 Port of Spain; 49938–44 San Rafael; 49945 Plaisance Mayaro; 49946 Morne Bleu Ridge; 49947–49950 Brickfield; 109749 Cascade; 217232, 218779 Arima Valley. USNM 166717, Arima Valley; 166718 near Matura. Tobago—USNM 167505 Bloody Bay- Charlotteville Rd. at the 29.34 milepost; 195010, Roxborough-Parlatuvier Rd., vic. of 5 milepost; 195139, 228072, 228074, 228076, 228077 vic. of Charlotteville; 228070 Bloody Bay; 228071 Speyside; 228080 Anse Fourmi; 228081–2 Merchiston; 228083 Hillsborough Dam; 233979 Cambleton.

Liophis reginae ssp.

Map 91. Plate 139.

Liophis sp.: Hardy, 1982:86. *Liophis reginae* ssp.: Dixon, 1983a:137.

Distribution: This undescribed race is known from northeastern Tobago, and is a Caribbean Coastal Range-Tobago endemic. It is currently known from three specimens, two of which have been examined by the author.

Identification: 362 mm SVL, 120 mm tail. Rostral visible from above; eight infralabials; eight supralabials; 9–10 infralabials; fourth and fifth supralabials enter the orbit; temporals number two primary and one secondary; one preocular; two postoculars; a divided anal plate. Dorsal scales are in 17 rows at midbody and reduced to 15 posteriorly; 143 ventrals; 77 subcaudals. A dorsolateral tan stripe distinguishes it from Trinidad specimens. The first and second scale rows are olive green; third scale row is olive green with a black smudge in the middle of the scale; fourth scale row is tan, possibly cream in life, with the lower edge black; the fifth scale row is tan with the upper one-third with green-black flecks; scale rows 6–10 are olive green. Ventrals and subcaudals are immaculate cream. Recently, a second specimen, a male, has been collected on Gilpin Trace (UF 91621). This animal differs from the specimen above in that the tan stripe is indistinct. The smudge of pigment on the third scale row is prominent, and on the posterior half of the body forms a dark stripe. Dorsal scale counts are the same as above except the ventral scales number 146, and the subcaudals number 66. Supralabials are 9/8, infralabials 11/11, the ocular scales are identical to the USNM specimen. The posterior of the venter has some light mottling.

Natural History: The specimen was active at 1500 hours. The area where it was collected is very old growth secondary forest.

Material: Tobago—UF 91621 Gilpin Trace. USNM 228069 Pigeon Peak Trace.

Liophis reginae zweifeli Roze

Map 91. Plates 140, 141.

Liophis reginae: Mole and Urich, 1894a:84. *Leimadophis reginae:* Roux, 1926:292. *Leimadophis reginae* (*reginae*): Amaral, 1935:238. *Leimadophis zweifeli* Roze, 1959:4. Type locality: "Rancho Grande in the state of Aragua, Venezuela, at an elevation of 1100 meters, in a cloud forest region." *Liophis reginae zweifeli:* Dixon, 1983a:126.

Common Names: "High woods coral snake" (Mole, 1914); "Reticulate snake" (Wehekind, 1960). Mole (1924) stated, "This extremely beautiful snake owes its second scientific name [*reginae*] to the fact that it was dedicated to a Queen of Sweden."

Distribution: *L. reginae* occurs in cis-Andean South America. *L. r. zweifeli* has a Caribbean Coastal Range distribution inhabiting Venezuela and Trinidad (Dixon, 1983a). On Trinidad it appears to be widely distributed, from near sea level to the highest mountains. Published Trinidad localities include: Arima Valley (Beebe, 1952); and Tamana Caves (Kenny, 1979). Field notes (JCM) add the Caura Valley. Museum material from Trinidad adds the following localities: Brickfield, Mayaro, Rio Grande Forest near Sangre Grande, St. Augustine, San Rafael, Tamana Caves, Talparo, Tamana Hill, near Valencia, and Vega de Oropouche.

Description: 437 mm SVL, 72 mm tail (damaged); tail 29.4–42.6% SVL; maximum total length may approach 800 mm. Rostral visible from above; divided nasal; single loreal; single preocular; no suboculars; two (occasionally one) postocular; seven to nine supralabials; 8–10 infralabials; 137–146 ventrals; divided anal plate; 61–80 paired subcaudals. Dorsal scales are smooth, in 17 rows at midbody reduce to 15 posteriorly. Dorsum olive green with each scale edged with black. Crown with a black blotch; black stripe posterior to the eye. Tail with black stripe on each side, venter red-pink or cream with black checkering on some scutes. The color pattern will distinguish this species from all other Trinidad *Liophis*, as well as other colubrid snakes. Mole (1924) wrote "They look as if they had pieces of black mosquito curtain strained over them. The young have a yellowish collar and an oblique yellowish, black-edged band on each side of the head."

Natural History: A forest and forest-edge snake; field notes (JCM) report three specimens on roads in secondary forests, one on a trail in secondary forest, three specimens in old growth secondary forest foraging in the leaf litter along small streams. Mole (1924) reported them from the vicinity of streams and mangrove swamps; the latter seems unlikely. Test

et al. (1966) found it to be the most commonly encountered snake in the cloud forests of Rancho Grande, Venezuela, and noted most of their 48 observations were made in forest openings such as streams, paths, clearings, and fallen logs. Field notes (JCM) report it feeding on *Leptodactylus validus*. Food includes frogs (*Hyla* sp., *Leptodactylus* sp., *Mannophryne trinitatis, Scinax rubra*), lizards (*Ameiva ameiva*) and small birds [Michaud and Dixon (1989) summarized the feeding habits of this species throughout its range]. Test et al. (1966) reported clutch size as three to five eggs; they marked nine of these snakes, two were recaptured three times in the same locality over a period of 6 weeks; and they reported predation by a hawk. The neck is flattened to form a small, narrow hood when it is disturbed (field notes, JCM).

Material: Trinidad—FMNH 215827, 217226–7, 219615 Arima Valley; 49957 San Rafael; 49958 Brickfield.

Mastigodryas boddaerti boddaerti (Sentzen)

Map 92. Plates 142, 143.

Coluber boddaerti Sentzen, 1796:59. Type locality: unknown. *Herpetodryas boddaertii:* Garman, 1887c:284. *Drymobius boddaerti:* Boettger, 1898:47. *Dryadophis boddaerti boddaerti:* Stuart, 1941:70. *Drymobius b. boddaerti:* Wehekind, 1955:10. *Mastigodryas boddaerti boddaerti:* Peters and Orejas-Miranda, 1970:193.

Common Names: "Machete couesse" (Mole and Urich, 1894a); "Grass machete" (Mole, 1924); "Machete" (Boos and Quesnel, 1968); "Couesse, grass snake" (Emsley, 1977).

Distribution: *M. boddaerti* ranges from Tobago and Trinidad over most of northern South America. *M. b. boddaerti* has an Amazonian distribution, and occurs from the lower slopes of the Andes to the mouth of Amazon River. This snake is also known from Trinidad. Published Trinidad localities include: Botanic Gardens in Port of Spain, Gasparee Island (Mole, 1924); and islands of Huevos and Chacachacare (Boos, 1975a); Monos Island (Manuel, 1965 and Boos, 1984c); Aripo savannas (Schwab, 1988). Trinidad localities based upon museum material are: Arima Valley; Bayshore, NW of Port of Spain; Chacachacare Island; Guayaguayare Rd. 3 mi from junction at Mayaro; Manzanilla-Mayaro Rd., vicinity of 41.75 milepost; Royal Rd. vicinity of 2.25 milepost, Maracas Valley; Marval; Mayaro; Princes Town; Tucker Valley.

Description: 877 mm SVL, 310 mm tail, tail about 35% of SVL. Rostral visible from above; loreal single; one preocular; no suboculars; two or three postoculars; 8–10 supralabials; 8–10 infralabials; 179–196 ventrals; divided anal plate; 106–124 divided subcaudals. Dorsal scales have apical pits, otherwise smooth and in 17 rows at midbody, reduce posteriorly to 15. Juveniles have a red-brown ground color, with 72 white dorsal crossbars, each bordered with black, which do not extend onto tail. White stripe on scale row 4 separates dorsal crossbars from lateral crossbars which are offset from dorsal bars. Chin mottled with black, grey, and white; the venter of the body and tail yellow. The tail's dorsum is uniform red-brown. Adults are uniform brown-grey or olive-brown with a light stripe on scale rows 4 and 5. Color light-

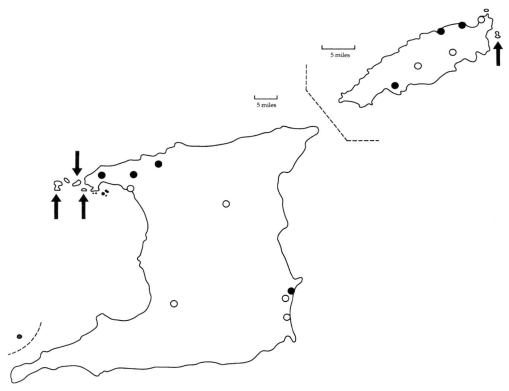

Map 92. *Mastigodryas boddaerti boddaerti* (Trinidad)
Mastigodryas boddaerti dunni (Tobago)

ens laterally; venter uniform off-white or yellow extending to the lower labials; venter may show partial mottling.

Natural History: A diurnal snake of forests and forest-edges. Field notes (JCM) describe specimens in secondary growth, active by day; one was crawling on leaves floating on the surface of a pond, and another sunning on a forest trail. Food includes frogs, lizards, reptile eggs, nestling birds, rodents, and grasshoppers (Beebe, 1946; Wehekind, 1960). Mole (1924) stated eggs are laid in May.

Material: Trinidad—FMNH 41677 no data; 40446 Tucker Valley. MCZ 126378–9, Marval. USNM 166685 Manzanilla-Mayaro Rd., vicinity of milepost 41.75; 166684 Maracas Royal Rd, vicinity of milepost 2.25. Chacahacare Island—MCZ 104398.

Mastigodryas boddaerti dunni (Stuart)

Map 92. Plate 144.

Eudryas dunni Stuart 1933:5. Type locality: Tobago Island, B.W.I. *Drymobius boddaertii:* Cope, 1879:276. *Dryadophis boddaerti dunni:* Stuart, 1941:76. *Dryadophis boddaerti dunni:* Brongersma, 1956b:178. *Drymobius boddaerti:* Underwood, 1962:104. *Drymobius b. boddaerti:* DeVerteuil, 1968:101. *Mastigodryas boddaerti dunni:* Peters and Orejas-Miranda, 1970:193.

Comment: Stuart's (1941) description of the range of *Mastigodryas amarali* stated, "Although this species is imperfectly known there is a reasonable probability that it inhabits the dry lands of northeastern Venezuela and the islands off the north coast, with the exception of Trinidad, to Tobago." He listed USNM 10137 as being from Tobago and

his Map 2 shows *amarali* as being on Tobago; this specimen was collected by Ober. Emsley (1977) suggested this location is invalid but does not cite evidence to suggest he looked at the specimen. Roze (1966) and Lancini (1979) also listed Tobago as a locality. All of these records are based on the single specimen collected by F. Ober in 1878. Tuck and Hardy (1973) have shown Ober's collection from Tobago actually had its origin on some other island. There is no other evidence for *M. amarali* occurring on Tobago.

Distribution: *M. b. dunni* is known only from the islands of Tobago and Little Tobago. Tobago localities based upon the literature include: Crown Point and Mt. Dillon (Brongersma, 1956b); Patience Hill and Scarborough (Mertens, 1972). Tobago localities based upon museum specimens include: Bacolet Rd., Bloody Bay, Cambelton, Charlotteville, Hillsborough Dam, Man of War Bay, Roxborough, Scarborough, and Little Tobago Island.

Description: 776 mm SVL, tail 105 mm (damaged). Rostral visible from above; loreal single; one preocular; no suboculars; two or three postoculars; 8–10 supralabials; 8–10 infralabials; 185–196 ventrals; divided anal plate; 119–124 divided subcaudals. Dorsal scales have apical pits, otherwise smooth and in 17 rows at midbody, reduction posteriorly to 15. Distinguished from the Trinidad population by a second stripe on the first and second scale rows. This stripe is indistinct and occurs in other populations (see Lancini, 1979, Fig. 50). Scale counts for the Trinidad and Tobago populations overlap, and it is probable that this race is not valid.

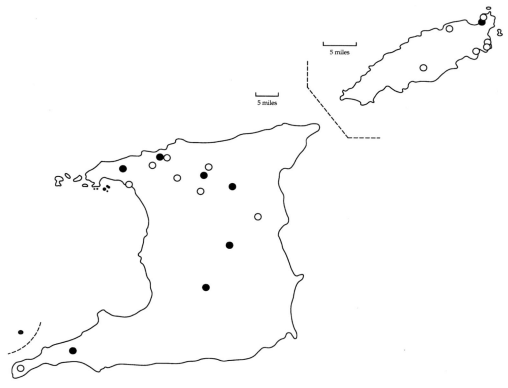

Map 93. *Ninia atrata*

Natural History: A forest and forest-edge snake; field notes (JCM) report one of these snakes on a steep, grass-covered road embankment being grazed by goats; one in a cacao planatation; one in a deciduous seasonal forest on Little Tobago.

Material: Tobago—FMNH 218534 Cambelton; MCZ 12071–2 Tobago; USMN 195126 Cambelton; 228085 Bloody Bay; 228086 Scarborough; 228087 Charlotteville; 228090 Roxborough. Little Tobago—AMNH 84228.

Ninia atrata **(Hallowell)**

Map 93. Plate 145.

Coluber atratus Hallowell, 1845:245. Type locality: within 200 miles of Caracas, Venezuela. *Ninia atrata:* Cope, 1860b:340. *Streptophorus atratus:* Boulenger, 1893:293. *Ninia atrata atrata:* Beebe, 1952: 175. *Ninia hudsoni:* Burger and Werler, 1954:649.

Common Names: "Coffee snake, collared snake, ringneck snake, white-collared snake" (Emsley, 1977).

Distribution: *N. atrata* is widespread, ranging from Honduras and Costa Rica to Ecuador and Venezuela. It also occurs on Trinidad and Tobago and the species is widespread on both islands. Published Trinidad locations include: Arima Valley (Beebe, 1952). Localities based upon museum material include: outskirts of Arima on Tunapuna Rd.; Brickfield; Diego Martin; La Seiva Valley; Maracas Valley; Morne Bleu Ridge; Mt. St. Benedict; Tamana Hill; Tucker Valley; Valencia, on Cuare Rd. Field note (JCM) localities: 0.5 mi east of Icacos; just south of Sangre Grande; at the 68.25 milepost on the Southern Main Rd.; and the summit of Mt. Tu-

cuche. Tobago localities based upon museum specimens include: Anse Fourmi, Charlotteville, Delford, Hillsborough Dam, Merchiston, and Roxborough.

Description: 290 mm SVL, 74 mm tail; tail 24–28% SVL. May reach a total length 460 mm. Rostral visible from above; nasal single; loreal single; prefrontals border front orbit; preoculars absent; suboculars absent; one postocular, sometimes divided; supralabials six or seven; infralabials six or seven; first pair of chin shields larger than second; ventrals 147–158; anal plate single; subcaudals 48–59. Dorsal scales keeled in 19 rows at midbody. Emsley (1977) described mature males with spiny projections on chin scales; I have not observed these structures. Dorsal coloration blue-black with a collar or blotch on the occipitals that may be orange, white or pink, or absent in old adults. The only Trinidad and Tobago snake with a collar and uniform blue-black color pattern; the venter is immaculate.

Natural History: *N. atrata* is a terrestrial-fossorial snake of forests as well as urban gardens. In Venezuela, Test et al. (1966) found it from sea level to 1900 ft. On Trinidad field notes (JCM) report it from sea level to about 3000 ft (the summit of Mt. Tucuche); 21 in secondary forest and agricultural areas, two in primary forest; microhabitats—one in rotting bamboo, one in a garbage dump, three under a piece of foam rubber along a trail, and the remainder were taken from the road. Emsley (1977) reported food as ". . . insects and soft-bodied arthropods." However, field notes (JCM) describe contents of 11 stomachs, four con-

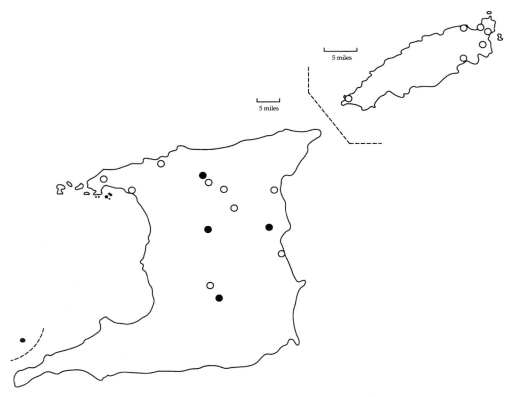

Map 94. *Oxybelis aeneus*

tained slugs (Gastropoda) and slug eggs, and a fifth stomach contained sand grains. Examination of another species in this genus (*N. sebae* from Costa Rica) also reveals remains of slugs; thus it appears at least two species of this genus may be specialized for feeding on these gastropods. The coral snake *Micrurus circinalis* regurgitated one of these snakes; it was partially digested and was accompanied by the microteiid *Bachia heteropa* and dipterous larvae. Emsley (1977) stated that they lay eggs; no data on clutch size available.

Material: Trinidad—FMNH 215821–2, 178481, 217236, 217259, 219585 Arima Valley; 49951–6, Brickfield; 219583, on the Southern Main Rd. about the 68.25 milepost. MCZ 12066 La Seiva Valley; 66020 Maracas Valley; 87333 Valencia, Quare Rd.; 100639 Tamana Hill, Tamana Caves; 12632–3 Diego Martin. Tobago—USNM 228093 Charlotteville.

Oxybelis aeneus (Wagler)

Map 94. Plates 146, 147.

Dryinus aeneus Wagler, 1824:12, pl 12. Type locality: Tefe, Amazonas, Brazil. *Oxybelis aeneus:* Wagler, 1830:183. *Dendrophis aurata:* Court, 1858:411. *Dryiophis aeneus:* Garman, 1887c:284. *Oxybelis acuminatus:* Mole and Urich, 1894a:86. *Oxybelis aeneus aeneus:* Beebe, 1952:175. *Oxybelis a. aeneus:* Wehekind, 1960:75. *Oxybelis ae. aeneus:* Mertens, 1972:18.

Common Names: "Ash-coloured horse-whip or rigoise-argentee" (DeVerteuil, 1858). "They are called by the Creoles 'Liguis,' a corruption of 'Rigoise' or 'horsewhip'" (Mole and Urich, 1894b). "Rigoise-Argentee, Liguez, Whip

Snake" (Mole, 1924). "Pike-headed snake, vine snake" (Emsley, 1977).

Distribution: *O. aeneus* is a widespread species, ranging from southern Arizona, United States, and southern Tamaulipas, Mexico, through Central America to southern Brazil. It occurs on Trinidad and Tobago from sea level to at least 300 m. Published Trinidad localities include: Tucker Valley (Johnson, 1946); Arima Valley (Beebe, 1952); Huevos Island (Boos, 1984c); Aripo savannas (Schwab, 1988). Field notes (JCM) list: Manzanilla-Cocos Bays' cocal; the 78 milepost on Icacos Rd.; and Simla, Arima Valley. Trinidad localities based upon museum material include: Heights of Aripo Rd. at milepost 2; Bayshore, near Port of Spain; Brickfield; Caura Valley; Heights of Guanapo; Maracas Valley; Mt. Harris; about 2 miles WNW of Rio Claro; San Rafael; Vega de Oropouche. Literature records for Tobago localities include: Milford Bay (Barbour, 1916a). Tobago localities based on museum material include: Cambelton, Charlotteville, Roxborough, and Speyside.

Description: 674 mm SVL, tail 317 mm (damaged); tail 54–77% SVL. This species may reach a total length of 2.0 m. A slender vine-like snake with an elongated, sharply pointed head. Rostral not visible from above; nasal single and elongate; loreal absent; one or two preoculars; no suboculars; one to three postoculars; seven to nine supralabials; seven to nine infralabials; three pairs of enlarged chin shields; ventrals 179–192; anal plate usually divided; subcaudals in males 171–179, in females 156–181. Dorsal scales are smooth or weakly keeled, number 17 at midbody

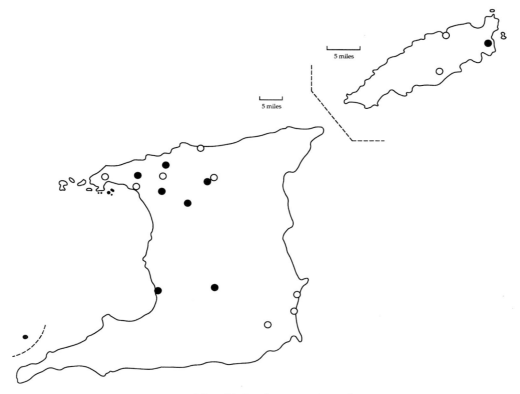

Map 95. *Oxyrhopus petola petola*

and reduce to 13 posteriorly. Mole (1924) reported apical pits in Trinidad specimens; Keiser (1974) found none. Trinidad specimens brown-grey dorsally, with black edging on some scales; some with a white streak above eye; region below eye from snout, across the upper and lower labials may be white-cream and continuous with color on the venter and the nape. Uniform cream or white venters were present in the specimens observed, but Keiser (1974) noted coloration is variable, and the venter may be mottled with brown or grey. This is the only "vine" snake with a uniform brown-grey body, lacking a loreal, and 17 scale rows at midbody; *Leptophis riveti* has a similar slender body form, but it has 15 scale rows at midbody; and *Imantodes cenchoa* is very slender but it has a blunt head much wider than its neck, a blotched pattern, and an enlarged vertebral scale row.

Natural History: A snake of dry scrub, secondary forest, and primary rainforest. On Trinidad it occurs from sea level to at least 700 m. Field notes (JCM) describe four of these snakes, two at sea level in palm forest, one at 240 m in secondary growth, and one at about 320 m in elevation in old secondary growth. Lizards are the most frequently taken prey, although frogs and birds are also eaten. Henderson and Binder (1980) reported on the feeding behavior of this diurnal snake, describing it as a sit-and-wait predator. When disturbed it does not hesitate to open its mouth and threaten the annoyance; the mouth is lined with blue membranes. At night it perches at higher sites than it does during the day. Mole (1924) reported a Trinidad specimen laid six eggs in June; on the mainland Beebe (1946) recorded three eggs in

March. Field notes (MB and RH) report behavior believed to be combat between two males: the snakes were located in a small tree for photographic purposes; one pursued the other through the branches, and at one point they came face to face with each other; they intertwined their bodies and hung down from a branch; one snake bit the other's head. The specimens were not retained and their sex, unfortunately, was not determined.

Material: Trinidad—FMNH 49974–5 Brickfield; 49976 Mt. Harris; 49977–85 San Rafael; 215838–9 Arima Valley.

Oxyrhopus petola petola (Linnaeus)

Map 95. Plates 148, 149.

Coluber petola Linnaeus, 1758:225. Type locality: Africa (in error).
Coluber petolarius: Linnaeus, 1758:225. Type locality: "Indiis."
Oxyrhopus doliatus: Reinhardt and Lutken, 1862:12. *Oxyrrhopus plumbeus:* Boulenger, 1891:285. *Oxyrrhopus petola:* Lonnberg, 1896:7. *Oxyrhopus petolarius:* Mole, 1924:252. *Oxyrhopus petola petola:* Beebe, 1946:37. *Oyxyrhopus p. petola:* Wehekind, 1960:74. *Pseudoboa petola:* Underwood, 1962:179.

Common Names: "False coral snake" (Wehekind, 1955); "Sombre false coral" (Emsley, 1977).

Distribution: *O. petola* is widespread, ranging from Veracruz, Mexico, southward to South America. *O. p. petola* has a Caribbean Coastal Range/Northern Forest distribution ranging from Villavicencio, Colombia, eastward to Guyana, and occurring on Trinidad and Tobago. On Trinidad and Tobago the species is widespread. Trinidad localities based on literature reports include: Arima Valley (Beebe, 1952); Port of Spain (Werner, 1899). Trinidad localities based upon field notes (JCM) are: the upper Guanapo Valley; and about 5 miles south of Rio Claro on Guayaguayare Road. Trinidad localities based upon museum material include: the intersection of Arima and Blanchisseuse Roads; Brickfield; Maracas Valley; Mt. St. Benedict; Mayaro Beach; Plaisance, Mayaro; near Piarco Airport; Pointe-à-Pierre; Marval; Port of Spain; St. Augustine; Teteron Bay; Tucker Valley. Published Tobago localities include: the road to Hillsborough Dam (Mertens, 1972). Hardy (1982) stated that this species is probably found throughout the highlands of Tobago. Field notes (JCM) report it on Bloody Bay Road, 4 km south of Bloody Bay. Tobago localities based upon museum material include: Lambeau Hill Crown Trace at Windward Rd.

Description: 611 mm SVL, tail 114 mm (damaged), tail 29–34% SVL. May attain a total length about 1.1 m. Rostral single, barely visible from above; nasal divided or semidivided; loreal elongate and single; one or two preoculars; no suboculars; two postoculars; seven or eight supralabials; eight or nine infralabials; 199–204 ventrals; anal plate single; 81–86 subcaudals. Dorsal scales smooth and in 19 rows (occasionally 17) at midbody. Mole (1924) describes four pattern morphs. Most of the specimens examined here are black with red annuli which do not extend onto the venter; however I have two specimens that are uniform black, both old adults. It is unknown if large specimens lose the red bands during growth or if they are born with that pattern; all of the animals lacking red bands are more than 550 mm SVL, suggesting a change with age. Mole (1924) also described animals with crossbars reduced to large spots. Venter uniform cream. There are no other Trinidad or Tobago snakes that have 19 or 17 rows of smooth dorsal scales, a single anal plate, a single nasal, and a banded pattern of red and black. *Drymarchon* has similar scale characters, but has a dark brown-grey coloration that lightens posteriorly and a divided nasal. Hatchlings at Villavicencio, Colombia, are black and white, with the posterior white bands turning peach colored before they turn red; the color change progresses anteriorly with growth (W. W. Lamar, personal communication). Trinidad and Tobago populations probably undergo a similar ontogenetic change; a juvenile observed on Tobago was black and white, and lacked red or peach coloration.

Natural History: A nocturnal, forest and savanna snake; field notes (JCM) report one road kill in secondary growth; one dead next to the Arima River; a road kill in a grassy area near the airport; one in lowland forest; one in montane forest, and two in a secondary forest/agricultural area. Emsley (1977) listed food as small mammals, lizards, and snakes; in Ecuador, Duellman (1978) found one that had eaten two diurnal lizards (*Kentropyx* and *Prionodactylus*). Field notes (JCM) describe one containing a broken tail from the lizard *Bachia heteropa*, another the remains of a *Gonatodes*, and a third containing remains of a mammal; the remains suggest this species forages in the leaf litter and possibly in low shrubs. Test et al. (1966) reported clutch size as seven eggs for a Venezuelan population; and Fitch (1970) reported

seven gravid females from Peru with 5–10 eggs, in March, September, and November.

Material: Trinidad—FMNH 215823-4 Arima Valley; 49987-9 Brickfield; 49986 Plaisance Mayaro; 218774 Piarco Airport Rd., between airport and Churchill-Roosevelt Highway. MCZ 28574, 66959 St. Augustine; 49067 Pointe-à-Pierre; 80998 0.75 milepost, Maracas Valley Rd.; 100632 Marval, Port of Spain; 100591 Emperor Valley Zoo, Port of Spain; 100592 Arima. USNM 166722 Arima Valley. Tobago—USNM 228112 Windward Rd. at Lambeau Hill Crown Trace.

Pseudoboa neuwiedii (Duméril, Bibron and Duméril)

Map 96. Plates 150, 151.

Scytale neuwiedii Duméril, Bibron and Duméril, 1854:1001. Type locality: Cote Ferme and Brazil, restricted by Hoge and Lancini (1960) to Cumana, Venezuela. *Scytale coronatum:* Gunther, 1858:188. *Tortryx scytale:* Court, 1858:441. *Tortrix scytale:* Court, 1884:382. *Oxyrrhopus* [sic.] *neuwiedi:* Boettger, 1897:211. *Pseudoboa guerini:* Werner, 1899:473. *Pseudoboa coronatus:* Mole, 1914:147. *Oxyrhopus neuwiedii:* Mole 1924:255. *Pseudoboa coronatus:* Wehekind, 1955:12. *Pseudoboa neuwiedii neuwiedii:* Roze, 1966:207. *Pseudoboa coronata:* Mertens, 1969:66. *Psuedoboa c. coronata:* DeVerteuil, 1968:103. *Pseudoboa neuwiedi:* Schwartz and Thomas, 1975:190.

Common Names: "Roulea" (DeVerteuil, 1858); "Mapepire velour" (Mole, 1914); "ratonera" (Wehekind, 1955); "ratonel" (Boos, 1975b); "moon snake" (Emsley, 1977). On Tobago, "Brown snake" (DeVerteuil, 1968).

Distribution: A widespread species, *P. neuwiedii* occurs from Panama and Colombia eastward to Suriname, and as far south as Brazil; and on Trinidad and Tobago. Its presence on Grenada has been questioned by Schwartz and Henderson (1991), and this record may be in error. It is widely distributed on Trinidad and Tobago at elevations below 1000 ft. Trinidad localities from the literature include: Port of Spain (Werner, 1899); Arima Valley (Beebe, 1952); Santa Cruz (Boos, 1975b); Bois Neuf, Nariva Swamp (Ramcharan et al., 1979); Gaspar Grande Island (Boos, 1984d); Aripo Savannas (Schwab, 1988). Trinidad localities based upon field notes (JCM): 2 miles east of Arima on Arima-Bypass; Erin; Manzanilla Bay Rd. at the 40 milepost; Penal; and Siparia. Trinidad localities based upon museum specimens include: Diego Martin Valley; Chaguaramas; Churchill Roosevelt Highway; Mayaro; Guayaguayare; Port of Spain; and Tucker Valley. Tobago localities based upon museum specimens include: Charlotteville; between Delford and Speyside; Milford Bay; Panama Bay; Scarborough; and the 7.75 milepost on the Windward Rd.

Description: 870 mm SVL; 215 mm tail; tail 22–33% SVL. Rostral single, slightly upturned, visible from above. Loreal single; one or two preoculars; no suboculars; two postoculars; eight supralabials; six to eight infralabials; 195–201 ventrals; single anal plate; and 68–78 single subcaudals. Dorsal scales smooth in 17 or 19 rows at midbody. Young red or pink above with a dark head and a cream collar fading with age. Each dorsal scale with a dark spot enlarging with age. Venter uniform cream, extending onto labials. Adult snakes are red-brown or pink-brown with a

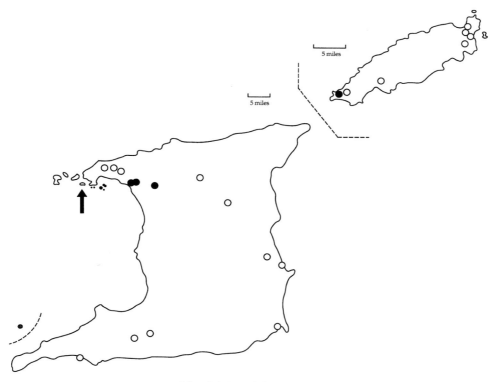

Map 96. *Pseudoboa neuwiedii*

darker brown-black head. This species has been confused with its close relatives *Clelia clelia* and *Oxyrhopus petola*. However, the single subcaudals and the dark color of the head extending on to the neck for eight or nine scale rows distinguish it from these two species, as well as all other Trinidad and Tobago snakes. Also, *Pseudoboa* has a unique spade-shaped rostral scale and an adult color pattern that is a uniform red-brown.

Natural History: A crepuscular-nocturnal snake of forest and savanna; *P. neuwiedii* is a common snake at low elevations, using almost all available habitats, including: agricultural areas, gardens, yards, and teak forest. Food includes: eggs, conspecifics, and most any appropriately sized vertebrate (Mole, 1924; Wehekind, 1960; Emsley, 1977); field notes (JCM) report snake scales in the stomach of one specimen. Captives killed rodents by constriction. Two of these snakes observed foraging at dusk in leaf litter accumulated in a streambed; one observed in primary forest (field notes, JCM). Boos (1975b) reported on the death of a cat from the bite of this snake, and notes an itching sensation in a human bitten on the index finger. Field notes (JCM) describe two captives housed together, one bit the other, and the bitten snake died within a few hours. Clutches of 3–9 eggs laid in nests of leaf cutting ants (*Atta* and *Acromyrmex*) in July, September, January, and February (Mole, 1924; Emsley, 1977, field notes, JCM).

Material: Trinidad—FMNH 77900 Port of Spain; 217228 Eastern Main Road, ca. 2 mi east of Arima. MCZ 66960 St. Augustine; 79813 Lady Young Rd., Port of Spain. Tobago—MCZ 11993, 11998, 12000 Milford Bay; 17612, 18841 Panama Bay.

Pseustes poecilonotus polylepis (Peters)

Map 97. Plates 152, 153.

> *Ahaetulla polylepis:* Peters, 1867:706. Type locality: Suriname. *Coluber poecilostoma:* Mole and Urich: 1894a:84. *Phrynonax eutropis:* Mole and Urich, 1894a:85. *Phrynonax fasciatus:* Boettger, 1898:49. *Phrynonax poecilonotus polylepis:* Amaral, 1930a:156. *Pseustes [poecilonotus polylepis]:* Brongersma, 1937:6. *Pseustes poecilonetus polyepis:* Wehekind:1960:73.

Common Names: "cutlah" (Mole, 1924); "liana snake, bird-eating snake" (Wehekind, 1955). "Dos-cocrite" (Schwab, 1988).

Distribution: *P. poecilonotus* occurs from the Isthmus of Tehuantepec and Yucatan, Mexico, through Central America to Amazonia. *P. p. polylepis* inhabits Amazonia and Trinidad. Published Trinidad localities include: Caparo, Cunupia, Marval, Mayaro, Santa Cruz (Mole, 1924); Mt. St. Benedict (Brongersma, 1956b). Trinidad localities based upon museum material include: Arima Valley; near Cumaca; upper Guanapo Valley; 120 milepost on Naparima-Mayaro Rd., near San Fernando; Rio Grande Forest, Sangre Grande; Scotland Bay; and Tucker Valley.

Description: 850 mm SVL; tail 41–49% SVL; may reach or slightly exceed 2 meters in total length. Rostral visible from above; single loreal; single preocular, no suboculars, two postoculars; seven supralabials, 10–11 infralabials, 193–203 ventrals, single anal plate, 125–126 subcaudals. Scale rows at midbody number 21 or 23, and reduce posteriorly to 15. Dorsal scales have two apical pits that are difficult to observe. Emsley (1982) reported that females have

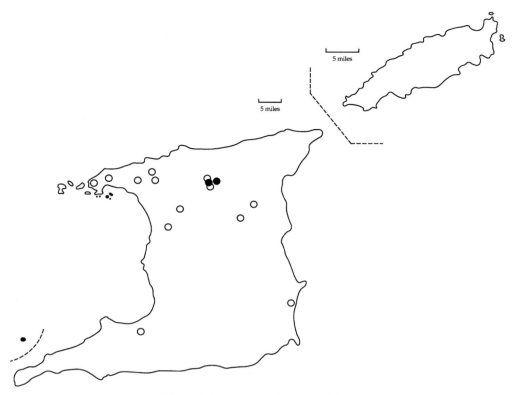

Map 97. *Pseustes poecilonotus polylepis*

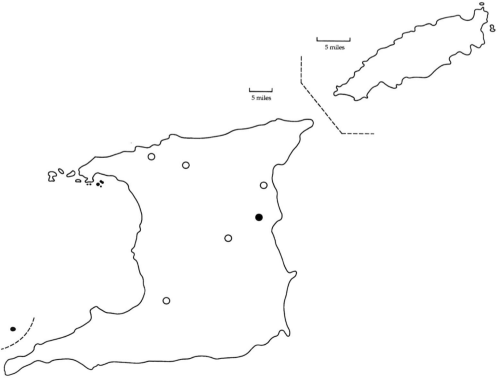

Map 98. *Pseustes sulphureus sulphureus*

5 middorsal rows of keeled scales, whereas males have 7–11 middorsal rows of keeled scales. Wilson and Meyer (1982) found slightly different variation in the Honduras population of this species (3–4 rows for females and 7–13 rows for males). Young are brown or brown-gray with dark brown crossbands, while adults are uniform olive-brown in color with yellow labials and chin. An indistinct vertebral stripe may be present. Ventrals more or less uniform yellow or green-grey. Dixon and Soini (1977) noted the crossbands are present in individuals less than 900 mm in total length; the largest Trinidad specimen with crossbands is 495 mm in total length; all other specimens larger than 900 mm in total length. The only Trinidad and Tobago colubrid with some keeled dorsal scales in 21 or 23 rows; *Pseustes sulphureus* is black and yellow and has 25 scale rows. It may also be superficially confused with *Chironius carinatus,* which has a similar olive-green dorsum and a yellow venter; however *Chironius* has only 12 dorsal scale rows at midbody.

Natural History: A diurnal, arboreal-terrestrial snake of forest and forest-edge. Field notes (JCM) report three road kills in secondary forest; two sunning on a lawn adjacent to secondary forest. Mice, birds, and lizards are eaten (Mole, 1924; Beebe, 1946; Emsley, 1977); in Peru, Dixon and Soini (1977) found one in a nest of Spix's guan that had eaten an egg of the bird; field notes (JCM) report one of four specimens contained orthopteran remains. Beebe (1946) noted seven oviductal eggs from a female collected in June. This snake will contort its body into a shape that resembles a liana, rendering it difficult to detect in leaf litter (Emsley, 1977; field notes, JCM). Defense behavior for this species in Central America includes lateral compression of the body, spreading of the lower jaw, inflation of the lungs, a gaping mouth, striking, and vibrating the tail (Rand and Ortleb, 1969); all of these behaviors are described in field notes (JCM) for Trinidad specimens.

Material: Trinidad—FMNH 215831, 218778, 219605 Arima Valley; 217223 Gunapo Valley.

Pseustes sulphureus sulphureus (Wagler)

Map 98. Plate 154.

Natrix sulphureus Wagler, 1824:26, pl 9. Type locality: shoreline forest along the Rio Japura, Brazil. *Phrynoax sulphureus:* Mole, 1914:144. *Pseustes sulphureus sulphureus:* Brongersma, 1937:6, figs. 1a–1b.

Common Names: Mole (1924) stated there is no local common name for this snake. Wehekind (1955) uses the name "yellow belly puffing snake" and later (1960) "yellow-bellied puffing snake." Emsley (1977) used the name "liana snake," a name that is more appropriately applied to *Pseustes poecilonotus polylepis.*

Distribution: *P. sulphureus* has an Amazonian distribution. *P. s. sulphureus* has an Amazonian distribution inhabiting the entire range of the species except southeast Brazil. Published Trinidad localities include: Arima Valley (Beebe, 1952); Tamana Cave (Boos, 1975d; Kenny, 1979). Trinidad

localities based upon museum material include: Mt. Harris; Maracas waterfall; Princes Town; and Vega de Oropouche.

Description: 977 mm SVL; 547 mm tail; tail 56% SVL; may exceed 3 m in total length (Roze, 1966). Rostral visible from above; nasal semidivided; loreal single; one preocular; no suboculars; three postoculars; eight supralabials, 10 infralabials; 208–226 ventrals; single anal plate; 125–145 paired subcaudals. Scale rows at midbody 21, reduce to 13 or 15 posteriorly, all but first two rows keeled. Head and neck tan, with some yellow on labials, chin, throat, and anterior venter; posteriorly the venter becomes black; anterior crossbands also yellow; dorsum otherwise black. Distinguished from *P. poecilonotus polylepis* by its coloration and 25 scale rows. Other species that it may be superficially confused with are *Clelia, Drymarchon,* and *Spilotes;* none of these species has 25 scale rows.

Natural History: A diurnal, forest and forest-edge snake. While this snake is usually associated with forests, William Montgomery (personal communication) describes finding one in Aripo Savanna, at an open, unforested locality. In Peru, Dixon and Soini (1977) found two in low bushes; in Ecuador, Duellman (1978) reported one from the forest floor. Its rarity may be in part due to it spending time in the forest canopy; but at least two specimens have been taken inside Tamana Caves. Field notes (RH and MB) report a road kill in primary forest. Food includes lizards, birds, and mammals (Mole, 1924; Beebe, 1946; Duellman, 1978) Emsley, 1977). Goode (1989) described two females from Suriname laying clutches of 7 and 14 eggs in August, with the young emerging on 24 and 26 October after 84–86 days of incubation. The hatchlings are quite large, 350–418 mm SVL from one litter, and 486–591 mm SVL in another.

Material: FMNH 53649 Mt. Harris.

Sibon nebulata nebulata (Linnaeus)

Map 99. Plate 155.

Coluber nebulatus Linnaeus 1758:222. Type locality: America. *Leptognathus nebulatus:* Mole and Urich, 1894a:87. *Petalognathus nebulatus:* Boulenger, 1894:239. *Sibon sibon:* Amaral, 1930a:194. *Sibon nebulatus:* Roze, 1952b:96. *Sibon nebulata nebulata:* Peters, 1960: 199. *Sibon n. nebulata:* DeVerteuil, 1968:103. *Sibon nebulatus nebulatus:* Mertens, 1972:15.

Common Names: "Mapepire corde violin, fiddle string mapepire" (Mole, 1914); "Cloud snake" (Wehekind, 1955); "Cloudy snake" (DeVerteuil, 1968); "Slug-eating snake" (Emsley, 1977).

Distribution: A widespread species, *Sibon nebulata* ranges from Veracruz and Nayarit, Mexico, to Brazil and Ecuador. *S. n. nebulata* occurs in the northern portion of this range, including Trinidad and Tobago. Published Trinidad localities include: Arima Valley (Beebe, 1952); Huevos Island (Emsley, 1977). Trinidad localities based on field notes (JCM): 3 mi south of Rio Claro. Trinidad localities based on museum material include: Brickfield; Caura; Marval; Macqueripe Bay; Mt. St. Benedict; Point Radix; Port of Spain; St. Augustine; St. Joseph; Sangre Grande; San Rafael;

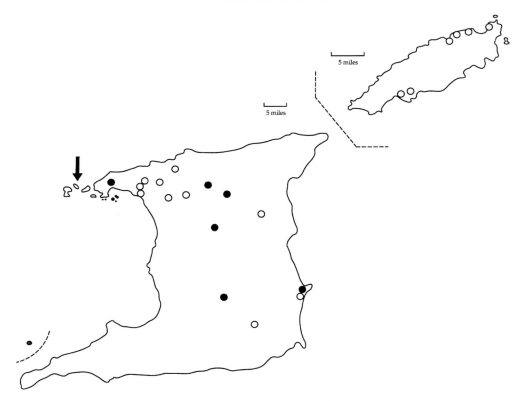

Map 99. *Sibon nebulata nebulata*

Tucker Valley; Mt. Tucuche. Published Tobago localities include: Scarborough (Barbour, 1916b); Bacolet River, Scarborough (Peters, 1960). Tobago localities based upon museum material include: Anse Fourmi; Bloody Bay; Charlotteville; and Hermitage.

Description: 440 mm SVL; 158 mm tail; tail 30–35% SVL; total length about 1 meter. Rostral barely visible from above; nasals divided; loreal touches the orbit, and may be fused with the preocular, which is usually absent; no suboculars; two to four postoculars, usually two; seven or eight supralabials; 8–10 infralabials; 174–187 ventrals; a single anal plate; 81–105 paired subcaudals. Smooth dorsal scales in 15 rows at midbody with no posterior reduction; vertebral scale row is slightly enlarged. Dorsum gray-brown with 36–41 black-brown blotches, many of which may form bands that extend onto or across the venter. One specimen from Tobago was very brown in color compared to Trinidad specimens. Head distinct from neck and mottled with gray-brown pigment. Labials cream with dark bars. Crown mottled; some specimens have the first crossband forming a collar. Venter cream or off-white with flecks of pigment, and intrusive dorsal crossbands. Distinguished from its relative *Dipsas variegata trinitatis* by the presence of a midline mental groove (on chin) and its grey coloration. *Dipsas* is mostly brown and lacks a mental groove.

Natural History: A nocturnal snake of forests and forest-edges; Mole (1924) stated it spends the day coiled in a bromeliad, under fallen leaves, or in decaying vegetation. It is known to feed only on slugs (Gastropoda) and Mole

(1924) noted that the slugs may be swallowed with the strike. Emsley (1977) found eggs laid in May, June, and September, but no information on clutch size is given. Urich (1931) considered this snake rare because of predation by the mongoose, stating it, ". . . is still common in gardens out of town." Depredation by the mongoose seems unlikely considering its nocturnal habits. Field notes (JCM) describe 13 specimens in the secondary forest–agricultural mosaic of the Arima Valley, all on the road after dark.

> **Material:** Trinidad—FMNH 40441–2 Tucker Valley; 49959, San Rafael; 49960–1, Brickfield; 171331, Point Radix (SE); 217229, 219590–2, Arima Valley; 218777, Eastern Main Rd. at the 34.5 mile-post.

Siphlophis cervinus (Laurenti)

Map 100. Plate 156.

> *Coronella cervina* Laurenti, 1768:88. Type locality: America. *Lycognathus cervinus:* Boulenger, 1896:57. *Siphlophis cervinus cervinus:* Beebe, 1946:42. *Siphilophis C.* [*sic.*] *cervinus:* Wehekind, 1955:10. *Siphlophis cervinus:* Hoge, 1964:43.

Common Names: "Checker belly (chequerbelly), variegated snake" (Emsley, 1977).

Distribution: *S. cervinus* is widespread, ranging from the Canal Zone of Panama southward to central Bolivia and Maranhao, Brazil; it also occurs on Trinidad. The secretive nature of this snake and the resulting few specimens make general statements about its distribution difficult. Published Trinidad localities include: Ortinola Estate, Maracas Valley (Mole, 1925 in Boos, 1975a); Manzanilla Road (Kenny in

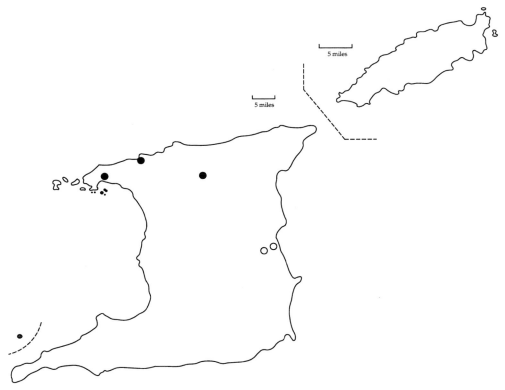

Map 100. *Siphlophis cervinus*

Smith and Seeberan, 1979); and Brigand Hill, in Nariva Swamp (Smith and Seeberan, 1979). Jack Price (personal communication) reports this snake at Simla, Arima Valley. Trinidad localities supported by museum specimens include: Arima Valley; Maracas Bay Rd., near the 2 milepost; and Tucker Valley.

Description: 634 mm SVL, 173 mm tail; tail 27–32% SVL. Maximum expected total length 1.3 m. Rostral visible from above with rounded edge; nasals single; elongate loreal single; one or two preoculars (usually one); no suboculars; two postoculars; seven to nine supralabials; eight or nine infralabials with fourth and fifth enlarged; 240–273 ventrals; anal plate single; 97–116 paired subcaudals. Smooth dorsal scales in 19 rows at midbody, reduce to 15 or 17 posteriorly. Dorsum is pink or red; head and nape red with black-edged scales, a black collar present. Black bars, spots, or chevrons are evenly or unevenly distributed over the dorsum and separated by yellow or white areas containing black tipped scales. Venter and first and second scale rows yellow or white with black spots or bars, giving the underside a checkered appearance. A very distinctive serpent unlikely to be confused with any other species, but because of brightly colored crossbands it may be mistaken for a coral snake or coral snake mimic (*Erythrolamprus* or *Oxyrhopus*). The checkered belly pattern should readily separate it from these snakes.

Natural History: A secretive snake of forest and forest-edge situations. Emsley (1977) found it on the ground, crawling up the side of a building and in the tops of tall coconut palms. Smith and Seeberan (1979) found a juvenile

(35 cm total length) specimen basking between 0830 and 0900 h on the concrete base of the radio mast on Brigand Hill. They observed the snake in captivity for 3 days and reported it more active between dusk and dawn than during the day. In Peru, Dixon and Soini (1977) found it in secondary and primary forest, one at the base of a large tree. Lizards may form the bulk of the prey; in Ecuador, Duellman (1978) reported one containing a lizard in the genus *Bachia*, suggesting it forages in leaf litter; W. W. Lamar (personal communication) reports one containing the arboreal lizard *Tropidurus umbra,* and found captives feed on anoles.

Material: Trinidad—AMNH 98185 Arima Valley. FMNH 40443 Tucker Valley. USNM 227710 Arima Valley; 227711 St. George Co., Maracas Bay Rd., near milepost 2.

Spilotes pullatus pullatus (Linnaeus)

Map 101. Plates 157, 158.

Coluber pullatus Linnaeus, 1758:225. Type locality: Asia (in error). *Coluber variabili* Court, 1858:441. *Spilotes pullatus:* Reinhardt and Lutken, 1862:8.L. *Spilotes variabilis:* Mole and Urich, 1894b:509. *Spilotes pullatus ater:* Sternfield, 1920:185 (Tobago). *Spilotes pullatus pullatus:* Amaral, 1930a:157. *Spilotes p. pullatus:* DeVerteuil, 1968:101.

Common Names: "Clibo, or cribo noir" (DeVerteuil, 1858). The use of these names for this species suggests confusion with *Drymarchon corias.* Mole and Urich (1891) write, "There is a larger variety entirely black, which is known as the widow." This suggests confusion with *Clelia clelia.* "Tigre" (Mole and Urich, 1894a); "Tigre or tigro"

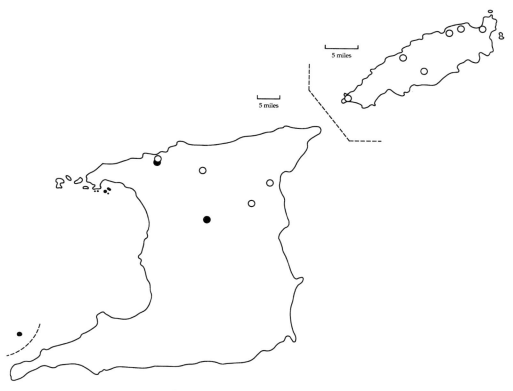

Map 101. *Spilotes pullatus pullatus*

(Mole, 1914); "rat snake, tiger snake, El Tigre, black and yellow rat snake" (Emsley, 1977).

Distribution: A widespread species, *S. pullatus* occurs from Tamaulipas, Mexico, through Central America to Argentina. *S. p. pullatus* ranges from Costa Rica and Panama to Paraguay and northern Argentina and Trinidad and Tobago. Published Trinidad localities include: Arima Valley (Beebe, 1952). Trinidad localities based upon museum material include: Maracas Bay Rd.; Maracas Falls; St. Michael Estate, St. George Co.; San Rafael; Sangre Grande; Vega de Oropouche at junction with Toco Rd. Field notes (JCM) report it at the 29 milepost on the Northside Rd. Published Tobago localities include: Milford Bay (Barbour, 1916b); and Mt. Dillon (Brongersma, 1956b). Tobago localities based upon museum material include: Anse Fourmi; Charlotteville; Hillsborough Dam; Man of War Bay; and Speyside.

Description: 1753 mm SVL, 558 mm damaged tail; tail 31–38% SVL; expected total length 3.6 m (Emsley, 1977); hatchlings about 250 mm total length. Rostral visible from above; nasal divided or semidivided; loreal usually present; one or two preoculars; no suboculars; one or two postoculars; six to eight supralabials; six to eight infralabials; 209–226 ventrals; anal plate single; the paired subcaudals number 116–129. First two rows of dorsal scales smooth, others keeled; dorsal scales in 16–18 rows at midbody, reduce to 10 posteriorly. Dorsum black-brown above with up to 14 yellow spots on anterior half of the body; these yellow spots may be greatly reduced or absent in Tobago specimens. Ven-

ter black-brown with some yellow ventrals on anterior half. Hardy (1982) considered the Tobago population to be distinctly melanistic compared to Trinidad and mainland populations; Tobago specimens have almost no yellow and may be mistaken for *Clelia* from a distance. It is the only Trinidad and Tobago snake with keeled scales in an even number of scale rows; this and the distinctive black and yellow pattern make this snake relatively easy to distinguish from all other snakes in the area.

Natural History: A diurnal, arboreal snake inhabiting forests and forest-edges; field notes (JCM) report three in old secondary growth, one in an open grassy area at forest-edge. Food includes mammals (mice, rats, and squirrels), birds and their eggs. Prey is killed by constriction (Mole, 1924); field notes (JCM) report mammal hair in one specimen. When approached it distends the neck and throat region with modified tracheal rings (Brongersma, 1957) to produce an impressive auditory and visual display. Mole (1924) observed an interspecific mating with *Pseustes*. In Brazil, Amaral (1930b) stated that 8–12 eggs are laid in early summer. Field notes (JCM) report a hatchling on 7 July. Urich (1931) considered the population of this species on Trinidad to have been reduced by the mongoose. Remains of two large individuals killed with a machete in the Arima Valley suggest local people are not tolerant of these large, harmless snakes (field notes RH, JCM, RS).

Material: Trinidad—FMNH 49996–49999 San Rafael; 215816, 219608 Arima Valley. MCZ 100501 Maracas Bay Rd.; 104404 Maracas Falls, St. Joseph Co.

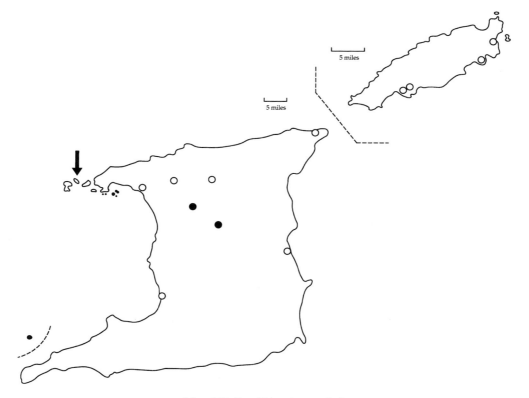

Map 102. *Tantilla melanocephala*

Tantilla melanocephala (Linnaeus)

Map 102. Plate 159.

> *Coluber melanocephalus* Linnaeus, 1758:218. Type locality: America. *Homalocranium melanocephalum:* Mole and Urich, 1894a:85. *Tantilla melanocephala:* Amaral, 1930a:221. *Tantilla melanocephalum:* Wehekind, 1955:12. *Tantilla melanocephala melanocephala:* Mertens, 1972:16.

Common Names: "Pink headed snake" (Wehekind, 1955); "blackhead" (Emsley, 1977).

Distribution: A widespread species, *T. melanocephala* ranges from Guatemala to Uruguay. Published Trinidad localities include: Port of Spain (Werner, 1899); Arima Valley (Beebe, 1952); SW of Caura on Tucuche Rd. (Brongersma, 1956b); Huevos Island (Emsley, 1977). Field notes (JCM) report it from the cocal at Manzanilla Bay. Trinidad localities based upon museum material include: Mt. Catherine, Piarco, Pointe-à-Pierre, Port of Spain, San Rafael, and Toco. Tobago localities based upon museum material include: Bacolet Guest House, Charlotteville, Roxborough, Scarborough, Speyside.

Description: 120 mm SVL; 34 mm tail; tail about 28% SVL; Roze (1966) reported it to reach 486 mm in total length. Rostral visible from above; nasal divided; loreal touches the orbit, preocular absent or fused with the loreal; no suboculars; two postoculars; seven supralabials; six infralabials; 143–151 ventrals; anal plate single; 48–59 paired subcaudals. Smooth dorsal scales in 15 rows at midbody, with no reduction posteriorly. Dorsum brown, with a black head and nape; pattern striped with a dark longitudinal line on the eighth scale row. Labials cream or white. Pattern and scale counts distinguish this species from other Trinidad and Tobago snakes. Venter white or cream. Snakes with which it may be superficially confused are *Atractus trilineatus* and *Atractus univittatus;* however, these species lack the black head and nape and have 32, or fewer, subcaudal scales.

Natural History: A nocturnal, terrestrial-fossorial snake of the forest floor; it hides in moist, shaded litter (Mole, 1924; Emsley, 1977); field notes (JCM) report it in coconut palm leaf litter at Manzanilla Bay. Food included centipedes and insects (Mole, 1924; Beebe, 1946; Wehekind, 1960). Most members of the genus produce a large number of ovarian eggs, but resorb most of them and produce clutches of 1–3 eggs (Fitch, 1970). Dixon and Soini (1977) found three oviductal eggs in Peruvian specimen.

Material: Trinidad—FMNH 40445 Piarco; 49970 San Rafael.

Thamnodynastes sp.

Map 103. Plate 160.

> *Thamnodynastes strigatus:* Boos, 1984a:3.

Comment: This undescribed species will be described by J. Bailey and R. Thomas with a revision of the genus.

Distribution: Coastal Suriname through eastern Venezuela (both uplands and the Orinoco Delta) and southwest Trinidad (J. Bailey, personal communication). This snake is a lowland Guiana endemic.

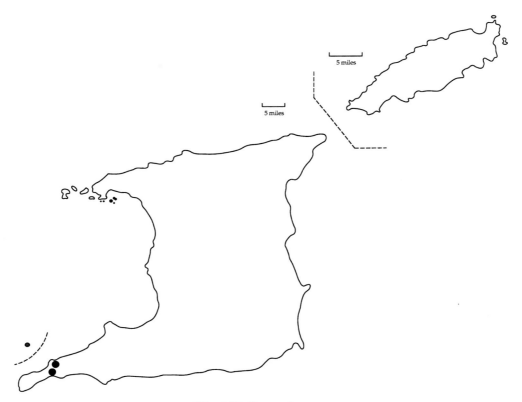

Map 103. *Thamnodynastes* sp.

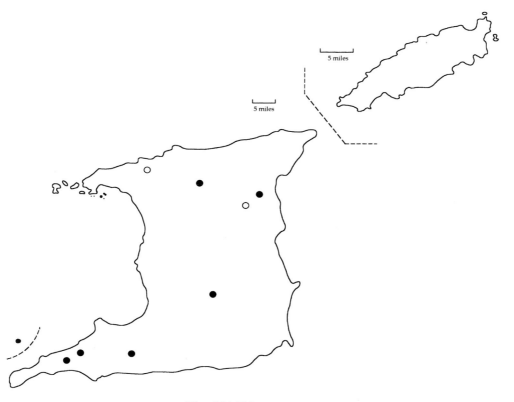

Map 104. *Tripanurgos compressus*

Identification: This information is based up *Thamnodynastes strigatus* which this species resembles. 403 mm SVL; tail 105 mm. Rostral barely visible from above; nasals entire; one preocular; two postoculars; two primary temporals; eight supralabials, with the fourth and fifth entering orbit; eight lower labials with the first four touching the anterior pair of chin shields; smooth dorsal scales in 19 rows at midbody, reduce to 17 posteriorly; ventrals 149; anal divided; paired subcaudals are expected to number 59–75. Dorsum brown-grey with light dorsolateral stripes and dark brown stripes; venter striped and flecked with small dark brown spots; a black postocular stripe. The only snake on the island of Trinidad with 19 rows of smooth scales, light colored dorsolateral stripes and a venter flecked with brown pigment.

Natural History: A poorly known snake. The known habitat is secondary forest and agriculture; most likely a semiaquatic species that eats frogs.

Material: Trinidad—FMNH 217230 just west of the 70 milepost on the Southern Main Rd. between Bonasse and Cedros. A second specimen collected 26 April 1984 at the intersection of the Southern Main Rd. and Cruel-Mandel Rd., near a bridge (not numbered). Both specimens are badly damaged. The latter was photographed along with the habitat, and the specimen is in collection of H. E. A. Boos.

Tripanurgos compressus (Daudin)

Map 104. Plates 111, 112.

Coluber compressus Daudin, 1803:247. Type locality: Suriname.
Trypanurgos compressus: Boulenger, 1896:58. *Tripanurgos compressus:* Underwood, 1962:179.

Common Names: "False false coral snake, pseudofalse coral snake" (Emsley, 1977).

Distribution: A widespread species with a disjunct range from Panama to Brazil. Published Trinidad localities: Forest Reserve at Sangre Grande (Mole, 1924). Museum material documents: Arima Valley; Brickfield; Valencia Rd. at the 7 milepost; the Southern Main Road at mileposts 63 and 69.5; at Quarry Rest House near Siparia; and Santa Cruz Valley. These locations suggest the species is widespread, and that it extends into the Northern Range to elevations of at least 300 m.

Description: 851 mm SVL; 272 mm tail; tail 32–34% SVL. Rostral visible from above; nasals divided; loreal single; one preocular, rarely two; no suboculars; two postoculars; seven to nine supralabials; eight or nine infralabials; 228–257 ventrals; anal plate single; 110–125 paired subcaudals. Smooth dorsal scales in 19 rows at midbody, reduce to 15 posteriorly; vertebral scale row enlarged. A red snake with about 45–50 black crossbands or alternating spots on the dorsum; head distinct from neck, a slender body compressed laterally. The dull red coloration makes this animal so distinctive it is difficult to confuse with any other species. *Oxyrhopus petola* has red and black bands, but lacks the enlarged vertebral scale row. Mole, (1924) reported this snake from Trinidad for the first time and wrote "The eyes are prominent, ruby-red, with elliptical pupils placed diagonally. Over the eyes and the muzzle there was a dark shade of brick-red. The hinder part of the head was a lighter hue. Two inches behind the head was a blotch of dark grey. The ground-colour of the remainder of the body was dull red." Young *Pseudoboa* are red but have single subcaudal scales and lack black crossbars; young *Clelia* are red but have a relatively short tail, fewer than 93 subcaudals, and lack black crossbars; both of these species lack the enlarged vertebral scales.

Natural History: A forest and forest-edge snake that is crepuscular and nocturnal, field notes (JCM) describe this snake active at dusk and very early in the morning (0600 hours) as well as at 2400 hours. The species is terrestrial and arboreal. Seven specimens observed, all but one were on the ground, the other climbing in a shrub. Emsley (1977) listed food as lizards and arthropods; in Ecuador, Duellman (1978) found a microteiid lizard in one specimen; field notes (JCM) record remains of a *Tropidurus plica* in a Trinidad specimen. Riley and Winch (1985b) found 12 eggs in the nest of the leaf-cutting ant *Atta cephalotes* on 1 May and suggested this represents two clutches laid by two different females, because the eggs fit into distinct size categories, six in each clutch; five eggs hatch between 6–8 May.

Material: Trinidad—FMNH 49972 Brickfield; 218771 Arima Valley; 21877, Valencia Rd. at the 7 milepost; 219593 on the Southern Main Rd. about the 63 milepost; 219594 near Siparia, at Quarry Rest House; 219595 on the Southern Main Rd. at about the 69.5 milepost.

Order Squamata: Suborder Serpentes
Family Elapidae: Front-fanged Snakes

Elapidae is comprised of about 240 species in 61 genera. This family includes cobras, mambas, kraits, and coral snakes, all of which have hollow, fixed front fangs for venom delivery. Most species are tropical, although some have invaded temperate latitudes; most species lay eggs in small numbers, and usually feed on ectothermic prey. Only two genera, *Micrurus* and *Micruroides,* occur in the terrestrial environments of the Western Hemisphere. Two species of coral snakes in the genus *Micrurus* occur on Trinidad. These are poisonous serpents and bites from these snakes can be life-threatening to humans.

Mole (1924) included the following anecdotes in his species account for *Elaps margravii* [= *Micrurus lemniscatus*]. They are cited here because DeVerteuil orginally considered only one coral snake to be present on the island, *Elaps coralinus.* The species responsible for the first anecdote is undoubtedly *M. lemniscatus,* based upon the length of 4 feet given in the account; there are no clues as to what species is involved in the second account. DeVerteuil (1858) cited two instances of human deaths caused by this species.

Casualties from the bite of the Coral snake (*Elaps corallinus*), must be very rare, since many persons even regard

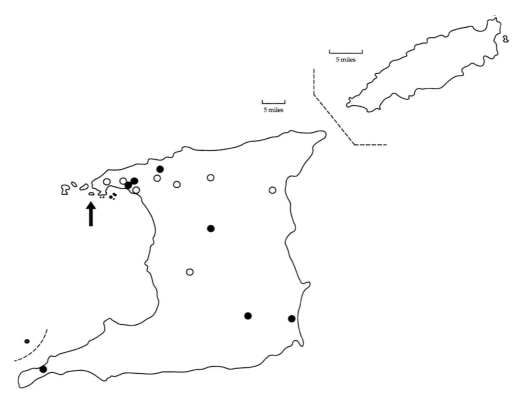

Map 105. *Micrurus circinalis*

it as perfectly innocuous: this opinion I myself entertained for a long time, and until I had too convincing a proof of the contrary in the death, within a few hours, of two robust African labourers. . . . These two men were at work in a cane field, on "La Marguerite" estate, in the ward of St. Joseph; having discovered a coral snake, they laid hold of it by way of amusement. Of the warning given by their fellow-labourers they took no notice, but, on the contrary, continued to tease the reptile, and even put its head into their mouths. They were both bitten, one on the lip and the other on the tongue; this happened about 1 P.M. The one who had apparently most irritated the snake, soon began to reel about like a drunken man, and was next taken with convulsions; he died abouth eight o'clock, and the other about nine, the same day. This coral has been preserved by Dr. Court, and measures four feet and a half.

Mole (1924) reported another case,

The Hon. Albert Carr relates a more recent incident. At Brasso Caparo a . . . man, heavily loaded with cacao, stepped into a drain and then onto the road. In the drain, he trod on and was bitten by a Coral. The injury was on the thin skin between the toes. Mr. Carr did not see the victim until many hours after the occurrence, when remedies were too late to be of any use. The man died the next morning.

Micrurus circinalis (Duméril, Bibron and Duméril)

Map 105. Plate 163.

Elaps circinalis Duméril, Bibron and Duméril, 1854, 7:1210. Type locality: Martinique (in error); Roze (1989) restricted the type locality to Trinidad, West Indies, he selected MNHN 3912, a female from an unknown locality as the lectotype; and noted that other two syntypes of *Elaps circinalis* that still exist in the Paris Museum do not belong to this species. *Elaps corallinus:* Court, 1858:441. *Elaps corallinus* var. *E. Riisei:* Reinhardt and Lutken, 1862:6. *Elaps riisei:* Garman, 1887c:285. *Micrurus (Elaps) micrurus:* Field, 1942:40. *Micrurus corallinus:* Wehekind, 1955:12. *Micrurus circinalis:* Schmidt, 1936:192. *Micrurus psyches circinalis:* Roze, 1967:40. *Micrurus psyches psyches:* Lancini, 1979: 189 (photo on p. 190–191) (in error).

Comment: Campbell and Lamar (1989) suggested that the populations now considered to be *Micrurus psyches* probably include several biological species not currently recognized, Roze (1994) reestablished *M. circinalis* as a full species.

Common Names: "Coral snake, Serpent-Corail and Corail" (Mole, 1924). Mole (1924) wrote,

Here it would be as well to remark on the word "Coral" that the writer has been informed that as applied to this snake and the next. "Coral" is the corruption of the Spanish word "Corro," meaning a ring. This is a good description of these creatures, which are girdled with red, black, and white rings. When referring to the colour of a snake—that is, a coral-tinted serpent: a young *Oxyrhopus coronatus,* [= *Pseudoboa neuweidii*] for instance, the South American

Spaniards say "Corallile." The Trinidad peasant, who loves to clip his words as much as possible, with much ease abbreviates this to "Coral," imagining that the red is the distinctive marking, and not the rings, and thus in referring to these ringed venomous serpents the significance of a most expressive descriptive word is lost. Moreover, the country people of the colony consider that the difference in the arrangement of the colors of this and the next species indicates the sexes, the present one being the "male."

Distribution: *M. circinalis* is restricted to Trinidad and adjacent mainland Venezuela, a Caribbean Coastal Range distribution. Published Trinidad localities include: Arima Valley (Beebe, 1952); Gaspar Grande Island (Boos, 1984d). Localities based upon museum material include: St. Augustine; San Rafael; Maracas Valley; the Microbiological Institute, St. Clair; Marval; San Juan; Botanic Gardens, Port of Spain; near Matura; 1 mile south of Rio Claro on Guayaguayare Rd.; Mt. St. Benedict; on the western edge of Cedros; St. Ann; Champs Fleurs; Tucker Valley; Caura; Petit Valley, Diego Martin; Brasso; Mayaro Beach; and Gasparee Island off the northwest peninsula.

Description: 494 mm SVL, tail 49 mm; tails of males 15–19% SVL, tails of females 9–10% SVL; total expected length 800 mm. Head small, about same width as neck. Rostral visible from above; nasal divided; one preocular; two postoculars; seven supralabials; seven infralabials; males 174–193 ventrals; females have 194–209 ventrals; anal plate divided; males with 40–50 subcaudals that are usually paired; females with 30–35 subcaudals that are usually paired. Smooth dorsal scales in 15 rows. Black rings complete and number 21–31; black rings edged with yellow and separated by long red interspaces. Female's tail with 5–8 black rings, male's tail with 8–12 black rings. Tail coloration is predominately black with some narrow white bands separating the black rings. All red and white scales are tipped with black. It can be readily distinguished from the other coral snake *Micrurus lemniscatus diutius* because of the very short white rings, usually less than one middorsal scale in length. Similarly, it can be readily distinguished from *Oxyrhopus* because the latter lacks white or yellow markings on Trinidad. The absence of a loreal will readily distinguish it from all the banded colubrids on Trinidad except *Hydrops,* which has black and red-purple bands of about equal widths.

Natural History: A snake of forest and savanna. Campbell and Lamar (1989) describe the habitat for this species as lower montane wet forest and lowland rainforest. Boos and Quesnel (1986) wrote, ". . . often found in gardens in the middle of town and it possibly gets there in loads of manure and compost that are brought in from the country for use as fertilizer." Emsley (1977) described the habitat as ". . . burrowing in soil and under forest litter." Field notes (JCM) describe one in primary rainforest, one in old secondary growth forest, and two in agricultural areas (one very near an occupied house). Emsley (1977) stated, ". . . at higher altitudes in the hills they become less common and seem to be replaced

by *M. lemniscatus.*" Field notes (JCM) report one in a lowland agricultural situation within 20 m of a large specimen of *M. lemniscatus;* and this species was seen at elevations above 300 m, where *M. lemniscatus* also occurs; thus, these snakes are not separated by altitude. Mole and Urich (1894b), Mole (1924), and Emsley (1977) report this snake feeding on *Atractus.* Stomach contents of three specimens (11 were empty) include: one *Atractus trilineatus,* one with unidentified snake scales, and one containing *Ninia atrata,* the lizard *Bachia heteropa,* and a dipterous fly larva. Mole (1924) observed copulation in January, and reported a clutch of two eggs laid in July. Emsley (1977) reported copulation from January to May, with two to six eggs laid from July to September. Field notes (JCM) report two females containing three and four eggs. Wehekind (1955) described predation by the larger coral snake *M. lemniscatus;* ffrench (in Quesnel, 1986) described predation by the marine toad *Bufo marinus.*

Material: Trinidad—FMNH 49963–4, 190746 no data; 75958–60 St. Ann's Port of Spain; 75951 Maracas Valley; 75953, 75956 Marval; 215820 1 mi south of Rio Claro on Guayaguayare Rd.; 219589 at the 72.75 milepost of the Southern Main Rd., on edge of Cedros; 75952 Port of Spain, Microbiological Inst.; 75954 Port of Spain, Botanic Gardens; 75955 San Juan; 49962 San Rafael; 41682 St. Augustine.

Micrurus lemniscatus diutius Burger

Map 106. Plate 164.

Elaps lemniscatus: Gunther, 1858:234. *Elaps marcgravii:* Boettger, 1898:126. *Micrurus lemniscatus:* Beebe, 1919:216. *Elaps marcgravi:* Roux, 1926:292. *Micrurus lemniscratus* [*sic*]: Wehekind, 1955:12. *Micrurus lemniscatus diutius* Burger, 1955:40. Type locality: Tunapuna, Trinidad.

Common Names: "Coral Snake (female), Corail" (Mole, 1914), "Large coral" (Emsley, 1977). See comments in the "Common Names" section for *Micrurus circinalis.*

Distribution: *M. lemniscatus* has an Amazonian distribution, occurring from Trinidad, eastern Venezuela, and the Guianas to the Amazon Basin. *M. l. diutius* inhabits Trinidad, eastern Venezuela, and the Guianas; and is a lowland Guiana endemic. On Trinidad it is widespread. Published Trinidad localities include: Port of Spain (Werner, 1900); and Arima Valley (Beebe, 1952). Couva; La Marguerite Estate, Ward of St. Joseph; Caparo; Brasso; and Port of Spain (Mole, 1924). Field notes (JCM) list: south of Rio Claro on Guayaguayare Road. Museum material supports the following localities: Tunapuna; Diego Martin; Braemer Rd., Port of Spain; Sangre Grande; Rio Grande Rd. 5 mi from Sangre Grande; Cedros; vicinity of Cheeyou; on Valencia Rd., about 3.8 km west of junction with Toco Rd.; St. Ann's River, St. Ann; Tucker Valley; Waller Field; Simla, Arima Valley.

Description: 1100 mm SVL; 100 mm tail; tail 6.8–9.8% SVL. Snout blunt and rounded; rostral visible from above; nasal divided; loreal absent; six or seven supralabials; six or seven infralabials; one preocular; two postoculars; 216–236

Map 106. *Micrurus lemniscatus diutius*

ventrals; and 25–35 paired (usually) subcaudals. Dorsal scales are smooth and in 15 rows. A very distinctive snake with bright, bold colored rings. Black rings in 7–13 triads, groups of three black rings each separated by a white or yellow ring form a single triad; each triad separated by a wide red ring. Tip of nose black followed by a white preocular ring, followed by a red collar. *M. circinalis* lacks the triad pattern and has large red rings separated by short black bands. Each of these black bands is outlined by a very short white ring. *Oxyrhopus petola* in Trinidad has a black and red pattern without white. The ringed pattern of *Hydrops* consists of numerous rings of black separated by red or orange rings that are about equal in length. Distinguishing this coral snake from its colubrid mimics (or models), *Erythrolamprus aesculapii* and *E. bizona,* at a distance is not possible; *Erythrolamprus* have a loreal scale, the coral snake lacks it and *Erythrolamprus* has paired black annuli. Only two specimens of the mimics have been found on Trinidad, and caution is always the best approach when collecting coral snakes.

Natural History: A snake of forests and savannas, that frequents bodies of water; widely distributed on Trinidad at elevations below 300 m. Field notes (JCM) describe seven of these snakes encountered at night in disturbed areas: one in a wet, grassy area along the roadside in front of a house; one in a secondary forest clearing on a rock wall; five were taken off the road in secondary forests, and agricultural areas. Mole and Urich (1894b) reported them in sugar estates and cacao plantations, and nocturnal in habits; in Venezuela,

Beebe (1946) observed them active on overcast days. Mole and Urich (1894b) described captives feeding on the snakes *Liophis melanotus* and *Mastigodryas boddaerti.* Schmidt (1957) found *Synbranchus* eels in their stomachs. Field notes (JCM) report a 1100 mm SVL female containing two eggs, 15 x 20 mm, collected on 5 July.

Material: Trinidad—FMNH 34472 Tunapuna (type specimen); 75949 Diego Martin; 75950 Braemer Rd., Port of Spain; 75957 Sangre Grande; 77897 Rio Grande Rd., 5 miles from Sangre Grande; 77898 Southern Main Rd., Cedros; 217240, 219607 Arima Valley; 219619 on Valencia Rd. 3.8 km west of the junction with Toco Rd.

Order Squamata: Suborder Serpentes
Family Leptotyphlopidae: Thread Snakes

Leptotyphlopidae has two genera containing about 78 species. The family is distributed in the Neotropics with some species invading North America and the West Indies. It is also represented in Africa and western Asia. These are small, slender, burrowing snakes with teeth in the lower jaw only. They are frequently associated with ants and termites, which they feed on, and are not capable of biting a human. One species of *Leptotyphlops* inhabits Trinidad and possibly occurs on Tobago. Of the species found on Trinidad DeVerteuil (1858) writes, ". . . another smaller one, provided with a sting at the end of the tail, may possibly be the *Stenostoma Albifrons* of Duméril." The probing action of the tail may startle a human handling this animal, but no known snake species has a tail capable of producing a sting.

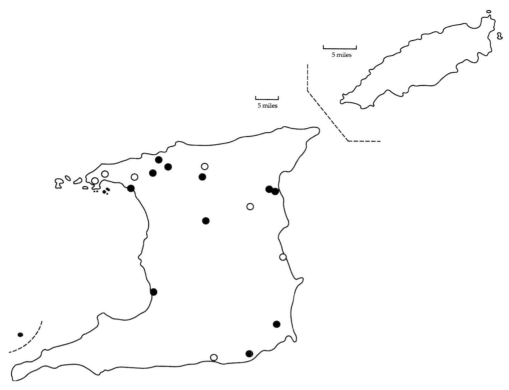

Map 107. *Leptotyphlops albifrons*

Leptotyphlops albifrons (Wagler)

Map 107. Plate 165. Figure F.

> *Stenostoma albifrons* Wagler, 1824:68. *Stenostoma albifrons:* Garman, 1887c:278. *Glauconia albifrons:* Boulenger, 1893, vol. 1:63. *Leptotyphlops albifrons:* Barbour, 1916a:441. *Leptotyphlops tenella* Klauber, 1939:59. Type locality: Kartabo, Guyana. *L. a. tenella:* Roze, 1952a:156. *L. albifrons:* Winstel, 1984b:9.

Comment: The name of the Trinidad population of this snake has been in dispute. Here I follow Hoogmoed and Gruber (1983) in assigning it to *L. albifrons* instead of Klauber's *L. tenella.*

Common Names: "Worm snake, Ground Puppy" (Boos and Quesnel, 1968:15) "White-faced worm snake" (DeVerteuil, 1968), "Blind snake" (Emsley, 1977).

Distribution: Trinidad, the Guianas, and the Amazon basin, it is categorized here as an Amazonian species. Its presence on Tobago is undocumented to date. Woodcock's (1867) *History of Tobago* contains the following statement, "It is a curious fact that a snake is almost always found an inhabitant with the ants in their nest, apparently dwelling with them in perfect harmony." This statement may refer to *Leptotyphlops* or it may refer to *Typhlops trinitatus* which superficially resemble each other; both may be associated with ants and termites. DeVerteuil (1968) includes it in his Tobago herpetofaunal list, as does Mertens (1972). However, Hardy (1982) has pointed out, there are apparently no known specimens of this snake from Tobago, and this investigation has not produced additional information on this point. Pub-

lished Trinidad localities include: Arima Valley (Beebe, 1952); Moruga (Quesnel, 1980). On Trinidad it is known from the following locations based upon museum material: Arima Valley, numerous localities; Mt. St. Benedict; Chaguaramas; Guayaguayare Forest; Maracas Rd. in St. Joseph; Manzanilla Bay Road; Matura Bay; Melajo Forest, Sangre Grande; Morne Bleu Ridge; Pointe-à-Pierre; Port of Spain—Bayshore and Marval; San Rafael; Trinity Hills Forest Reserve; Mt. Tucuche; Tucker Valley; Vega de Oropouche Road.

Barbour (1930b) stated, "This tiny burrowing snake has an erratic distribution and has probably been carried about by primitive man, being occasionally introduced with material intended for garden planting." This may account for the single, questionable record of this species from Antigua in the Lesser Antilles (see Schwartz and Henderson, 1991.)

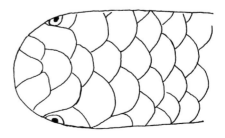

Figure F

Description: 185 mm SVL; tail 12 mm; tail extremely short 5.6–6.3% SVL; it may reach 275 mm TL (Roze, 1966). Head no wider than neck. Eyes large, in ocular shield that extends downward to form the fifth labial scale. Nostrils located on a scale forming the second labial. Scale rows at midbody number 14, and form 219–229 transverse rows. Ventrals not enlarged, same size as dorsal scales. Tail ends in a sharply pointed scale; 15–20 subcaudal scales. Mole (1924) described this snake as looking like it is made from polished steel. Each scale row has a stripe, the dorsal and lateral stripes are dark, the ventral stripes are lighter in color; there are seven dark stripes and seven light stripes. Head and tail with central yellow spots, thereby making it difficult to distinguish head from tail at first glance. Hoogmoed and Gruber (1983) wrote ". . . large round eyes not covered by skin, the large pentagonal ocular scales not covered with pits, the quadrangular yellow (white) spot on the tip of the snout, the yellow-tipped tail and the dorsal pattern of wide blackish brown longitudinal stripes separated by narrow, light zig-zag lines. . . . can be found in one eastern Amazonian species. . . . *L. albifrons*." The color pattern, shiny appearance, and lack of specialized enlarged ventrals will readily separate this snake from all other Trinidad and Tobago snakes except *L. goudotii*, (should it be found to be present on Trinidad.) *L. albifrons* can be distinguished from this species by having the supraocular extending in front of the eye and in contact with the supralabials; *L. goudotii* does not exhibit this condition, but almost all Trinidad *L. albifrons* do (one specimen I have seen lacks this on one side of the head). It may be confused superficially with *T. trinitatus* (both have yellow spots on head and tail), but the number of scales around the body will distinguish it (*T. trinitatus* has 20 scale rows.) *T. brongersmianus* has a different pattern, and a much thicker body diameter, and has 20 scales around the body. And, the anomalepid has yellow spots on head and tail but has 18 scale rows around midbody.

Natural History: A fossorial snake using forest and savanna macrohabits. Field notes (JCM) report this snake in and around buildings in the Arima Valley, and one specimen was climbing on a rock wall. Wehekind (1960) stated it is frequently found in Port of Spain gardens. Boos and Quesnel (1968) described the habitat as ". . . under rocks and fallen logs, and also under the loose bark of trees where it ventures to lay its eggs and to find food." Mole (1924) described taking one from a termite nest and having it vomit termites. Wehekind (1960) reported that it feeds on ants, termites, and millipedes (the latter seems improbable). Boos and Quesnel (1968) listed eggs of insects, as well as termites. Emsley (1977) found ants of the genera *Atta* and *Acromyremex* in the stomachs of these snakes. Watkins et al. (1967) described North America *Leptotyphlops* using pheromone trails laid down by ants to locate ant nests. Field notes (JCM) describe a specimen trailing an ant column next to a building, in a secondary forest clearing and a second specimen collected in a kitchen where ants were abundant. When handled the snake probes with the sharp pointed scale on the tip of the tail, and the stinglike sensation may startle a predator; it will also release an odorous musk when annoyed (field notes JCM; Boos and Quesnel, 1968).

Material: Trinidad—FMNH 42721–2 no data; 69769 Fishing Pond; 217237–8, 217238 Arima Valley; 190745, 200292 Port of Spain; 49914 San Rafael. MCZ 28208 Maracas Rd., St. Joseph; 32520 Mt. Tucuche; 38660 Trinity Hills Forest Reserve; 48774 Mt. St. Benedict; 49064 Pointe-à-Pierre; 60801 Guayaguayare Forest; 96538–9 Matura Bay; 160087 Manzanilla Bay.

Order Squamata: Suborder Serpentes
Family Typhlopidae: Typical Blind Snakes

The Typhlopidae includes one to three genera depending on whose classification is used, containing about 170 species. They have teeth only in the upper jaw and are small slender snakes not capable of biting a human. Like the leptotyphlopids they tend to be associated with ants and termites, which they feed upon. *Typhlops* is pantropical, excluding Australia. At least 10 species occur in continental South America, and another 22 species occur in the West Indies. Two species are known from Trinidad and one of these occurs on Tobago. Both are more closely related to the mainland forms, as opposed to the species inhabiting the West Indies.

Typhlops brongersmianus Vanzolini

Map 108. Plate 166. Figure G.

Typhlops reticulatus: Mole and Urich, 1894a:82. *Typhlops* sp.: Underwood, 1962:179. *Typhlops brongersmai* Vanzolini, 1972a:27. Type locality: Baira de Itaipe, Ilheus, Bahia, Brazil. *Typhlops brongersmianus*—Vanzolini, 1976:247 (replacement name for *brongersmai*).

Common Names: "Blind snake, worm snake, reticulated worm snake" (Emsley, 1977).

Distribution: An Amazonian species, ranging from Colombia, Venezuela, the Guianas, and Brazil, southward to Argentina and Paraguay (Dixon and Hendricks, 1979). Emsley (1977) noted the locality of two specimens from Trinidad as Tucker Valley in the northwest peninsula of Trinidad. USNM 227713 documents Waller Field, Aripo Savanna as a locality.

Description: 285 mm SVL; tail 6 mm; tail 2.1% SVL; a total length 325 mm has been reported by Dixon and Hendricks (1979). Rostral visible from above; nasals large and semi-divided; four supralabials; eyes distinct but under ocular shields. Scales around body number 20, reduce to 19 or 18 posteriorly; dorsal scales from rostral to tail spine range

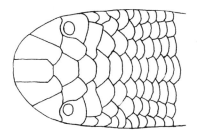

Figure G

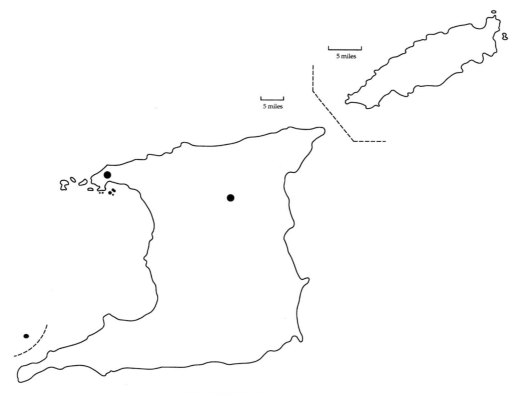

Map 108. *Typhlops brongersmianus*

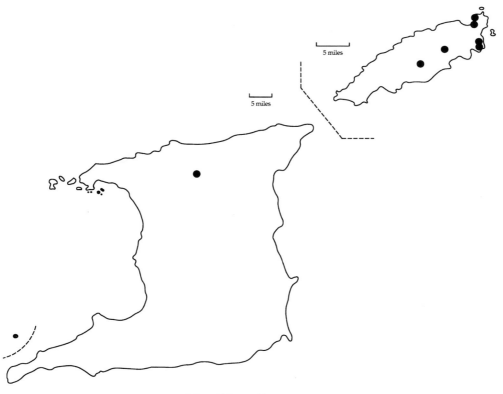

Map 109. *Typhlops trinitatus*

from 195 to 287 (average 233.1) as reported by Dixon and Hendricks (1979). However they note the Trinidad population, as well as some of the mainland populations to the south and east are characterized with low numbers of dorsals. Subcaudals 8–14 (average 10.6). Tail wider than long, ending in a conical spine. This snake resembles a cigar in shape and color, making it easy to identify. Its congener, *T. trinitatus*, has a striped pattern with yellow blotches at each end, making it similar in appearance to *Leptotyphlops albifrons*. This species has three light spots on the head, a large central spot and a smaller one on each side. Eleven dorsal scale rows with yellow-brown or red-brown pigment, snout may be streaked with dark brown that forms fan-shaped spots; nine ventral scale rows are yellow or pink.

Natural History: This species inhabits rainforest leaf litter and soils. Emsley (1977) described this snake as, "Subterranean, burrowing in damp soil, humus and rotting vegetation. . . . Nocturnal and very secretive, the poorly developed eyes cannot form an image but can detect changes in light intensity." Wehekind (1960) reported it in the nests of ground ants and termites, and under stones, compost heaps and roots; and that it feeds on insects and termites. Emsley (1977) stated they probably feed on termites and bachac (leaf-cutter) ants. Notes (JCM) describe one specimen palped (AMNH 64467) containing seven or eight eggs.

Material: Trinidad—AMNH 64467, 101343 Tucker Valley. USNM 227713 Waller Field, Aripo Savanna.

Typhlops trinitatus Richmond

Map 109. Plate 167. Figure H.

Typhlops trinitatus Richmond, 1965:121. Type locality: Trinidad, in log beside Arima road, 3 mi above Simla. *Typhlops* cf. *lehneri:* Emsley, 1963:577. *Typhlops lehneri:* Emsley, 1977:232.

Common Name: "Lineated worm snake" (Emsley, 1977).

Distribution: *T. trinitatus* is known only from the islands of Trinidad and Tobago. It is probably best considered a Venezuelan Coastal Range form, and may eventually be found on the mainland. On Trinidad this species is known only from the type locality in the Arima Valley. On Tobago museum material documents Roxborough-Parlatuvier Rd. at the 6.4 milepost; Kings Bay at dam on Kings Bay River; Pirate Cove, Charlotteville; Merchison; and Hillsborough Dam.

Description: 237 mm SVL; tail 3 mm; tail 1.2% SVL. Snout projects over the mouth; small, single preocular in contact with second and third labials; nasal divided; dorsal scales from rostral to tail spine number 388–389; subcaudals in 10 rows; 20 scale rows around midbody. Third and fourth labials similar in size; both taller than long; ocular scale small. Pattern of 11–13 dark brown stripes; the yellow head and tail spots make it difficult to distinguish one end from the other. It superficially resembles *Leptotyphlops albifrons* which has 14 scales around the body. *Typhlops brongersmianus* has a larger diameter body, the pattern is not striped, and it has a complete nasal cleft. The undescribed anomale-

pidid also has a yellow tipped head and tail, but has 18 scale rows at midbody.

Natural History: Probably a forest and forest-edge species. "Likely to be found in rotting logs, leaf litter and loose soil where they probably feed on insects" (Emsley, 1977). May be associated with ants or termites.

Material: Trinidad—AMNH 89870 Holotype. Tobago—MCZ 55670; USNM 228131–7.

Order Squamata: Suborder Serpentes Family Viperidae: Vipers

The vipers inhabit every continent except Antarctica and Australia, and while most species are tropical, some are quite successful in cold temperate latitudes. There are 14 genera and about 187 species. Vipers tend to be stout, short-tailed snakes with numerous heavily keeled scales. They have folding, front fangs connected to a venom gland and many are dangerously venomous to humans. All Western Hemisphere vipers are in the subfamily Crotalinae, and possess an infrared (heat) sensing pit located between the eye and the nostril, usually associated with the labial scale. The pit is a sense organ used to locate prey and direct the feeding strike. Two species representing two genera occur on Trinidad; none is known from Tobago.

Remedies for the bites of these snakes on Trinidad are mentioned by DeVerteuil (1858):

Although venomous serpents are numerous and common in Trinidad, accidents arising from their bite are of rare occurrence, either because the Mapepire and the Cascabel (*Crotalus mutus,* and *Trigonocephalus Tararaca* [*sic*.]) [*Lachesis muta* and *Bothrops asper* respectively] being very sluggish, are easily avoided, or even do not attack or inflict wounds, except on their being disturbed in the enjoyment of repose; or again, because those who are more exposed to their encounter, such as sportsmen, are in the possession of good antidotes. The guaco, however, and the roots of the manaco palm—both rather common plants—are the favourite remedy for the bite of serpents. Dogs, in the woods, as also horses and mules, in the underbrush, are common victims of the Cascabel and Mapepire.

Cooper and Bacon (1981), noted that the plant reideparel, *Rauwolfia ligustrina* (Apocynaceae), is reputed to be useful for snakebites and scorpion stings, and that it contains reserpine-

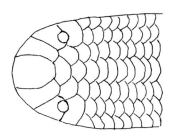

Figure H

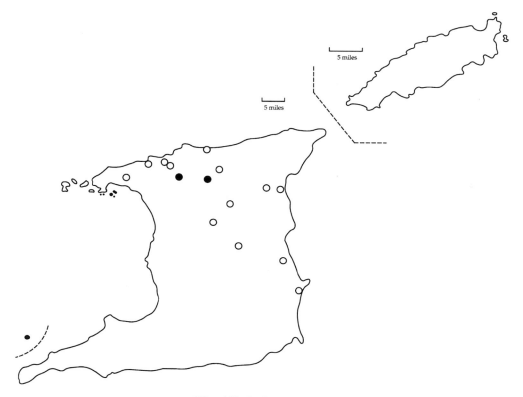

Map 110. *Bothrops asper*

like tranquilizer alkaloids. They also report the use of the bitter cassava tuber, *Manihot esculenta* (Euphorbiaceae), as an antidote for snakebite; the plant is known to contain cyanide. None of these are likely to be useful in treating envenomation from a poisonous snake.

Bell (1889) stated, "In Trinidad, not only is the rattlesnake anything but a rare sight . . ." and then described going through the inventory used by a sorcerer, or Obeah man [on Grenada], "In a little tin canister I found the most valuable of the sorcerer's stock, namely, seven bones belonging to a rattlesnake's tail—these I have known sell for five dollars each, so highly valued are they as amulets or charms . . ." There are no rattlesnakes known to occur on Trinidad or Grenada. The confusion may have resulted from the use of the common name "cascabel" which is applied to tropical rattlesnakes on the mainland but to the boid *Corallus hortulana* on Trinidad. *Crotalus* and *Bothrops* are both absent from Grenada, and *Crotalus* is not present on Trinidad or Tobago, but does occur on Venezula's Península de Paria.

Bothrops asper Garman

Map 110. Plates 168, 169.

Trigonocephalus asper var, n.c. *lanceolati* Garman, 1884 Bull. Mus. Comp. Zool. 8:124. Type locality: Opispo, Isthmus of Darien, Panama. *Trigonocephalus jacaraca:* Court, 1858:441. *Bothrops lanceolatus:* Cope, 1879:276. *Lachesis lanceolata:* Boettger, 1898:137. *Bothrops atrox:* Mole and Urich, 1894a:87. *Lachesis atrox:* Mole, 1924:271. *Bothrops atrox atrox:* Beebe, 1952:175. *Bothrops asper:* Campbell and Lamar, 1989:250.

Comment: Campbell and Lamar (1989) wrote, "*Bothrops asper* also appears to be the species . . . occurring on Trinidad, but the situation there is complicated owing to its proximity to the Orinoco Delta, a region where *B. asper* and *B. atrox* may be sympatric." In reading their species accounts and keys, it is apparent that the only external morphological characters identified to date that distinguish *B. asper* from *B. atrox* are the presence of a light stripe dorsal to the postorbital bar and the length of the keels on the scales. This suggests the systematics of the two species and related species are confused and are in need of clarification. Considering the medical importance of these snakes this is more than a academically interesting question. The arrangement of Campbell and Lamar is followed here.

Common Names: Joseph (1838) gave names for three pit vipers on Trinidad, and uses the names "Cascabelle" and "Mapapero" in addition to the common name for *Lachesis*. Undoubtedly the first two names can be applied to this species. DeVerteuil (1858) lists the common name of this species as "Cascabel." Mole and Urich (1894b) stated that it is called "Mapepire Balsain," which is said to mean striped. They also stated that at some localities it is called "Valsain" which they suggest means dancing (from the French), because of the circling motion exhibited during defense behavior. Lindblad (1966) suggested that balsain means basin, and that the name applies to the damp places with small runnels that the snake is reputed to prefer. Mole (1924) added "Mapepire Barcin" as a local name, and notes that the young are called "Rabo Frito." In Mole's 1924 account he uses the name "Fer de Lance." It would appear that "Balsain," "Valsain," and "Barcin" are all phonetically derived from the same root.

Distribution: The *B. asper* is widespread and trans-Andean. It ranges from Yucatan southward through Middle America to the Pacific versant of Colombia and Ecuador and across northern Venezuela to the Orinoco River and occurs on Trinidad. Published Trinidad localities include: Arima Valley (Beebe, 1952); Mt. Aripo (Ditmars and Bridges, 1935; Lindblad, 1966); Blanchisseuse Reserve (Brongersma, 1956b); Bush-bush Island, Narvia Swamp (Worth, 1967); Caparo River (Mole, 1924); and Aripo Savannas (Schwab, 1988). Field notes (JCM) describe a specimen within 10 m of the summit of Mt. Tucuche, an elevation of almost 1000 m; on Valencia Road, between Valenica and Toco Road; and on Toco Road between its junctions with Valencia Road and Vega de Oropuche Road. Trinidad museum material adds the following localities: Arima Valley (numerous localities); near milepost 3 on Heights of Aripo Road; Diego Martin; Lopinot; Coast Road above La Vache Bay; St. Joseph, Maracas Valley; eastern slope of Tamana Hill; Port of Spain; San Rafael.

Description: Campbell and Lamar (1989) reported it may exceed a total length of 2500 mm. The largest specimen measured in this study was 1390 mm SVL; tail 200 mm; tail 13–17% SVL; a specimen exceeding 1500 mm SVL observed, but not measured; smallest measured 140 mm SVL, probable size at birth. Rostral quadrangular and barely visible from above; nasals lateral, divided; nostrils open posterior-lateral; nasals separated by two internasals which overlap from the dorsal to lateral face. Scales on crown small, overlapping and keeled. Supraoculars with an outer lateral ridge and, separated by seven to nine small scales. Two or three preoculars, one to three suboculars; two to four postoculars. Labial pit surrounded by three or four scales; upper labials number six to eight, the fourth or fifth is the largest, the third and fourth or just the fourth is under the orbit but separated from it by the suboculars and other rows of small scales; lower labials number 8–11 and the first three are in contact with the first pair of chin shields. The first pair of chin shields are larger; the second pair are separated by a small pair of scales; gulars number four or five. Dorsal scales at midbody number 23, 25, or 27 rows; they are heavily keeled, elongated, and overlapping. The normal looking keels will distinguish it from *L. muta* with conical keels on the mid-dorsal scales. Ventrals number 201–212; subcaudals paired and number 57–68. Anal plate is single. A dark postocular streak present with some individuals having a light margin above the dark streak. Dorsum has 19–23 dark rhomboidal or triangular blotches outlined in white or yellow. Venter mottled with yellow and black-brown. Venter at base of the tail is similar to the body venter; distal portion mostly yellow. In juveniles the tail tip is yellow above.

Natural History: A snake of forest and savanna; micro-habitats include swamps, bushes, muddy stream banks, forested stream banks, rocky gullies, and human habitations in rural areas (DeVerteuil, 1858; Mole and Urich, 1894b; Mole, 1924; Ditmars and Bridges, 1937; Boos and Quesnel, 1968; Emsley, 1977). Field notes (JCM) describe habitats as: front yards of human dwellings, agricultural areas, secondary forests and primary forests of the upper elevations of the Northern Range; none of these specimens was directly associated with a stream or other body of water. Climbing in bushes is noted by Mole and Urich (1894b); field notes (JCM) report one specimen crawled 2 meters to a small tree trunk and immediately ascended the tree; and a specimen within 10 meters of the summit of Mt. Tucuche was basking at 0630 h, lying on top of a bank of ferns, about 1 meter above the ground.

Mole also reported the species feeding on wood rats, mice, and frogs. Food includes small mammals, lizards, frogs, birds, and crayfish (Emsley, 1977); Mole (1924) cited a story by A. B. Carr examining a decapitated 61-inch specimen containing a "Manicou Cros Yeux" (*Didelphis marsupialis*) oppossum. Field notes (JCM) describe one specimen containing the remains of the snake *Ninia atrata,* suggesting that this pit viper forages, at least sometimes, in the leaf litter.

Emsley (1977) recorded copulation in May, June, and July and gave the litter size as 12. Mole (1924) observed young are born between September and January, and lists litters of 29, 30, 32, and 56. He also described caudal luring, observing a young snake luring the frog *Mannophryne trinitatis* close enough to grasp. All of the young observed (three specimens) in this study had yellow tail-tips.

Mole and Urich (1894b) and Mole (1924) reported venom "spitting," the latter report is more extensive and is quoted here.

Rough usage, sudden movements, and teasing will work the Fer de Lance into a perfect fury. He will strike at his aggressors again and again, and each time he does so he will spread wide his gaping jaws and extend his formidable teeth. If he is in good condition and has not used his venom for some time, and the poison-fangs are full, he will even send tiny jets of poison from his perforated teeth to a considerable distance. On one occasion, says Mr. Carr, the venom thus ejected struck the face of a woman who was watching the proceedings from a distance of twelve feet. I myself have seen one throw fine jets a distance of at least six feet . . .

Recent reviews (Greene, 1988) of antipredator mechanisms in snakes have overlooked or dismissed this account. Klauber (1972) discusses rattlesnake's spitting venom and concludes that they do not normally do so, but that saliva may be ejected during a defense display, and that a snake with an injured mouth may spray venom. Mole's account is quite specific and his observations, and those of Carr, on snake habits tend to be accurate. It seems unlikely that this is a regular defense strategy of *B. asper,* but this species may be capable of this behavior under some conditions (e.g., mouth injuries or extreme stress).

Map 111. *Lachesis muta muta*

Field notes (JCM, MM) describe a specimen on the road in the lower Arima Valley trying to avoid capture by crawling forward then turning to face the collectors. It then leaped about 0.8 m off the pavement and at least 1 meter forward. The snake was less than 1 meter in length. It was placed in a bag, and found dead the following morning, apparently hit by a car before it was collected.

Mole (1924) described placing a *B. asper* in a cage with a South American rattlesnake. The *B. asper* apparently bit the rattlesnake and killed it. He also recounted two specimens of *B. asper* biting each other, both recovered but one exhibited some swelling; both were quiescent after the injuries. One of the snakes was a gravid female that gave birth to a litter of 27, and all but one were dead upon birth. Mole suggested they died because of the envenomation of the female.

Mole and Urich (1894b) noted that this species suffers from large parasitic worms in their lungs; field notes (JCM) report pentastomtids in several specimens dissected.

Folklore surrounding this snake is abundant; Mole (1924) related the following: "Trinidad woodsmen say that the mother Fer de Lance crawls along in one direction as she deposits her young ones, and that when the last one is born, she turns around and retraces her journey, swallowing all of the young ones she can find en route." Mole also relates a story from A. B. Carr, about a man carelessly handling a large fer de lance in a village shop. Carr warned the man of the danger, and the snake charmer replied that he "had a powerful L'Oraison to protect him . . ." Upon inspection of the snake Carr found it to have its mouth sewn shut with black thread.

Material: Trinidad—FMNH 219618 Arima Valley; USNM 17731–4 no data; 166679 Arima Valley, 166681 Lopinot, 286957, 286962, 306172 Arima Valley.

Lachesis muta muta (Linnaeus)

Map 111. Plates 170, 171, 172.

> *Crotalus mutus* Linnaeus, 1766:373. Type locality: Suriname. *Lachesis mutus* Daudin, 1803, 5:351. *Lachesis mutus:* Mole and Urich, 1891:477. *Lachesis muta [muta]*: Taylor, 1951:184. *Lachesis muta muta:* Beebe, 1952:175. *Lachesis muta:* Underwood, 1962:179.

Common Names: Joseph (1838) wrote, "I have lately seen a specimen of what is called the Pine Apple Snake . . . It was of bright yellow colour, spotted with brown. . . . his scales were in the form of lozenges, like the rind of a pineapple, hence the name." DeVerteuil (1858) provided a similar explanation, "The scales of the mapepire are oval, and carinated as those of the others, but they are not so flat, and there is besides, on each a prominence, giving it the appearance of a pine-apple eye; hence its local name of 'Mapepire Ananas' . . ." "Mapepi" (Mole and Urich, 1891).

Distribution: This is a widespread snake, and Campbell and Lamar (1989) described its distribution as consisting of four disjunct populations. One population ranges from the Atlantic lowlands of southern Nicaragua through Costa Rica and Panama into northwestern Colombia and Ecuador; a second population occurs in the Pacific lowland of southeastern Costa Rica; the third population inhabits the area east of the Andes in the upper Amazon and on Trinidad; and a fourth population occurs in the Atlantic forests of Brazil. The race

L. m. muta is the most widespread race, occurring in the upper portion of greater Amazonia and on Trinidad. It appears to be widespread on Trinidad. Published Trinidad localities include: Las Cuevas (Joseph, 1838); Mayaro; between Caroni and Tamana; near the river Tumpuno (DeVerteuil, 1858); Arima Valley (Beebe, 1952); Diego Martin and Arima (Boos and Quesnel, 1968); Mamural Valley (Mole, 1924); 1.5 km east from where Lalaja-Paria road crosses the Aripo trail (Read, 1986a); Aripo Savannas (Schwab, 1988). Localities based upon museum material include: Arima Valley; Caparo; Maracas Valley; Oropouche Cave; Heights of Aripo; Lalaja Trace; Mt. Harris; and San Rafael.

Description: 1825 mm SVL; tail 170 mm; tail about 9% SVL; may reach 4.267 m in total length. DeVerteuil (1884) reported an 11 foot specimen killed at Covua, Trinidad; Emsley (1977) stated any Trinidad specimen over 8 feet or 2440 mm is exceptional; Trinidad specimens examined were mostly skins with attached heads, making accurate lengths impossible to obtain. Triangular rostral not visible from above; nostrils very anterior; orifice opens laterally in a divided nasal; heat-sensing pits located in the second labial scale which is fused with the prelacunal scale. Preocular large and separated from nasal by a small loreal; postoculars number two or three and are very small. Two pairs of enlarged scales located above the nasals; remaining scales on the crown are small and somewhat granular, with the exception of the large supraoculars; a subocular scale elongate in Trinidad specimens, but divided in specimens from elsewhere in the range; subocular separated from the upper labials by four rows of small scales. Upper labials number 9–10, lower labials number 12–17. Temporal scales indistinguishable from occipital scales. First pair of lower labials form the mental groove with the single pair of enlarged chin shields; gulars number four or five. Dorsal scales in first row are smooth and ovate, scales in rows 2–6 are smooth to weakly keeled; and scales closest to midline are lanceolate, strongly keeled with raised conical keels. Dorsal scale rows at midbody number based on other published reports range from 31–39; however one Trinidad animal has 27 scale rows at midbody, if some small abnormal scales are omitted from the count. Ventrals number 200–247, anal plate single, 43–56 subcaudals are paired proximally and divided into four or five rows of tiny scales distally. Crown of head uniform or slightly spotted with dark blotches. Dark postocular stripe that extending above and past the corner of mouth. Body with about 25 transverse blotches that may fuse on the midline; blotches narrow toward ventrals and expand toward midline. Dark pigment predominates on tail and is separated by narrow tan or orange-brown rings. Ground color of body tan to orange-brown. On Trinidad this species and *Bothrops asper* are the only pit vipers. *L. muta* has conical keeled scales, 9 or 10 upper labials and the distal subcaudals are divided into four or five rows of tiny scales. *B. asper* has normally keeled scales, seven or eight upper labials, and paired subcaudals at the tail tip.

Natural History: A forest snake. DeVerteuil (1858) stated, "The mapepire shows a preference for high grounds, and is very common in Mayaro, as also between Caroni and Tamana, near the river Tumpuno. It is often found together with the lapo in the same hole; and, in certain localities, hunters are obliged to act with great caution, in order to protect their dogs or themselves from its poison fangs. There is, I believe, no authentic record of a lapo having ever been found killed in its recess by a mapepire." The lapo, lappe, lapa or paca is the large, herbivorous dasyproctid rodent *Agouti cuniculus paca*. Boos and Quesnel (1968) stated that *Lachesis* is a rare snake, seen in the deep forests, as well as in outlying districts such as Diego Martin or Arima. Campbell and Lamar (1989) described this species as a snake of primary rainforests that receive more than 2000 mm of rain per annum, and usually more than 4000 mm of rain per annum; often found near large, buttressed trees, or adjacent to fallen trees, and they suggest that when it occurs in secondary forest, the locations have been recently cleared areas or areas adjacent to primary forests. Barbour (1930a) reported it to be nocturnal. Dowling (1961) described the microhabitat of a Trinidad bushmaster from the Arima Valley as,

. . . about 1200 feet and on a west facing slope. The snake was coiled under the arum plants that formed a blanket-like ground cover about 18 inches high. The time was 3:50 P.M.—the hottest part of the day for this location. The resting place of the snake was 75° when measured, and may have been warmed somewhat by the brush having been cut from around it. It is notable that only three feet directly above this hiding place the temperature was five degrees higher (80° F). Since there was no cover nearby and the entire plantation had been cleared of underbrush three times during the past year, it seemed likely that this particular snake had recently moved into the plantation from the forest above . . . Thus, the ecological situation under which Bushmasters live is most 'untropical'. These inhabitants of foggy montane regions emerge after dark when the temperature has dropped below 70° F. They apparently avoid sunlight and retreat to underground burrows when temperatures are too high or humidity too low. A temperature of 75° must be nearly the maximum they ever encounter in nature—and this only when foraging outside the forest during the height of the dry season.

The bushmaster is the only Western Hemisphere pit viper known to lay eggs. Mole (1924) reported the observations he made in July 1903 when he returned home to find that a large captive had laid, "ten or twelve eggs, larger than those of a duck." The female was 7.5 feet long, and Mole commented that the female, "looked like she was trying to incubate them." In a letter to Raymond Ditmars published in the same paper, Mole wrote, "I have learned that similar bunches of eggs have been occasionally found by hunters in the holes inhabited by the Paca . . . and the Armadillo and other burrowing animals in which specimens of *Lachesis mutus* are often found. I have seen these snakes dug out of such holes, but I have only seen the eggs laid in my cage."

Mole and Urich (1894b) noted that this species suffers from large parasitic worms in its lungs. Ditmars and Bridges (1937) reported on an autopsy done at New York's Bronx Zoo indicate that a captive bushmaster died of a lung worm (Linguatulidae) infection.

Mole and Urich (1894b) and Mole (1924) related several instances of dogs being bitten by bushmasters where the owners used a local snake bite remedy, "Melidor's Cure for Snake Bite." In one case the dog died in 45 minutes, in a second the dog died in 15 minutes, and in a third the dog survived. It seems improbable the local remedy had any effect on the venom, for it was, ". . . composed of certain roots, barks, seeds and rum" and said to be, ". . . pleasant though strong balsamic bitter."

A. B. Carr was bitten by a bushmaster; the account given in Mole (1924) is reprinted here.

Whilst Lappe hunting on the low hill-ranges which line the Mamural Valley, accompanied by my brother Reggie and a faithful friend and servant, Sammy, we started a Lappe which sought cover in a hole on the slope of a thinly-wooded hill. We set to work in the usual way, with cutlass and spade, to dig out the quarry. In about an hour it was stabbed, and withdrawn from the burrow. Noticing that the end of the hole had not been reached, and knowing that it often happened that there was another Lappe, or an Armadillo, in the same hole, which was there before the entry of the one we had pursued, I inserted a thin and pliant rod, and at once touched some living creature three or four feet further in. To find out what it was, I thrust in my hunting knife and arm as far as I could reach, and moved it gently up and down and felt what I thought was the scaly hind quarters of an Armadillo. I noticed no movement but a light kick to the blade. I paid no attention to it, and never for a moment suspected the presence of a snake, as I had on many occasion noticed a similar movement and had afterwards taken a Lappe or Armadillo, but never seen a snake, although I had been hunting for many years. In later years, however, I found Mapepire Z'Ananna occasionally in both Lappe and Armadillo holes, but principally in the former. If I had had any doubt, it would have been soon laid to rest, for Sammy called out "I hear it, Sir! its a Lappe; let me probe the hole." Probing means finding out the direction before digging is undertaken, and I again inserted my hunting-knife and was immediately bitten on the inner side of my left thumb. As I withdrew my hand, I saw the head of a large Mapepire Z'Ananna holding on to my thumb. It was only for a fraction of second, and then the snake let go and withdrew into the burrow. As quick as though I called my brother to open my haversack and take out my penknife and a phial of "Melidor's Antidote to Snake Bite." At the same time I gripped my wrist with all the power of my right hand, and I called to Sammy to cut a long pendant root of *Philodendron* (Seguin) with which to make a ligature. But these orders given, imagine

my dismay when the penknife was nowhere to be found, and the antidote on which I pinned my faith (as it had to my knowledge been used with success in more than one case where dogs had been bitten) had been reduced to one half-dose by leakage through a faulty cork. Failing the penknife, my brother used his hunting-knife, which had been blunted during the progress of the day. After sawing across the puncture (it could not be called cutting) in two directions, a little of the antidote was applied, and I drank the rest. Sammy, meanwhile, had applied the ligature. The whole of the treatment did not occupy more than three or four minutes.

The first sensation experienced was that of a sharp stab. Then followed intense pain, accompanied by a feeling of cold, attended by shivering and giddiness. The last two sensations disappeared on my taking a draught of the antidote, which I presumed was due to there being alcohol in it. The thumb and hand became much inflamed, and the forearm and wrist were extremely painful. The dressing of the wound over, the next best thing to be done was to hurry home as quickly as possible, and there was but an hour of daylight before nightfall, and a distance of three miles to traverse through the forest with all its natural impedimenta of lianes and thorny vines, there was none too much time. Some loose earth was thrown into the hole, which should have been tightly rammed. The trees were blazed round it. Then we set off, I leading as the others were not sure of the way. The Lappe was shouldered by Sammy, and I carried a large Agouti, which, being hung as a sling, afforded a soft and partly warm support for my very sore and fast swelling hand and arm. After a rapid tramp for an hour, during which we picked up a large Morocois (tortoise), home was reached—not the well-founded home where stimulants and a medical chest exist — simply a large airy, thatched ajoupa, containing none of the accompaniments of modern civilization. The excitement of walking over, a quarter of an hour later my terrible troubles began. My hand had begun to take the shape, and threatened to assume the dimensions, of a three-quarter sized football, which it actually did towards midnight. My sufferings throughout the night and in the early hours of next morning were most intense, and it is difficult to say in which part of my body the pain was most acute—at the wound, in the armpit, the heart, or the abdomen. I am inclined to think the last named was where the pain seemed to be a death-racking cramp. At 8 P.M. being unable any longer to bear the pain caused by the ligature at the wrist, I had another placed over the elbow, and then removed the first one. I then took to my bed, and an hour later a fit of vomiting came on, which continued at frequent intervals until 1 A.M. The vomit was mainly black, and I thought it consisted of congealed blood from the lungs. This added to the great pain I had undergone for so many hours, did not tend to make matters any better for me, but rather resulted in completely prostrating me, and it was not until 7 A.M. next day that I was somewhat revived after taking a few sips of black coffee—the first food of any kind to pass my lips since noon on the previous day. From that time until five weeks later I was unfit for all work. The thumb, meanwhile, had undergone a great change, for practically all the flesh and the nail fell off. The new flesh grew slowly, and when quite healed over, the thumb was only about three quarters of its original size, while for years it was perfectly numb. There was no treatment beyond that administered in the woods. My brother sat up all night with me, and measured my arm at intervals of fifteen minutes and made notes thereof. These showed that the swelling increased until 1 A.M., and then began to decline and by daybreak had very considerably decreased, as also had the pain.

Within a fortnight of the bite, my brother Artie, proceeding on the description of the hill and environment which I gave him, succeeded in finding the hole, and to his and my disappointment found that the snake had made its escape through the loosely packed earth which had been hurriedly thrown into it. His mission, however, was not altogether a failure, as he found the freshly-cast skin of a large Mapepire Z'Ananna within a few feet of the hole where I was bitten. A few persons, all townspeople, and among them Mr. J. H. Hart, Superintendent of the Botanic Gardens and botanist, questioned my statement that I had been bitten by a Mapepire Z'Ananna. Mr. Hart claimed that as the snake had escaped, no reliance could be placed on my narrative. All Trinidad woodsmen know positively, and their knowledge of woodcraft is quite sufficient for me, that none of our venomous snakes but the Mapepire Z'Ananna lives in the burrows of Lappe and Armadillo, and that the only other large poisonous ophidian of the island, viz. the Mapepire Barcin, or Trinidad Fer de lance, inhabits the banks of muddy streams, such as the Caparo and the Cumuto.

Very few people lived in Caparo in those days, but the news spread, and the very next day the only woman within miles came to see me, and to warn me that if before I was well I met an expectant human mother I would surely die. I laughed, and feeling stronger the next day, made the journey to town, when I met not one, but many, and yet, I am still, 27 years later, alive to tell the tale. (Sgd.) A. B. Carr.

Ditmars and Bridges (1937) related stories of bushmasters being attracted to lights at night. These may be based on a story A. B. Carr told to Mole (1924). "Some East Indians were out on a nocturnal hunting expedition, and one of them carried a light. They halted for a moment, when they were suddenly horrified at seeing slowly rising out of the undergrowth the great head and flickering tongue of an enormous Mapepire which was approaching the lantern. A Creole who was there dexterously beheaded the creature before it satisfied its curiosity."

An additional folktale about the bushmaster in Trinidad culture is related by Ditmars and Bridges (1937). The story deals with a Trinidadian who collects a reward by leading a search party to the body of a crashed aviator in the Northern Range. The boy claimed a mapipire z'ananna had whispered the location of the wreckage.

Material: Trinidad—FMNH 49992.

Glossary

amplexus The sexual embrace of amphibians. The male may clasp the female behind her arms, or in front of her hind legs.

anal Pertaining to the anus, the terminal end of the digestive system. In reptiles this term refers to scales immediately preceding and covering the cloaca.

annulus (pl. annuli) A ring of pigment or scales.

apical pit A pit or depression in a scale; usually difficult to see, even with a good microscope.

arboreal Tree-dwelling.

areola The center of a scale on a turtle shell that acts as a center for new growth.

autotomy The spontaneous loss of part of the body. Refers to the ability of lizards to break off their tail to escape predation.

axial (leaf) The location where a leaf joins the stem of a plant. Some plants have leaf axials which collect water and serve as egg-laying sites for frogs and nurseries for tadpoles.

axillary Pertaining to the armpit.

barbel A fleshy, elongated skin flap that has a sensory function.

bifurcate Branched, or divided, into two parts.

bridge The connection between the plastron and the carapace of a turtle's shell.

bromeliad A plant in the family Bromeliaceae; these plants may have leaves that collect water in their leaf axials; they may grow on the ground, or on branches of trees.

canthus Used here as shorthand for canthus rostralis, the area between the anterior corner of the eye and the snout. It may form a distinct ridge, be rounded, or be concave.

carapace The dorsal portion of the shell of a turtle or tortoise, usually composed of dermal bone, each covered with a scale.

chevron A V-shaped mark, the apex of the V is usually on the midline of the animal.

chromatophore A cell containing pigment and contributing to the color of the animal.

cis-Andean Organisms that are found east of the Andes Mountains.

cloaca A common chamber into which the digestive system, urinary system, and reproductive system open. All amphibians and reptiles have one.

columnar Column-like, often used to describe the leg shape of tortoises.

compressed Vertically flattened, sides of body pushed toward each other.

conical Cone-shaped, used to describe the cone-shaped keels on the scales of *Lachesis*.

costal scutes A plate on the carapace of a turtle between the vertebrals and marginals, thus it covers the ribs.

cranial crest Raised, bony ridge(s) on top of the head.

cycloid Refers to scales, or other structures, with rounded, almost circular edges.

depressed Dorsoventral flattening of the body.

dermal Pertaining to the skin.

dewlap A throat fan, may be permanently extended as in *Iguana,* or retractable as in *Anolis*.

discoidal disk Disk-like fold of skin, as those found on the ventral side, around the perimeter of the abdomen, of many leptodactylid frogs.

distil The part of a structure that is most distant from the center of the body.

dorsum The upper surface of the body.

dorsolateral The area of the body between the dorsum and the sides.

endemic   Native to a particular geographic area.

escutcheon   An area of strongly differentiated scales, usually on the venter of a lizard.

eyespot   Usually a rounded, dark blotch with a light center. Often on the concealed surfaces of the thighs of frogs. These may serve to intimidate predators.

femoral pore   A relatively large hole in a scale found on the ventral side of the thigh in many lizards. In some species the pores extend onto the body anterior to the vent and are then called preanal pores.

fossorial   Living in the ground, burrowing through soil.

frontal   A large, medial scale located between the eyes of lizards and snakes.

frontonasal   A large, medial scale(s) located between the internasals, prefrontals and loreals.

frontoparietal   A scale formed by the fusion of the frontal and parietal scales.

genus (pl. genera)   A group of species that are closely related, that is they share an immediate common ancestor.

granular   Scales having a grainy or pebbled appearance. These scales would not overlap each other.

heterogeneous   Objects that are different from each other. Scales that are of mixed sizes or shapes on a single organism.

hemipenis (pl. hemipenes)   One of the paired copulatory organs of lizards and snakes which are located in the base of the tail.

hind limb/SVL   The length of the hind limb divided by the snout-vent length.

homogeneous   Objects that are the same to each other. Scales that are of similar shapes and sizes.

humerus   The upper arm region.

infradigital   The underside, or venter, of a digit.

infralabial   The scales bordering the mouth on the lower jaw.

inguinal   Pertaining to the region of the groin.

intercalary cartilage   A cartilage phalanx between the ultimate and penultimate phalanges in the digits of hylid frogs.

internasal   A scale or scales between the scales containing the nostrils.

interorbital   Refers to the area between the orbits on the top of the head.

interparietal   A scale, or scales, on top of the head between the parietals. In some lizards this scale contains the parietal eye's external opening.

juxtaposed   Refers to scales which lie next to each other without overlapping.

keel   A ridge or raised area, usually refers to an area on a scale that is raised. Its position on the scale may have taxonomic significance.

km   The abbreviation for kilometer.

lamellae   A group of soft plates lying in an orderly series. Used here to refer to the structures on the underside of lizard digits.

lateral   Pertaining to the sides of an animal, between the dorsal and ventral surfaces.

longitudinal   Pertaining to the long axis of the animal.

loreal   The scale, or scales, located between the preocular and nasal scales.

marginals   The scale, or epidermal plate, on the outer margin of a turtle's carapace.

medial   Refers to a scale, blotch, stripe, or other structure in a midline position on an animal.

melanophores   A cell with dark brown or black pigment.

mental groove   A deep groove on the midline of the chin, between the chin shields. Most Trinidad and Tobago snakes have this; its absence is useful for identification.

metamorph   A recently metamorphosed frog or toad, one that has just changed from a tadpole to a miniature adult.

metamorphosis   The process of change from a tadpole (frog or toad larva) to a miniature frog or toad.

m   The abbreviation for a meter.

mm   The abbreviation for a millimeter.

nasal   The scale, or scales, on the head containing the nasal opening or nares.

nuchal   Pertaining to the region of the neck. In turtles the scale or epidermal plate lying on the dorsal midline of the carapace is called the nuchal.

oblique   Parts of a pattern than run at an angle to the midline of the long axis.

occipital   The region behind the parietal area. In most snakes and lizards this area contains dorsal scales; however, distinctive elements of the pattern may be present in this region. Also, the scale arrangement in this region of a crocodilian has significance for identification.

ocellus (pl. ocelli)   An eye-like blotch, usually round with a dark or colored center.

ocular Pertaining to the eye. A scale containing the eye, or scales surrounding the eye.

ontogenetic Refers to events that occur during the development, maturity, and aging of an individual. It may refer to changes in structure, or changes in food or habitat.

osteoderm A bony plate or scale in the skin of an animal. In most reptiles with these structures there is one osteoderm per scale.

oviposition Egg laying.

parietal(s) Usually referred to here as the pair of scales immediately behind the frontal of snakes and lizards, the most posterior head scales that can be distinguished from body scales.

parotid gland A gland located behind the eye that may extend to the neck and shoulder, and farther.

pectoral Pertains to the ventral chest region of lizards and frogs.

peritoneum The internal membrane that lines the body cavity and internal organs. Some of these are transparent, others are pigmented. The transparent nature of these membranes allows many of the internal organs of centrolenid frogs to be visible; and the membranes that are transparent and pigmented vary from species to species, and are therefore used in identification.

phalanges The bones of the fingers and toes.

pit Refers to a hole, cavity, or depression in a scale. Apical pits are microscopic openings on scales. The loreal and labial pits of vipers and boid snakes are readily visible and contain infrared sensors which are used to locate prey.

plastron The ventral portion of a turtle's shell composed of paired bones, each overlaid by a scale.

ppt Abbreviation for parts per thousand, used in measuring the salinity of water.

posterior The back end, or tail end of an animal.

preanal The area anterior to the cloaca; the preanal area may contain distinctive pores in lizards, or distinctive scales in snakes.

prefrontal As used here it refers to the head scales immediately anterior to the frontal.

preocular The scale(s) touching the anterior edge of the eye's orbit.

protuberant A structure which extends beyond the surface on which it lies.

rhomboid A diamond-shaped marking.

rostral The scale at the tip of the snout that separates the right and left labial rows.

rudimentary An structure that is reduced or degenerated in a species, reduced thumbs in frogs (pollex), or reduced legs in *Bachia*.

s Abbreviation for seconds.

sacral Refers to the region at the end of the vertebral column on the dorsum.

scapular Refers to the area in the shoulder area on the dorsum.

scute Any large, plate-like scale.

serrations Tooth-like projections, may be on a jaw margin or a keel on a scale.

subcaudal The area on the ventral side of the tail. Usually refers to scales which may be single, paired, or both.

subgular The area under (ventral to) the throat.

subnasal The area under (ventral to) the nostrils.

superciliary The area above the eye, may refer to a spiny process that protrudes over the eye in lizards or snakes.

supralabials The scales bordering the upper jaw at the margin of the mouth.

supranasals The scales located immediately above the nostril.

supraocular semicircle Refers to numerous small scales that form a half-circle on the crown of the head above the eye in *Anolis* and some other lizards.

supratympanic Above the tympanum.

suture The joint between two scales.

SVL Snout-vent length.

symphysis Used here to refer to the point at which the two halves of the lower jaw come together on the anterior midline of the chin.

tarsal fold A fold of skin on the foot of a frog between the metatarsals and the joint with the tibia-fibula.

tectonic Refers to movements of the Earth's crustal plates.

temporals Scales behind and touching the postoculars, may be plate-like or indistinguishable from scales on body. May be present in three rows; the first row is said to be the primary temporals, the second row, secondary temporals.

terrestrial Land-dwelling.

tibia   The lower portion of the back legs between the femur and foot. The length of this in relationship to the SVL is often useful in identifying closely related frogs.

trans-Andean   Species found on both sides of the Andes Mountains.

transparent   Light can pass through a transparent material, and an image can be discerned. Some centrolenid frogs have transparent skin.

transverse   Anything that is perpendicular to the long axis of the body.

triad   A cluster of three. Here it is used to describe groups of three black rings on a coral snake.

truncated   Cut off, not as elongate as usual. Refers here to the shape of the face of an animal when viewed in profile.

tubercles   Small round bumps on the skin. They may be glands or have a sensory function.

tympanum   The ear drum.

vertebral   Pertaining to the vertebrae or back bones.

vocal sac   An inflatable sac present in many male frogs, may be single or double, used in sound production.

Literature Cited

Abel, J. J., and D. I. Macht. 1911. The poisons of the tropical toad *Bufo agua*. *Journal of the American Medical Association* 6:1531–1536.

Aitkens, T. H. G., C. B. Worth, and E. S. Tikasingh. 1986. Arbovirus studies in Bush Bush Forest, Trinidad, W. I. (September 1959–December 1964). III. Entomological Studies. *American Journal of Tropical Medicine and Hygiene* 17(2):253–268.

Alexander, T. R. 1964. Observations on the feeding behavior of *Bufo marinus* (Linne). *Herpetologica* 20(4):255–259.

Alford, C. E. R. 1968 (7th ed. re-edited by K. N. Alford.) *The Island of Tobago (The West Indies)*. London: Ranelagh Press.

Alkins-Koo, M. 1990. The aquatic fauna of two intermittent streams in the southwestern peninsula, Trinidad. *Living World, Journal of the Trinidad and Tobago Field Naturalist's Club* 1989–1990:36–42.

Altig, R. 1979. *Toads Are Nice People*. Columbia and Eldon, Missouri: Gates House and Manco.

Amaral, A. 1930a. Estudos sobre ophidios neotropicos XVIII—Lista remissiva dos ophidios da regiao neotropica. *Memorias do Instituto Butantan* 4:129–271.

———. 1930b. Notes on *Spilotes pullatus*. *Bulletin of the Antivenin Institute of America* 3:96–99.

———. 1935. Collecta herpetologica no centro do Brasil. *Memorias do Instituto Butantan* 9:235–246.

Andre, E. 1904. *A Naturalist in the Guianas*. London: Smith, Elder, & Co.

Anonymous. 1897. Additions to the museum. 1896. *Proceedings of the Academy Natural Science, Philadelphia* 48(1896):595–602.

Anonymous. 1926. Harmless and useful snakes. *Zoological Society Bulletin* 1926:31–35.

Anonymous. 1991. A good year for the turtles. *Spring Hill-Simla News Update*. Bulletin of the Asa Wright Nature Centre and Lodge. July 1991. Pages unnumbered.

Ashtine, E. 1966. *Crick-Crack! Trinidad and Tobago Folktales*. University of the West Indies, Extra-Mural Department, Trinidad.

Auffenberg, W. 1965. Sex and species discrimination in two sympatric South American tortoises. *Copeia* 1965:335–342.

———. 1971. A new fossil tortoise with remarks on the origin of South American testudines. *Copeia* 1971(1):106–117.

Bacon, P. R. 1967. Leatherback turtles. *Journal of the Trinidad Field Naturalist's Club* 1967:2–3.

———. 1969. The leatherback turtle project progress report 1967–1968, and recommendations. *Journal of the Trinidad Field Naturalist's Club* 1969:8–9.

———. 1970a. *The Ecology of Caroni Swamp, Trinidad*. The Central Statistical Office Printing Unit, Trinidad. 68 pp.

———. 1970b. Studies on the leatherback turtle, *Dermochelys coriacea* (L.), in Trinidad, West Indies. *Biological Conservation* 2(3):213–217.

———. 1973. *The Status and Management of the Sea Turtle Resources of Trinidad and Tobago*. Report to Permanent Secretary, Ministry of Agriculture, Lands and Fisheries, Trinidad and Tobago. 40 pp.

———. 1975. *Review of Research, Exploitations, and Management of the Stocks of Sea Turtles*. UN-FAO Fisheries Circular (334):1–19.

———. 1978. *Flora and Fauna of the Caribbean: An Introduction to the Ecology of the West Indies*. Port of Spain, Trinidad:Key Caribbean Publications. 320 pp.

————. 1981. *The Status of the Sea Turtles Stock Management in the Western Central Atlantic.* West Central Atlantic Fisheries Commission Studies 7:1–38.

————, and G. K. Maliphant. 1971. Further studies on sea turtles in Trinidad and Tobago. *Journal of the Trinidad Field Naturalist's Club* 1971:2–17.

Barbour, T. 1914. Contributions to the zoogeography of the West Indies, with especial reference to amphibians and reptiles. *Memoires of the Museum of Comparative Zoology, Harvard College* 44(2): 209–395.

————. 1916a. Amphibians and reptiles of the West Indies. *Zoologische Jahrbuchen* 11(4):437–442.

————. 1916b. Amphibians and reptiles from Tobago. *Proceedings of the Biological Society of Washington* 29:221–224.

————. 1923. A new *Pipa. Proceedings of the New England Zoology Club* 10:25–31.

————. 1930a. The bushmaster in the Canal Zone. *Bulletin of the Antivenin Institute of America* 4(1):11.

————. 1930b. A list of Antillean reptiles and amphibians. *Zoologica* 11(4):61–116.

————. 1930c. The anoles. 1. The forms known to occur on the neotropical islands. *Bulletin of the Museum of Comparative Zoology, Harvard* 70(3):105–144.

————. 1935. A second list of Antillean reptiles and amphibians. *Zoologica* 19(3):77–140.

————, and G. K. Noble. 1915. A revision of the lizards of the genus *Ameiva. Bulletin of the Museum of Comparative Zoology* 59(6):417–479.

Beard, J. S. 1944. The natural vegetation of the island of Tobago, British West Indies. *Ecological Monographs* 14(2):137–163.

————. 1946. The natural vegetation of Trinidad. *Oxford Forest Memorial,* Number 20. Oxford: Claredon Press, 152 pp.

————. 1953. The savanna vegetation of northern tropical America. *Ecological Monographs* 23:149–215.

Beebe, W. 1919. The higher vertebrates of British Guiana with special reference to the fauna of Bartica District. Number 7. List of Amphibia, Reptilia and Mammalia. *Zoologica* 2(7):205–227.

————. 1925. Studies of a tropical jungle, one quarter of a square mile of jungle at Kartabo, British Guiana. *Zoologica* 6(1):1–193.

————. 1944a. Field notes on the lizards of Kartabo, British Guiana, and Caripito, Venezuela. Part 1. Gekkonidae. *Zoologica* 29:145–160.

————. 1944b. Field notes on the lizards of Kartabo, British Guiana and Caripito, Venezuela. Part 2. Iguanidae. *Zoologica* 29(4):195–216.

————. 1945. Field notes on the lizards of Kartabo, British Guiana, and Caripito, Venezuela. Part 3. Teiidae, Amphisbaenidae and Scincidae. *Zoologica* 30(1):7–31.

————. 1946. Field notes on the snakes of Kartabo, British Guiana, and Caripito, Venezuela. *Zoologica* 31:11–52.

————. 1952. Introduction to the ecology of Arima Valley, Trinidad, B.W.I. *Zoologica* 37(13):157–183.

Bell, H. J. 1889 (1970). *Obeah; Witchcrcaft in the West Indies.* Negro Universities Press, Westport, Conn. 200 pp.

Belluomini, H. E., and A. R. Hoge. 1958. Operacao cesariane realizada en *Eunectes murinus* (Linnaeus, 1758) (Serpentes). *Memorias do Instituto Butantan* 28:187–194.

————, T. Veinert, F. Dissman, A. R. Hoge, and A. M. Pehna. 1976–77. Notas biologicas a respeito do genero *Eunectes* Wagler, 1830 "Sucuris" [Serpentes:Boinae.] *Memorias do Instituto Butantan* 40–41:79–115.

Blainville, H. de. 1816. Prodrome d'une nouvelle distribution systematique du regne animal. *Bulletin de la Société Philomathique de Paris* (3)3:113–124.

Boettger, O. 1892. *Katalog der Batrachien-Sammlung im Museum der Senchkenbergischen Naturforschenden Gesellschaft.* Frankfort: Druck von Gebruder Knauer. 73 pp.

————. 1893. *Katalog der Reptilien-Sammlung im Museum der Senckenbergischen Naturforschenden Gesellschaft. (Rhynchocephalen, Schildkroten, Krokodile, Eidechsen, Chamaleons) Frankfurt, Druck von Gebruder Knauer. 140 pp.*

————. 1894a. *Geschenke und Erwerbungen.* B. Im Tausch erworben. I. Für die Reptilien- und Batrachiersammlung. Berichte der Senckenbergischen Naturforschenden Gesellschaft.

————. 1894b. *Sphaerodactylus molei* Bttgr. n. sp. And, *Hylodes urichi,* Bttgr, n. sp. Page 88. In A preliminary list of the reptiles and batrachians of the island of Trinidad. R. Mole and F. W. Urich (eds.), 80, 88. *Journal of the Trinidad Field Naturalist's Club,* 2(3):77–90.

————. 1895. A contribution to the herpetological fauna of the island of Tobago. *Journal of the Trinidad Field Naturalist's Club* 2(6):45.

————. 1897. *Geschenke und Erwerbungen*. Frankfurt: Berichte der Senckenbergischen Naturforschenden Gesellschaft.

————. 1898. *Katalog der Reptilien-Sammlung im Museum der Senckenbergischen Naturforschenden Gesellschaft (Schlangen)*. Frankfurt: Druk von Gebruder Knauer, 160 pp.

Boie, F. 1827. Ueber Merrem's Versuch eines Systems der Amphibien, Marburg, 1820. Erste Lieferung: Ophidier. *Isis Von Oken* 20:508–566.

Bokermann, W. C. A. 1950. Redescriçao e nova nome generico para *Coelonotus fissilis* Mir. Rib. 1920. *Papeis Avulosos do Departamento de Zoologia* (Sao Paulo) 9(14):215–222.

————. 1968. Notas Sobre *Phyllodytes auratus* (Boul. 1917) (Amphibia, Hylidae). *Revista Brasileira de Biologia*, 28(2):157–160.

Bonnaterre, P. J. 1789. Erpetologie. In *Tableau Encyclopedique et Methodique des Trois Règnes de la Nature*. Volume 1. Paris: Pnachoucke.

Boos, H. E. A. 1974. The ocellated gecko. *International Wildlife* (U.K.) 16(6):280–81.

————. 1975a. Checklist of Trinidad snakes. *Journal of the Trinidad and Tobago Field Naturalist's Club* 1975:22–28.

————. 1975b. Report on the effects of the venom of the colubrid snake the 'Ratonel' *Pseudoboa neuwiedii*. *Journal of the Trinidad and Tobago Field Naturalist's Club* 1975:28–30.

————. 1975c. The rediscovery of the yellow-tailed cribo, *Drymarchon corais*, in Trinidad. *Journal of the Trinidad Field Naturalist's Club* 1975:84–85.

————. 1975d. Following the snake trail. *International Wildlife* (U.K.) 17(2):74–75.

————. 1977a. The geckos of Trinidad and Tobago (Part 1). *Trinidad Naturalist*, 1(7):26–29.

————. 1977b. The geckos of Trinidad and Tobago (Part 2). *Trinidad Naturalist* 1(8):28–29.

————. 1977c. Iguanas (Part 1). *Trinidad Naturalist* 1(10):32–35, 37.

————. 1977d. Iguana—relict of the dinosaur age (Part 2). *Trinidad Naturalist* 1(11):24–30.

————. 1979a. The teiids (Part 1). *Trinidad Naturalist* 2(5):26–33.

————. 1979b. Teiids (Part 2). *Trinidad Naturalist* 2(7):25–28.

————. 1979c. The skinks and legless lizards. *Trinidad Naturalist* 2(12):54–55, 84–86.

————. 1981. Spiny gecko. *Trinidad Naturalist* 3(7):48.

————. 1984a. A new snake for Trinidad. *Living World, Journal of the Trinidad and Tobago Field Naturalist's Club* 1983–84:3

————. 1984b. Reptiles of Soldado Rock, Trinidad. *Living World, Journal of the Trinidad and Tobago Field Naturalist's Club* 1983–1984:12.

————. 1984c. The terrestrial reptiles of Monas Island. *Living World, Journal of the Trinidad and Tobago Field Naturalist's Club* 1983–1984:14–18.

————. 1984d. A consideration of the terrestrial reptile fauna on some offshore islands northwest of Trinidad. *Living World, Journal of the Trinidad and Tobago Field Naturalist's Club* 1983–1984:19–26.

————. 1984e. *The Status and Distribution of Important Reptiles and Amphibians in Trinidad and Tobago*. New York: FAO United Nations. 19 pp.

————. 1990. Additions to the terrestrial fauna of the offshore islands northwest of Trinidad. *Living World, Journal of the Trinidad and Tobago Field Naturalist's Club*, 1989–1990:9.

————. 1992. A note on the 18.5 ft. *Boa constrictor* from Trinidad. *British Herpetological Society Journal*, 1992(42):15–17.

————, and V. Quesnel. 1968. *Reptiles of Trinidad and Tobago*. Ministry of Education and Culture, Trinidad and Tobago. 39 pp.

————, and ————. 1994. Additional notes on the fauna recorded for the off-shore islands north-west of Trinidad. *Living World, Journal of the Trinidad and Tobago Field Naturalists' Club*, 1993–1994:6–7.

Boos, J. O., and V. C. Quesnel. 1971. Notes on *Kentropyx striatus* in Trinidad, West Indies. *Herpetologica*, 27(4):477–481.

————, and F. C. Urich. 1986. Notes on curious methods of locomotion in two iguanids from Trinidad, West Indies. *Living World, Journal of the Trinidad and Tobago Field Naturalist's Club*, 1985–1986:26.

Boulenger, E. G. 1911. On a new tree frog from Trinidad, living in the Society's Gardens. *Proceedings Zoological Society London*, 15:1082–1083.

Boulenger, G. A. 1882. *Catalogue of the Batrachia, Salientia s. Ecaudata in the collection of the British Museum, London*, 2nd edition. London: Trustees of the British Museum. 503 pp.

————. 1885. *Catalogue of the Lizards in the British Museum (Natural History)* 2nd ed. London: Taylor and Francis. Volumes 1–3, 436 pp, 497 pp, 512 pp.

————. 1889a. *Catalogue of the Chelonians, Rhynchocephalians and Crocodilians of the British Museum.* London: Trustees of the British Museum. 311 pp.

————. 1889b. Description of a new batrachian of the genus *Eupemphix* from Trinidad. *Annals and Magazine of Natural History,* Series 6, 3(16):307–308.

————. 1891. On reptiles, batrachians and fishes from the Lesser West Indies. *Proceedings Zoological Society of London* 1891(3):351–357.

————. 1893. *Catalogue of Snakes in the British Museum (Natural History).* London: Trustees of the British Museum, Vol. 1, 448 pp.

————. 1894. *Catalogue of Snakes in the British Museum (Natural History).* London: Trustees of the British Museum Vol. 2, 382 pp.

————. 1896. *Catalogue of Snakes in the British Museum (Natural History).* London: Trustees of the British Museum Vol. 3, 727 pp.

————. 1898. A list of the reptiles and batrachians collected by the late Professor L. Balzan in Bolivia. *Annali dell Museo Civico di Storia Naturale di Genova* 19(2):128–133.

————. 1917. On a second group of the batrachian genus *Amphodus. Annals and Magazine of Natural History* 8(16):184–185.

Bowman, H., and J. Bowman. 1939. *Crusoe's Island in the Caribbean.* Indianapolis: The Bobbs-Merrill Co. 339 pp.

Bratttstrom, B. H., and R. M. Yarnell. 1968. Aggressive behavior in two species of leptodactylid frogs. *Herpetologica* 24(3):222–228.

Brongersma, L. D. 1937. Herpetological notes. XIV–XVI. *Zoologische Mededelingen* 20:1–10.

————. 1956a. On some reptiles and amphibians from Trinidad and Tobago, B.W.I. I. *Proceedings Koninklijke Nederland Akademie van Wetenschappen* Series C, 59(2):165–176.

————. 1956b. On some reptiles and amphibians from Trinidad and Tobago, B.W.I. II. *Proceedings Koninklijke Nederland Akademie van Wetenschappen* Series C, 59(2):176–188.

————. 1957. Notes upon the trachea, the lungs, and the pulmonary artery of snakes. I–II. *Proceedings Koninklijke Nederland Akademei Wetenschappen* 60:299–313.

Burger, W. L. 1955. A new subspecies of coral snake, *Micrurus lemniscatus* from Venezuela, British Guiana and Trinidad; and a key for the identification of associated species of coral snakes. *Boletin de la Sociedad Venezolana de Ciencias Naturales* 1:35–50.

Burger, W. L., and J. E. Werler. 1954. The subspecies of ring-necked coffee snake, *Ninia diademata,* and a short biological and taxonomic account of the genus. *University of Kansas Science Bulletin* 36(2):643–672.

Burt, C. E., and M. D. Burt. 1930. The South American lizards in the collection of the United States National Museum. *Proceedings of the United States National Museum* 78(6):1–52.

Caldwell, D. K., A. Carr, and T. R. Hellier. 1955. A nest of the Atlantic leatherback turtle, *Dermochelys coriacea coriacea* (Linnaeus), on the Atlantic coast of Florida, with a summary of American nesting records. *Quarterly Journal of the Florida Academy of Sciences* 18(4):279–284.

Caldwell, J. P. 1989. Structure and behavior of *Hyla geographica* tadpole schools with comments on classification of group behavior in tadpoles. *Copeia* 1989(4):938–950.

Campbell, J. A., and W. W. Lamar. 1989. *The Venomous Reptiles of Latin America.* Ithaca, NY: Comstock Publishing. 425 pp.

Cannatella, D. C., and W. W. Lamar. 1986. Synonymy and distribution of *Centrolenella orientalis* with notes on its life history (Anura: Centrolenidae). *Journal of Herpetology* 20(3):307–317.

Carr, A. 1956. *The Windward Road.* New York: Alfred A. Knopf. 258 pp.

Carr, A. F., A. Meylan, J. Mortimer, K. Bjorndal, and T. Carr. 1982. *Surveys of Sea Turtle Populations and Habits in the Western Atlantic.* National Ocean and Atmospheric Administration Technical Memorandum. National Marine Fisheries Service, South East Fisheries Center 91:1–82.

Case, J. E., T. L. Holcombe, and R. G. Martin. 1984. Map of geologic provinces in the Caribbean region. In The Caribbean-South American plate boundaries and regional tectonics. W. E. Bonini, R. B. Hargraves, and R. Shagman (eds.) 1–30. *The Geological Society of America Memoirs* 162.

Censky, E. 1988. *Geochelone carbonaria* (Reptilia: Testudines) in the West Indies. *Florida Scientist* 51(2):108–114.

Chadee, D. D., A. Le Maitre, R. Ganesh, and R. C. Persad. 1984. Ectoparasite of a "galap," *Rhinoclem-*

mys punctularia (Daudin) in Trinidad. *Living World, Journal of the Trinidad and Tobago Field Naturalist's Club* 1983–1984:15.

Chippaux, J. P. 1986. Les serpentes de la Guyane Française. *Collection Faune Tropicale* 27:1–165.

Clark, A. H. 1916. The present status and breeding season of the giant toad (*Bufo aqua*) in Barbados, St. Vincent, Trinidad and Demerara. *Copeia* 1916(27):13–14.

Cochran, D. M. 1955. Frogs of southeastern Brazil. *United States National Museum Bulletin* 206:1–423.

———. 1961. *Living Amphibians of the World*. Garden City, New York: Doubleday and Company. 199 pp.

———. and C. J. Goin. 1970. Frogs of Colombia. *Bulletin of the Smithsonian Institution*, No. 285, 655 pp.

———, and H. C. Dessauer. 1993. Unisexual and bisexual whiptail lizards of the *Cnemidophorus lemniscatus* complex (Squamata: Teiidae) of the Guiana Region, South America, with descriptions of new species. *American Museum Novitates* 3081. 30 pp.

———, ———, and A. L. Markezich. 1993. Missing link found: the second ancestor of *Gymnophthalmus underwoodi* (Squamata: Teiidae), a South American unisexual lizard of hybrid origin. *American Museum Novitates* (3055):1–13.

———, ———, and C. R. Townsend. 1983. Isozymes reveal hybrid origin of Neotropical unisexual lizards. *Isozyme Bulletin* 16:74.

———, ———, ———, and M. G. Arnold. 1990. Unisexual lizards of the genus *Gymnophthalmus* (Reptilia: Teiidae) in the Neotropics: genetics, origins and systematics. *American Museum Novitates* (2994):1–29.

———, C. R. Townsend, H. C. Dessauer, and L. M. Hardy. 1989. A lizard foretold. *Natural History* 1989(5):12, 14–17.

Conant, R., and J. T. Collins. 1991. *A Field Guide to Reptiles and Amphibians of Eastern and Central North America*. Boston: Houghton-Mifflin. 450 pp.

Cooper, St. G. C., and P. R. Bacon (eds). 1981. *The Natural Resources of Trinidad and Tobago*. London: Edward Arnold. 223 pages. [References to this paper refer to anonymous appendices.]

Cope, E. D. 1860a. Catalogue of Colubridae in the Museum of the Academy of Natural Sciences in Philadelphia with notes and descriptions of new species. Part 2. *Proceedings of the Academy of Natural Sciences of Philadelphia* 12:241–266.

———. 1860b. Notes and descriptions of new and little known species of American reptiles. *Proceedings of the Academy of Natural Sciences of Philadelphia* 12:339–345.

———. 1861. Notes and descriptions of anoles. *Proceedings of the Academy of Natural Sciences of Philadelphia* 13:208–215.

———. 1863. Descriptions of new American Squamata in the museum of the Smithsonian Institution, Washington. *Proceedings of the Academy of Natural Science of Philadelphia* 15:100–106.

———. 1864. Contributions to the herpetology of tropical America. *Proceedings of the Academy of Natural Sciences of Philadelphia* 16:166–181.

———. 1868. An examination of the Reptilia and Batrachia obtained by the Orton expedition to Ecuador and the upper Amazon, with notes on other species. *Proceedings of the Academy of Natural Sciences of Philadelphia* 20:96–140.

———. 1879. Eleventh contribution to the herpetology of tropical America. *Proceedings of the Academy of Natural Sciences of Philadelphia* 18(4):261–277.

Cott, H. B. 1926. Observations on the life-habits of some batrachians and reptiles from the lower Amazon: and a note on some mammals from Marajo Island. *Proceedings of the Zoological Society London* 2:1159–1178.

Court, J. 1858. Catalogue of Reptiles. *In Trinidad: Its Geography, Natural Resources, Administration, Present Condition, and Prospects*. ed. L. A. A. G. DeVerteuil, 440–441. London: Ward and Lock.

———. 1884. Catalogue of Reptiles. In *Trinidad: Its Geography, Natural Resources, Administration, Present Condition, and Prospects*, ed. L. A. A. G. DeVerteuil, 381–382. Second Edition. London: Cassell and Company.

Cracraft, J. 1974. Continental drift and vertebrate distribution. *Annual Review of Ecology and Systematics* 5:215–261.

Cuiver, G. 1807. Sur les différentes espèces de crocodiles vivants et sur leurs charactères distinctifs. *Annals des Sciences Naturelles* 10:8–86.

Darevsky, S., L. A. Kupriyanova, and T. Uzzell. 1985. Parthenogenesis in reptiles. Pages 412–526. In *Biology of the Reptilia*, Vol. 15, eds. C. Gans and F. Billett, 412–526. New York: John Wiley and Sons.

Darlington, P. J., Jr. 1957. *Zoogeography, the Geographical Distribution of Animals.* New York: John Wiley and Sons. 675 pp.

Daudin, F. M. 1801–1803. *Historie naturelle des rainettes des grenoulle et des crapauds.* Paris: F.Dufart, 8 vols.

Dawson, A. G. 1992. *Ice Age Earth, Late Quaternary Geology and Climate.* New York, Routledge. 293 pp.

Debusk, J., and J. R. Glidewell. 1972. Social dominance in the South American iguanid lizard *Plica plica.* *Journal of Herpetology* 6(2):139–141.

Demeter, B. J., and D. L. Marcellini. 1981. Courtship and aggressive behavior of the streak lizard (*Gonatodes vittatus*). *Herpetologica* 37(4):250–256.

Despax, R. 1910. Mission geodesique de l'Equateur. Collections recueillies par M. le Dr. Rivet. Liste des ophidiens et description des especes nouvelles. *Bulletin du Museum National d'Historie Naturelle* 16:368–376.

Dessauer, H. C., and C. J. Cole. 1989. Diversity between and within nominal forms of unisexual teiid lizards. In *Evolution and Ecology of Unisexual Vertebrates.* ed. R. M. Dawley and J. P. Bogart, 49–71. New York State Museum Bulletin Number 466.

DeVerteuil, J. P. 1968. Notes on the snakes and lizards of Tobago. In *The Island of Tobago, The West Indies,* 7th Ed. ed. C. E. R. Alford (re-edited by K. N. Alford), 101–105. London: Ranelagh Press.

DeVerteuil, L. A. A. G. 1858. *Trinidad: Its Geography, Natural Resources, Administration, Present Condition, and Prospects.* London: Ward and Lock.

————. 1884. *Trinidad: Its Geography, Natural Resources, Administration, Present Condition, and Prospects.* Second Edition. London: Cassell and Company.

Diesing, C. M. 1850. Systema helminthum. Volume 1, *Sumpt. Acad. Caesar. Sci. W.* Braumuller, Vindobonae. 679 pp.

Dinsmore, J. J. 1970. Reptiles of Little Tobago Island, West Indies. *Quarterly Journal of the the Florida Academy of Sciences* 32(1969):307–309.

Ditmars, R. L., and W. Bridges. 1935. *Snake-hunters Holiday.* New York: D. Appelton-Century Company. 309 pp.

Dixon, J. R. 1973. A systematic review of the teiid lizards, genus *Bachia,* with remarks on *Heterodactylus* and *Anotosaura. University of Kansas Museum of Natural History Miscellaneous Publication* (57):1–47.

————. 1983a. Systematics of *Liophis reginae* and *L. williamsi* (Serpentes, Colubridae), with a description of a new species. *Annals of the Carnegie Museum* 52(6):113–138.

————. 1983b. The *Liophis cobella* Group of the neotropical colubrid snake genus *Liophis. Journal of Herpetology* 17(2):149–165.

————. 1989. A key and checklist to the Neotropical colubrid genus *Liophis* with country lists and maps. *Smithsonian Herpetological Information Service* (79):1–28 pp.

————, and F. S. Hendricks. 1979. The wormsnakes (Family Typhlopidae) of the neotropics, exclusive of the Antilles. *Zoologische Verhandelingen* (173):1–39 pp.

————, and E. J. Michaud. 1992. Shaw's black-backed snake (*Liophis melanotus*) (Serpentes: Colubridae) of Northern South America. *Journal of Herpetology* 26(3):250–259.

————, and P. Soini. 1975. The reptiles of the upper Amazon Basin, Iquitos Region, Peru. 1. Lizards and amphisbaenians. *Milwaukee Public Museum, Contributions in Biology and Geology,* 4:1–58.

————, and ————. 1977. The reptiles of the upper Amazon Basin, Iquitos Region, Peru. 2. Crocodilians, turtles and snakes. *Milwaukee Public Museum, Contributions in Biology and Geology* (12):1–91.

————, and M. Staton. 1976. Some aspects of the biology of *Leptodactylus macrosternum* Miranda-Riberio of the Venezuelan llanos. *Herpetologica* 32(2):227–231.

————, and ————. 1977. Arboreality in the teiid lizard *Cnemidophorus lemniscatus* (Reptilia, Lacertilia, Teiidae) in the Venezuelan llanos. *Journal of Herpetology* 11(1):106–108.

————, M. Staton, and F. S. Hendricks. 1975. Incubation of *Kentropyx striatus* eggs. *Journal of Herpetology* 9(4):363–364.

Dodge, R. E., R. G. Fairbanks, L. K. Benninger, and F. Maurrasse. 1983. Pleistocene sea levels from raised coral reefs of Haiti. *Science* 219:1423–1425.

Donoso-Barros, R. 1965. Nuevos reptiles y anfibios de Venezuela. *Not. Mens. Mus. Hist. Nat.* (Santiago, Chile) 9(102):1–3.

————. 1966. Dos nuevos *Gonatodes* de Venezuela. *Publicacion Ocasional Museo Nacional de Historia Natural* (Santiago, Chile) 11:1–32 pp.

————. 1968. The lizards of Venezuela. *Caribbean Journal of Science* 8(3–4):105–122.

Dowling, H. G. 1960. A bushmaster in the zoo again. *Animal Kingdom* 63(3):109–111.

————, and W. E. Duellman. 1978. *Systematic Herpetology: A Synopsis of Families and Higher Categories*. New York: HISS Publications.

Dowling, M. 1960. Interlude at Simla. *Animal Kingdom* (63)4:137–139.

Downie, J. R. 1984. How *Leptodactylus fuscus* tadpoles make foam, and why. *Copeia* 1984(3):778–780.

————. 1988. Functions of the foam in the foam-nesting leptodactylid *Physalaemus pustulosus*. *Herpetological Journal* 1:302–307.

————. 1989. Observations on foam-making by *Leptodactylus fuscus* tadpoles. *Herpetological Journal* 1:351–355.

————. 1990. Functions of foam in foam-nesting leptodactylids: antipredator effect of *Physalaemus pustulosus* foam. *Herpetological Journal* 1:501–503.

————. 1993. Functions of the foam in foam-nesting leptodactylids: the nest as a post-hatching refuge in *Physalaemus pustulosus*. *Herpetological Journal* 3:35–42.

————. 1994a. Developmental arrest in *Leptodactylus fuscus* tadpoles (Anura: Leptodactylidae). I. Descriptive analysis. *Herpetological Journal* 4:29–38.

————. 1994b. Developmental arrest in *Leptodactylus fuscus* tadpoles (Anura: Leptodactylidae). II. Does a foam-borne factor block development? *Herpetological Journal* 4:39–45.

Drajeske, P. W. 1983. Husbandry and captive reproduction of the mata mata, *Chelus fimbriatus* (Schneider). *Bulletin of the Chicago Herpetological Society* 18(3–4):73–81.

Duellman, W. E. 1956. The frogs of the hylid genus *Phrynohyas* Fitzinger, 1843. *Miscellaneous Publication of the Museum of Zoology University of Michigan* (96):1–47 pp.

————. 1958. A monographic study of the colubrid snake genus *Leptodeira*. *Bulletin American Museum of Natural History* 114:1–152.

————. 1960. A record size for *Drymarchon corias melanurus*. *Copeia* 1960:367–368.

————. 1963. Amphibians and reptiles of the rainforest of southern El Petèn, Guatemala. *University of Kansas Publications, Museum of Natural History* 15(5):205–249.

————. 1965. A biogeographical account of the herpetofauna of Michoacan, Mexico. *University of Kansas Publications, Museum of Natural History* 15(14):627–709.

————. 1971a. A taxonomic review of South American hylid frogs, genus *Phrynohyas*. *Occasional Papers of the Museum of Natural History, University of Kansas* (4):1–24.

————. 1971b. The nomenclatural status of the name *Hyla boans* (Linnaeus) and *Hyla maxima* (Laurenti) (Anura: Hylidae). *Herpetologica* 27(4):397–405.

————. 1974. A reassessment of the taxonomic status of some neotropical hylid frogs. *Occasional Papers of the Museum of Natural History, The University of Kansas* (27):1–27.

————. 1977. Liste der rezenten amphibien und reptilien—Hylidae, Centrolenidae, Pseudidae. *Das Tierreich* (95):1–225.

————. 1978. The biology of an equatorial herpetofauna in Amazonian Ecuador. *Miscellaneous Publication of The University of Kansas Museum of Natural History* (65):1–352.

————. (ed.) 1979. The South American herpetofauna: its origin, evolution and dispersal. *Monograph of the Museum of Natural History University of Kansas* (7):1–485.

————. 1993. *Amphibian Species of the World: Additions and Corrections*. The University of Kansas Museum of Natural History Special Publication No. 21.

————, and P. Gray. 1983. Developmental biology and systematics of the egg brooding hylid frogs, genera *Flectonotus* and *Fritziana*. *Herpetologica* 39(4):333–359.

————, and J. D. Lynch. 1981. Nomenclatural resolution of the identities of *Hyla aurantiaca* and *Hyla lactea*. *Journal of Herpetology* 15(2):237–239.

————, and S. J. Maness. 1980. The reproductive behavior of some hylid marsupial frogs. *Journal of Herpetology* 14(3):213–222.

————, and L. Trueb. 1986. *Biology of Amphibians*. New York: McGraw-Hill Book Company. 670 pp.

————, and J. Wiens. 1992. The status of the hylid frog genus *Ololygon* and the recognition of *Scinax* Wagler 1830. *Occasional Papers Museum Natural History University Kansas* 151:1–23.

Dugan, B. A. 1982. The mating behavior of the green iguana, *Iguana iguana*. In *Iguanas of the World:*

Their Behavior, Ecology, and Conservation, ed. G. M. Burghardt and S. A. Rand, 320–341. Park Ridge, NJ: Noyes Publications.

Duméril, A. M. C., and G. Bibron. 1836. *Erpétologie générale ou Histoire naturelle compléte des reptiles.* Volume 3. Librairie Encyclopédique de Roret. 517 pp.

————, and ————. 1837. *Erpétologie générale ou Histoire naturelle compléte des reptiles.* Volume 4. Librairie Encyclopédique de Roret. 571 pp.

————, ————, and A. Duméril. 1854. *Erpétologie générale ou Histoire naturelle compléte des reptiles.* Volume 7, Part II. Librairie Encyclopédique de Roret. 781–1536 pp.

Duncan, R. A., and R. B. Hargraves. 1984. Plate tectonic evolution of the Caribbean region in the mantle reference frame. In *The Caribbean-South American Plate Boundaries and Regional Tectonics,* ed. W. E. Bonini, R. B. Hargraves and R. Shagman, 81–93. The Geological Society of America Memoirs 162.

Dunn, E. R. 1935. Notes on American *Mabuyas. Proceedings of the Academy Natural Sciences of Philadelphia* 87:533–557.

————. 1942. The American caecilians. *Bulletin Museum of Comparative Zoology* 91(6):439–540.

————. 1944. Los generos de anfibios y reptiles de Colombia. III Tercera parte. Reptiles. Orden de las Serpientes. *Caldasia* (Bogota) 3:155–224.

————. 1949. Notes on South American frogs of the family Microhylidae. *American Museum Novites* No. 1419:1–21.

————, and J. R. Bailey, 1939. Snakes from the uplands of the Canal Zone and of Darien. *Bulletin of the Museum of Comparative Zoology* 86:1–22.

————, and R. Conant. 1936. Notes on anacondas with descriptions of two new species. *Proceedings Academy Natural Sciences of Philadelphia* 88:503–506.

Eckert, S. A., D. W. Nellis, K. L. Eckert, and G. L. Kooyman. 1986. Diving patterns of two leatherback sea turtles (*Dermochelys coriacea*) during internesting intervals at Sandy Point, St. Croix, U.S. Virgin Islands. *Herpetologica* 42:381–388.

Eckert, K. L., and C. Luginbuhl. 1988. Death of a giant. *Marine Turtle Newsletter* 43:2–3.

Edwards, S. R. 1971. Taxonomic notes on South American *Colostethus* with descriptions of two new species (Amphibia, Dendrobatidae). *Proceedings Biological Society of Washington* 84(18):147–167.

Emerson, S. B. 1988. The giant tadpole of *Pseudis paradoxa. Biological Journal of the Linnean Society* 34:93–104.

————. 1994. Testing pattern predictions of sexual selection: a frog example. *The American Naturalist* 143(5):848–869.

————, and D. Berrigan. 1993. Systematics of Southeast Asian ranids: multiple origins of voiceless in the subgenus *Limnonectes. Herpetologica* 49:22–31.

Emsley, M. G. 1963. A consideration of the snakes recorded from Trinidad. *Copeia* 1963(3):576–577.

————. 1966a. The status of the snake *Erythrolamprus ocellatus* Peters. *Copeia* 1966:128–129.

————. 1966b. The mimetic significance of the snake *Erythrolamprus ocellatus* Peters from Tobago. *Evolution* 20:663–664.

————. 1977. Snakes, and Trinidad and Tobago. *Bulletin of the Maryland Herpetological Society* 13(4):201–304.

Ernst, C. H. 1981. *Rhinoclemmys punctularia. Catalog of American Amphibians and Reptiles* 276.1–2.

Eschscholtz, J. F. 1829. *Zoologischer atlas, enthaltend Abbildungen und Beschreibungen neuer Thierarten während des Flottcapitains von Katzebue zweiter Reise um die Welt, auf der Russisch-Kaiserlich Kriegsschlupp Predpriaetie in den Jahren 1823–1826.* Berlin: G. Reimer I:1–28, 25 plates.

Estes, R. 1975. Fossil *Xenopus* from the Paleocene of South America and the zoogeography of pipid frogs. *Herpetologica* 31:263–278.

Etheridge, R. 1970. A review of the South American iguanid lizard genus *Plica. Bulletin of the British Museum of Natural History (Zoology)* 19(7):235–256.

Everard, C. O. R., and H. E. A. Boos. 1975. Aspects of the ecology of the lizard, *Tupinambis nigropunctatus. Journal of the Trinidad Field Naturalist's Club* 1975:16–21.

Everard, C. O. R., B. Tota, B. Basssett, and C. Ali. 1979. *Salmonella* in wildlife from Trinidad and Grenada, W.I. *Wildlife Diseases* 15(2):213–219.

Fairbanks, R. G. 1989. A 17,000 year glacio-eustatic sea level record: influence of glacial melting rates on the Younger Drays event and deep-ocean circulation. *Nature* 342:637–642.

Farfan, P. 1985. An outline of the geology of Trinidad. In *Field Guide, 1st Geological Conference of the Geological Society of Trinidad and Tobago,* 6–10. July 10–12, 1985, Port of Spain, W. I.

ffrench, R. 1990. The birds and other vertebrates of Soldado Rock, Trinidad. *Living World, Journal of the Trinidad and Tobago Field Naturalist's Club* 1989–1990:16–20.

Field, H. 1942. *Handbook of Trinidad and Tobago.* Typescript. 172 pages. Field Museum of Natural History. [Pages 38–41 list the herpetofauna of Trinidad, no scientific names given for Tobago herpetofauna.]

Fielden, G. St. Clair. 1914. Birds. Notes on some birds of Trinidad and Tobago. *Bulletin of the Department of Agriculture, Trinidad and Tobago* 13(77):25–33.

Fitch, H. S. 1970. Reproductive cycles in lizards and snakes. *The University of Kansas Museum of Natural History Miscellaneous Publication* (52):1–247.

Fitzinger, L. J. F. J. 1826. *Neue classification der Reptilien nach ihern naturlichen Verwandtschaften nebst einer Verwandtschafts-Tafel und einem Verzeichnisse der Reptilien-Sammlung des K. K. zoologischen Museums zu Wien.* Vienna: J. G. Huebner. 66 pp.

———. 1843. *System reptilium Fausciculus primus Amblyglossae.* Vienna: Braumuller et Seidel. 106 pp.

Forcart, L. 1951. Nomenclature remarks on some generic names of the snake family Boidae. *Herpetologica* 7(4):197.

Formanowicz, D. R. Jr., E. D. Brodie, Jr., and S. C. Wise. 1989. Foraging behavior of matamata turtles: the effects of prey density and the presence of a conspecific. *Herpetologica* 45(1):61–67.

Fouquette, M. J. 1968. Some frogs from the Venezuelan Llanos, and the status of *Hyla misera* Werner. *Herpetologica* 24(4):321–325.

———, and A. J. Delahoussaye. 1977. Sperm morphology in the *Hyla rubra* Group (Amphibia, Anura, Hylidae), and its bearing on generic status. *Journal of Herpetology* 11(4):387–396.

Fretey, J., and R. Bour. 1980. Rediscovery du type de *Dermochelys coriacea* (Vandelli) (Testudinata, Dermochelyidae). *Bolletino dei Musei di Zoologia* 47:193–205.

Frost, D. R. (ed.) 1985. *Amphibian species of the world: a taxonomic and geographical reference.* Allen Press and the Association of Systematic Collections, Lawrence, Kansas. 732 pp.

———. 1992. Phylogenetic analysis and taxonomy of the *Tropidurus* group of lizards (Iguania.Tropiduridae). *American Musuem Novitates* (3033):1–68.

Frost, D. R., and R. Etheridge. 1989. A phylogenetic analysis and taxonomy of Iguanian lizards (Reptilia: Squamata). *University of Kansas, Museum of Natural History Miscellaneous Publication* (81):1–65.

Funkhouser, A. 1957. A review of the neotropical treefrogs of the genus *Phyllomedusa. Occasional Papers of the Natural History Museum of Stanford University* 5:1–90.

Gallagher, D. S. 1979. *A systematic revision of the South American lizard genus* Kentropyx *(Sauria: Teiidae).* Texas A & M University, Ph.D. Dissertation, 256 pp.

———, and J. R. Dixon. 1980. A new lizard (Sauria, Teiidae: *Kentropyx*) from Brazil. *Copeia* 1980(4):616–620.

Gallardo, J. M. 1961. On the species of Pseudidae. *Bulletin of the Museum of Comparative Zoology,* Harvard University 125:11–134.

———. 1964. Consideraciones sobre *Leptodactylus ocellatus* (L.) (Amphibia, Anura) y especies aliadas. *Physis* 24(68):373–384.

———. 1965. The species *Bufo granulosus* Spix (Salientia: Bufonidae) and its geographic variation. *Bulletin of the Museum of Comparative Zoology* 134:107–138.

Gans, C. 1962. Notes on amphisbaenids (Amphisbaenia, Reptilia) 5. A redefinition and a bibliography of *Amphisbaena alba* Linne. *American Museum Novitates* (2105):1–31.

Garman, S. 1884 [dated 1883]. The reptiles and batrachians of North America. *Memoirs of the Museum of Comparative Zoology* 8:1–185.

———. 1887a. On West Indian Iguanidae and On West Indian Scincidae in the collection of the Museum of Comparative Zoology at Cambridge, Mass. *Bulletin of the Essex Institute* 19:1–28.

———. 1887b. On West Indian reptiles and batrachians in the Museum of Comparative Zoology. *Bulletin of the Essex Institute* 19:1–24.

———. 1887c. On West Indian reptiles in the Museum of Comparative Zoology, at Cambridge, Mass. *Proceedings of the American Philisophical Society* 24:278–286.

Gascoyne, M., G. T. Benjamin, and H. P. Schwartz. 1979. Sea-level lowering during the Illinoian glaciation: evidence from a Bahama "Blue Hole". *Science* 205:806–808.

Gilmore, R. M., and J. C. Murphy. 1993. On large anacondas, *Eunectes murinus* (Serpentes: Boidae), with special reference to the Dunn-Lamon record. *Bulletin of the Chicago Herpetological Society* 28(9):185–188.

Goode, M. 1988. Reproduction and growth of the chelid turtle *Phrynops* (*Mesoclemmys*) *gibbus* at the Columbus Zoo. *Herpetological Review* 19(1):11–12.

———. 1989. Life history: *Pseustes sulphureus*. Reproduction. *Herpetological Review* 20(3):73.

Gorham, S. W. 1962. Liste der rezenten Amphibien und Reptilien. Gymnophiona. *Das Tierreich* (78):1–25.

Gorman, G. C. 1969. Intermediate display of a hybrid *Anolis* lizard (Sauria:Iguanidae). *Zeitschrift für Tierpsychologie* 26:390–393.

———. 1976. Observations on the distribution of *Anolis extremus* (Sauria, Iguanidae) on St. Lucia, West Indies. A "colonizing" species. *Herpetologica* 32(2):184–188.

———, and L. Atkins. 1968. Natural hybridization between two sibling species of *Anolis* lizards: chromosome cytology. *Science* 159:1358–1360.

———, and J. O. Boos. 1972. Extinction of a local population of *Anolis* lizard through competition with a congener. *Systematic Zoology* 21(4):440–441.

———, and Y. J. Kim. 1978. The genetics of colonization: loss of variability among introduced populations of *Anolis* lizards (Reptilia, Lacertilia, Iguanidae). *Journal of Herpeptology* 12(1):47–51.

———, and P. Licht. 1975. Differences between the reproductive cycles of sympatric *Anolis* lizards on Trinidad. *Copeia* 1975(2):332–337.

———, ———, H. C. Dessauer, and J. O. Boos. 1971. Reproductive failure among the hybridizing Anolis lizards of Trinidad. *Systematic Zoology* 20(1):1–18.

Gorzula, S. 1982. Life History: *Leptodeira annulata ashmeadii*. Envenomation. *Herpetological Review* 13(2):47.

Gosner, K. L. 1960. A simplified table for staging anuran embryos and larvae with notes on identification. *Herpetologica* 16:183–190.

Granger, O. E. 1982. Climatic fluctuations in Trinidad, West Indies and their implications for water resource planning. *Caribbean Journal of Science* 17(1–4):173–201.

Grant, C. 1958. A new *Gymnophthalmus* (Reptilia, Teiidae) from Barbados, BWI. *Herpetologica* 14(4):227–228.

Grant, G. S., and D. Ferrell. 1993. Leatherback turtle, *Dermochelys coriacea* (Reptilia: Dermochelidae): Notes on near-shore feeding behavior and association with cobia. *Brimleyana* 19:77–81.

Graves, L. 1819. Sur deux nouvelles espéces de crocodile. *Annales Générales des Sciences Physiques. (Bruxelles)* 2:343–353.

Gray, J. E. 1831a. A synopsis of the species of the class Reptilia. In *The Animal Kingdom Arranged in Conformity with Its Organization by G. Cuvier, with Additional Descriptions of All the Species Hitherto Named, and of Many not before Noticed,* ed. E. Griffith and E. Pidgeon, Appendix to E. London: Whittaker, Treacher, and Co. 110 pp.

———. 1831b. *Synopsis Reptilium, or Short Descriptions of the Species of Reptiles. Part 1. Cataphracta, Tortoises, Crocodiles and Enyaliosaurians.* London: Treuttle, Wurtz and Co.

———. 1840. Catalogue of the species of reptiles collected in Cuba by W. S. MacLeory, Esq.—with some notes on their habits extracted from his M.S. *Annals and Magazine of Natural History* 5:108–115.

———. 1842. Synopsis of the species of prehensile-tailed snakes, of the family Boidae. *Zoologica Miscellanea* (2):41–46.

———. 1845. *Catalogue of the Specimens of Lizards in the Collection of the British Museum.* London: Taylor and Francis. 289 pp.

———. 1849. *Catalogue of the Specimens of Snakes in the Collection of the British Museum.* Trustees of the British Museum, London. 125 pp.

———. 1868. Notice of *Hydrapsis gordoni*, a new species from Trinidad, living in the Gardens of the Society. *Proceedings of the Zoological Society of London* 1868:563–564.

Greene, H. W. 1988. Antipredator mechanisms in reptiles. In *Biology of the Reptilia,* Vol. 16, Ecology B, Defense and Life History. ed. C. Gans and R. B. Huey, 1–152. New York: Alan R. Liss, Inc.

Greenhall, A. M. 1959. Notes on local mongoose. *Journal of the British Guiana Museum of Zoology* 22:29–30.

Groombridge, B. 1982. *The IUCN Amphibia-Reptilia Red Data Book, Part 1. Testudines, Crocodylia, Rhynchocephalia.* Gland, Switzerland: IUCN 426 pp.

Guichenot, A. 1855. *Animaux nouveaux ou rares recueillis pendent l'expédition dans les parties centrales de l'Amérique du Sud. de Rio de Janeiro á Lima, et de Lima au Pará; exécutée par order du govuvernement françaias pendant les année 1843 a 1847, sous la direction du Comte Francis de Castelnau 1847. Part 7. Zoologie,* (Vol. 2, Reptiles, 95 p). P. Bertrand, Paris.

Gunther, A. C. L. G. 1858. *Catalogue of Colubrine Snakes in the Collection of the British Museum.* London: Taylor and Francis, 281 pp.

Guyer, C., and J. M. Savage. 1986. Cladistic relationships among anoles (Sauria: Iguanidae). *Systematic Zoology* 35:509–531.

Haas, C. A. 1991. Evolution and biogeography of West Indian *Sphaerodactylus* (Sauria: Gekkonidae): A molecular approach. *Journal of Zoology,* London 225:525–561.

Haddad, C. F. B. 1991. Satellite behavior in the neotropical treefrog *Hyla minuta. Journal of Herpetology* 25:226–229.

Haffer, J. 1979. Quaternary biogeography of tropical lowland South America. In *The South American Herpetofauna: Its Origin, Evolution, and Dispersal,* ed. W. E. Duellman, 107–140. Monograph of the Museum of Natural History, The University of Kansas No. 7.

Halliday, T. R., and K. Adler. 1986. *The Encyclopedia of Reptiles and Amphibians.* New York: Facts On File. 143 pp.

Hallowell, E. 1845. Description of reptiles from South America, supposed to be new. *Proceedings of the Academy of Natural Sciences of Philadelphia* 2:241–247.

———. 1855. Contributions to South American herpetology. *Journal of the Academy of Natural Science of Philadelphia* 2(3):33–36.

———. 1860 [1861]. Report upon Reptilia of the North Pacific Exploring Expedition under command of Capt. John Rogers, USN. *Proceedings of the Academy of Natural Sciences of Philadelphia* 1860:480–509.

Harding, K. A. 1983. *Catalogue of New World Amphibians.* New York: Pergamon Press. 406 pp.

Hardy, J. D., Jr. 1971. Zoogeography in action. Observations on the movements of terrestrial vertebrates across open water. *Maryland Herpetological Society Newsletter* 1971(1):4–6.

———. 1977. Frogs, islands, and evolution (Abstract). In *Eastern Seaboard Herpetological League Abstracts of 10th Biannual Meeting,* p. 5. March 5, 1977.

———. 1982. Biogeography of Tobago, West Indies, with special reference to amphibians and reptiles, a review. *Bulletin of the Maryland Herpetological Society* 18(2):37–142.

———. 1983a. A new frog of the genus *Colostethus* from the island of Tobago, West Indies (Anura: Dendrobatidae). *Bulletin of the Maryland Herpetological Society* 19(2):47–57.

———. 1983b. Tobago—The forgotten island. *Naturalist Magazine* (Trinidad) 4(7):8–10,12,14, 17–19, 21–22.

———. 1984a. Frogs, egg teeth, and evolution: preliminary comments on egg teeth in the genus *Eleutherodactylus. Bulletin of the Maryland Herpetological Society* 20(1):1–11.

———. 1984b. Herpetology of Tobago: additions, deletions, and taxonomic changes. *Bulletin of the Maryland Herpetological Society* 20(1):12–19.

———. 1984c. Systematic status of the South American frog *Phyllobates mandelorum* (Amphibian, Dendrobatidae). *Bulletin of the Maryland Herpetological Society* 20(3):109–111.

———. 1984d. A new subspecies of *Centrolenella orientalis* (Anura: Centrolenidae) from Tobago, West Indies. *Bulletin of the Maryland Herpetological Society* 20(4):165–173.

———, and H. A. E. Boos. 1995. Snakes of the genus *Erythrolamprus* (Serpentes: Colubridae) from Trinidad and Tobago, West Indies. *Bulletin of the Maryland Herpetological Society* 31:158–190.

Hardy, L. M., C. J. Cole, and C. R. Townsend. 1989. Parthenogenetic reproduction in the neotropical unisexual lizard, *Gymnophthalmus underwoodi* (Reptilia: Teiidae). *Journal of Morphology* 201:215–234.

Harris, D. M. 1982. The *Sphaerodactylus* (Sauria: Gekkonidae) of South America. *Occasional Papers of the Museum of Zoology University of Michigan* (704):1–31.

Harris, P. 1980. Excavation report: Loves Retreat Period IV, Tobago. In *Proceedings of the 8th International Congress for the Study of Pre-Columbian Culture of the Lesser Antilles,* Arizona State University, ed. S. M. Lewensteind (22):524–552.

Hart, J. 1890 [1891]. *Annual Report of the Royal Botanic Gardens.* Trinidad, 1890:25.

Hemming, F. (ed.) 1958. Opinion 520. Suppression under the Plenary Powers of the specific name *tibiatrix* Laurenti, 1768 as published in the combination *Hyla tibiatrix,* and of the generic name *Acrodytes* Fizinger, 1843, and interpretation under the same species *Rana venulosa* Laurenti, 1768 (Class Amphibia). Opinion Declaration, *International Commission of Zoological Nomenclature* 19:169–200.

Henderson, R. W. 1974a. Aspects of the ecology of the neotropical vine snake, *Oxybelis aeneus* (Wagler). *Herpetologica* 30(1):19–24.

———. 1974b. Aspects of the ecology of the juvenile common iguana (*Iguana iguana*). *Herpetologica* 30(4):327–332.

———. 1991. Distribution and preliminary interpretations of geographic variation in the Neotropical tree boa, *Corallus enydris:* a progress report. *Bulletin of the Chicago Herpetological Society* 26(5):105–110.

———. 1993. On the diets of some arboreal boids. *Herpetological Natural History* 1(1):91–96.

———, and M. H. Binder. 1980. The ecology and behavior of vine snakes (*Ahaetulla, Oxybelis, Thelotornis, Uromacer*): A review. *Milwaukee Public Museum Contributions in Biology and Geology* 37:1–38.

———, and H. E. A. Boos. 1994. The tree boa (*Corallus enydris*) on Trindad and Tobago. *Living World, Journal of The Trinidad and Tobago Field Naturalist's Club* 1993–1994:3–5.

———, and S. B. Hedges. 1995 (in press). Origin of West Indian populations of the geographically widespread boa *Corallus enydris* inferred from mitochondrial DNA sequences. *Molecular Phylogeny and Evolution.*

———, and M. A. Nickerson. 1976. Observations on the behavioral ecology of three species of *Imantodes. Journal of Herpetology* 10(3):205–210.

———, ———, and S. Ketcham. 1976. Short term movements of the snakes *Chironius carinatus, Helicops angulatus* and *Bothrops atrox* in Amazonian Peru. *Herpetologica* 32(3):304–310.

Hero, J.-M., and U. Galatti. 1990. Characteristics distinguishing *Leptodactylus pentadactylus* and *L. knudseni* in the central Amazon rainforest. *Journal of Herpetology* 24(2):227–228.

Heyer, W. R. 1968. The proper name for the type species of the genus *Leptodactylus. Copeia* 1968(1): 160–162.

———. 1969. The adaptive ecology of the species groups of the genus *Leptodactylus* (Amphibia, Leptodactylidae). *Evolution* 23:421–428.

———. 1972. The status of the *Leptodactylus pumilio* Boulenger (Amphibia: Leptodactylidae) and the description of a new species of *Leptodactylus* from Ecuador. *Natural History Museum of Los Angles County Contributions in Science* (231):1–8.

———. 1974. Systematics of the *marmoratus* group of the frog genus *Leptodactylus* (Amphibia, Leptodactylidae). *Los Angeles County Museum of Natural History, Contributions in Science* (253):1–46.

———. 1978. Systematics of the *fuscus* group of the frog genus *Leptodactylus* (Amphibia, Leptodactylidae). *Natural History Museum of Los Angeles County, Science Bulletin* (29):1–85.

———. 1994. Variation within the *Leptodactylus podicipinus-wagneri* complex of frogs (Amphibia: Leptodactylidae). *Smithsonian Contributions to Zoology* (546):1–124.

———, and J. A. Peters. 1971. The frog genus *Leptodactylus* in Ecuador. *Proceedings of the Biological Society of Washington* 84(19):163–170.

———, and S. A. Rand. 1977. Foam nest construction in the leptodactylid frogs *Leptodactylus pentadactylus* and *Physalaemus pustulosus* (Amphibia, Anura, Leptodactylidae). *Journal of Herpetology* 11(2):225–228.

———, and P. Silverstone. 1969. The larva of the frog *Leptodactylus hylaedactylus* (Leptodactylidae). *Fieldiana* 51(11):141–145.

Hillis, D. M., and R. De Sa. 1988. Phylogeny and taxonomy of the *Rana palmipes* Group (Salienta: Ranidae). *Herpetological Monographs* 2:1–26.

Hoge, A. R. 1964 [1960–1962]. Sur la position systematique de quelques serpents du genre *Siphlophis* Fitzinger 1834 W. *Memorias do Instituto Butantan* 30:35–50.

———, and A. R. Lancini. 1960. Notas sobre la ubicacion de la tierra typica de varias especies de "serpentes" colectadas por M. Beauperthuis en la "Cote Ferme" y en la "Province de Venezuela." *Boletin de la Sociedad Venezolana de Ciencias Naturales.* (Caracas) 6–7:58–62.

———, and S. A. R. W. L. Romano-Hoge. 1979. Poisonous snakes of the world. Part. 1. Checklist of the pit vipers Viperoidae, Viperidae, Crotalinae. *Memorias do Instituto Butantan,* 42–43:179–310.

Holmstrom, W. F., Jr. 1978. Preliminary observations on prey herding in the matamata turtle, *Chelus fimbriatus* (Reptilia, Testudines, Chelidae). *Journal of Herpetology* 12(4):573–574.

Hoogmoed, M. S. 1973. Notes on the herpetofauna of Suriname. IV. The lizards and amphisbaenians of Suriname. *Biogeographica* 4:1–419. The Hague: W. Junk.

———. 1979a. Resurrection of *Hyla ornatisma* Noble (Amphibia, Hylidae) and remarks on related species of green tree frogs from the Guiana area. Notes on the herpetofauna of Suriname VI. *Zoologische Verhandelingen* (127):1–46.

———. 1979b. The herpetofauna of the Guiana region. In The South American herpetofauna: its origin, evolution, and dispersal, ed. W. E. Duellman, 217–240. *Monograph of the Museum of Natural History, University of Kansas* No. 7.

———. 1980. Revision of the genus *Atractus* in Suriname, with the resurrection of two species (Colubridae, Reptilia). Notes on the herpetofauna of Suriname, VII. *Zoologische Verhandelingen* (175): 1–47.

———. 1981. Introduced species of reptiles in Suriname. Notes on the herpetofauna of Suriname VIII. *Amphibia-Reptilia* 1(3–4):277–285.

———. 1983 [dated 1982] Snakes of the Guiana region. *Memorias do Instituto Butantan* 46:219–254.

———. 1986. Erganzende beobachtungen on *Lithodytes lineatus* (Schneider, 1799). *Salamandra* 22 (2–3):215–217.

———, and S. J. Gorzula. 1979. Checklist of the savanna inhabiting frogs of the El Manteco region with notes on their ecology and the description of a new species of tree frog (Hylidae, Anura). *Zoologische Mededelingen* 54(13):183–216.

———, and U. Gruber. 1983. Spix and Wagler type specimens of reptiles and amphibians in the Natural History Musea in Munich (Germany) and Leiden (The Netherlands). *Spixiana Supplement* 9:319–415.

Hopkins, D. M. 1982. Aspects of the paleoecology of Beringia during the Late Pleistocene, In *Paleoecology of Beringia*, 3–28. ed. D. M. Hopkins et al. New York: Academic Press.

Houttuyn, M. 1782. Het onderscheid der Salamanderen van de Haagdissen in 't algemeen, en van de Gekkoes in 't byzonder aangetoond. *Verhandelingen Zeeuwsch Genootschap der Wetenschappen te Vlissingen* (1) 9 (2):304–336.

Ingle, R. M., and F. G. Smith. 1949. *Sea Turtles and the Turtle Industry of the West Indies, Florida and the Gulf of Mexico, with Annotated Bibliography.* The Marine Laboratory, University of Miami and Caribbean Research Council. University of Miami Press. See pages 56–57.

IUCN. 1989. *Tortoise and Freshwater Turtles. An Action Plan for Their Conservation.* Gland, Switzerland: International Union for Conservation of Nature and Natural Resources. 47 pp.

Iverson, J. B. 1992. *A Revised Checklist with Distribution Maps of the Turtles of the World.* Privately Printed, John B. Iverson, Earlham College, Richmond, Indiana. 363 pp.

James, C. 1983. Endangered species: the leatherback turtle and the pawi. Pages 39–49. In *Highlighting Wildlife: Basic Information on Wildlife Conservation in Trinidad and Tobago.* ed. C. James. Forestry Division, Ministry of Agriculture, Lands, and Food Production, Port of Spain, Trinidad. 1–72 pp.

Jan, G. 1862. Enumerazione sistematica delle specie d'ofidi del gruppo Calamaridae. *Archivio per la Zoologia, l'Anatomia e la Fisiologia* 2:1–76.

———. 1863. Enumerazione sistematico degli ofidi appartenenti al gruppo Coronellidae. *Archivio per la Zoologia, l'Anatomia e la Fisiologia.* 2(2):211–330.

Johnson, M. L. 1946. Herpetological notes from Trinidad. *Copeia* 1946:108.

Joseph, E. L. 1838. *History of Trinidad.* London: Henry James Mills. 269 pp.

Joy, W. 1992. World record boa constrictor "de-discovered." *Notes From NOAH,* July 26, 1992.

Kaiser, H., C. M. Dwyer, W. Feichtinger, and M. Schmidt. 1996. A new species of *Eleutherodactylus* (Anura: Leptodactylidae) from Tobago, West Indies and its morphometric and cytogenetic characterization. *Herpetological Natural History* 3(2):151–163.

Kaplan, M. 1994. A new species of frog of the genus *Hyla* from the Cordillera Oriental in northern Colombia with comments on the taxonomy of *Hyla minuta. Journal of Herpetology* 28(1):79–87.

Kearney, P. 1972. Nocturtles of Trinidad. *International Turtle and Tortoise Society Journal* 6(2):10–11, 32–33.

Keiser, E. D. 1974. A systematic study of the neotropical vine snake, *Oxybelis aeneus* (Wagler). *Texas Memorial Museum Bulletin* (22):1–51.

Kenny, J. S. 1966. Nest building in *Phyllomedusa trinitatis* Mertens. *Caribbean Journal of Science* 6:15–22.

———. 1969. Amphibia of Trinidad. *Studies on the Fauna of Curacao and Other Caribbean Islands* 29(54):1–78.

———. 1971. A further contribution on the Amphibia of Trinidad. *Journal of the Trinidad Field Naturalist's Club* 1971:24–25.

————. 1977. The Amphibia of Trinidad—an addendum. *Studies on the Fauna of Curacao and Other Caribbean Islands* 51:91–95.

————. 1979a. Floorplan, environment and fauna of Tamana caves. *Living World, Journal of the Trinidad and Tobago Field Naturalist's Club* 1978–1979:5–9.

————. 1979b. Some recent colonizations. *Journal of the Trinidad and Tobago Field Naturalist's Club* 1978–79:27.

Kenny, J. S., and P. R. Bacon. 1981. Aquatic resources. Pages 112–144. In *The Natural Resources of Trinidad and Tobago.* ed. St. G. C. Cooper and P. R. Bacon. London: Edward Arnold. 223 pp.

King, W. 1962. The occurrence of rafts for dispersal of land animals into the West Indies. *Quarterly Journal of the Florida Academy of Sciences* 25(1):45–52.

King, F. W., and R. L. Burke. 1989. *Crocodilian, tuatara, and turtle species of the world. A taxonomic and geographic reference.* Washington, DC: Association of Systematics Collections. 216 pages.

King, F. W., H. W. Campbell, and P. E. Moler. 1982. Review of the status of the American crocodile. In *Crocodiles. Proceedings of the 5th Working Meeting of the Crocodile Specialist Group of the Species Survival Commission of the International Union for the Conservation of Nature and Natural Resources, 84–98. Convened at the Florida State Museum, Gainesville, FL, USA. 12–16 August. 1980.* IUCN Publication, New Series.

Kingsley, C. 1890. *At Last: A Christmas in the West Indies.* New York: MacMillan and Co. 334 pp.

Klauber, L. M. 1939. Three new worm snakes of the genus *Leptotyphlops. Transactions of the San Diego Society of Natural History* 9(14):59–66.

————. 1972. *Rattlesnakes, Their Habits, Life Histories, and Influence on Mankind.* 2 vol. Berkeley: University of California Press.

Kluge, A. G. 1967. Higher taxonomic categories of gekkonid lizards and their evolution. *Bulletin of the American Museum of Natural History* (135):1–60.

————. 1969. The evolution and geographical origin of the New World *Hemidactylus mabouia-brookii* complex (Gekkonidae, Sauria). *Miscellaneous Publication of the Museum of Zoology, University of Michigan* (138):1–78.

————. 1979. The gladiator frogs of Middle America and Colombia—a reevaluation of their systematics (Anura: Hylidae). *Occasional Papers Museum of Zoology University of Michigan* (688):1–24.

Krakauer, T. 1968. The ecology of the neotropical toad, *Bufo marinus,* in south Florida. *Herpetologica* 24(3):214–222.

Krintler, K. 1982. Auf den Spuren von Robert Mertens auf Tobago. *Herpetofauna* (Ludwigsburg) 4(16):10–14.

Lacepede, B. G. E. 1788. *Histoire Naturelle des Quadrupèdes Ovipares et des Serpens.* Paris, 2 vol. (Vol. 1:1–651.)

Lack, D. 1976. Island biology illustrated by the land birds of Jamaica. *Studies in Ecology* 3:1–445.

La Marca, E. 1992. *Catalogo taxonomico, biogeografico y bibliografico de las ranas de Venezuela.* Universidad de Los Andes, Facultad de Ciencias Forestales, Instituto de Geografia y Conservacion de los Recursos Naturales (9):1–197.

Lamotte M., and J. Lescure. 1977. Tendances adaptives a l'affranchissement du miliue aquatique chez les amphibiens anoure. *Terre et la Vie* 1977(2):225–312.

Lancini, A. R. 1963. Herpetofauna de la isla de Patos (Golfo de Paria, Venezuela). *Boletin de la Sociedad Venezolana de Ciencias Naturales* 23(103):247–254.

————. 1979. *Serpientes de Venezuela.* Ernesto Armitano (ed.). Transv. Avendia Principal de Boleita, Edificio Centro Industrial, Caracas, Venezuela. 262 pp.

La Riva, I. de. 1995. A new reproductive mode for the genus *Adenomera* (Amphibia: Anura: Leptodactylidae): taxonomic implications for certain Bolivian and Paraguayan populations. *Studies on Neotropical Fauna and Environment* 30(1):15–29.

Laurenti, J. N. 1768. *Specimen medicum exhibens synopsin reptillum emendatum cum experimentis incavenea et antidota reptillium austriacorum.* Vienna. 214 pp.

Lazell, J. D. 1972. The anoles (Sauria, Iguanidae) of the Lesser Antilles. *Bulletin of the Musuem of Comparative Zoology* 143(1):1–115.

————. 1973. The lizard genus *Iguana* in the Lesser Antilles. *Bulletin Museum of Comparative Zoology* 145:1–28.

————. 1989. *Wildlife of the Florida Keys, a Natural History.* Washington, DC: Island Press. 250 pp.

————. 1992. The family Iguanidae: disagreement with Frost and Etheridge (1989.) *Herpetological Review* 23(4):109–112.

————. 1993. Tortoise, cf. *Geochelone carbonaria,* from the Pleistocene of Anguilla, northern Lesser Antilles. *Journal of Herpetology* 27(4):485–486.

————. 1994a. Iguanians and the cladistic party line. *Herpetological Review* 25(1):9–10.

————. 1994b. A new *Sphaerodactylus* (Sauria:Gekkonidae) from Bequia, Grenada Bank, Lesser Antilles. *Breviora* (496):1–20.

————, and T. Sinclair. 1990. Geographic distribution: *Gymnophthalmus underwoodi.* SSAR *Herpetological Reivew* 21(4):96.

Leon, J. R., R. Donoso-Barros, and A. S. Prieto. 1970. Alimentacion de tres especies de lagartos de los alredeores de Cumana, Estado Sucre, Venezuela. *Boletin de la Sociedad de Biología de Conceptión* 42:349–354.

Lescure, J. 1972. Contribution a l'étude des amphibiens de Guyane francaise. II. *Leptodactylus fuscus* (Schneider). Observation écologiques et éthologiques. *Ann. Mus. Hist Nat. Nice* 1(1):91–100.

————. 1980. Le peuplement en reptiles et amphibiens des Petites Antilles. *Bulletin de la Societe Zoologique de France* 112(3–4):327–342.

Lichtenstein, M. H. C. 1856. *Nomenclature reptilium et amphibiorum Museu Zoolgici Berolinensis. amenverzeichniss der in der Zoologischen Sammmlung der Königlichen Universität zu Berlin aufgestellten Arten von Reptilien und Amphibien nach ihren Ordnungen, Familien und Gattungen.* Berlin: Köningl. Akad. Wiss. 48 pp.

Liddle, R. A. 1946. *The Geology of Venezuela and Trinidad.* Ithaca, NY. 1–890 pp.

Lindblad, J. 1968. *Journey to the Red Birds.* New York: Hill and Wang. 170 pp.

Linnaeus, C. 1758. *Systemna Naturae per Regna Tria Naturae, Secundum Classes, Ordines, Genera, Species cum Characteribus, Differentiis, Synonymis, Locis.* Tenth ed. Vol. 1. L. Salvius, Stockholm. 826 pp.

————. 1766. *Systema Nature per Regna Tria Naturae, Secundum Classes, Ordines, Genera, Species cum Characteribus, Differentiis, Synonymis, Locis.* Twelfth ed. Stockholm: L. Salvivus. 532 pp.

Lonnberg, E. 1896. Linnaean type specimens of birds, reptiles, batrachians and fishes in the zoological museum of the R. University in Uppsala. *Bihang till Kongliga Svenska Vertenskaps-Akademiens. Handlingar,* 22(4):1–45.

Lutz, A. 1927. Notes on batrachians from Venezuela and Trinidad. *Memorias do Instituto Oswaldo Cruz,* 20:35–65.

Lutz, B. 1973. *Brazilian Species of Hyla.* University of Texas Press, Austin and London. 260 pp.

Lynch, J. D. 1970. Systematic status of the American leptodactylid frog genera *Engystomops, Eupemphix,* and *Physalaemus. Copeia* 1970(3):488–496.

————. 1971. Evolutionary relationships, osteology, and zoogeography of leptodactyloid frogs. *University of Kansas Museum of Natural History, Miscellaneous Publications* (53):1–238.

————. 1979. The amphibians of the lowland tropical forests. In W. E. Duellman (ed.) The South American herpetofauna: its origin, evolution, and dispersal, 189–215. *Monograph of the Museum of Natural History, The University of Kansas.* No. 7.

————, and E. La Marca. 1993. Synonymy and variation in *Eleutherodactylus bicumulus* (Peters) from northern Venezuela, with a description of a new species (Amphibia: Leptodactylidae). *Caribbean Journal of Science* 29(3–4):133–146.

Lynn, W. G. 1959. Some reptiles and amphibians from Trinidad. *Herpetologica* 15(3):113–117.

MacLean, W. P., R. Kellner, and H. Dennis. 1977. Island lists of West Indian amphibians and reptiles. *Smithsonian Herpetological Information Service* (40):1–47.

Manuel, R. L. 1965. Monas Island studies. *Journal of the Trinidad Field Naturalist's Club* 1965:16–24.

Marshall, R. C. 1934. *Physiography and Vegetation of Trinidad and Tobago.* Oxford Forest Mem. 17.

Mattson, P. H. 1984. Caribbean structural breaks and plate movements. In The Caribbean-South American plate bourdaries and regional tectonics. ed. W. E. Bonini, R. B. Hargraves, and R. Shagman, 131–152. *The Geological Society of America Memoirs* 162.

Maxwell, J. C. 1948. Geology of Tobago B. W. I. *Bulletin of the Geological Society of Amercia,* 59:801–854.

Maze, E. B. 1984. Jurassic La Quinta Formation in the Sierra de Perija northwestern Venezuela: geology and tectonic environment of red beds and volcanic rocks. In The Caribbean-South American plate bourdaries and regional tectonics, ed. W. E. Bonini, R. B. Hargraves, and R. Shagman, 263–282. *The Geological Society of America Memoirs* 162.

McBee, K., J. W. Bickman, and J. R. Dixon. 1987. Male heterogamety and chromosomal variation in Caribbean geckos. *Journal of Herpetology* 21(1):68–71.

McBee R. H., and V. H. McBee. 1982. The hind gut fermentation in the green iguana, *Iguana iguana*. In *Iguanas of the World: Their Behavior, Ecology, and Conservation,* ed. G. M. Burghardt and S. A. Rand, 77–83. Park Ridge, NJ: Noyes Publications.

McDiarmid, R. W., T'S. Toure, and J. M. Savage. 1996. The proper name of the Neotropical tree boa often referred to as *Corallus enydris* (Serpentes: Boidae). *Journal of Herpetology* 30(3):320–326.

McGinnis, S. M., and R. G. Moore. 1969. Thermoregulation in the boa constrictor, *Boa constrictor. Herpetologica* 25(1):36–45.

Medem M., F. 1960. Datos zoo-geograficos y ecologicos sobre los Crocodylia y Testudinata de los Rios Amazonas, Putumayo Caqueta. *Caldasia* 8:341–351.

———. 1981. *Los Crocodylia de Sur America, Vol. 1. Los Crocodylia de Colombia*. Bogota: Ministerio de Educacion Nacional, Fondo Colombiano de Investgaciones cientificas y Proyectos Especiales "Francisco Jose de Caldas" Colciencias. 354 pp.

———. 1983. *Los Crocodylia de Sur America, Vol. II. Venezuela, Trinidad, Tobago, Guyana, Suriname, Guayana Francesa, Ecuador, Peru, Bolivia, Brasil, Paraguay, Argentina, Uruguay*. Bogata: Universidad Nacional de Colombia y Fondo Colombiano de Investgaciones cientificas y Proyectos Especiales "Francisco Jose de Caldas" Colciencias. 270 pp.

Merrem, B. 1820. *Versuch eines Systems der Amphibien Tentamen systematis amphibiorum*. Marburg. 191 pp.

Mertens, R. 1926. Herpetologische Mitteilungen VIII—XV. *Senckenbergiana,* 8(3–4):137–155.

———. 1930. Zoologische Ergebnisse eine Reise von Otto Conde. 2. Amphibien und Reptilien. *Folia Zool. Hydrobiol. Univ. Lettlands, Riga* 1(2):161–166.

———. 1969. Herpetologische Beobachtungen auf der Insel Tobago. *Salamandra* 5(1–2):63–70.

———. 1970. Herpetologisch neues von der insel Tobago. *Salamandra* 6(1–2):42–44.

———. 1972. Herpetofauna tobagana. *Stuttgarter Beiträge zur Naturkunde* 252:1–22.

———. 1973. Uber falsche Korallennater auf Trinidad and Tobago. *Salamandra* 9(3–4):161–163.

———. 1974. Erganzende Bemerkungen zur Herpetofauna tobagana. *Salamandra* 10(2):79.

———, and L. Muller. 1928. Liste der amphibien und Reptilien Europas. *Abhandlungen der Senckenbergischen Naturforschenden Gesellschaft Frankfurt am Main* 41(1):1–62.

———, ———, and R. Rust. 1934. Systematische Liste der Lelenden Schildkroten. *Blatter fur Aquarien- und Terrarienkunde* 45:42–45, 59–67.

———, and H. Wermuth. 1955. Die rezenten Schildrkröten, Krokodile und Brückenechsen. Ein kritische Liste der heute lebenden Arten und Rassen. *Zoologische Jahrbücher Abtelung für Systematik, Ökologie und Geographie der Tiere.* 83(5):323–440.

Meylan, A. 1988. Spongivory in hawksbill turtles: a diet of glass. *Science* 239:393–395

Michaud, E. J., and J. R. Dixon. 1989. Prey items of 20 species of the neotropical colubrid snake genus *Liophis. Herpetological Review* 20(2):39–41.

Milstead, W. W. 1961. Notes on teiid lizards in southern Brazil. *Copeia* 1961(4):493–495.

Miranda-Ribiero, A. d. 1920. As Hylas coelonotas do Museu Paulista. *Revista do Museu Paulista* 12:321–328.

———. 1926. Notas para servirem ao estudo dos gymnobatrachios (Anura) Brasileiros. *Archivos do Museu Nacional Rio de Janeiro* 27:1–227.

Mittermeier, R. A., A. G. J. Rhodin, F. Medem, P. Soini, M. S. Hoogmoed, and N. C. de Espinoza. 1978. Distribution of the South American chelid turtle *Phrynops gibbus,* with observations on habitat and reproduction. *Herpetologica* 34(1):94–100.

Mole, R. R. 1892a. *Eunectes murinus. Journal of the Trinidad Field Naturalist's Club* 1(3):56–58.

———. 1892b. Babiche shooting in the Caroni. *Journal of the Trinidad Field Naturalist's Club,* 1(4):93–102.

———. 1895. A visit to the high woods of Caparo. *Journal of the Trinidad Field Naturalist's Club* 2(6):147–161..

———. 1910. Economic zoology in relation to agriculture. Part 1—Snakes. *Bulletin Department of Agriculture, Trinidad and Tobago* 9(65):140–141.

―――. 1914. Trinidad snakes. *Proceedings of the Agricultural Society Trinidad and Tobago* 14(603): 363–369.

―――. 1924. The Trinidad snakes. *Proceedings of the Zoological Society of London* (1):235–278.

―――, and F. W. Urich. 1891. Notes on some reptiles from Trinidad. *Proceedings of the Zoological Society of London* 1891:447–449.

―――. 1894a. A preliminary list of the reptiles and batrachians of the island of Trinidad. *Journal of the Trinidad Field Naturalist's Club* 2(3):77–90.

―――. 1894b. Biological notes upon some ophidia of Trinidad, B.W.I., with a preliminary list of the species recorded from the island. *Proceedings of the Zoological Society of London* 1894:499–518.

Moreau de Jonnes, A. 1818. Monographie du Mabouia des murailles, ou *Gecko Mabouia* des Antilles. *Bulletin de la Société Philomathique de Paris* 5(3):138–139.

Moskovits, D. K. 1988. Sexual dimorphism and population estimates of the two Amazonian tortoises (*Geochelone carbonaria* and *G. denticulata*) in northwestern Brazil. *Herpetologica* 44(2):209–217.

―――, and K. A. Bjorndal. 1990. Diet and food preferences of the tortoises *Geochelone carbonaria* and *G. denticulata* in northwestern Brazil. *Herpetologica* 46(2):207–218.

Muller, L. 1923. Zur nomenklatur der sudamerikanischen Kaiman-Arten. *Zoolgischer Anzeiger* 58:315–320.

―――, and W. Hellmich. 1936. *Wissenschaftliche Ergebnisse der Deutschen Gran Chaco—Expedition. (Leiten: Professor Dr. Hans Krieg, Munchen). Amphibien und Reptilien. I. Teil: Amphibia, Chelonia, Loricata.* Stuttgart: Strecker und Schroder. 120 pp.

Murphy, J. C. 1986. Babiche: the crocodilian with many names. *Bulletin of the Chicago Herpetological Society* 21(1–2):4–13.

―――, and R. H. Humbert. 1983. In search of the El Tucuche golden frog, *Phyllodytes auratus* (Boulenger). *Bulletin of the Chicago Herpetological Society* 18(1):24–29.

Myers, C. W. 1982. Blunt headed vine snakes (*Imantodes*) in Panama, including a new species and other revisionary notes. *American Museum Novitates* (2738):1–50.

Netting, M. G. 1930. The systematic status and breeding habits of *Eupemphix trinitatis* Boulenger. *Annals of the Carnegie Museum* 19:249–254.

Niddrie, D. L. 1980. *Tobago.* Gainesville: Litho Press. 243 pp.

Nieden, F. 1923. Anura I. Subordo Aglossa und Phaneroglossa. Section 1, Arcifera. *Das Tierreich* 1–584.

Ober, F. A. 1898. *Crusoe's Island: A Bird Hunter's Story.* New York: D. Appleton and Co. 273 pp.

Obst, F. J. 1977. Die herpetologische sammlung des Staatlichen Museums fur Tierkunde Dresden und ihre Typusexemplare. *Zoologische Abhandlungen* 34(13):171–186.

Oliver, J. A. 1942. A checklist of the snakes of the genus *Leptophis,* with descriptions of new forms. *Occasional Papers Museum Zoology University of Michigan* (462):1–19.

―――. 1948. The relationships and zoogeography of the genus *Thalerophis* Oliver. *Bulletin of the American Museum Natural History* 92:157–280.

―――. 1958. *Snakes in Fact and Fiction.* New York: The Macmillan Co.

Ottley, C. R. 1969 (1970). *A History of Place-Names in Trinidad and Tobago.* Little Books on Trinidad and Tobago, No. 5. Published by the author. Printed by Victoria Commercial Printers, 61 Ambercromby Street, Port of Spain, Trinidad. 33 pp.

Ovaska, K. 1991a. Reproductive phenology, population structure and habitat use of the frog *Eleutherodactylus johnstonei* in Barbados, West Indies. *Journal of Herpetology* 25(4):424–430

―――. 1991b. Diet of the frog *Eleutherodactylus johnstonei* (Leptodactylidae) in Barbados, West Indies. *Journal of Herpetology* 25(4):486–488.

Parker, H. W. 1926. Description of a new snake from Trinidad. *Annual Magazine of Natural History* 9(18):205–207.

―――. 1933. A list of the frogs and toads of Trinidad. *Tropical Agriculture* (Trinidad) 10:8–12.

―――. 1934. Some frogs and toads of Trinidad. *Tropical Agriculture* 11(5):123.

―――. 1935a. The frogs, lizards and snakes of British Guiana. *Proceedings of the Zoological Society of London* 1935:506–530.

―――. 1935b. The lizards of Trinidad. *Tropical Agriculture* (Trinidad) 12(3):65–70.

―――. 1935c. The new teiid lizard in Trinidad. *Tropical Agriculture* (Trinidad) 12(11):283.

―――. 1939. Luminous organs in lizards. *Linnaean Society Journal of Zoology* 40(275):685–660.

Peccinini-Seale, D. M. 1989. Genetic studies on bisexual and unisexual poulations of Amazonian *Cnemidophorus*. In Evolution and ecology of unisexual vertebrates, ed. R. M. Dawley and J. P. Bogart, 241–254. *New York State Museum Bulletin* 466.

Pendlebury, G. B. 1974. Stomach and intestine contents of *Corallus enydris:* a comparison of island and mainland specimens. *Journal of Herpetology* 8(3):241–244.

Peters, J. A. 1960. The snakes of the family Dipsadinae. *Miscellaneous Publications Museum of Zoolology University of Michigan* 114:1–224.

———, and R. Donoso-Barros. 1970. Catalogue of neotropical Squamata. Part II. Lizards and Amphisbaenians. *United States National Museum Bulletin,* Vol. 2, 297:1–293.

———, and B. Orejas-Miranda. 1970. Catalogue of the neotropical Squamata. Part I. Snakes. *United States National Museum Bulletin* Vol. 1, 297:1–347.

Peters, W. 1862. Eine Neue Gattung von Laubfroschen *Plectromantis* aus Ecuador vor. *Monatsberichte der Preussischen Akademie de Wissenschaften zu Berlin* 1862:232–233.

———. 1867. Uber Flederthiere und Amphibien. *Monatsberichte der Preussischen Akademie de Wissenschaften zu Berlin* 1867:703–712.

———. 1868. Uber einige neue oder weniger bekannte Amphibien. *Monatsberichte der Preussischen Akademie de Wissenschaften zu Berlin* 1868:640–642.

———. 1872. Uber eine Sammlung von Batrachiern aus Neu-Freiburg in Brasilien. *Monatsberichte der Preussischen Akademie de Wissenschaften zu Berlin* 1872:680–684.

Pope, C. H. 1967. *The Giant Snakes.* New York: Alfred Knopf. 289 pp.

Powell, J. H., Jr. 1971. The status of crocodilians in the United States, Mexico, Central America, and the West Indies. *First Working Group Meeting Crocodile Specialists, IUCN Publication* 32:72–82.

Poyntz, J. 1683. *The Perfect Prospect of the Famous and Fertile Island of Tobago: With a Description of the Situation, Growth, Fertility and Manufacture of the Said Island. To Which is Added, Proposals for the Encouragement of all Those That are Minded to Settle There.* London: George Larkin (printer), iv + 47. [Cited in Hardy, 1982.]

———. 1695. *The Perfect Prospect of the Famous and Fertile Island of Tobago; to the Southwest of the Island of Barbados. With a Description of the Situation, Growth, Fertility, and Manufacture of the Said Island: Setting Forth how that 100 1 Stock in Seven Years may be Improved to 5000 1 per Annum. To Which is Added Proposals for Encouragement of all Those That are Minded to Settle There.* 2nd Edition. London: John Atwood (printer), vi + 50 pp. [Cited in Hardy, 1982.]

Praderio M. J., and M. D. Robinson. 1990. Reproduction in the toad *Colostethus trinitatis* (Anura: Dendrobatidae) in a northern Venezuela seasonal environment. *Journal of Tropical Ecology* 6:333–341.

Presch, W. 1973. A review of the tegus, lizard genus *Tupinambis* (Sauria: Teiidae) from South America. *Copeia* 1973(4):740–746.

———. 1983. The lizard family Teiidae: is it a monophyletic group? *Zoological Journal of the Linnean Society* 77:189–197.

Pritchard, P. C. H. 1979. *Encyclopedia of Turtles.* Neptune, NJ: T.F.H. Publications, 895 pp.

———, and P. Trebbau. 1984. *The Turtles of Venezuela.* SSAR Contributions to Herpetology No. 2. 414 pp.

Quesnel, V. C. 1957. The life history of the streak lizard, *Gonatodes vittatus. Journal of the Trinidad Field Naturalist's Club* 1957:5–14.

———. 1979. The reproductive behavior of the lizard, *Ameiva ameiva tobagana. Living World, Journal of the Trinidad and Tobago Field Naturalist's Club* 1978–1979:16–18.

———. 1980. Field Naturalist's Club Activities. *Trinidad Naturalist* 3(3):47–48.

———. 1986. An unusual prey for the marine toad, *Bufo marinus. Living World, Journal of the Trinidad and Tobago Field Naturalist's Club* 1985–1986:25.

———, and J. S. Kenny. 1959. The anoles of the eastern Caribbean (Sauria, Iguanidae). II. Two sibling species of anoles in Trinidad. *Bulletin of the Museum Comparative Zoology* 121:189–191.

Rabb, G. B., and M. S. Rabb. 1960. On the mating and egg laying behavior of the Suriname toad, *Pipa pipa. Copeia* 1960(4):271–276.

———, and ———. 1963. Additional observations on breeding behavior of the Surinam toad, *Pipa pipa. Copeia,* 1963(4):636–642.

———, and R. S. Snedigar. 1960. Observations on breeding and development of the Surinam toad, *Pipa pipa. Copeia* 1960(1):40–44.

Ramcharan, E. K., G. Seeberan, and D. Chadee. 1979. Ecological observations on Bois Neuf. *Living World, Journal of the Trinidad and Tobago Field Naturalist's Club* 1978–1979:16–18.

Rand, S. A. 1982. Clutch and egg size in Brazilian iguanid lizards. *Herpetologica* 38(1):171–178.

———, and B. Dugan. 1980. Iguana egg mortality within the nest. *Copeia* 1980(3):531–534.

———, and H. W. Greene. 1982. Latitude and climate in the phenology of reproduction in the green iguana, *Iguana iguana*. In *Iguanas of the World: Their Behavior, Ecology and Conservation*. ed. G. M. Burghardt and A. S. Rand, 142–149. Park Ridge, NJ: Noyes Publications.

———, and E. P. Ortleb, 1969. Defensive display in the colubrid snake *Pseustes poecilonotus shropshirei*. *Herpetologica* 25(1):46–48.

Read, V. M. St. J. 1983. A new locality record for the bromeliad dwelling hylid *Phyllodytes auratus* (Boulenger) in Trinidad, the West Indies. *Bulletin of the Chicago Herpetological Society* 18(1):30–31.

———. 1986a. An onychophoran from the summit of Mt. Aripo, with notes on other animals from locality. *Living World, Journal of the Trinidad and Tobago Field Naturalist's Club* 1985–1986:28–30.

———. 1986b. Two new anurans from Trinidad. *Bulletin of the Chicago Herpetological Society* 21(1–2):29–31.

Reboucas-Spieker, R. 1981. Sobre uma nova especie de *Mabuya* do nordeste do Brazil (Sauria, Scincidae). *Papeis Avulsos do Departamento de Zoologia, Universidade de Sao Paulo* 34(9):121–123.

Reinhardt, J. T., and C. F. Lütken. 1863. Bidrag til det vestindiske Öriges og naunligen til de dansk-vestindiske Öers Herpetologie. *Videnskabelige Meddelelser frå Dansk Naturhistorisk Forening i Kjobenhavn* (4):153–291.

Richmond, N. D. 1965. A new species of blind snake *Typhlops* from Trinidad. *Proceedings of the Biological Society of Washington* 78:121–124.

Riley, J. 1986. The underground life of the Trinidad worm-lizard *Amphisbaena alba*. *Living World, Journal of the Trinidad and Tobago Field Naturalist's Club* 1985–1986:24–25.

———, and J. M. Winch. 1985a. Life history: *Leptodeira annulata ashmeadi*. *Herpetological Review* 16(1):29.

———. 1985b. Life history: *Tripanurgos compressus* eggs. *Herpetological Review* 16(1):29.

———, A. F. Stimson, and J. M. Winch. 1985. A review of squamata ovipositing in ant and termite nests. *Herpetologica Review* 16(2):38–43.

Rivero, J. A. 1961. Salientia of Venezuela. *Bulletin of the Museum of Comparative Zoology* 126(1):1–207.

———. 1968. Los centrolenidos de Venezuela. *Memoria de la Sociedad de Ciencias Naturales La Salle.* 28(81):301–334.

———. 1969. On the identity and relationships of *Hyla luteocellata* Roux (Amphibia, Salientia). *Herpetologica* 25(2):126–134.

———. 1971. Tres nuevas records y una nueva especie de anfibios de Venezuela. *Caribbean Journal of Science* 11(1):1–9.

———, and A. E. Esteves. 1969. Observations on the agonistic and breeding behavior of *Leptodactylus pentadactylus* and other amphibian species in Venezuela. *Breviora* (32):1–14.

———, J. A. Langone, and C. M. Prigioni. 1986. Anfibios anuros colectados por la expedicion del Museo Nacional de Historia Natural de Montevideo al Rio Caura Estado Bolivar, Venezuela; con la descripcion de una nueva especie de *Colostethus* (Dendrobatidae). *Communicacions Zoologicas del Museo de Historia Natural de Montivideo* 157(11):1–15.

Robertson, P., and K. Burke. 1989. Evolution of southern Caribbean Plate boundary, vicinity of Trinidad and Tobago. *The American Association of Petroleum Geologists Bulletin* 73:409–509.

Rodda, G. H. 1992. The mating behavior of *Iguana iguana*. *Smithsonian Contributions to Zoology* 534:1–40.

Rossman, D. A. 1973 (1974). Miscellaneous notes on the South American water snake genus *Helicops*. *HISS-New Journal* 1(6):189–191.

———. 1984. Life history. *Helicops angulatus*. Reproduction. *Herpetological Review* 15(2):20.

Roth, W. D., and C. Gans. 1960. The luminous organs of *Proctoporus* (Sauria; Reptilia)—a reevaluation. *Breviora* (125):1–12.

Rousseau. 1895. Report of club meeting. *Journal of the Trinidad Field Naturalist's Club* 2(11):263.

Roux, J. 1926. Notes d'erpetologie sud-americaine. 1. Sur une collection de Reptiles et d'Amphibiens de l'ile de la Trinite. *Revue Suisse de Zoologie* 33:291–299.

Rowley, K. C. 1979 [1985] Outline of the geology of Tobago. In *Field guide, 1st Geological Conference of the Geological Society of Trinidad and Tobago, 2–5. July 10–12, 1985,* Port of Spain, W. I.

Roze, J. A. 1952a. Contribucion al conocimiento de los ofidios de las familias Typhlopidae y Leptotyphlopidae en Venezuela. *Memorias de la Sociedad de Ciencias Naturales La Salle* 32(12):143–158.

———. 1952b. Coleccion de Reptiles del Professor Scorza de Venezuela. *Acta Biologica Venezuela* 1(5):93–114.

———. 1955(1957). Ofidios colecionados por la expedicion Franco-Venezolana al Alto Orinoco: 1951 a 1952. *Boletin de la Sociedad Venezolana de Ciencias Naturales* 1(3–4):179–195.

———. 1956. La herpetofauna de las islas los Roques y la Orchila. *Memorias de la Sociedad de Ciencias Naturales La Salle* 1956:79–86.

———. 1957. Resumen de una revision del genero *Hydrops* (Wagler) 1830 (Serpentes: Colubridae). *Acta Biologica Venezuela* 2(8):1–95.

———. 1959. Taxonomic notes on a collection of Venezuelan reptiles in the American Museum of Natural History. *American Museum Novitates* (1934):1–14.

———. 1961. El genero *Atractus* (Serpentes: Colubridae) en Venezuela. *Acta Biologica Venezuela* 3:103–119.

———. 1964. La herpetologia de la Isle de Margarita, Venezuela. *Memorias de la Sociedad de Ciencias Naturales LaSalle* 69(24):209–241.

———. 1966. *L Taxonomia y Zoogeografia de los Ofidios en Venezuela.* Caracas, Venezuela: Ediciones de la Biblioteca. 362 pp.

———. 1967. A checklist of the New World venomous coral snakes (Elapidae), with descriptions of new forms. *American Museum Novitates* (2287):1–60.

———. 1989. New species and subspecies of coral snakes, genus *Micrurus* (Elapidae), with notes on type specimens of several species. *American Museum Novitates* (2932):1–15.

———. 1994. Notes on taxonomy of venomous coral snakes (Elapidae) of South America. *Bulletin of the Maryland Herpetological Society* 30:177–185

———, and A. Solano. 1963. Resumen de la familia Caeciliidae (Amphibia: Gymnophiona) de Venezuela. *Acta Biologica Venezuela* 3(19):287–300.

Ruiz-Carranza P., and J. Lynch. 1991. Ranas Centrolenidae de Colombia I. Propuesta de una nueva clasificacion generica. *Lozania* 57:1–30.

Russo, R. M., and R. C. Speed. 1992. Oblique collision and tectonic wedging of the South American continent and Caribbean terranes. *Geology* 20:447–450.

Ruthven, A. G. 1922. The amphibians and reptiles of the Sierra Nevada de Santa Marta, Colombia. *Miscellaneous Publications of the Museum of Zoology University of Michigan* (8):1–69.

Ryan, M. J. 1985. *The Túngara Frog, A Study in Sexual Selection and Communication.* Chicago: University of Chicago Press.

Sanderson, I. T. 1939. *Caribbean Treasure.* New York: The Viking Press. 292 pp.

Schluter. A., and J. Regos. 1981. *Lithodytes lineatus* (Schneider, 1799) (Amphibia: Leptodactylidae) as a dweller in the nests of the leaf cutting ant, *Atta cephalotes* (Linnaeus, 1758) (Hymenoptera, Attini). *Amphibia-Reptilia* 2(2):117.

Schmidt, K. P. 1936. Preliminary account of coral snakes of South America. *Zoology Series, Field Museum Natural History* 20(19):189–203.

———. 1953. *A Checklist of North American Amphibians and Reptiles.* 6th ed. University of Chicago Press. 280 pp.

———. 1957. The venomous coral snakes of Trinidad. *Fieldiana Zoology* 39:55–63.

Schneider, J. G. 1782. *Allgemeine Naturgeschichte der Schildkröten nebst einem systematischen Verzeichnisse der einzelnen Arten und zwey Kupfern.* Leipzig: J. G. Muller. 364 pp.

Schneider, J. G. 1799. *Historiae Amphibiorum Naturalis et Literariae.* Fr. Frommann, Jena. Vol. 1, 266 pp.

Schwab, S. 1988. Faunal checklist of the Aripo Savannas (Scientific Reserve). *Living World, Journal of the Trinidad and Tobago Field Naturalist's Club* 1987–1988:35–39.

Schwartz, A. 1967. Frogs of the genus *Eleutherodactylus* in the Lesser Antilles. *Studies of the Fauna of Curacao and Other Caribbean Islands* 23(91):1–62.

———, and R. W. Henderson. 1988. West Indian amphibians and reptiles: a checklist. *Millwaukee Public Museum Contributions in Biology and Geology* (74):1–264.

————, and ————. 1991. *Amphibians and Reptiles of the West Indies: Descriptions, Distributions and Natural History*. University of Florida Press, Gainesville. 720 pp.

————, and R. Thomas. 1975. A checklist of West Indian amphibians and reptiles. *Publications of the Carnegie Museum of Natural History* (1):1–216 pp.

Schweigger, A. F. 1812. Prodromus monographiae cheloniorum. Konigsberg. *Archiv für Naturwiss und Math.* 1:271–368, 406–458.

Schwenk, K. 1994. Systematics and subjectivity: the phylogeny and classification of Iguanian lizards revisited. *Herpetological Review* 25(2):53–57.

Sentzen, U. I. 1796. Ophiologische fragmente. In Meyer's *Zool. Arch.* 2:49–74.

Sexton, O. J. 1960. Notas sobre la reproducion de una tortuga venezolana la *Kinosternon scorpioides*. *Memorias de la Sociedad de Ciencias Naturales LaSalle* 20:187–197.

Shackleton, N. J. 1987. Oxygen isotopes, ice volume and sea level. *Quaternary Science Reviews* 6:183–190.

Smith, H. M. 1942. Mexican herpetology miscellany. *Proceedings of the United States National Museum* 92(3153):349–395.

————, and E. H. Taylor. 1950. Type localities of Mexican reptiles and amphibians. *Kansas University Science Bulletin* 33(8):313–380.

————, and R. B. Smith. 1977. *Synopsis of the Herpetofauna of Mexico. Vol. 5. Guide to Mexican Amphisbaenians and Crocodilians, Bibliographic Addendum II*. North Bennington, VT: John Johnson. 187 pp.

————, and ————. 1979. *Synopsis of the Herpetofauna of Mexico. Vol. 6. Guide to Mexican Turtles, Bibliographical Addendum III*. North Bennington, VT: John Johnson. 1044 pp.

Smith, R., and G. Seeberan. 1979. Occurrence of the rare checkerbelly snake, *Siphlophis cervinus*, in the Nariva Swamp, Trinidad. *Living World, Journal of the Trinidad and Tobago Field Naturalist's Club* 1978–1979:11.

Solano, H. 1987. Algunos aspectos de la biologia reproductiva del sapito silbador *Leptodactylus fuscus* (Schneider) (Amphibia: Leptodacylidae). *Amphibia-Reptilia* 8:111–128.

Speed, R. C. 1985. Cenozoic collision of the Lesser Antilles Arc and continental South America and the origin of the El Pilar fault. *Tectonics* 4:41–69.

Speed, R., R. Russo, J. Weber, and K. C. Rowley. 1991. Evolution of southern Caribbean plate boundary, vicinity of Trinidad and Tobago: discussion. *The American Association of Petroleum Geologists Bulletin* 75(11):1789–1794.

Spix, J. B. von. 1824a. *Animalia Nove, Siva Species Novae Testudinum et Ranarum, quos in itenere per Brasiliam, Annis 1817–20 . . . collegit et descripsit . . . Vol 3*. Munich. 37 pages.

————. 1824b. *Serpentium Brasiliensium . . . Species Novae ou Historie Naturelle des Espèces Nouvelles de Serpens, Recueillis et Observées Pendant le Voyage dans L'intérieur du Brésil dans les Années 1817–1820. Vol. 2*. Munich. 74 pages.

————. 1825. *Animalia Nova Sive Species Novae Lacertarum Quos in Itinere per Brasiliam Annis 1817–1820 . . . Vol. 1*. Munich 26 pages.

Stahel, G., and D. C. Geijskes. 1939. Ueber den Bau der Nester von *Atta cephalotes* L. und *Atta sexdens* L. (Heym. Formicidae). *Review de Entomologia* 10(1):27–78. [Cited by Hoogmoed, 1973.]

————, and ————. 1940. De parasolmieren enhunne bestriigding. *Dep. Landbouwprofstation in Suriname Bull.* 56:1–8. [Cited by Hoogmoed, 1973.]

Stamps, J. A. 1977. Rainfall, moisture and dry season growth rates in *Anolis aeneus*. *Copeia* 1977(3): 415–419.

————, and D. P. Crews. 1976. Seasonal changes in reproduction and social behavior in the lizard *Anolis aeneus*. *Copeia* 1976(3):467–476.

Staton, M. A., and J. R. Dixon. 1977a. The herpetofauna of the central Llanos of Venezuela; noteworthy records, a tentative checklist and ecological notes. *Journal of Herpetology* 11(1):17–24.

————, and ————. 1977b. Breeding biology of the spectacled caiman, *Caiman crocodilus crocodilus*, in the Venezuelan llanos. *U. S. Department of the Interior, Fish and Wildlife Service Wildlife Research Report* (5):1–21.

Stejneger, L. H. 1899. Reptiles of the Tres Marias and Isabel islands. *North American Fauna* (14):63–71.

————. 1904. The herpetology of Porto Rico. *Report United States National Museum* 129:549–724.

————. 1917. Cuban amphibians and reptiles collected for the United States National Museum from 1899 to 1902. *Proceedings United States National Museum* 53(2205):259–291.

Sternberg, J. 1981. *The Worldwide Distribution of Sea Turtle Nesting Beaches.* New York: Sea Turtle Rescue Fund, Center for Environmental Education.

Sternfield, R. 1920. Zur systematik der schlangen-Gattung *Spilotes. Senckenbergiana* 2:181–186.

Strimple, P. S. 1993. Overview of the natural history of the green anaconda (*Eunectes murinus*). *Herpetological Natural History* 1:25–35.

Stuart, L. C. 1933. Studies on Neotropical Colubrinae. II. Some new species and subspecies of *Eudryas* Fitzinger, with an annotated list of the frogs of *Eudryas boddaertii* (Stentzen). *Occasional Papers of the Museum of Zoology, University of Michigan* (254):1–10.

————. 1939. A description of a new *Gymnophthalmus* from Guatemala with notes on other members of the genus. *Occasional Papers of the Museum of Zoology, University of Michigan* (409):1–10.

————. 1941. Studies on Neotropical Colubrinae. VIII. A revision of the genus *Dryadophis* Stuart 1939. *Miscellaneous Pubications of the Museum of Zoology, University of Michigan* (4):1–106.

————. 1955. A brief review of the Guatemalan lizards of the genus *Anolis. Miscellaneous Publications Museum of Zoology, University of Michigan* (91):1–31.

Stull, O. G. 1935. A checklist of the family Boidae. *Proceedings of the Boston Society of Natural History* 40(8):387–408.

Taylor, E. H. 1951. A brief review of the snakes of Costa Rica. *Kansas University Science Bulletin* 34(1):3–188.

————. 1968. *The Caecilians of the World: A Taxonomic Review.* University of Kansas Press, Lawrence. 848 pp.

Teixeira, D. M., and M. Porto. 1991. Life history notes: *Leptophis ahaetulla,* feeding behavior. *Herpetological Review* 22(4):132.

————, M. L. Lorini, V. G. Persson, and M. Porto. 1991. Life history note: *Clelia clelia,* feeding behavior. *Herpetological Review* 22(4):131–2.

Test, F. H., O. J. Sexton, and H. Heatwole. 1966. Reptiles of Rancho Grande and vicinity, Estado Aragua, Venezuela. *Miscellaneous Publication Museum of Zoololgy University Michigan* (128):1–63.

Thomas, R. 1965. The smaller teiid lizards (*Gymnophthalmus* and *Bachia*) of the southeastern Caribbean. *Proceedings of the Biological Society of Washington* 78:141–154.

Thorbjarnarson, J. B., and G. Hernández. 1993. Reproductive ecology of the Orinoco crocodile (*Crocodylus intermedius*) in Venezuela. I. Nesting ecology and egg and clutch relationships. *Journal of Herpetology* 27(4):363–370.

Toft, C. A., and W. E. Duellman. 1979. Anurans of the lower Rio Llullapichis, Amazonian Peru: a preliminary analysis of community structure. *Herpetologica* 35(1):71–77.

Troschel, F. H. 1848. Amphibien. In *Versuch einer Zusammenstellung der Fauna und Flora von British-Guiana,* Richard Schomburgk, 645–661. Vol. 3. Leipzig.

Tschudi, J. J. 1838. Classification der Batrachien, mit Berucksichtigung der fossilen Thiere dieser Abtheilund der Reptilien. *Mémoires de la Société Neuchâteloise des Sciences Naturelles,* Vol. 2, 99 pp.

Tuck, R. G. 1972. New Records: *Hemidactylus palaichthus. Herpetological Review* 4(3):93.

————, and J. D. Hardy. 1973. Status of the Ober Tobago collection, Smithsonian Institution, and the proper allocation of *Ameiva surinamensis tobaganus* Cope (Sauria: Teiidae). *Proceedings of the Biological Society of Washington* 86(19):231–242.

Underwood, G. 1956. A new lizard record for Trinidad. *Journal of the Trinidad Field Naturalist's Club* 1956:25–26.

————. 1959. The anoles of the eastern Caribbean (Sauria, Iguanidae). part III. Revisionary notes. *Bulletin of the Museum of Comparative Zoology* 121(5):191–226.

————. 1962. Reptiles of the eastern Caribbean. *Caribbean Affairs* (N.S.) (1):1–192.

————. 1964. Reptiles of the Eastern Caribbean, 1st Supplement. *Caribbean Affairs,* i–iv, 51, 52, 94a, 94b.

Urich. 1892. Report of club meeting. *Journal of the Trinidad Field Naturalist's Club* I(11):261. [Cited in Medem, 1983.]

Urich, F. W. 1931. The mongoose in Trinidad. *Tropical Agriculture* 8(4):95–97.

————. 1933. Snake v. mongoose. *Tropical Agriculture* 10(1):5.

Uzzell, T. M., Jr. 1958. Teiid lizards related to *Proctoporus luctuosus* with the description of a new species from Venezuela. *Occasional Papers of the Museum of Zoology, University of Michigan* (597):1–15.

Vandelli, D. 1761. *Epistola de Holothurio et Testudine Coriacea ad Celeberrimum Carolum Linnaeum Equitem Naturae Curiosum Dioscoridem II.* Conzatti, Padum.

Van Denburgh, J. 1898. Reptiles from Sonora and Jalisco, Mexico, with a description of a new species of *Sceloporus. Proceedings Academy of Natural Sciences of Philadelphia* 49:460–464.

Van Devender, R. W. 1982. Growth and ecology of spiny-tailed and green iguanas in Costa Rica, with comments on the evolution of herbivory and large body size. In *Iguanas of the World: Their Behavior, Ecology and Conservation,* ed. G. M. Burghardt and S. A. Rand, 162–183. Park Ridge, NJ: Noyes Publications, Van Meeuwen, H. M. 1977. De Trinidadse beekkikker, *Colostethus trinitatis. Lacerta* 36:3–11.

Vanzolini, P. E. 1951. *Amphisbaena fuliginosa.* Contributions to the knowledge of the Brasilian lizards of the family Amphisbaenidae Gray, 1925. 6. On the geographical distribution and differentiation of *Amphisbaena fuliginosa* Linne. *Bulletin of the Museum of Comparative Zoology,* 106(1):1–67.

————. 1961. *Bachia:* espécies brasilerias e conceito genérico (Sauria, Teiidae). *Papeis Avulsos Departamento de Zoologia, Universidade de Sao Paulo* 14:193–209.

————. 1968. Geography of the South American Gekkonidae. *Arquivos de Zoologia Universidade de Sao Paulo* 17(2):85–112.

————. 1970. Unisexual *Cnemidophorus lemniscatus* in the Amazonas Valley: a preliminary note (Sauria: Teiidae). *Papeis Avulsos do Departamento de Zoologia. Universidade de Sao Paulo* 23(7):63–68.

————. 1972a. *Typhlops brongersmai* spec. nov. from the coast of Bahia, Brazil (Serpentes, Typhlopidae). *Zoologische Mededelingen.* Rijksmuseum van Natuurlijke Historie, Leiden 47:27.29.

————. 1972b. Miscellaneous notes on the ecology of some Brasilian lizards (Sauria). *Papeis Avulsos Departamento de Zoologia. Universidade de Sao Paulo* 26(8):83–115.

————. 1976. *Typhlops brongersmianus,* a new name for *Typhlops brongersmai* Vanzolini, 1972, preoccupied (Serpentes, Typhlopidae). *Papeis Avulsos do Departamento de Zoologia. Universidade de Sao Paulo* 29:247.

————. 1978. On South American *Hemidactylus. Papeis Avulsos do Departamento de Zoologia. Universidade de Sao Paulo* 31(20):307–343.

————. 1981. Reptilia. In *Aquatic Biota of Tropical South America.* Part 2. Anarthropoda., ed. S. H. Hurlbert et al., 246–266. San Diego: San Diego State University.

————. 1990. Geographic distribution: *Gymnophthalmus underwoodi. Herpetological Reiview* 21(4):96.

————, and C. Morato de Carvalho. 1991. Two sibling and sympatric species of *Gymnophthalmus* in Roraima, Brazil (Sauria: Teiidae). *Papeis Avulsos do Departamento de Zoologia. Universidade de Sao Paulo* 37(12):173–226.

————, and R. Reboucas-Spieker. 1973. Notes on the ecology and limb proportions of Amazonian *Mabuya mabuya. Papeis Avulsos do Departamento de Zoologia. Universidade de Sao Paulo* 26(17):215–226.

————, and E. E. Williams. 1970. South American anoles: the geographic differentiation and evolution of the *Anolis chrysolepis* species group (Sauria, Iguanidae). *Arquivos de Zoologia. Museu de Zoologia, Universidade de Sao Paulo* 19(1–4):1–298.

Vasquez de Espinoza, A. 1628. *Compendium and Description of the West Indies.* Translated by C. U. Clark. Washington, DC: National Museum Natural History, 1941. 826 pp.

Vierbuchen, R. C. 1984. The geology of the El Pilar fault zone and adjacent areas in northeastern Venezuela. In The Caribbean-South American plate bourdaries and regional tectonics, ed. W. E. Bonini, R. B. Hargraves, and R. Shagman, 189–212. *The Geological Society of America Memoirs* 162.

Vitt, L. J. 1991. Ecology and life history of the scansorial arboreal lizard, *Plica plica* (Iguanidae) in Amazonia, Brazil. *Canadian Journal of Zoology* 69:504–511.

————., and D. G. Blackburn. 1991. Ecology and life history of the viviparous lizard *Mabuya bistriata* (Scincidae) in the Brazilian Amazon. *Copeia* 1991(4):916–927.

————, and C. M. de Carvalho. 1992. Life in the trees: the ecology and life history of *Kentropyx striatus* (Teiidae) in the lavrado area of Roraima, Brazil, with comments on the life histories of tropical teiid lizards. *Canadian Journal of Zoology* 70:1995–2006.

Wagler, J. G. 1824. *Serpentum Brasilensium Species Novae ou Historie Naturelle des Espèces Nouvelles de Serpens, Recueillies et Observées Pendant le Voyage dans L'intérieur du Bresil dans les Annees 1817, 1818, 1819, 1820, Exécuté par Order de Sa Majesté le Roide Baviére, Publiée par Jean de Spix . . . , Écrite D'après les Notes du Voyageur par Jean Wagler.* Franc. Serraph. Hübschmann, Monachii. 75 pp.

————. 1828. Auszuge aus seinen Systema Amphibiorum. *Isis von Oken* 21:740–744.

————. 1830. *Naturliches system der Amphibien mit voranghender classification der Saugethiere und Vogel Ein Beitrag zur vergleichender Zoologie.* Munich, 354 pp.

Watkins, J. F., II, F. Gehlbach, and R. Baldridge. 1967. Ability of the blind snake, *Leptotyphlops dulcis* to follow pheromone trails of army ants. *Southwestern Naturalist* 12(4):455–462.

Wehekind, L. 1955. Notes on the foods of the Trinidad snakes. *British Journal of Herpetology* 2:9–13.

————. 1960. Trinidad snakes. *Journal of the British Guiana Museum of Zoology* 27:71–76.

Wells, K. D. 1980. Social behavior and communication of a dendrobatid frog (*Colostethus trinitatis*). *Herpetologica* 36(2):189–199.

————. 1981. Territorial behavior of the frog *Eleutherodactylus urichi* in Trinidad. *Copeia* 1981(3): 726–728.

————, and K. M. Bard. 1988. Parental behavior of an aquatic-breeding tropical frog, *Leptodactylus bolivianus. Journal of Herpetology* 22:361–364.

Wiegmann, A. F. A. 1834. *Herpetologia Mexicana seu Descriptio Amphibiorum Novae Hispaniae quae Itinerbus Comitis de Sack, Ferdinandi Deppe et Chr. Guil. Schiede in Museum Zoologicum Berolinense Pervenerunt. Pars prima, Sasurorum Species Amplectans, Adiecto Systematis Saurorum Prodromo, Additisque Multis in Hunc Amphibriorum Ordinem observationbus.* Berlin: C. G. Lëderitz 54 pp.

Werner, F. 1899. Ueber Reptilien und Batrachier aus Columbien und Trinidad. *Verhandlungen der Zoologisch-Botanischen Gesellschaft in Wien* 49:470–484.

————. 1900. Ueber Reptilien und Batrachier aus Colimbien und Trinidad, II. *Verhandlungen der Zoologisch-Botanischen Gesellschaft in Wien* 50:262–272.

White, G. 1988. Notes on two localized frogs. *Living World, Journal of the Trinidad and Tobago Field Naturalist's Club* 1987–1988:40.

Wied-Neuwied, M. 1824. *Abbildungen zur Naturgeschichte Brasiliens.* Weimar. pl. 47.

Williams, E. E. 1960. Two species of tortoises in northern South America. *Breviora* (120):1–13.

————. 1989a. Old problems and new opportunities in West Indian biogeography. In *Biogeography of the West Indies: Past, Present, Future,* ed. C. A. Wood, 1–46. Gainesville, FL: Sandhill Crane Press.

————. 1989b. A critique of Guyer and Savage (1986): cladistic relationships among anoles (sauria: Iguanidae): are the data available to reclassify the anoles? In *Biogeography of the West Indies: Past, Present, Future,* ed. C. A. Wood, 433–478. Gainesville, FL: Sandhill Crane Press.

Williams, R. O., et al. 1928. *Flora of Trinidad and Tobago.* (Incomplete.) Trinidad.

Wilson, L. D., and C. E. Mena. 1980. Systematics of the *melanocephala* group of the colubrid snake genus *Tantilla. Memoirs of the San Diego Society Natural History* 11:1–58.

————, and J. R. Meyer. 1982. *The Snakes of Honduras.* Milwaukee Public Museum, Milwaukee. 159 pp.

Winer, L., and H. E. A. Boos. 1990–1991. Agouti to zandolie: fauna in the dictionary of Trinbagonian. *Living World, Journal of the Trinidad and Tobago Field Naturalist's Club* 1990–1991:25–28.

Wing, E. S., and E. J. Reitz. 1982. Prehistoric fishing economies of the Caribbean. *Journal of New World Archeology* 5(2):13–31.

Winstel, A. 1984a. Reptiles of Trinidad. Part 1. *The Forked Tongue, Greater Cincinnati Herpetological Society* 9(1):8–10.

————. 1984b. Reptiles of Trinidad. Part II. *The Forked Tongue, The Greater Cincinnati Herpetological Society* 9(2):9–11.

————. 1984c. The amphibians of Trinidad. *The Forked Tongue, Greater Cincinnati Herpetological Society* 9(11):9–11.

Woodcock, H. I. 1867. *A History of Tobago.* Printed for the author by Smith and Grant. Ayrshire Express Office, Ayr. 195 pp.

Worth, C. B. 1967. *A Naturalist in Trinidad.* New York: J. B. Lippincott Co. 291 pp.

Wunderle, J. M., Jr. 1981. Avian predation upon *Anolis* lizards on Grenada, West Indies. *Herpetologica* 37(2):104–108.

Yang, S. Y., M. Soule, and G. C. Gorman. 1974. *Anolis* lizards of the eastern Caribbean: a case study in evolution. 1. Genetic relationships, phylogeny and colonization sequence of the *roquet* group. *Systematic Zoology* 23:387–399.

Zug, G. R. 1977. The matamata (Testudines: Chelidae) is *Chelus* not *Chelys! Herpetologica* 33:53–54.

————. 1993. *Herpetology, An Introductory Biology of Amphibians and Reptiles.* New York, Academic Press. 527 pp.

————, and P. B. Zug. 1979. The marine toad, *Bufo marinus.* A natural history resume of native populations. *Smithsonian Contributions to Zoology* (284):1–58.

Index to Scientific Names

Numbers in bold are plate numbers.